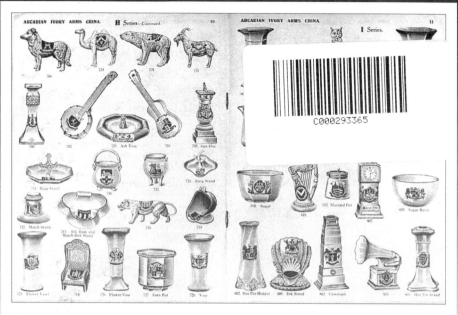

Pages from an Arcadian Ivory Arms China Catalogue for the 1920s.

Any shape could be ordered by an agent and pieces would be supplied with the local coat of arms of the retailer.

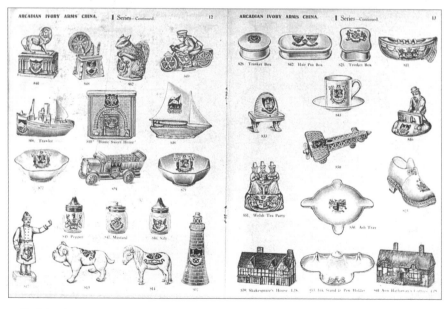

All of the shapes on the pages shown are relatively common, and can be found with a wide range of crests.

THE 2000
PRICE GUIDE
TO CRESTED CHINA

THE 2000
PRICE GUIDE
TO CRESTED CHINA

Nicholas Pine

Published by Milestone Publications
Goss & Crested China Ltd,
62 Murray Road,
Horndean, Waterlooville, Hants. PO8 9JL .

Typeset by Hilite, 82 Portswood Road, Southampton, Hants

Printed and bound in Great Britain by
MPG Books Ltd., Bodmin, Cornwall

British Library Cataloguing in Publication Data

The price guide to crested china.
  2000
  A catalogue record for this book is available from the British Library

ISBN 1-85265-129-6

Contents

Acknowledgements

I would like to thank all those who have informed the author and the Goss & Crested China Club of previously unrecorded pieces. The result has been this 2000 edition, into which has been incorporated the factory marks and factory histories taken from *Crested China* by Sandy Andrews.

The original compilation of these listings was undertaken by Sandy Andrews in 1980 and I am very grateful for her permission to include extracts from *Crested China* in this book and for her providing original research into Crested China.

I am also grateful to Lynda Pine, who is responsible for the prices in this guide, and the staff of Goss & Crested China Ltd who carefully check through stock which passes through their hands, and continually update values, dimensions, variations and new models. I wish, in particular, to thank Patricia Welbourne, the Milestone Publications in-house editor of this book, who has recorded all new information collected by Goss Crested China Ltd.

I thank Len Harris for his work on Locke & Co, Worcester.

Special thanks go to Stephen Godly, David Wiscombe and Bob Southall for their continuing contributions and to Michael Shears for carefully reading and checking the text.

Also a big thankyou to Ray Clarke for all his help during his many years as my manager, and for his excellent photographic contributions. Trevor Glover has drawn the factory marks and Janet Ward has also contributed in this area. I thank them both. I have made extensive use of the *Encyclopaedia of British Pottery and Porcelain Marks* by Geoffrey A. Godden FRSA and thank its author for producing such a definitive book.

But the biggest thankyou of all must go to Lionel Hemsley who has conducted a particular study of heraldic porcelain and who has contributed hundreds of different pieces of information, most of them material. His knowledge of crested china is encyclopaedic and he has, once again, made a significant contribution to this edition.

When the heraldic souvenir ware industry faded in the 1930s, no-one could have foreseen that its popularity would return a second time. No records were kept by the potteries as they either closed down or were taken over, or switched to different lines of production in order to survive. It is to the credit of collectors today that we have amassed such a comprehensive listing of shapes made, but there are certainly many more. So please, if you have come across any pieces not listed in this book, write to me and the Goss & Crested China Club at the address at the back of this book with the relevant details.

Nicholas Pine

The following collectors have all forwarded lists, new information, photographs, or details to be included in this edition, and we are extremely grateful to them.

R. Alexander, D. Arbory, Valerie Arthur, Moira & Tony Askew, Mr M. Bannister, Mrs K. Barker, Christopher Bartle, Douglas Bates, Mrs J. Barnes, Ann and John Bavin, Peter Bolton, R. Boydell, N. Bradberry, Alan Brook, P. Brookes, A. Bullen, Mrs J. Bush, W.J. Burton, A.R. Chadwick, P. Cheeseman, Miss C. Clark, Mrs. R. Clayton, Sue Cook, M.A. Coombs, Bill Cover, Mr & Mrs A.E Cole, M. G. Cook, M.A. Coombs, R. Cording, T. Cousins, Ann Daniels, R. Day, Mrs E. Davis, Mrs V.A. Daynes, K.P. Dunne, Mrs Elizabeth Edwards, Ron Edwards, Mrs A Elfick, Bill Elkington, R. Field, R.A. Fowler, Denise Fox, Mrs M.J. Frizzle, C.J. Garbutt, G. Goodchild, Gwyn Griffiths, A. S. Guy, Mrs M. Growns, Peter Hacker, Mr & Mrs C. Hayter, P. Hawker, K. Harrison, G. Hall, Maureen & John Hall, Martin Hanlon, B. Higgs, Ron Holmes, H.E. Hoyle, Mr & Mrs Hulse, M & M Jacques, Mrs Jenvey, Mrs R. A. Johnson, Mrs M. Johnson, C.L. King, Les Killick, B.D. Knight, J.B. Learman, Malcolm Lee, D. Lewis, G. Lewis, Mrs Lockley, Mr Lubbock, I. Marlow, D. Mills, A.J. Mitchell, M.N. Morgan, N. Morse, A. Munday, Barry Mursell, Mrs J. V. Palin, C. Parker, D.A. Payne, Jim Poolman, Mrs S. Pratt, D. Newton, G. Nicholls, A. Pfleger, E. Pote, John Proud, A. Reeve, Mr & Mrs Brian Prindiville, J. Roberts, Graham Robinson, M. Rogers, C.P Ryan, R. Segal, Bob Southall, Jean Smith, W. Smith, G. Sowell, K. Spencer, George Sturrock, K. Stevenson, J. Sweeney, Dorothy H. Sutton, Mr & Mrs J.V. Tate, Oliver J. Thompson, Brian Thacker, Robert Toghill, B. Triptree, V. Trump, B. Wales, Mrs V.A. Withnall, J.C Wood, Mrs Webb, Sue Westbrook, M. Woods, Allan J. Woodliffe, John Whipp, John B. White, Mr Whitehouse, A.J.L. Wright, Margaret & Michael Younger, John Yallop and several anonymous contributers.

Please continue to send details of any new models to Milestone Publications for inclusion in future editions of *The Price Guide to Crested China*.

Preface

This volume is essentially a listing of all pieces produced, with the exception of mundane jugs, pots, vases and similar shapes, with sizes thereof, with full descriptions of each factory where known, and an example of each variation of factory mark. The total number of recorded pieces is now in excess of 10,000. If you have accurate information on any piece or factory mark that cannot be located in this Guide, please inform the publishers in order that it may be included in a future edition.

To find the value of any piece first look up the correct manufacturer; this will be found by reference to the mark on the base of the piece in question. All items are listed in the order of the headings given on Page 22.

This guide is designed to represent average prices that one would expect to pay from a dealer. The market has continued to rise strongly since publication of the 1992 edition. Both common and rare pieces have risen in price substantially. As the years go by, it is becoming clearer which pieces are scarce and which are not, so we are able to set prices more accurately, or rather, the market sets the prices for we can only respond to supply and demand, reflecting the 'collectibility' of a piece. We constantly assess and discuss prices and alter our master listings every working day. There are even some pieces which have gone down in price.

In order to assist the reader, we have included a section where over 1000 pieces are illustrated and valued including items in every theme and price range. This section should allow one to quickly obtain the approximate value of any item and will be of use to market traders and dealers who do not specialize but need to value pieces rapidly when buying or selling. This, when used in conjunction with the illustrations in the previous (1992) edition will assist the reader to build up a comprehensive record of illustrated price information.

Values quoted in this guide represent the prices charged by Goss and Crested China Ltd in 2000 and are, in our opinion, fair and true values of the current retail selling price, net of any Value Added Tax.

Goss & Crested China Ltd are the leading dealers in heraldic porcelain and whilst we do not have every piece we do have a constantly changing stock of several thousand pieces to interest the collector. We produce *Goss & Crested China* an illustrated monthly catalogue containing 28 pages of items for sale. This is available by subscription, please enquire for details of this and our range of publications on the subject of heraldic china, a full list of which will be found at the back of this book. Visitors are welcome to view our stock at the Goss & Crested China Centre and Museum, our Hampshire showroom.

We run the Goss & Crested China Club, the leading collectors club, membership of which is free to subscribers to *Goss & Crested China* or to regular customers. Please ask for details.

Any notable decorations will add value to a piece, i.e. transfer printed scenes, views, birds, animals or floral decorations or indeed some pieces may be found solely coloured in blue, red, black or yellow. A premium should be added for any piece having an unusual or attractive decoration or verse. Inscriptions have been omitted from the guide unless they are essential in determining the nature of the piece. Some models have military inscriptions, i.e. details of particular engagements during the Great War. For such pieces, usually produced by Savoy, £10-£15 should be added. Matching crests are very few and far between on models produced by factories other than W.H. Goss and may be disregarded in most instances. In the case of buildings, monuments and the like a small premium should be paid for the correct arms although many items will be found to display local crests as they were usually sold in those areas.

Much domestic ware was produced, often carrying coats of arms as an afterthought as much as by design. Such pieces, including cups and saucers, plates, milk jugs, large pots and vases, are only worth around £5-£10 each but tend to be the most overpriced items at fairs, markets etc. Such ware is not very collectable. Ordinary small vases, jugs, pots, ewers, etc. from factories are worth £3-£5 and named models £5-£10. Those of German or Czechoslovakian descent are worth half these values.

Many similar pieces carry different factory marks on their bases, for example Arcadian, Swan and Clifton were all made by Arkinstall & Son Ltd. Where the same piece could have been produced with several different marks the reader's attention is drawn in such cases to the names of the factories and chapters under which one should look if the piece cannot be found listed under the factory or mark shown on the base. To aid the reader a table of the principal manufacturers of crested china and their trademarks, subsidiaries and firms using their products will be found on page 19. Manufacturers were constantly merging, being taken over, ceasing production and selling their designs and moulds to other potters so pieces continually appear with different marks.

Many pieces can be found bearing no factory mark. In the majority of such cases, it is obvious to the trained eye which factory produced them. Having no factory mark reduces the value of such pieces by very little if at all.

Many items which are normally found coloured can also be found white, either with or without gilding and sometimes having no factory mark. All these variations are individually listed and priced, but in general, such items would normally be worth approximately $1/2$ to $2/3$ of the value of the coloured version. Similarly, a piece normally found white glazed only would be increased in value by $1/2$ to $3/4$ should a coloured variety be found. Likewise, a piece bearing no inscription would require a price reduction of some 20% from that of one priced in this guide with an inscription, and vice-versa.

New items are constantly coming to light, if you have a piece for which you cannot find an entry as it is not listed under the appropriate heading in this guide, one must refer to the table of principal manufacturers on page 19 and check under all other relevant factory headings. Many known models were produced with different factory marks, these are all worth the same as identical pieces listed elsewhere.

One point that needs to be clearly made is that pieces from one factory are not worth more than those from another. For example, Savoy is not worth any more than Swan or for that matter Carlton, Grafton or Shelley etc. Over the years one has often been told by amateur dealers and stall holders that Arcadian is worth more than other factories. This is not so. The only reasons for the uttering of this myth I would venture are that firstly Arkinstall & Son Ltd were more prolific than most and that there are hundreds of Arcadian pieces to be found, dealers therefore would usually have a number in stock and these would be preferred to items with no factory mark or a lesser known - in fact little-known marks are definitely rarer, but, alas they are not worth a premium either. Secondly, this fallacy has been passed on over the years and in this vacuum of knowledge, such gems as this have thrived. I am pleased to say that I have heard it little during recent years.

The value of crested china may be determined by three factors: theme, rarity and condition - in that order. The most popular themes are: Great War; Buildings; Animals (including birds); Transport; Memorials; Monuments; Statues; Cartoon/ Comedy Characters; Comic/Novelty; Sport; Alcohol and Musical Instruments. This list is by no means exhaustive but it does cover the main spheres of interest among collectors. Rarity is self explanatory; a 'Bomb Thrower' is rarer than a 'Cenotaph' and therefore it is worth more. These two factors may be summed up as 'Collectability', for example a scarce animal would be worth far more than, say, a unique billiken because there is far more demand for the animal from theme collectors. Thus supply and demand play an important part. It should always be borne in mind that even the most attractive and rare crested cup and saucer will never be worth more than a few pounds whereas a rare military piece could command a price in excess of £500.00.

Condition is another factor which affects price. Whilst not as important as with Goss china, it still affects the value of an item considerably and the following remarks should be noted. Crested china produced by other manufacturers was never as fine as that of the Goss factory. William Henry Goss conducted over one thousand experiments which took many years before he perfected the parian body which he used as his medium. With few exceptions the other producers were not interested in the high standards that Goss set himself, they were only concerned with jumping on the crested china bandwagon and producing wares as quickly and as cheaply as possible for the profitable souvenir trade which was rapidly developing. Some factories were better than others and Grafton, Carlton and Alexandra in particular produced some very detailed and delicate models, all in porcelain. Most foreign ware (mainly German or Czechoslovakian) is of poor quality, tending to be rather crude and heavy, and is therefore worth less as a general rule than English china.

Having made the point that crested china factories were not that particular about the quality of their products it follows that many pieces were substandard even before leaving the factory. The producers were not usually too concerned about this and many pieces were sold having firing cracks, chips (under the glaze) or other flaws; rubbed, poorly applied or non-existent gilding, imperfect transfers, crooked or poorly painted coats of arms and inscriptions as well as having indifferent glazing. This was sometimes incomplete and often heavy and too liberally coated, leading to a green-grey tinge in grooves and internal corners where the glaze has built up. This latter occurrence often leads to crazing appearing in such build ups of glaze. This does not affect values unless really bad. In addition, pieces were often wrongly named on the base, or not named at all as many of the paintresses could not read or write!

Minor defects such as those given above are commonplace and do not affect value although naturally a piece completely free of such manufacturers' imperfections would be preferable. Such items however number less than a third of all crested china produced so to restrict a collection to these pristine items only would be frustrating if not impossible. If one seeks perfection then W.H. Goss is the only factory that can be considered by the serious collector, indeed, many if not most Goss collectors consider all other crested china to be inferior and would not dream of collecting it themselves. It does however have charms other than those of complete perfection to commend it. Pieces with particularly bad factory defects were often sold off without factory mark, crest or inscription, such items are worth around 50% of the price of a normal item. Other plain items were travelling salesmen's examples.

Damage occuring in the period subsequent to manufacture such as cracks or chips affect values and any sub-standard piece with minor damage would be worth less than 50% of the perfect price. The same applies with restoration. In the past ten years, as prices of perfect items have risen, those of sub-standard items have risen by a higher percentage due to such pieces being cheaper and more plentiful.

I urge you however, to be especially vigilant when buying from market stalls, antique fairs and shops where dealers seem to disregard damage when endeavouring to sell their wares. Damaged items are usually overpriced, if indeed the damage has even been noticed by the dealer concerned, it must be fully allowed for in the price when buying. It is only when one comes to sell that the wisdom of this advice will become apparent. It is however, perfectly acceptable to buy damaged pieces at damaged prices.

No forecast can be made as to whether prices will rise or fall in the future, that will depend upon economic factors. During the last decade however, prices have risen strongly with rarer items increasing many times faster than the smaller pots and vases and the more common shapes. Over the years crested china has been a very good investment with all the fun of collecting thrown in. This price guide, now in its fifth edition, can only further interest in the hobby.

The Goss & Crested China Club would be pleased to hear of any pieces or unusual or notable crests or decorations (apart from non-models and domestic ware) that are not mentioned in the listings in this guide or in the main book for inclusion in future editions.

Should you wish to sell please note that the prices in this guide are used as a basis for purchasing and that we will pay good, fair market prices for all items offered. Please send us a list of the pieces that are for sale or part-exchange stating in each case the factory, height, crest and condition in order to receive our individual offers.

Nicholas Pine

Introduction

Collecting heraldic porcelain miniatures became a national craze in late Victorian and Edwardian times when it is thought that some 90% of all homes contained some 'crested china' as it is now popularly known. Between 1890 and 1930 no holiday or trip to the seaside was complete without a porcelain memento, with the arms of the place in which it was purchased. For dedicated collectors, the trip away was merely a means of acquiring the next prized piece, for agencies were quite strict in only stocking local arms. To get a Llandudno crest one really did have to go to Llandudno!

Sales of souvenirs were boosted by the introduction of Bank holidays in 1871, paid holidays for workers and improved wages. These factors, combined with improved travel by train, paddlesteamer, charabanc and bicycle, saw the advent of a nation that was becoming more inquisitive and acquisitive.

In the 1880s, the pottery firm of W.H. Goss of Stoke-on-Trent had begun a new line, miniature souvenir ware for Queen Victoria's Jubilees and for pupils of public schools. The eldest son of William Henry Goss who had invented his own particular type of parian, Adolphus Goss, hit on the idea of reproducing miniatures of famous antiquities found in museums all over the country, and decorating them with the relevant coats of arms. These 'matching' crests as they were popularly termed soon gave way to agents (appointed originally by Adolphus who was also the firm's traveller), being able to order any of his shapes with their own respective local arms. These artefacts and models started off a whole national craze, with Goss producing miniature cottages after 1893 and increasing their range to historic models, early religious crosses, animals and fonts.

The 1880s and 1890s were hard times for the British pottery industry, virtually all centred in the Staffordshire pottery towns, and hundreds of other manufacturers leapt to cash in on the Goss prosperity and fame. Whilst the Goss factory kept to the exact and sober representation of objects of historic importance, often found in museums or famous landmarks other potteries took a new lead in producing more light-hearted souvenirs, with comical, puzzling, exaggerated and amusing connotations of every conceivable theme, ranging from alcoholic souvenirs, hats, shoes, black cats, musical instruments, pillar boxes to modes of transport and even everyday domestic items. In short, they brought a sense of fun into collecting which suited the mood of the country and the humour of the day

The Germans had always competed against the British china industry and souvenir ware was their speciality. It was mostly ornate domestic shapes including ribbon plates, baskets, jug and bowl sets and tankard mugs that were made, heavily decorated with gilded scrolls, bouquets of flowers, or even completely bright pink. Transfer scenes were used more than crests.

The German, Austrian and Czechoslovakian potteries were flooding the British market, with even the inmates of the German prisons being used as cheap labour to produce their own souvenir ware. They were unwilling to compete with their own potteries at home, so they decorated their wares with British emblems and exported to the UK with determination. After and even during the first world war, they disguised the origins of their wares by using Austrian and Czechoslovakian marks and exporting via these countries.

Often the spelling of the crest was incorrect, which rather adds to the charm. They used greyish, hard paste porcelain or very white bisque which was less expensive to produce than porcelain, up to date kilns and cheap labour, so even with the added cost of exporting, they were able to supply wares more cheaply than British potters and so were successful commercially. In 1905 a German firm 'Mosanic' could take an order for a reproduction model of a building in Britain, send back a postcard photograph of it to their German pottery, and have the order in the British shops within a fortnight. Their British counterparts maintained that their own slow delivery was due to the care and skill in manufacture. An over-used advertising slogan in the Staffordshire pottery industry at the time was 'Best English China at foreign prices'. Stockists of crested china varied from newspaper stands at railway stations, lending libraries, tea rooms, fancy goods shops and chemists to specialist china shops, Boots and W.H. Smith.

The Goss factory was the most accurate in its use of arms. Where there was none, or permission had not been obtained, the registration seal (No 77966) was used, together with some emblem within the seal to represent the particular place. Other potteries simply invented their own designs instead to fulfil orders. Some rather odd creations can be found masquerading as correct heraldic devices. This does, however add interest when collecting a particular town or area.

Most crested ware was decorated after it was glazed. For a full account of how crested china was made, fired and decorated, see *William Henry Goss – The Story of the Staffordshire Family of Potters who Invented Heraldic Porcelain* by Lynda and Nicholas Pine (Milestone Publications).

Coats of arms were decorated by means of a transfer of the black outline of the crest being affixed, then coloured in, each different colour needing time to dry before the next was applied. Some items were in themselves coloured partly or fully, and the Arcadian and Willow black boy series was typical of its time - it certainly could not be produced now. The sales of transfer printed view wares declined with the popularity of the picture postcard, at the turn of the century and therefore transfers are very much less common than coats of arms.

By 1910 *The Pottery Gazette* was predicting that the craze would soon be over. Indeed, all through the regular weekly copies published over the decades during 'crest china' production, *very* little is mentioned apart from advertisements, possibly because many suspected its popularity would be short-lived.

The charm of heraldic china lays in its representing a bygone era. The transfer scenes show buildings long gone, deserted narrow lanes where by-passes now rule the day, ladies in long skirts and leg o'mutton sleeved blouses, and gentlemen, wearing boaters, walking with canes. Captured in porcelain are the comedians of the day like Ally Sloper, Jackie Coogan, and cartoon characters such as Felix the Cat and Bonzo. Even those funny little seated billikens, sometimes found named 'God of Luck', invented by Florence Pretz in America in 1908, soon found their way over here. Who knows who 'Dr Beetle' and Teddytail' are now?

The First World War caught Britain at the height of its collecting craze, and although the nation's men were drafted to the Front, the potteries soldiered on and carried out a good trade in producing tanks, guns, military figures, shells and grenades. After the war, memorials were none too popular, apart from the Cenotaph, and the majority are scarce.

When a fresh mood swept the nation after peace had been signed in 1919, the craze for crests was on the decline. Out with the old, in with the new. The older amongst us will possibly remember their parents consigning collections to the dustbin. I have lost count of the number of times I have been told that 'Mother threw out a bathful after the war'. It is quite likely that only 10% of what was originally made now exists.

From the late sixties onwards, boxes of crested china were to be found unwanted in corners of second-hand shops, at a penny a piece, with few takers. By the seventies the Crested Circle, now defunct and Goss & Crested China Ltd. had been formed and John Magee's monthly auction and magazine, *Goss News,* were gaining in popularity. 1980 saw the publication of *Crested China* by Sandy Andrews and the first *Price Guide* to *Crested China* soon after. We started publishing a monthly catalogue of Goss china for sale in 1970 and have never missed a month since then. The Goss & Crested China Club now has over 2,000 members and continues to thrive. This book is now in its fifth edition and its popularity shows that collecting heraldic porcelain is indeed a craze again.

Nicholas Pine

Manufacturers and Trade Marks

The plethora of different manufacturers, wholesalers, retailers, marks and names found on the bases of crested china can be confusing to those not familiar with heraldic china. There are perhaps only eight major and a further two relatively important manufacturers who accounted for the bulk of crested china produced. These are followed by over one hundred very minor firms, which are usually only responsible for the production of a handful of pieces, and often only then as a sideline to their main areas of manufacture.

In order that the original manufacturer of a piece may be ascertained more easily, the following table should be referred to as an aid to identification. Under the name of the manufacturer that firm's main trade name has been given in bold in each case. Under this name will be found all known trade marks that can be attributed to that firm.

Therefore, if you have a piece that does not appear in the listings for that particular mark, try looking it up in the following table and check under firstly, the main and then under the subsidiary marks until it is located, you can then note the value of the item.

I have therefore included below a table of manufacturers showing the various trademarks that they used. Often these are retailers, agents or wholesalers.

Every known example of factory mark has been drawn and illustrated in its relevant listing.

Table of the principal manufacturers of Crested China and their Trade Marks, Subsidiaries and other firms using their products

Arkinstall & Son
Arcadian China
Albion China
Aldwych China
Amber China
Arcadian China
Avon China
Birks Crest China
Botolph
Boots
Bute China
Carmen China
Christop China
C.J.B. & Co
Clarence China

Clifton
Coronet Ware
Endor China
Excelsior
Ford & Pointon
FL
FP & S
The Griffin China
Grosvenor Series
Hamilton China
Iceni Crest China
JW
Kensington China
Kingsway Art or Crest China
LAB

Lion Brand
Lynton China
C McDMann & Co Ltd
Nelson China
One and All
Palatine China
Porcelle
Queens Crest China
R & L
Robinson & Beresford
Robinson & Leadbeater
Rostrevor
Raphael China
Shamrock China
Skareb
Snowdon China
Sporting Series
Sussex China S.P. Co.
Swan China
Tuskar Rock China
Vectis
Victis
Warwick China
Waverley China
Wembley China
Zuyder Zee China

Belleek Pottery
Belleek Pottery
Colleen China
Shamrock China

Wiltshaw & Robinson Ltd.
Carlton Ware
Aldwych China
Alpha China
Balmoral China
Bramwell China
Caledonia Heraldic China
Cambrian China
Carlton China
Craven China
Crown China
Cyclone
Eclipse China

Kahess China
Kangaroo Brand
Lion China
Lynton China
The Milton China
Mother Shipton China
Queens Crest China
Eugene Rimmel
Syren China

Sampson, Hancock & Sons
Corona
Alexandra
Anglo-Heraldic Co.
British Manufacture
C.J.B. & Co
The Corona China
Corona Ware
Dolphin
The Duchess China
Exceller
FL
Granic China
Grosvenor Ware
Heraldic China
JBM
Mayfair Ware
Melba China
Raleigh China
Regency Ware
Success Art China
Sussex China
Sussex China S.P. Co.
Talbot China
Triood
Tudor Arms China
Unity China
Victoria China
Waterloo Ware
Willper Heraldic China

E. Hughes & Co.
Fenton
Fenton China
E. Hughes & Co.
Royal China

Taylor & Kent
Florentine
Albion China
Atlas Heraldic China
Bell China
Bute China
C&SC
Cable China
Caledonia China
Civic
Coronet Ware
The Crown Duchy English China
Cyclone
The Dainty Ware
Doric Herald
Empress China
English China
English Manufacture
English Souvenir China
Excelsior
Filey China
Florentine China
Gladstone China
Griffin China
Hamilton China
Ionic Heraldic
Keltic
Kent Bone China
Lion Brand
Lochinvar
Poppyland China
Premier
Queen China
Royal Vale China
Taylor & Kent
Viking China

Charles Schmidt & Co.
Gemma
Alexandre
Empire
Empire Gem
Empress China
Durbar

Elite
Fairy Ware
Gemma
Manx Legs
Ness China
Rococco
Victoria

Alfred B. Jones & Sons Ltd.
Grafton China
ABJ & Sons
Argosy
Aurelian China
Best English Make
CP & Co.
Diamond China
Elite
Elite H.M. & Co.
English China
English Make
English Herald China
Grafton China
Herald China
Herald Series
King China
Maxem China
C.L. Reis & Co.
Royal Grafton
Wil-Wat China

Wm. Kutzscher & Co;
Impero
Imperial
Princess China
Regent China
St. George China
W.H.H. and S.
Unmarked
Saxony
Made in Saxony

Edwin Leadbeater
H&L
Leadbeater Art China
Marine Art China

Nornesford China
Panorama
R&M

James MacIntyre
MacIntyre
Argonauta Porcelain
Caledonia China
Caledonia Heraldic China

Max Emanuel & Co.
Mosanic
Maxim China
Unity China
Austria
Czechoslovakia
Foreign
Germany

Nautilus Porcelain Co.
Nautilus Porcelain
British Nautilus
Celtic Porcelain
Lochinvar

Podmore China Co.
Podmore
Strand China

Robinson & Leadbeater
Robinson & Leadbeater
R&L
Royal Ivory Porcelain
Ryecroft China Series
Victorian Porcelain
Wy Not?

Birks, Rawlins & Co.
Savoy China
Aldwych China
Birks China
Birks Rawlins & Co.
Bow China
B.S. & Co.

Caledonia China
Caledonia Heraldic China
Diamond China
Do! Do! Crest China
Empire China
Endor China
Ivora Ware
JW & Co.
Mermaid
Niagara Art China
Patriotic China
Porcelle
Queens China or Ware
C.L. Reis & Co.
Rex China
Savoy China
Universal Series
W.R.F.S.

Wileman & Co
Shelley China
E.B. & Co.
Foley Bone China
Foley E.B. & Co.
The Foley China

R.H. & S.L. Plant Ltd.
Tuscan China
Nornesford China
Rowena China
Shamrock Crest China

Charles Waine & Co.
Venetia China
CW & Co.
Etruscan China
Kyle Series

James Reeves
Victoria China
Botolph China
English Emporium China
Gothic China
J.R. & Co.

Hewitt and Leadbeater

Willow Art China
Abbey China
Alexandra China
Asbury China
Balmoral China
Cable China
Caledonia Heraldic China
Cascade China
Challenge China
Clays
Curzon Art
Dainty Crest China
Devonia Art China
Diamond China
Disa Art China
Do! Do! Crest China
Dougall's "Castle" Series
Eglinton China
Elite China Series
English Manufacture
Esbeco
Famous Henley China
FCCH
H&L
H&S
JBC
Jerusalem & Orient Bazaar
Kangaroo Art China
Kensington China
Kingsway Art China
Kingsway Crest China
Kursaal China
Lochinvar
Marine Art China
Meir Arms China
The Milton China
Niagara Art
Norfolk Crest China
Oxford Art China
Palmer
Panorama
Pearl Arms China
Ramshorn

Real English China
Regis
Reliance Art China
Royal Ivory Porcelain
Roman Bath China
J. Shaw
Signal China
St. Pauls
Star Bazaar Art China
Success (Art) China
Sussex Ware
Thistle China
T.C. & P.G.
T.M.W. & Co & S Ltd.
Tourist Art China
Towy China
Tudor Arms China
Victoria Arms China
Viking China
Waterfall Heraldic China
W.H.H. and S.
Wilco Series
Wordsworth Art China
Willow China
W and R
Why Not
Wy Not

Explanation of Entries

Entries have been arranged by trademark in alphabetical order, with manufacturer's name, if known, and recorded models after each mark.

The models have been grouped into types of souvenirs and have been arranged for the most part in the order in which they would have been made. Two themes are now listed under their own heading, namely hats and footwear, formerly included under Miscellaneous. The headings are as follows:

Ladies and Figures, Coloured

Unglazed/Parian
Parian busts are also found under this heading.

Ancient Artefacts
Models of historic interest.

Buildings - Coloured

Buildings - White
Including bridges

Monuments (including Crosses)

Historical/Folklore

Traditional/National Souvenirs
These have been listed in the following order: Britain, England, Ireland, Scotland, Wales, other countries.

Seaside Souvenirs
These have been listed in the following order: Bathing Machines, Crafts, Fishermen/ Lifeboatmen, Lighthouses, Shells, People and Punches.

Bathing Belles/Twenties Flappers

Figures
These listings include only the figures which do not belong under any other heading.

Countryside

Animals
These listings include animals which are really regional symbols as the Sussex Pig. Most collectors would include these in an animal collection. Also includes Black cats.

Birds (including Eggs)
These listings also include regional or national emblems such as the Kiwi.

Great War
These models have been grouped as follows: Personnel, Aeroplanes / Airships / Zeppelins, Ships / Submarines, Armoured Cars / Red Cross Vans / Tanks, Guns / Mortars, Small arms, Shells, Bombs, Grenades, Mines Torpedoes,

Personal Equipment, Memorabilia and Memorials. Where a factory is known to have produced regimental badges, a list of these precedes the listing in that section. (Florence Nightingale statues are always included in Great War collections although she died before 1914. Certainly the statue was offered for sale at the same time, so it is listed under this heading).

Home/Nostalgic

Comic/Novelty
Includes Black Boys

Cartoon/Comedy Characters
Includes Felix the Cat and other copyrighted characters.

Alcohol

Sport/Pastimes
This section includes card trump symbols and chess pieces. Sporting items have been listed first, then those used for pastimes.

Musical Instruments

Transport

'Modern' Equipment
'Modern', that is, at the time it was made.

Hats

Footwear
These listings also include regional or national symbols such as the Lancashire clog and Dutch sabot.

Miniature Domestic

Domestic

Miscellaneous

> Under these headings models are listed alphabetically, if that is possible. All inscriptions and verses are printed in *italics*.
>
> If a model is best described by its inscription this will be placed at the beginning of an entry in *italics*.
>
> Sizes are height unless otherwise stated.
>
> All values are given in £ and p in Sterling currency.

Crested China Manufacturers

A

Abbey China

Trademark probably used by J.A. Robinson Ltd. (usual trademark Arcadian) for a Cornish retailer. One small has been seen with the above trademark. It has the crest of Rostrevor, Cornwall.

Trademark used by J.A. Robinson Ltd. and Hewitt & Leadbeater for a fancy goods retailer or wholesaler in Tewkesbury. Usual trademarks Arcadian and Willow Art.

Stock numbers where known as Willow Art.

For details of this china and manufacturers see Arcadian China, Willow Art and Willow China. C C of Tewkesbury must have been a wholesaler as crests from several places have been recorded; these include Cheddar, Devizes, Upton on Severn and Winscombe as well as Tewkesbury. Possibly the firm owned a chain of souvenir shops. No view ware or late transfers have been found on models with this mark.

Abbey Models
Ancient Artefacts
Puzzle Jug No. 68/89 73mm.   7.00

Seaside Souvenirs
Lighthouse pepper pot. 110mm.   7.50
(There is almost certainly a
   matching salt pot.)

Animals
Black Cat, operating radio. (Arcadian
   Registered Series No. 13). 68mm.   115.00
Cat, sitting, one ear down. 102mm.   16.00
Dog, sitting, red eyes. Bow to neck
   No. 23. 67mm   16.00

Birds
Peewit posy holder. 78mm long.   10.00

Home/Nostalgic
Grandfather Clock, inscribed: *Make
use of time let not advantage slip.
Shakespeare.* No. 149. 140mm.   15.00

Cartoon/Comedy Characters
Baby with arms outstretched,
   inscribed: *Cheerio.* Some
   colouring on face. 125mm.   30.00

Alcohol
Toby Jug. 80mm.   15.00

Sport/Pastimes
Cricket Cap. 62mm. long.   50.00

Domestic
Barrel Jug with grapevine in relief
   90mm.   8.00

ABJ & Sons

Trademark used by Alfred B. Jones and Sons
   Ltd., Grafton Works, Longton, Staffs.
For all details of manufacturer and china,
   please see Grafton China entry.

Wm. Adams & Sons

Adderleys

Usually found without the addition of
  Egyptian Heraldic shields, which refers
  to a particular range.
JW Adams & Sons, Tunstall produced some
  ornamental ware and domestic china with
  crests for Langhams China Shop, Bury St
  Edmunds.
The pieces produced are worth £5.00 or
  more.

A 78mm vase in a matt black finish
  with a yellow and orange pattern around
  the neck has been recorded.   12.50

This vase has been found with the above
  trademark overstamped with *Egyptian
  Heraldic* bearing the arms for Burns.

Used 1912-1926.

Used 1912-1926.

Trademark used by Adderleys Ltd. Daisy
  Bank Pottery, Longton.
Adderleys Ltd., established in 1906
  manufactured china and earthenware
  throughout the 'crested china' period.
  They did not as far as is known
  manufacture crested ware but they did
  produce a range of 'smalls' to
  commemorate the Great War, these are
  inscribed: 1914 EDITION, and are often
  found in Great War china collections.

Range of 'smalls' to commemorate
  the Great War - inscribed: 1914
  WAR EDITION.   from 10.00

A.F. & S.

1887-1901.

Trademark used by Alfred Fenton & Sons, Brook Street, Hanley.
No details of this factory or its products are available.

Alba Pottery

Trademark used by a British pottery for exported goods. The only model found has an Honduras crest.

Alba Model
Monuments
Iona Cross. 110mm.   14.00

Albion China
(Robinson & Beresford)

1907-1910.

This mark originally thought to be a variation of the Albion China T.C. & P. mark now appears clearly to be a mark used by J.A. Robinson Ltd. (Usual mark Arcadian). As they took over Robinson & Beresford (see below) they presumably went on using the 'Albion China' trademark.

In 1901 Mr W.H. Robinson set up as a china manufacturer in Longton, specialising in Queens White Ware. In 1903 Mr Robinson had need to take into partnership a Mr Beresford and the firm was then known as Robinson and Beresford. The firm seems to have been under financed from the start and by 1907 Harold Taylor Robinson (see Arcadian China) had gained control and merged Robinson and Beresford with Charles Ford (see Swan China). In 1910 these firms were made branches of J.A. Robinson Ltd.

All known models with the Albion China mark are exactly the same as Arcadian and Swan pieces. It is unlikely that Robinson and Beresford made crest china before the merger, and as only early models and 'smalls' have been recorded it seems that the Albion mark was not used after 1910.

Numbering System. The stock numbers found on the base of Albion models are exactly the same numbers as found on Arcadian models and are listed below. The dashes and other painted symbols found near the trademark are paintresses' marks.

Albion (Robinson and Beresford) Models

Ancient Artefacts

Ancient Tyg, Model of. 68mm.	5.50
Exeter Vase. 65mm.	5.50
Glastonbury Bowl, No.55. 50mm.	5.50
Kendal Jug 75mm.	5.50
Lincoln Jack, inscribed: *Model of the Lincoln Jack from original in museum.* No.50. 63mm.	5.50
Loving Cup originated by Henry of Navarre King of France. 2 or 3 handled. No.579. 40mm.	6.50
Newbury Leather Bottle. No. 83. 65mm.	5.50
Portland Vase. No. 52. 45mm.3.00	5.50
Shrewsbury Salopian Ewer, inscribed: *Roman Salopian Ewer found at Uriconium now in Shrewsbury museum.* No. 613. 75mm	5.50
Silchester Vase. No. 54. 60mm.	5.50

Historical/Folklore

Ancient Coaching Hat, Model Of. No. 687. 65mm long.	12.50

Albion China (T.C. & P)

Usual mark 1913-25.

Mark only rarely found and thought to be a variation used by the firm.

Mark only seen on a model of a leather-bound 60mm book.

Trademark used on china made for a Scottish wholesaler by Taylor and Kent (Ltd.) Florence Works, Longton. (Usual trademark Florentine.)

For details of this china and manufacturer see Florentine China.

'Smalls' and models found with this mark have Scottish crests or coloured transfer printed views. Some useful crested domestic ware has been recorded including plates, beakers, bagware vases and a money box with a handle 70mm long. (Stock numbers were not used by Taylor and Kent).

The initials T. C. and P are probably those of the wholesalers. They are remarkably similar to the initials T.C. and P.G. which appear on Thistle China, manufactured for L.M. Mack, Ayr. However, we have no further evidence to suggest any connection between the two.

Albion (T.C. and P) Models
Ancient Artefacts

Aberdeen Bronze Pot. 57mm.	5.50
Canterbury Roman Vase. No. 289.	5.50
Glastonbury Bowl. 40mm.	5.50
Irish Bronze Pot. No.62. 42mm.	5.50
Newbury Leather Bottle 64mm.	5.50
Puzzle Jug. 67mm.	6.50
Scarborough Jug 53mm.	5.50
York Roman Ewer Inscribed: *Roman Ewer from the original in Hospitium. Found at York*	

Buildings - White

Blackpool Tower. 120mm.	12.50

Historical/Folklore

Mother Shipton. 72mm.	8.50

Traditional/National Souvenirs

Welsh Hat with blue or white band. 62mm.	7.50

Seaside Souvenirs

Lighthouse on rocky base. 100mm.	7.50
Whelk Shell. 100mm long.	5.50
Yacht. 130mm.	12.00

Animals

Camel, kneeling. 100mm long.	16.50
Cat sitting, very furry coat. 90mm.	17.00
Cat, Cheshire - inscribed: *Always smiling* 90mm.	15.00
Cat, Manx. 90mm long.	30.00
Dogs, 2 Spaniel pups in top hat. 72mm.	20.00

Dolphin Jug. 100mm.	6.50
Elephant kneeling. 88mm long.	25.00
Frog Jug. 80mm long.	10.00
Hare. 95mm long.	12.50
Pig standing. Can be found with the inscription: *The Pig that won't go.* 90mm long.	16.00
Toad. 35mm.	30.00

Birds

Canary on rock 98mm.	12.00
(Giant) Hen, brooding. 91mm long.	12.00
Pelican Jug. 83mm long.	7.00
Swan posy holder. 80mm.	5.00

Great War

Bust of Sailor. 85mm.	45.00
Monoplane with roundels and 4-bladed movable propeller. 170mm long.	115.00
Tank, (wide Florentine mould with side guns standing proud.) 125mm long.	50.00
With guns adjacent	50.00
Shell. 75mm.	7.50
Bury St. Edmunds Bomb. 75mm.	17.50

Home/Nostalgic

Book. 60mm	10.00
Firebucket. 65mm.	5.00
Old Armchair, The with verse. 85mm.	10.00
Lamp. 69mm.	5.00
Pillar Box. 76mm.	12.00
Portmanteau. 60mm long.	5.00
Shaving Mug. 56mm.	7.50

Comic/Novelty

Negro Minstrel, bust, some colouring. 100mm.	40.00

Modern Equipment

Box Gramophone. 58mm.	25.00

Musical Instruments

Grand Piano. 83mm long.	16.00
Harp. 92mm.	7.00

Alcohol

Carboy. 76mm.	5.00

Footwear

Boot,with gold buckle. 95mm long.	5.00
Lancashire Clog. 88mm long.	5.00

Oriental Slipper. 100mm long.	5.00

Miniature Domestic

Coffee Pot with lid. 76mm.	9.00
Dish, circular with 3 handles. 80mm.	4.00
Jelly Mould. 53mm.	10.00
Tea Pot with lid. 60mm.	9.00
Tea Pot with lid, squat. 35mm.	9.00

Domestic

Candle Stick and holder with snake curled around stem. 105mm.	6.00

Aldwych China

Mark used on wares manufactured by Arkinstall & Son Ltd.

Mark used on wares manufactured by Birks, Rawlins & Co.

Mark used on wares manufactured by Wiltshaw & Robinson Ltd.

ALDWYCH CHINA
SAMUELS, STRAND, LONDON

Printed mark for items with bases too small to receive the normal marks.

Trade name used by the retailer, Samuels, The Strand, London on crested china manufactured by Arkinstall and Son Ltd. (usual trademark Arcadian), Birks, Rawlins and Co. (usual trademark Savoy), Wiltshaw and Robinson Ltd. (usual trademark Carlton) and Hewitt and Leadbeater (usual trademark Willow Art).

Stock numbers where known coincide with those used on other models made by above firms.

Samuels either changed their supplier often or all four companies produced crested wares for them at the same time. For details of the china and manufacturer see the appropriate entry in these lists. Many 'smalls' have also been recorded.

Aldwych (A and S) Models
Mark used on wares manufactured by Arcadian.

Parian/unglazed

Bust of George V. 130mm.	47.50
Bust of Queen Mary. 130mm.	47.50

Ancient Artefacts

Puzzle Jug. 67mm.	7.00

Buildings - White

St. Paul's Cathedral. 103mm.	22.00

Monument

Nelson's Column. 169mm.	80.00

Peter Pan

Statue. 140mm.	65.00

Animals

Elephant. 75mm long.	30.00
Monkey sitting.	
Hand to mouth. 77mm.	30.00
Tortoise. 72mm. long.	10.00

Birds

Cock, standing, inscribed: *Cock o'*	
the South. 100mm.	22.00
Swan. 50mm. long.	8.50

Great War

Tommy in Sentry Box, not named.	
105mm.	85.00
Cannon Shell, inscribed: *Jack*	
Johnson. 90mm.	8.50
Steel Helmet with EP on side.	
70mm long and only 24mm high.	47.00
HMHS Anglia 108mm. long	90.00

Home/Nostalgic

Grandfather clock, inscribed.	
2 sizes: 100mm.	10.00
108mm.	12.50
Village pump with trough 90mm.	7.50

Miscellaneous

Horseshoe. 55mm long.	4.00

Aldwych (BR and Co) Models
Mark used on wares manufactured by Savoy.

Most pieces found with this mark are small vases etc. Only one model has been recorded.

Countryside

Acorn, model of. No. 110. 56mm.	7.50

Aldwych (W & R) Models
Mark used on wares manufactured by Carlton.

Monuments

Nelson's Column with four lions at	
base. 165mm.	75.00

Birds (including eggs)

Swan 55mm.	8.50

Great War

Tank inscribed: *HMLS Creme de*	
Menthe. 150mm long.	47.00
Zeppelin with moulded iron cross	
on side 118mm.	150.00

Alexandra China

This mark can be found with with the word IVORY replacing CEBL.

Marks used on china made by Hewitt Bros.

Mark found on some domestic ware.

Mark used on London buildings and black cat transfers supplied by Hewitt and Leadbeater, (usual trademark Willow Art). This mark can be found with the word IVORY replacing CEBL.

Marks thought to be used by Sampson, Hancock & Sons (usual trademark Corona)

Trademark used by a wholesaler, china manufactured by several leading producers of crested china, particularly Sampson Hancock (Corona Pottery) and Hewitt & Leadbeater (Willow). CEB must have been a wholesaler for souvenir china with showrooms in London. Many such companies advertised in the *Pottery Gazette*, but so far I have been unable to place these initials. Alexandra China has presented an enormous problem for researchers, the china is of good quality and many of the buildings are not found in other ranges. All the buildings with the exception of the Bottle Oven are to be found in London, and many Alexandra models carry London crests. Once one had realised that the china was not made by one manufacturer and that the buildings were probably (with the exception of the Bottle Oven) made by Hewitt Bros (see Willow China) this mark is not so problematic.

It would seem that before the war CEB probably sold cheaper German china wares as there are very few early 'crested' models in the range. Most of the models in the Great War, animals and home/nostalgic categories appear to have been made for the firm by Sampson Hancock and Sons (see Corona China) during the war years. Many of the Alexandra models listed below will also be found in the Corona range including that puzzling Bottle Oven. Hewitt Bros seem to have become the supplier after the Great War, working to a higher standard than usual. The buildings are not recognisably Willow but one finds that hardly any London buildings are found marked Willow, the exception being Nelson's Column. A Cenotaph has been found bearing a Willow mark as well as an Alexandra mark which goes some way to proving this theory correct. Later 'smalls' and models with 'Lucky Black Cat' transfers were very obviously made by Hewitt Bros, the paintresses' marks and the stock numbers being identical. Many of the models listed below will also be found in the Willow range.

It is quite probable that other manufacturers made china for this wholesale firm and hopefully other clues will indicate which these were.

No view ware or foreign crests have been found with these marks, but 'Lucky Black Cat' transfers have been found on some later wares. No 'Lucky White Heather' devices have been found. The only war badges are Aldershot Command – Blackdown Camp, Aldershot Command – Deepcut Camp, Longmoor Camp and Cranwell.

Numbering System. Unfortunately stock numbers have not been recorded with any regularity. This is a pity as they would help in identifying manufacturers. Numbers are given where known.

Alexandra (Sampson Hancock) Models
Ancient Artefacts

Aberdeen Bronze Pot.	5.50
Bronze Bowl. 50mm.	5.50
Puzzle Jug No. 148. 73mm.	6.00

Buildings - White

Marble Arch. 75mm.	30.00
Bottle Oven. No. 233. 82mm.	20.00
St Pauls Cathedral.	
3 sizes: 90mm.	22.00
135mm.	40.00
142mm.	40.00
Tower Bridge.	
2 sizes: 140mm. long	45.00
150mm. long	50.00
Westminster Abbey, West Front.	
3 sizes: 90mm.	20.00
114mm.	22.00
130mm.	27.50

Monuments

Cleopatra's Needle. 130mm high,	
130mm wide.	150.00
Monument, The. 159mm.	150.00
Nelson's Monument. Trafalgar Square.	
165mm.	75.00

Historical/Folklore

Ark. 85mm long.	6.50
Burns and Highland Mary (also	
impressed WILLOW).117mm.	30.00
Man in the Moon. 35mm.	30.00
Peter Pan Statue. 144mm.	65.00

Traditional/National Souvenirs

Welsh Harp. No. 292. 95mm.	7.50
Welsh Hat. 50mm.	10.00

Seaside Souvenirs

Bathing Machine. 73mm.	12.00
Canoe. 106mm long.	9.00
Lighthouse. No. 192.	6.50
Scallop Shell hatpin holder on coral base	
2 sizes: 80mm.	10.00
92mm.	10.00
Shell. No. 56. 83mm long.	5.00

Animals

Bear, Polar. 185mm long.	50.00
Bear, Polar, sitting up. 100mm.	50.00
Cat in Boot. 93mm long.	26.50
Cat Candle Snuffer. 53mm.	17.00
Cat, sitting, with ruff of fur. 100mm.	30.00
Cat, sitting, very long neck. 68mm.	10.00
Cat, Manx, 75mm long.	30.00
Dog, Bulldog Puppy. 55mm.	30.00
Dog, Bulldog, standing. 63mm.	16.50
Can be found inscribed 'Duggie Haig' with Union Jack on back. 63mm.	200.00
Dog, Bulldog in Kennel (just face visible) 67mm.	25.00
Dog, Bulldog standing. 120mm long.	17.00
Dog, Scottie with glengarry 88mm.	15.00
Dog, Labrador Puppy, sitting. 80mm.	12.00
Fish,120mm long.	7.50
Fish Vase, 63mm.	5.00
Monkey holding coconut. 75mm.	25.00
Pig, standing, 80mm long.	17.00
Rabbit, crouching, ears back. 67mm long.	12.00
Shetland Pony 110mm long.	40.00
Teddy Bear sitting upright.	25.00

Birds

Swan, 51mm.	9.00
Swan posy holder. 78mm.	6.00
Wise Owl with verse. 110mm.	25.00

Great War

Monoplane, with movable prop. 145mm long.	77.50
British Airship on stand. 130mm long.	30.00
Battleship with 2 guns forward and 1 aft. 120mm long.	30.00
Lusitania. 163mm long.	140.00
Submarine, inscribed: E4. 110mm long.	30.00
Red Cross Van. 98mm long.	37.50

Tank with inset trailing wheels. 100mm long.	30.00
Renault Tank. 115mm long.	95.00
Field Gun. 130mm long.	30.00
Howitzer. 120mm long.	32.50
Torpedo. 150mm long.	55.00
Cannon Shell. 80mm.	9.00
Bell Tent. 85mm.	20.00
Bugle 72mm	30.00
Flash Lamp, flat. 90mm.	13.00
Gurkha Knife. 140mm long.	20.00
Ad Astra, Royal Air Force Memorial with inscription: Unveiled by HRH Prince of Wales July 16th 1923. gilded top. 170mm.	165.00
Cenotaph, inscribed: The Glorious Dead MCMXLV-MCMXLX, with green wreaths.	
3 sizes: 105mm.	8.50
145mm.	12.00
184mm.	15.00
Edith Cavell Memorial, London.	
2 sizes: 115mm.	19.00
155mm.	20.00
Florence Nightingale Statue. 146mm.	16.00

Home/Nostalgic

Anvil. 48mm.	5.00
The Old Armchair, with inscription. 95mm.	10.00
Baby in Bootee. 76mm.	14.50
Basket,1 handle. 58mm.	5.00
Cigarette Case. 70mm.	15.00
Hip Bath. 95mm long.	12.00
Chair, high backed. 105mm.	12.00
Desk, with inkwells. 58mm wide.	13.00
Grandfather Clock. 138mm.	16.00
Jardiniere and stand, one piece. No. 214. 85mm.	6.00
Pillar Box with GVR monogram, inscribed: If you haven't time to post a line, here's the pillar box. 78mm.	25.00
Pillar Box 70mm.	15.00
Sundial with verse. 112mm.	7.50
Tobacco Pouch. 75mm long.	9.00
Watering Can. 70mm.	10.00

Comic/Novelty

Baby standing, arms outstretched inscribed: Cheerio! 12mm	45.00
Hand holding flower. 80mm.	5.00
Man's Head, Cream Jug. 78mm.	10.00

Alcohol

Barrel on Stand. 65mm.	6.00
Hand holding a beaker. 50mm.	10.00
Spirit Flask.	
2 sizes: No. 242 65mm.	13.00
89mm.	13.00
Tankard No. 109. 63mm.	7.00

Sport/Pastimes

Club Trump indicator. 66mm.	6.00
Castle, chess piece. 67mm.	9.00
King chess piece.	
2 sizes: 82mm.	30.00
110mm.	40.00
Queen chess piece. 84mm.	30.00

Musical Instruments

Harp. 96mm.	6.00
Upright Piano. 62mm.	17.00

Transport

Petrol Can. No. 249. 66mm.	16.00

Modern Equipment

Gas Cooker. 70mm.	13.00
Gramophone, box. 55mm.	30.00

Footwear

Boot with buckle. 75mm long.	7.50
Ladies' Button Boot. 65mm.	12.00
Lancashire Clog. 83mm long.	6.00
Ladies' Riding Shoe with square toe and blue laces and tie.	
No. 118. 114mm long.	15.00
Ladies' 18th Century Shoe. 2 sizes:	
70mm & 85mm long.	7.50
Ladies' lace-up Walking Shoe, scalloped edge, button up.	
114mm long.	14.00
Sabot. 102mm long.	5.00

Miniature Domestic

Bagware Jug. 48mm.	4.00
Bowl with handle. 50mm.	4.00
Cheese Dish, 1 piece.	
2 sizes: 70mm long. No. 407.	7.50
82mm long.	7.50
Cheese Dish and cover.	
2 sizes: 50mm.	7.50
60mm.	7.50
Coffee Pot with lid. 75mm.	9.00
Kettle with lid. 85mm.	9.00
Tea Pot with lid, bagware. 70mm.	10.00
Tea Pot with lid, bulbous. 56mm.	10.00

Domestic

Candlestick. 84mm.	4.00
Initial Jug, "C" formed by handle.	
42mm.	15.00

Alexandra

Alexandra China H & Co.

Trademark used by C. Schmidt and Co., Carlsbad (Bohemia).

A wide range of domestic shapes and trinket boxes with lids coloured beige with maroon or green trim and a heavy embossment of gold around the coat of arms is found with this mark, together with similar ware marked Durbar, Gemma, Rococco, Victoria and Empire. Some also have gold bows painted above the arms, and numbers painted on the bases in gold. An important feature of this ware is the sprays of pink roses and rosebuds found on a pastel-coloured background with a glazed area for the crest.

Alexandra Model
Domestic
Pepper Pot. 75mm.   8.00

Trademark used by an unknown manufacturer for a Liverpool retailer.

The only model to have been recorded with the above mark is a 40mm. jug, valued at £4.00.

Alpha China

Amber China

"ALPHA" CHINA
A.O. & C?
B.

Trademark used by Wiltshaw and Robinson Ltd. (usual trademark Carlton). Presumably the initials, A.O. & Co. refer to a retailer.

Only a 75mm ewer has been recorded, this having the Yorkshireman's arms and verse.   14.00

Trademark used by a retailer or wholesaler probably in Manchester on pottery manufactured by Arkinstall & Son Ltd. (usual trademark Arcadian).

Amber Model
Great War
Tank with inset steering wheels.
110mm long.   30.00
Peaked Cap, amber coloured.
72mm long.   17.00

Anglo Heraldic Co

Trademark used by Sampson Hancock (& Sons), Bridge Works, Stoke (usual trademark Corona).

For details of this china and the manufacturer see Corona China.

Sampson Hancock appear to have used this mark before the Great War, as most pieces found with this mark are 'smalls', ancient artefacts (unfortunately un-named and therefore not often recorded as such) and the usual animals, shoes, etc. made before 1914.

Some pictorials and views are found on china with this mark but as yet only monochrome (black) transfers have been recorded. (Stock Numbers are the same as Corona models, and are listed where known).

Anglo Heraldic Models
Ancient Artefacts

Canterbury Leather Bottle. No.156.	5.50
Chichester Roman Ewer.65mm.	5.50
Glastonbury Bowl. 40mm.	5.50
Lincoln Jack. No.123. 57mm.	5.50
Loving Cup, 3 handled. No.135. 50mm.	6.50
Puzzle Jug with verse. No.148. 70mm.	6.00

Countryside

Milk Churn. No.168. 70mm.	6.50

Animals

Teddy Bear, sitting. 85mm.	25.00
Bulldog, standing.112mm long.	17.00

Cheshire Cat always smiling, The.

2 sizes: 85mm.	9.00
95mm.	10.00
Pig, standing. 84mm long.	17.00

Home/Nostalgic

Coal Scuttle.64mm.	5.00
Shaving Mug.58mm.	7.50
Watering Can. 70mm.	8.50

Footwear

Ladies' Button Boot. 65mm.	12.00
Ladies' 18th Century Shoe. No.146. 90mm long.	7.50

Miniature Domestic

Cheese Dish and cover.50mm.	8.50
Tankard. No. 178. 50mm.	7.00
Tea Pot with lid, frilled top. No.122. 65mm.	8.50
Tea Pot with lid. 65mm.	8.50

Arcadian China

From 1903.

Probably introduced 1910.

Probably introduced 1912.

ARCADIAN CHINA

Mark used on models with small bases
1903-20's.

ARCADIAN CHINA

Mark used on models with small bases
1920's.

Mark found on late domestic wares.

Mark used on wares to be sold in non-English speaking countries.

Trademark used from 1904 by Arkinstall & Son Ltd., Arcadian Works, Stoke on Trent subsequently a branch of J.A. Robinson & Sons, later Cauldon Ltd., and finally Coalport China Co. (John Rose & Co.) Ltd. and Aynsley.

Arkinstall & Sons were the largest British producers of crested china over the longest period, therefore, it follows that the history of the firm and its wares is of great importance to collectors and anyone interested in the development of popular china souvenirs from the early part of this century to just before the Second World War. The story of Arcadian China has to be the story of its owner Mr Harold Taylor Robinson, possibly the most interesting and important person in the Potteries during the period crested china was made. He was the central figure in the production and promotion of cheap china souvenirs for the lower end of the market. One cannot imagine that he did so with the integrity and enthusiasm for quality of some potters, the Goss family for example. He was first and foremost the entrepreneur, a brilliant and daring business man (his critics would add almost reckless), interested in china only as a marketable commodity. During his amazing career he managed to draw many of the most important crested china manufacturers, including Goss, into his enormous empire; a study of his business dealings and eventual bankruptcy does much to explain why so many identical pieces of crested china can be found with different marks.

Harold Taylor Robinson began his career as a traveller for Wiltshaw & Robinson (the makers of Carlton China) in 1899 when he was twenty-two years old. He was paid £156 per annum plus commission, and one can only assume that he managed to earn a huge amount of commission because he was able, four years later, in 1903 to start out on his own as a china manufacturer. With capital of approximately £1,500, which he claimed represented his savings, he formed the company Arkinstall & Son. Using the tradename 'Arcadian', Arkinstall produced china novelties and souvenirs, and was probably the only company formed specifically to manufacture crested china. Mr Robinson continued some kind of association with Wiltshaw and Robinson Ltd and became a partner in that firm by 1906. (The early Arcadian and Carlton crested wares were very similar). Mr Wiltshaw seems to have been unwilling to be taken over and he managed to keep the ownership and control of the company in his own hands. From 1903 to 1920 however Harold Taylor Robinson was interested alone or jointly in the acquisition of a number of china and earthenware manufacturing concerns, either for resale or to form new companies to take them over and run them.

He was particularly active in 1910; having gained control of Robinson & Leadbeater (R & L) he merged this firm with Arkinstall. This explains the number of R & L parian busts found with Arcadian marks. Later in August of that year having gained control of more firms he formed a new company, J.A. Robinson and Sons, Ltd. (J.A. Robinson was his father, the directors included Harold Taylor, his father and his brother, Hubert Alcock Robinson), to carry on the businesses of Robinson & Leadbeater, Charles Ford (Swan China) and Wardle's Art Pottery Ltd. Arkinstall became a branch of J.A. Robinson in 1912 and Ford & Pointon (Coronet), having been taken over by Mr Robinson, became yet another branch in 1919. From the dates of their amalgamation models marked Arcadian, Coronet and Swan are from the same moulds and were obviously produced in the same works.

At the 1920 British Industries Fair, J.A. Robinson presented a huge exhibit showing all types of ornamental and domestic china and earthenware, but this was just proof of the first stage of Harold Taylor Robinson's empire building. In April of that year he bought Cauldon (Brown, Westhead, Moore & Co) Ltd for £100,000 and promoted Cauldon Potteries Ltd to amalgamate most of the concerns he by then either owned or in which he had controlling interest. These included J.A. Robinson & Sons, Ltd. and branches, F.R. Pratt & Co. Ltd. (Greekware and sundries for chemists), Henry Alcock Pottery Co. (Fancy Goods), Grindley Hotel Ware (Hotel Vitrified Ware), Geo. L. Ashworth & Bros (Manufacturers of Masons ironstone), and Brown Westhead, Moore & Co. (Cauldon China, earthenware and fire proof ware).

Between 1910 and 1930, through a series of share deals, which although not dishonest were rather questionable morally, as he

was often the Managing Director of the firms buying and selling the shares, he managed to gain control of some of the bigger names in the china industry. Ridgways (Bedford Works) Ltd., Wedgwood & Co. Ltd., Tunstall (not to be confused with Josiah Wedgwood & Sons), Bishops & Stonier Ltd., The Coalport China Co., Royal Crown Derby Porcelain Co. Ltd., and Royal Worcester Porcelain were all in some way controlled by him. He moved into the sanitary ware side of the business too, gaining control of F. Winkle & Co. Ltd. and Baker & Co. Ltd.

On the way he picked up the almost bankrupt firms of W.H. Goss and Hewitt Bros. ((Willow)), forming in 1925 Willow Potteries Ltd. as part of the Cauldon Group and in 1930 W:H. Goss Ltd. He continued to use the moulds and marks of both companies, but from this date the quality of Goss China was never what it had once been. Most of these late Goss pieces are marked Goss England now termed Third Period, but this is not always the case. Models from the Arcadian and Willow ranges are often found with the Goss mark. In recent years, prices of items marked Arcadian or Willow have often exceeded those of those marked W H GOSS ENGLAND. The production of late coloured crested Arcadian and Willow China was obviously combined at the Arcadian Works in Stoke, the only difference between late Arcadian or Willow Black Boys being the mark printed on the base. The Willow mark was not used after 1930, there being no demand for it as crested china was already out of fashion.

During this period, 1920-30, Harold Taylor Robinson had become the largest employer in North Staffordshire, his interest in the fine china trade being such that he dominated it. His turnover during these years was between £850,000 and £900,000 per annum and he was the director of thirty-two companies. His ultimate scheme was to form an amalgamation of all the companies of which he obtained control into one huge company (perhaps he was a little before his time; such companies exist in the china industry today). It is not surprising, given his speculative genius, that at this stage he started buying into the companies of his suppliers, Parkhouse Collieries Ltd. and Goldenhill & Clive's Marl Co. Ltd. in order to provide cheap fuel and clay for his works.

Mr Robinson told the court during his bankruptcy hearing that he had been assured by a very important and respectable accountant that if outside events had not overtaken him he would by 1932 have been a millionaire; who could doubt it? Unfortunately, like so many other large concerns at the time, this enormous monument to enterprise he had so cleverly built came crashing down in that year, unable to withstand the crippling effects of world depression. He had had to face a series of disasters, beginning with the coal strike in 1921; the loss of foreign markets, notably America, Australia, West Canada and Brazil, as trade internationally was unsettled; the loss of the 'West End' trade in London (for the Depression hit the rich as well as the poor), and Britain going off the gold standard in 1924. He is quoted in the *Pottery Gazette* at his Bankruptcy Proceedings in 1932:

'When I saw the depression was developing to the extent it was, I left my country house and came to live practically next door to the works and I have been working fifty weeks out of fifty-two to try and circumvent the terrible effects of that depression.

'When you get down to basic facts you will realise that as the largest potter in North Staffordshire I have been the largest victim.'

In his frantic efforts to save his empire, his financial dealings became more and more wild. He borrowed money from the banks that he had no hope of repaying, he distributed money and stocks from one of his firms to another in an enormous and over optimistic attempt to keep afloat. His efforts came to nothing and when he was declared bankrupt most of his firms were already in the hands of the Receiver.

Throughout his bankruptcy and discharge proceedings (for which he petitioned in 1934) no one had call to question his honesty, but his dealings could only be described as unorthodox and disturbed and often puzzled the judge, but not as

much as his behaviour while still a bankrupt. The Secretary of the Cauldon Potteries had been buying up the debts on the debtors' behalf for very small sums. Fifty-three creditors had sold their debts amounting to £3,733 for £593. Rates varied alarmingly, ranging from 1s.5d. to 20s. in the £. Some of these people were creditors who would have received nothing out of the bankruptcy, whereas preferential creditors got nothing at all.

'Do you suggest that he is only acting for the debtor in this matter?' asked the judge.

'I say that he is the bankrupt's catspaw,' answered a very heated Official Receiver.

Harold Taylor absolutely denied any knowledge of the transactions. The judge refused to discharge Mr Robinson for a further two years.

Proving once more that it had been impossible to keep a 'good' man down, Mr Robinson had already been appointed Sales Organiser of the newly formed company, George Jones and Sons Ltd. in 1933 when the old established firm of George Jones had been merged with Bishops & Stonier. The new company continued to use the Crescent Potteries that had always been the home of the George Jones firm. Mr Robinson must have been a fairly good Sales Organiser, for George Jones and Sons Ltd. soon bought up the old and well-known firm of Allertons. Later in 1933 Cauldon merged with Coalport China Co. (John Rose & Co.) Ltd.; the Arcadian trademark was still being used, as was Goss. One could almost guess what would happen next! In 1937 the Coalport China Co. was amalgamated with George Jones and Sons, Cauldon, Coalport, Allertons, Crescent and Goss china were all produced at the Crescent Pottery. Arcadian had disappeared without trace and the Goss trademark was not listed by the firm after the Second World War. It probably was not used after 1939. What happened to Harold Taylor Robinson after 1933 is not clear: an employee at the Crescent Potteries in the late thirties has no recollection of him, and he is certainly not listed as an officer of that firm. He was by then in his sixties and it may well be that he had retired. The two surviving companies from this last merger have both been sold, Cauldon Potteries Ltd. was acquired by Pountney & Co. Ltd. of Bristol in 1962 and Coalport became a division of the Wedgwood Group in 1977.

Having considered his career, it is not at all surprising to learn that Mr Robinson made a huge commercial success out of his first company, Arkinstall and Sons. W.H. Goss had an agent in every reasonably sized town in Britain; Arkinstall's Arcadian was sold in just about every conceivable retail outlet across Britain; bazaars, lending libraries, cafés, pubs, seaside kiosks, stationers, fancy emporiums, pharmacies, subpost offices as well as china shops. The wares of the company were not advertised in trade journals, probably because Arcadian retailers were unlikely to read them, and Harold Taylor Robinson relied on a large team of travellers to bring back the orders. They obviously left no stone unturned!

Arcadian China is not particularly fine, it cannot be compared with Shelley or Grafton wares, but it is adequate and really quite well produced when one considers the selling price. ('Smalls' were usually sold for less than a shilling). Early wares for the most part were copies of the historic shapes sold by Goss on the one hand and the small animals and grotesques of the German souvenir industry on the other. It is very difficult to assess which of these early models were original Arcadian moulds and which were brought to the firm as a result of all the mergers. It was during the war years that Mr Robinson showed his flair for innovation, when Akinstalls' provided the war-minded public with an enormous range of crested military souvenirs. Often these models were designed from newspaper descriptions and are therefore very unlike the real thing, but as the public had not seen them either no one seemed to mind. As each new weapon was brought into the war Mr Robinson showed great speed in making a china model of it. The day after the *Daily Mail* ran a photograph of the first tank, Mr Robinson registered his model (Rd. No. 658588). The tank had seen some action and had lost one of its steering wheels. Unfortunately this was not explained, and the first china tanks also had only one wheel, and looked very

odd! He soon corrected his mistake. Mr Robinson had the copyright on models of British tanks, so I doubt if he lost much sleep over it as he collected the dues from all the other manufacturers. (Nearly all the early tanks carry the same registration number).

It was during the war years and immediately afterwards that Arcadian became the brand leader in the china souvenir field. (They were particularly busy after the war making the Memorials which were sold for many years). In 1921 Arkinstalls were described to trade as 'Manufacturers of Arms China Miniatures and Coats of Arms Tea Ware' and apart from Goss they were the only firm who made little else. By the mid-1920s they were offering models with a great deal of colouring and introduced their popular Black Cat series. A catalogue from this period has been discovered; although undated it must have been produced around 1925. It is particularly short on words but visually it provides us with an enormous amount of information. The Black Cats were obviously a new and important line as they were the only items illustrated in colour. The cheapest Black Cats sold for 12/- per dozen to the retailer, the most expensive for 18/-. 'Smalls' were only 4/6 per dozen and small animals 6/-, whereas models of St. Paul's were as much as 36/- per dozen. Certain items were sold to retailers as singles, these being large domestic pieces such as fern pots and tobacco jars; one of these, a delightful Art Deco 'Ballet Girl Puff Box' priced at 5/- has not as yet been found by collectors, presumably few were made as they were so expensive. At this time the catalogue offers any of the models in 'Arms China, Black Cat, 'Good Luck From', Lucky White Heather or Coloured Views'.

After 1925, for the most part, only coloured models were added to the range. These include Black Boys, cute children and novelty, joke items, all unique to this firm and particularly appealing. The crests found on these models are purely incidental and one suspects they would have sold just as well with a simple 'Souvenir from' message. The craze for crests was nearly over so it is surprising to find a large advertisement in the *Daily*

Mail 22nd May 1928 for 'Arcadian Arms China'. It reads:
'Arcadian Arms China can be obtained from over 10,000 Retail Fancy Goods Stores in practically every town and village in Great Britain, decorated in correct colours with local Coat-of-Arms.

If not already collecting Arcadian Arms China, START AT ONCE! It is a fascinating hobby.

The collection of Arcadian Arms China creates an added interest and preserves pleasant recollections of a holiday. Friends will appreciate nothing better than a gift of Arcadian Arms China on your return.

No other souvenir is so conveniently carried home.'

Arcadian China can be found decorated with a great number of other devices and designs. View ware, both monochrome (black only) and polychrome, was produced throughout the life of the company. A huge number of views and pictorials of reasonable quality can be found, usually on small vases and named artefacts but occasionally on animals, Great War and other unlikely models. Transfer prints of a regional nature are very desirable; these include: *Devonshire Dumplings, Hampshire Hog, Somerset Cuckoo, Trusty Servant, Yorkshireman's Advice, Welsh Teaparty* and various tartans.

Later, other transfer prints were introduced, the most popular being the Lucky Black Cats which can be found in great quantity on small pieces and domestic ware. Less easily found transfers are the range of tropical looking birds on branches; these can be coloured yellow, yellow and brown, pink and brown and pink and blue; they are usually found inscribed: *A Gift from . . .* or more unusually *A Souvenir from . . . .*

Other transfer prints have some hand colouring added, the same technique as used on crests. These include *Lucky White Heather,* Raphael Tuck Cartoons and an early range of beautifully and brightly coloured cocks and hens. The Lucky White Heather device is found on many small models and domestic ware, either of which can have a lustre finish or be made in cream ware. The Raphael Tuck cartoons, usually of a small Dutch boy and

girl, or Darby & Joan figures in Dutch costumes are found on small and domestic china including nursery ware. 'By Special Permission of Raphael Tuck & Sons Ltd', is usually found printed on domestic ware. Various mottoes accompany these cartoons, including such gems as:

He that is satisfied is rich.
None but the brave deserve the fair.
No life can be dreary when work is a delight.
Deeds are fruits, words are but leaves.
A good life and health are a man's best wealth.
Tis deeds alone must win the prize.
He loves me! He loves me not! He loves me!

Cockerel or Hen transfers have only been found on small vases and jugs of various sizes and they are quite rare. These too are found with rather trite mottoes and sayings, but oddly not the same as the ones above. They are:

Joy, temperance and repose slam the door on the Doctor's nose.
If you can't be aisy, be as aisy as you can.
All the world's a stage and man in his time plays many parts.
Little and often fills the purse.
To err is human to forgive divine.
A handsome shoe often pinches the foot.

Pieces bearing mottoes invariably also have Green Trim.

How many relatives were irrevocably offended by receiving one of these offerings is not recorded.

Floral transfer decorations are also rarely found, red poppies being the most visible, but forget-me-nots and much later floral designs of sprays of mixed flowers were also used, although they are difficult to find, as are the transfer prints of butterflies, but they do exist.

In 1921 Arkinstalls advertised 'Nursery Rhyme Ware', but very little of this has survived. One example is a child's plate with a charming hand coloured transfer print of *Ride a Cock Horse.*

Pieces with transfer prints other than Views can be found edged in colour rather than gilt orange (Black Cats and Lucky White Heather); green or blue (Black Cats, Flowers, Nursery Ware, Cockerels and Cartoons) and black (tropical birds).

Arcadian was exported and many foreign crests have been recorded; models for non-English speaking countries were marked Porcelaine Arcadienne. Crests of the Allies are often found on models made during the Great War, as are Military Crests. These are much collected by Great War enthusiasts, the following have so far been recorded:

Army Ordnance Corps
Army Service Corps
Berkshire Regiment
Black Watch
Canadian Forces
Canadian General Service Corps
Cheshire Regiment
Coldstream Guards
Denbighshire Regiment
Denbighshire Hussars
Derbyshire Regiment
Devonshire Regiment
Devonshire Regiment 11th Foot
Duke of Cambridge's own Middlesex Regiment
Duke of Cornwall's Light Infantry
2nd Dragoon Guards (Royal Scots Greys)
3rd Dragoon Guards
5th Dragoon Guards
Durham Light Infantry
East Kent Regiment 'The Buffs'
East Surrey Regiment
East Yorkshire Regiment
Essex Regiment
Gloucestershire Regiment
Gordon Highlanders
Hampshire Regiment
11th Hussars
18th Hussars
Inns of Court OTC
Irish Guards
Kings Own Liverpool Scottish
Kings Own Scottish Borderers
Kings Own Yorkshire Light Infantry
Lancashire Fusiliers
Lancashire Fusiliers (20th Foot)
Lancaster Regiment
Leicestershire Regiment 17th Foot
1st Life Guards
2nd Life Guards
Light Infantry
Lincolnshire Regiment
Liverpool Regiment (8th Foot)
Liverpool Regiment (11th Foot)
Liverpool Scottish, The King's
London Scottish
Machine Gun Corps
Manchester Regiment
Middlesex Regiment 57th & 77th Foot
Middlesex Regiment
5th Norfolk Regiment

Northamptonshire Regiment
Northumberland Fusiliers
North Staffs Regiment; 64th & 98th Foot
Notts & Derby
Officers Training Corps Omagh
Oxfordshire & Buckinghamshire Light Infantry
Prince Albert's Own Hussars
Prince Albert's Somerset Light Infantry
Prince Consort's Own Rifle Brigade (Swan)
Prince of Wales North Staffordshire Regiment
Queens Bays
Queens Own Cameron Highlanders
Queens Own Royal West Surrey Regiment
Queens Own Royal West Kent Regiment
RAE Ewshott
RFA Ewshott
Royal Artillery
Royal Aircraft Establishment
Rifle Brigade - The Prince Consort's Own
Royal Air Force (2 versions)
Royal Army Medical Corps
Royal Berkshire Regiment, 49th & 66th Foot
Royal Bucks Hussars
Royal East Kent Mounted Rifles - Imperial Yeomanry
Royal West Kent (The Queen's Own)
Royal Engineers
Royal Field Artillery
Royal Flying Corps
Royal Fusiliers, 7th Foot
Royal Garrison Artillery
Royal Gloucestershire Hussars
Royal Irish; 5th Lancers
Royal Irish Regiment 18th Foot
Royal Irish Dragoon Guards
Royal Horse Artillery
Royal Marines
Royal Military College Camberley
Royal Munster Fusiliers, 101st & 104th Foot
Royal Naval Air Service
Royal Navy
Royal Scots Greys 2nd Dragoons
Royal Shropshire Light Infantry
Royal Staff College Camberley
Royal Sussex Regiment
Royal Tank Corps
Royal Warwickshire Regiment
Royal Welsh Fusiliers
Royal West Surrey Regiment
Shropshire Light Infantry
South Staffordshire Regiment
South Wales Borderers
Staffs Regimental Insignia (Staffordshire Knot)

Stafford & Staffs Regt.
Staffordshire Imperial Yeomanry
Suffolk Regiment
Tank Corps
Walmer Camp
West Riding Regiment
Wiltshire Regiment (62nd & 69th Foot)
Worcestershire Regiment
York & Lancaster Regiment, Victoria Mary,
  Princess of Wales
H.M.S. Achilles (Transfer view of ship)
H.M.S. Barham
H.M.S. Colossus
H.M.S. Hercules
H.M.S. Queen Mary
H.M.S. Thunderer
Apart from Great War flags of the allies transfer *United we stand*, very few commemoratives seem to have been produced, the only ones known being: *South Africa 1900-1901* and *British Empire Exhibition 1924 and 1925*.

It is not surprising that the very late products of the firm are eagerly sought and have risen in price over the last ten years. Unlike other firms Arkinstall did not make a range of uncrested coloured models in the early 1930s, except for female figures. These are of particular interest as they are very like the Goss England flower girls and were made at the same time. The Arcadian ladies are more detailed and rather more delicate than the Goss England versions. The range was wide, and includes male figures, as well as seated and other less traditional forms.

Late lustre ware marked Arcadian is suspiciously like that marked Goss, and one wonders if they were produced by the same hands. Vases, bowls and domestic ware can be found, but not all that often with mother-of-pearl, orange, green, mauve, purple, turquoise and yellow lustre finishes.

Numbering System. Printed stock numbers are found on early models and these have been given where known in the following lists. It must be emphasised that registration numbers printed on later Arcadian models are notoriously unreliable and are often found not to be the number that the piece was actually registered under. Mr Robinson registered up to twenty models at a time and given

that more moulds became available with each new merger presumably no one could be bothered to check that the correct number was being used on each model. (Printing any number or 'Registration applied for' was an indication that the model was registered and therefore copyright). The Registration Number most often found on a model, whether it is the correct one or not has been given in the lists – hopefully this will help with identifying an un-named item. The tiny numbers, initials and marks often found painted on the base of Arcadian china are paintresses' marks.

Arcadian Models
Coloured Ladies/Figures

Antoinette.	125.00
Aristocrat, taking pinch of snuff. 150mm.	100.00
Miss Ascot, wearing large Ascot hat. 145mm.	155.00
Ballet Girl, seated on three-legged stool, wearing a crimson or green dress. 164mm.	140.00
Balloon Lady, old lady in pink dress, mauve apron and green shawl holding balloons. No. 43.145mm.	125.00
Breeze. No.15.95.00	140.00
Bridesmaid, wearing pink, yellow or blue dress and holding flowers. No. 6 or No. 15. 135mm.	120.00
Cavalier, with Van Dyke style beard. 150mm.	80.00
Costermonger. 160mm.	100.00
Cherry Ripe, wearing yellow dress and holding basket of flowers. 175mm	160.00
Cherry Ripe, with feather in hat, holding skirts and a basket of cherries, wearing yellow, blue and red dress. 163mm.	160.00
Clarissa, tying her bonnet. No. 142. 200mm.	160.00
Doris, curtseying, wearing green dress and bonnet. No. 66. 118mm.	120.00
Fair Huntress, holding hat and lurcher dog. 175mm.	125.00
Grace. 84mm.	110.00
Miss Holland, dressed in mauve, pink, red or black, wearing a cap long plaits and hands on hips. 127mm.	145.00
Joan, young girl wearing mob cap and green dress, holding hands together. 113mm.	120.00

Jester, seated figure. No. 222.	
150mm.	85.00

June, wearing bonnet and wide yellow
crinoline, holding a single rose.

No. 70. 115mm.	125.00

Lady Bountiful, wearing red dress
carrying basket o fruit on her right

arm. No. 122. 170mm.135.00	170.00
Lady Maria, 105mm.	100.00

Lady Marie, wearing yellow dress,

sitting on rock. 125mm.	115.00

Lady Marie, wearing green dress.

No.21. 145mm.	115.00
Her Ladyship, large seated figure in	
turquoise dress. No.182. 150mm.	140.00

Lucy. There are no details of dress or

size available.	150.00

Market Woman, old lady in blue
dress and red shawl, holding a

basket of fruit. No.43. 155mm.	130.00

Market Woman, similarly dressed
holding a basket of inticately

handmade flowers. No.2. 153mm.	130.00

Monk, from Lilleshall Abbey
wearing black robe, with tankard.

96mm.	95.00

Pauline, wearing black and yellow
tight dress with fur stole and

cuffs. 100mm.	180.00

Peggy, curtseying to side, holding

flower. 100mm.	120.00

Miss Prudence, sitting on settee,

holding fan and book. 108mm.	160.00

Miss Prudence, wearing a green
dress and pink hat, holding a

spray of flowers. No. 50. 175mm.	155.00

Tinker, wearing green or brown
jacket and yellow trousers, carrying
bag in left hand. No. 210. Two
sizes have been recorded,

150mm and 182mm.	145.00
Town Crier 160mm	120.00
Tulip Boy, in Dutch costume. 150mm.	110.00

Tulip Girl, in Dutch costume, with
basket of tulips at her feet. No. 133.

2 sizes: 130mm.	150.00
150mm.	150.00

Victorian Belle, wearing yellow and
green dress with blue shawl and
frilled crinoline, holding fan,
with flowers in hair, which is in

ringlets. 193mm.	170.00
Wendy, Medieval Lady.	135.00

Boy/Girl, sitting figure on stool.

150mm.	90.00

Parian/unglazed

Bust of King Edward VII in military
uniform, later models found with
inscriptions. On circular glazed
base. Add £5 for matching arms.

2 sizes: 130mm.	47.50
140mm.	47.50

Bust of King Edward VII wearing
trilby, overcoat and suit, on
circular glazed base. With

inscription. 125mm.	65.00

Bust of Queen Alexandra, on
circular glazed base.

2 sizes: 120mm.	47.50
140mm.	47.50

Smaller size can be found named
in blue lettering.

Bust of King George V, can be found
with circular glazed or keyhole
base. With inscription.

2 sizes: 125mm.	47.50
135mm.	47.50

Bust of King George V, robed,
holding orb, on circular-shaped

base. 140mm.	55.00

Bust of Queen Mary, can be found
with a glazed circular or keyhole
base, with inscription.

2 sizes: 125mm.	47.50
135mm.	47.50

Bust of Prince of Wales (later
Edward VIII) in midshipman's
uniform, can be found inscribed
*HRH The Prince of Wales born June
23rd 1894* in red and blue. On

glazed circular base. 135mm.	80.00

(Any of the above can be found with
matching crests on their glazed
bases, for which £10.00 may be added).

Bust of *HRH The Prince of Wales*
(later Edward VIII), wearing suit.

Rectangular glazed base. 90mm.	80.00

Bust of *Burns*, found with poem by
Wordsworth. On circular glazed

base. 120mm.	35.00

Bust of *Napoleon*, on square glazed

base. 125mm.	75.00

Bust of *Nelson*, on square glazed base.

2 sizes: 120mm.	75.00
140mm.	75.00
Bust of *John Peel*, with verse. 120mm.	75.00

Bust of *Scott*, on circular glazed

base. 120mm.	40.00

Bust of Duke of Wellington on

glazed base. 130mm.	75.00

Bust of Albert *King of the Belgians*
on square glazed base, sculpted
by W.C. Lawton .
2 sizes: 155mm.   60.00
 175mm.   65.00
Bust of *Sir Douglas Haig* on square
glazed base, sculpted by S.R.
Sanders. 150mm.   75.00
Bust of *Sir John French* on square
glazed base, sculpted by W.C.
Lawton. 155mm. Add £20 for
Arms of Sir John French.   75.00
Bust of *Sir John Jellicoe* on square
glazed base, sculpted by W.C.
Lawton. 170mm.   75.00
Bust of *General Joffre* on square
glazed base, sculpted by W.C.
Lawton.
3 sizes: 155mm.   75.00
 162mm.   75.00
 175mm.   75.00
Bust of *Lord Kitchener* on circular
glazed base. 119mm.   40.00
Bust of *Lord Kitchener* on square
glazed base, sculpted by W.C.
Lawton. Add £20 for Arms of
Lord Kitchener.
3 sizes: 155mm.   70.00
 162mm.   75.00
 175mm.   75.00
Bust of Chamberlain on circular
glazed base. 115mm.   40.00
Bust of David Lloyd George on
circular glazed base. 135mm.   50.00
Bust of *Lord Roberts* on square
glazed base, in uniform. Sculpted
by W.C. Lawton. 155mm. Add £20
for Arms of Lord Roberts.   100.00
Bust of Rt. Hon. W.S. Churchill on
square glazed base, sculpted by
W.C. Lawton. 160mm.   125.00

Ancient Artefacts
Most inscriptions begin *model of*, so
this will not be repeated
throughout the listing. These
models are sometimes found not
named and numbered.
Aberdeen Bronze Pot. 74mm.   5.50
Ancient Bronze British Pot. No. 618.
 68mm.   5.50
*Ancient Roman Vase now in
Wedgwood Museum, Burslem.*
No. 202. 65mm.   6.00
Ancient Tyg, 1 or 2 handles. No. 58.
 70mm.   5.50

Ancient Urn. No. 85. 35mm.   5.50
Ashbourne Bushel, with inscription.
No. 99. 67mm dia.   10.50
Bath Roman Ewer, inscribed: *Roman
Ewer in Dorset Museum found at
Bath.* No. 69. 70mm.   5.50
Butterpot, old, of 17th Century. 45mm. 5.50
Cadogan teapot, working model of.
 45mm.   14.50
Cambridge Roman Jug. No. 67.
2 sizes: 60mm.   6.50
 75mm.   8.50
Canterbury Roman Ewer. 2 shapes:
No. 23. 60mm.   5.50
No. 25. 75mm.   5.50
Canterbury Roman Vase, inscribed:
*Roman Vase found near Canterbury
original in Canterbury museum.*
9 different shapes:
No. 21. 65mm.   5.50
No. 22. 60mm.   5.50
No. 24. 66mm.   5.50
No. 27. 66mm.   5.50
No. 28. 70mm.   5.50
No. 29. 60mm.   5.50
No. 30. 60mm.   5.50
No. 31. 80mm.   5.50
No. 32. 63mm.   5.50
Canterbury Leather Bottle. 40mm.   5.50
Celtic Water Bottle. No. 625. 63mm. 5.50
Chester Roman Jug. No. 133. 80mm. 5.50
Chester Roman Vase, inscribed:
*Roman vase now in Chester
Museum.* 3 different shapes:
No. 131. 56mm.   5.50
No. 134. 70mm.   5.50
No. 136. 60mm.   5.50
Chester Roman Vase, inscribed:
*Roman vase found at Chester from
original in Museum.* No. 263.
58mm.   5.50
*Chinese vase, original in Hanley
Museum.* No.127. 38mm.   5.50
Colchester Vase.   5.50
Derby Roman Vase. No.26. 63mm.   5.50
Devon Oak Pitcher. No. 165. 60mm.   5.50
Dogger Bank Bottle. No. 206.
2 sizes: 50mm.   6.50
 70mm.   6.50
Dorchester Jug. No. 66. 55mm.   5.50
Eddystone Spanish Jug. No. 585.
 60mm.   5.50
Egyptian Urn. No. 130.   5.50
Egyptian Vase, ancient, about 230 BC.
No. 155. 45mm.   5.50
Egyptian Water Bottle, 60mm.   5.50

Etruscan Vase, 4th Century original in Stoke-on-Trent Museum No. 205. 50mm. 5.50
Exeter Vase from original in Museum. No. 70. 68mm. 5.50
Fountains Abbey Cup. No. 64. 50mm. 5.50
Glastonbury Bowl. No. 55. 40mm. 5.50
Glastonbury Bronze Bowl. No. 74. 40mm. 5.50
Glastonbury Vase. No. 642. 55mm. 5.50
Grecian Bronze Pot found at Pompeii. No. 138. 50mm. 5.50
Greek Cauldron, Ancient. No. 288. 44mm. 5.50
Hastings Kettle. No. 237. 62mm. 5.50
Hereford Terracotta Kettle with lid. 12.50
Highland Whisky Jar No. 679. 72mm. 6.50
Highland Quaich or Whisky Bowl. No. 529. can be inscribed: *Scaub Asi.* 134mm wide. 12.00
Horsham Vase, inscribed: *13th century vase found at Horsham.* No. 201.
2 sizes: 45mm. 5.50
　　　　　75mm. 6.50
Ipstones Jug. No. 73. 60mm. 5.50
Irish Bronze Pot, Ancient. No. 62. 50mm. 5.50
Irish Kettle. No. 95. 70mm. 6.00
Jersey Milk Can, Ancient, with lid. No. 523. 72mm. 10.00
Kendal Jug. No. 9. 75mm. 6.50
Lichfield Jug. No. 60. 70mm. 6.00
Lincoln Jack from original in museum. No. 50. 62mm. 5.50
Lincoln Vase from original in the museum. No. 80. 66mm. 5.50
Loving Cup originated by Henry of Navarre King of France. 2 or 3 handled. No. 579.
2 sizes: 40mm. 6.50
　　　　　49mm. 7.50
Newbury Leather Bottle, inscribed: *Leather bottle found on battlefield of Newbury 1044 now in museum.* No. 83.
2 sizes: 45mm. 5.50
　　　　　65mm. 6.50
Norwich Cinerary Urn 50mm. 5.50
Norwich Cinerary Urn No. 135 5.50
Peterborough Tripod, unnamed. 40mm. 5.50
Phoenician Vase original in Stoke-on-Trent museum. No. 257. 60mm. 5.50
Pompeian Vessel. No. 208. 55mm. 5.50
Pompeii Lamp inscribed *Model of Eastern Lamp found at Pompeii* No. 603. 90mm long. 5.50

Portland Vase now in British Museum. No. 52. 60mm. 5.50
Puzzle Jug original in South Kensington Museum. No. 147. 70mm. 8.50
Puzzle Teapot. 50mm. 14.50
Roman Urn. No. 305. 63mm. 5.50
Salisbury Jack. 5.50
Salisbury Kettle. No. 90. 107mm. 5.50
Salt Maller. 5.50
Scarborough Jug. No. 82. 52mm. 5.50
Scotch Coggie, inscribed: *Model of Scotch Coggie used by the Highlands before the introduction of earthenware.* No. 149. 80mm. 8.50
Shakespeare's Jug, 60mm. 7.50
Shrewsbury Salopian Ewer. No. 613. 75mm. 6.00
Silchester Vase. No. 54. 55mm. 5.50
Southwold Jar. No. 627. 95mm. 5.50
Suffolk Palace Jug, inscribed: *Model of antique jug found on site of Suffolk Palace Hull now in museum.* No. 122. 60mm. 5.50
Toby Jug, inscribed: *This is an exact copy in miniature of the old toby jug.* No. 253. 75mm. 14.00
Tutankhamun's Cup, inscribed: *Kings wishing cup found in King Tut-Ankh-Amen's tomb at Luxor.* 55mm. 30.00
West Malling Elizabethan Jug or stoup. No. 152. 75mm. 12.00
Winchelsea Roman Cup. No. 137. 50mm. 5.50
Winchelsea Vase, inscribed: *Model of Roman Cup found near Winchelsea.* No. 68. 55mm. 5.50
Winchelsea Vase, inscribed: *Model of Vase found near Winchelsea.* No. 87. 75mm. 5.50
Winchester Bushel, blue feet and handle. 83mm dia. 40.00
Winchester Vase. 5.50
Windsor Roman Urn. No. 123. 50mm. 5.50
Wokingham Tankard. No. 88. 78mm. 5.50
York Roman Ewer. No. 57. 60mm. 5.50

Buildings - Coloured
These buildings are not normally found crested.
Alton Round House, inscribed: *The Ancient Lock Up. Light brown* colour. 86mm. 165.00

Ann Hathaway's Cottage.
50mm long.   17.50
Bridlington Priory Church, model of.
Light brown colour. 68mm long.   82.50
Burns Cottage. 68mm long.   22.00
Dean Goodman's Birthplace.
85mm long.   135.00
First and Last House with annexe.
2 sizes: 100mm long: 75.00
          136mm long: 105.00
Guildhall, Thaxted, 88mm.   215.00
Jean Mac Alpines Inn, Famous Inn in
'Rob Roy' where the scene of a
fray between Bailie Nicol Jarrie
and the Highlanders took place.
Unglazed. 104mm long.   125.00
*Old Blacksmith's Shop and Marriage
Room, Gretna Green, 85mm long*
(late Willow mould).   40.00
Old Star Inn, Alfriston. 80mm.   150.00
Shakespeare's House.
2 sizes: 63mm long.   20.00
          127mm long.   30.00
Wells Cathedral. Stone coloured
with some colouring on doors
and windows. 110mm long.   75.00

Buildings - White
Aberystwyth University 110mm long. 125.00
Alton, The Round House. 83mm.   80.00
Ann Hathaway's Cottage.
2 sizes: 83mm long: 12.00
          100mm long.   14.00
Bath Abbey, front. 107mm.   37.50
Big Ben, also found inscribed:
City of London.
3 sizes: 92mm.   17.00
          135mm.   22.50
          150mm.   25.00
Blackpool Tower, inscibed: *The Tower*
87mm.   10.00
Blackpool Tower. 144mm.   10.00
Blackpool Tower with Buildings.
107mm.   16.50
Blackpool Tower with Buildings on
heavy base.
2 sizes: 135mm.   12.50
          165mm.   14.50
Boston Stump.
2 sizes: 89mm long.   47.50
          110mm long.   65.00
The Bridge, Clacton-on-Sea
136mm long.   30.00
Bunyan's Cottage.
2 sizes: 83mm.   22.50
          95mm.   25.00

Burn's Cottage. 112mm long.   35.00
Canterbury Cathedral. West front.
126mm.   40.00
Canterbury, Westgate. 93mm.   30.00
Chester Cathedral. 120mm long.   45.00
Chesterfield Parish Church AD 1037.
Model of. 125mm and 80mm.   55.00
Clifton Suspension Bridge.
175mm long.   75.00
Cottage, very detailed.
2 sizes: 50mm and 100mm
(See Shakespeare's)
Cottage on rectangular base usually
found with no inscription.
80mm long.   15.00
Can be found inscribed: *Model of
Highland cottage, Welsh cottage or
Irish Cottage.* 60mm.   22.00
Douglas Jubilee Clock Tower. 125mm. 55.00
Ely Cathedral. 140mm long.   75.00
Fair Maid's House, Perth. 84mm.   50.00
*Farringtons Girl School Chapel,
Chislehurst Kent.* 125mm long.
(Very rare). Unglazed.   200.00
*First and Last Refreshment House in
England.* Often found without
'refreshment' inscription.
75mm long.   15.00
Also found with annexe.
2 sizes: 100mm long.   30.00
          138mm long.   40.00
Forth Bridge. 158mm long.   47.50
Gloucester Cathedral. 128mm long. 47.50
God's Providence House Chester.
82mm.   40.00
Grimsby Hydraulic Tower. 170mm. 42.50
Hastings Castle Ruins. 96mm.   40.00
Hastings, Clock Tower.
2 sizes: 135mm.   13.00
          152mm.   16.00
Hop Kiln. 86mm.   47.50
Houses of Parliament. 73mm long. 40.00
Irish Round Tower. 106mm.   16.00
King Alfred's Tower, inscribed: *You
well-poised tower, sublimely eminent,
shows to the curious passer by the
spot where Alfred, England's Patriot
King, uncurled the Saxon banner
against the Northern Foe.* 92mm.   125.00
Lantern Hill Church. Ilfracombe.
98mm long.   30.00
Launceston Castle. 112mm long.   85.00
Lincoln Cathedral, West Front.
2 sizes: 98mm.   40.00
          115mm.   42.50

Lincoln Stonebow. 88mm long.	30.00
Lloyd George's Early Home, with	
Annexe Llanstymdwy, Criccieth.	
120mm long.	47.50
London Bridge. Ye olde.	
2 sizes: 88mm long.	34.00
170mm long.	39.00
Marble Arch also found inscribed:	
Hyde Park, London.	
4 sizes: 45mm.	22.00
65mm.	17.00
76mm.	20.00
80mm.	22.00
Margate Clock Tower, sometimes	
inscribed: Clock Tower.	
2 sizes: 140mm.	17.00
152mm.	17.00
Martello Tower, with inscription:	
'Erected for Coast Defence 1804'.	
73mm dia.	39.00
Morpeth Clock Tower, not found	
named. 122mm.	18.00
Mundesley-on-Sea Castle Ruins.	
105mm.	100.00
Norwich Cathedral. 105mm long.	55.00
Old Curiosity Shop. Immortalized by	
Charles Dickens. No. 14 Portsmouth	
Street.	
2 sizes: 70mm long.	30.00
95mm long.	30.00
If found named, add £10.00.	
Old Pete's Cottage (near Ramsey).	
2 sizes: 75mm long.	40.00
100mm long.	40.00
Pegwell Bay, Clock Tower, 135mm.	27.00
Plymouth, Clock Tower.	
2 sizes: 150mm.	15.50
180mm.	16.50
Portsmouth, Guildhall. 60mm long.	40.00
Queen Mary's Dolls House.	
3 sizes: 75mm.	40.00
95mm.	40.00
118mm.	42.50
Two smaller sizes are often found	
as boxes with loose roof lids.	
(These models can be found with	
the 'Cauldon' mark as well as	
'Arcadian'.-Same price.)	
Rochester Castle, dating from 1126.	
70mm.	47.50
Rowton Tower, with inscription:	
King Charles 1st stood on this tower,	
Sept. 24th 1645 and saw his army	
defeated on Rowton Moor. 88mm.	40.00

St Albans. The Clock Tower. 125mm.	40.00
St. Nicholas Chapel, Ilfracombe.	
100mm long.	30.00
St. Pauls Cathedral. No. 114.	
3 sizes: 72mm.	22.00
95mm.	22.00
130mm.	25.50
St. Tudno's Church, Llandudno.	
73mm.	65.00
Can sometimes be found as a	
money box.	
St. Winifred's Bath, Holywell. 75mm.	65.00
Salisbury Cathedral. 120mm long.	75.00
Salisbury Clock Tower, not found	
named. 130mm.	17.00
Shakespeare's House.	
3 sizes: 50mm long.	10.50
83mm long.	14.00
100mm long.	16.00
Skegness, Clock Tower, 125mm.	16.00
Smallest House in Great Britain. (at 10	
Lower Gate Street, Conway)	
3 sizes: 88mm.	22.00
97mm.	25.00
115mm.	30.00
Southampton, the Bargate. 66mm.	30.00
Temple Bar.	
2 sizes: 60mm.	25.00
95mm.	38.50
Tom Tower, Christchurch, Oxford.	
88mm.	25.00
Tower Bridge.	
2 sizes: 80mm long.	30.00
135mm long.	40.00
Tower of Refuge, Douglas I.O.M.	
68mm.	40.00
Tudor House, L shaped. 80mm.	42.00
Tudor House, two chimneys & four	
gable windows, found with the	
Wellingborough crest. 95mm.	30.00
Tynwald Hill, Model of, with lengthy	
inscription. 110mm dia.	125.00
Wembley Sports Stadium, with	
capacity details. 136mm long.	95.00
Westminster Abbey, West Front.	
2 sizes: 72mm.	25.00
118mm.	28.00
Weymouth Jubilee, Clock Tower on	
octagonal base. 128mm.	39.00
Wimborne Minster. 127mm long.	65.00
Windmill with movable sails.	
85mm.	40.00
Very rarely found inscribed:	
Windmill, Woodhouse.	50.00

Windsor Castle. 55mm high,
80mm long.   35.00
Windsor Round Tower.
2 sizes: 58mm.   30.00
90mm.   30.00
Worcester Cathedral.
2 sizes: 127mm long.   35.00
140mm long.   40.00
York Minster. 105mm.   60.00

Monuments (including Crosses)

Banbury Cross, with nursery
rhyme: *Ride a cock horse.* 160mm.   42.50
Bloody Corner, Ilfracombe with very
lengthy inscription of slaying of
King Hubba on all 3 sides. Same
mould as Rufus Stone. 100mm.   65.00
Bunyan Statue. 140mm.   20.00
Burns, Monument with dog. 70mm   30.00
Caister on Sea Lifeboat Memorial.
150mm.   30.00
Castleton Village Cross. 140mm.   95.00
Celtic Cross. 125mm.   12.00
Conway *We are Seven* Grave, with
inscription: 'The Grave
immortalized by Wordsworth's
Poem' and 'Two of us in the
churchyard lie'. This is a
triangular tube shaped tomb with
seven small towers. 110mm long.   65.00
Drake Statue. 160mm.   19.50
Ethelfreda Memorial. 150mm.   75.00
'Fisherman's Memorial', appears with
crest of Fleetwood. 155mm.   19.50
Gibbet Cross, Hindhead with
inscriptions. 136mm.   12.00
(The) Globe, Swanage, Model of.
80mm.   40.00
Hull Fisherman's Memorial, with
inscription. 155mm.   22.00
Hull Soldier's War Memorial, with
inscription (Boer War). 155mm.   40.00
Iona Cross. 142mm.   12.00
Irish Monument, not named but
appears with Irish Crests.
Circular base with man standing
on top. 138mm. This is the metal
man at Tramore.   56.50
Joan of Arc, statue on plinth. 60mm.   50.00
King *Alfred the Great,* Statue.
Winchester. Rd. No. 521701. 170mm.   55.00

Lion of Belfort. *Aux Defenseurs de
Belfort 1870-71.* Lion lying on
rectangular plinth with arrow
& feathers under paw. Inscribed
on reverse *S B Schmitt Editeur
Belfort.* Commemorates the seige
of Belfort by German troops
between Nov. 1870 and Feb. 1871.
130mm long.   50.00
Lytham St Annes Fishermens Memorial
145mm.   20.00
*Maiwand Memorial, Forbury Gardens,
Reading.* (Lion on base). Can be
found with black lion, add £10.00.
100mm.   25.00
Margate Surf Boat Memorial. Lifeboatman standing on plinth.
2 sizes: 118mm.   20.00
125mm.   20.00
Margate Surf Boat memorial, rock-
shaped with lifebelt, gilded anchor
& weeping girl *In memory of nine
heroic men who lost their lives by the
capsizing of the Margate surf boat
"Friend to all nations" in attempting
to assist a vessel in distress at sea
2nd Dec. 1897.* Rare 84mm   70.00
Nelson's Column.
2 sizes: 102mm.   45.00
170mm.   75.00
Nelson Monument, Great
Yarmouth. 206mm.   160.00
Newton Statue. 165mm.   38.50
Plymouth Armada Memorial.
181mm.   35.00
Queen Victoria Statue, Windsor
133mm   38.00
Richmond, Yorks, Market Cross.
135mm.   30.00
*(The Great) Rock of Ages, Burrington
Coombe, near Cheddar, Som.* with
three verses of hymn. 83mm.   13.00
Robert the Bruce Statue, standing
on rock, with sword. 130mm.   50.00
Rufus Stone. 100mm.   10.00
St. Anne's on Sea Fisherman's
Memorial. 155mm.   30.00
Sailor's Stone, Hindhead. 100mm.   12.50
Saxon Lady and Child, both with
swords, on glazed base. 153mm.   150.00

Series of at least three figures standing on a square plinth. (These are not easily identifiable and could be statesmen, industrialists or literary figures. It is thought that one is Joseph Chamberlain, one is Lloyd George and another is Charles Dickens); inscribed: *Industry is the parent of success.* Edged in green. 135mm. Each 65.00

Toad Rock. 85mm. 20.00

Tom Hughes Monument, Rugby School. 142mm. 30 00

Victorian Lady and Gentleman figure group on base, inscribed: *He that is satisfied is rich.* Found with colour transfer of children. 115mm. 65.00

Statue found with York Crest, Lion and three Imps or Satyrs on a square pedestal. 115mm. 44.50

Sir William Wallace Statue, holding left hand outstretched and sword tip resting on ground, held in right hand, Aberdeen. 125mm. 75.00

Historical/Folklore

Archbishop of Canterbury's Chair now in cathedral AD5541. 95mm. 19.00

Bell, squashed appearance. Inscription in red relief: *CAMPAN Athgme.* Usually found with the Canterbury Arms. 58mm. 32.00

Burns with Plough on rectangular base. 120mm. 75.00

Coaching Hat, can be found inscribed: *Model of ancient coaching hat. No. 687.* 65mm long. 7.50

Coronation Chair, inscribed: *Model of Chair on which King George V was crowned Westminster Abbey June 22nd 1911* and on the back: *All the world's a stage and man in his time plays many parts.* 107mm. 15.00

Devil looking over Lincoln. 108mm. 16.00

Ducking Stool, 2 pieces, hinged together. With long details of its last employment in Leominster in 1809 and 1817. 120mm long. 85.00

English Folksong Bride beside chest. 93mm. 55.00

Execution Block with Axe. 50mm. 35.00

Henry V Cradle, Monmouth. 78mm high, 96mm long. 75.00

Jenny Geddes Stool 1637, 3 legged. 40mm. More often found unnamed. 10.00
Named. 17.50

Judge Bust.
2 sizes: 55mm. 20.00
75mm. 35.00
Can be found inscribed: *Defend the children of the poor and punish the wrong doer.* Add £10.00.

Judge in his box, reading book, with Old Bailey inscription. 82mm. 55.00

Lady Godiva, Coventry, on horseback, circular base.
3 sizes: 76mm. 26.00
85mm. 30.00
115mm. 35.00

Lady Godiva on horseback, on heart shaped base. 80mm. 30.00

Miner's Lamp, inscribed: '1836'. 85mm. 22.00

Mother Shipton, can be found with verse.
2 sizes: 76mm. 10.00
115mm. 12.00

Mrs Gummidge (identical to Mother Shipton). 115mm. 18.00

Peeping Tom, bust. 110mm. 17.00

Man in the Sun. 94mm. 47.50

Man standing in Pillory, can be found inscribed: Time for *reflection. AD1600.* 190mm. 17.00

Man sitting in Stocks, can be found inscribed: *Time for reflection* and very rarely: *Berkswell stocks, The stocks, Dartmouth* or *The Brading Stocks.* 88mm. 20.00
30.00

Nottingham Oak (base of trunk) 40.00

Shakespeare's Desk from the original in the museum, model of. Can be found in lustre. 62mm long. 75.00

Trusty Servant on ornate rectangular base, with verse. Fully coloured and without crest. 137mm. 170.00

Trusty Servant on small square base, can be found with verse. Fully coloured with crest and unglazed. 130mm. 150.00

Wishing Chair, Giants Causeway. 75mm dia. 55.00

Witches Cauldron with inscription. 47mm. 5.50

Yorick's Skull, inscribed: *Alas poor Yorick.* 57mm. 16.00

Traditional/National Souvenirs

John Bull, bust.

3 sizes: 65mm.	17.00
85mm.	25.50
96mm.	30.00

Largest 2 sizes found with a black hat.

'ARRY, bust of Pearly King. 86mm.	55.00
'ARRIET, bust of Pearly Queen.	80.00

Blackpool Big Wheel.

3 sizes: 60mm.	14.00
78mm.	16.00
110mm.	19.00

Bolton Trotter, hand holding.

110mm long.	10.00

Boy Scout, inscribed: *Be prepared.*

105mm.	85.00

Cheddar Cheese, Prime, with slice out.

2 sizes: 54mm high.	12.50
35mm high, 65mm diameter.	12.50

Cornish Pasty, with verse.

98mm long.	12.50

Devonshire Dumpling. 45mm.	22.50

Isle of Wight, relief map standing upright on pintray. Coloured.

106mm long.	55.00

Lancashireman's Jug with verse.

75mm.	10.00

Lincoln Imp. 110m.	12.00

Lincoln Imp, on pedestal.

125mm.	15.00
Manx Legs, flat. 85mm dia.	17.00

Manx Legs on stand, can be found

in lustre. 101m.	16.00
Manx Legs on rock. 51mm.	30.00

Melton Mowbray Pie, with verse.

54mm.	25.00

Mill Lass, bust, shawl draped round

head and shoulders. 60mm.	26.00

Sometimes inscribed:

Lancashire Lass.	30.00
Ripon Hornblower, with verse. 130mm.	15.00

The Winton Imp on pedestal. (Thin buddha with hand in mouth).

135mm.	95.00
Yorkshireman's Jug with verse. 83mm.	13.00
Yorkshireman bust. 67mm.	14.00
Irish Colleen, fully coloured on	55.00

ashtray base. 105mm. (One of a series of ashtrays, *see also* **Comic/ Novelty**.

Irishman and pig on shamrock ashtray base. 100mm long. (One of a series of ashtrays, *see also*

Comic/Novelty.	100.00

Irish Harp with green shamrocks.

108mm.	10.50

Irish Jaunting Car, Model of. With

horse and driver. 120mm long.	110.00

Irish Lady, bust, inscribed: *My simple graceful Nora Criena.*

2 sizes: 63mm.	26.00
85mm.	35.00

Irishman bust, wearing black hat, Inscribed: *If the liquors pure, sure Paddy McClure, will drain the ewer, if the liquors bad, He'll leave it bedad.*

78mm.	40.00
Pat the Irishman, bust. 80mm.	30.00
Shamrock shaped dish. 80mm long.	4.00
Bagpipes. 110mm long.	50.00

Gretna Green, Anvil from, with verse.

2 sizes: 66mm, white.	8.00
85mm, coloured.	14.50
Scotsman, bust of. 65mm.	22.00
If named *Harry Lauder*	30.00

Scotsman, coloured, holding

Matches container. (Late). 90mm.	65.00

Souter Johnny, sitting figure on chair

with verse. Some colouring. 130mm.	40.00

Tam o'Shanter (bonnet) inscribed: *Tha can sit on the thistle noo.* Coloured feather and pompom.

95mm dia.	40.00
Thistle candlestick. 50mm.	6.00

Thistle on stalk base (Candlestick or: Vase) inscribed: *Tha can sit on the thistle noo.*

2 sizes: 85mm.	6.50
113mm.	8.50

Thistle vase, wide necked.

4 sizes: 45mm.	5.00
55mm.	5.00
70mm.	5.00
85mm.	7.00
Thistle Vase on ornamental base. 55mm.	7.00

Ladies of Llangollen, the. Standing figures on base, dressed in black riding habit. These two Irish Ladies

eloped to live in Llangollen. 100mm.	125.00

Welsh Harp, with leek in relief on rear.

80mm.	10.50
Welsh Coracle. 75mm wide.	15.00

Welsh Hat, Model of. Often unnamed. Can be found with longest Welsh place name round brim, for which add £3.00

2 sizes: 52mm.	9.50
72mm.	12.00

Welsh Hat, much wider brim, large
blue bow. Reg. No. 450915. 49mm.   14.00
Welsh Lady Bust, can be found fully
coloured or with black hat & red
band, inscribed: *Wales! Wales!*
My Mother's Sweet Home.
3 sizes: 65mm.   17.00
      85mm.   25.00
     106mm.   30.00
Welsh Lady with stick sitting on
bench on oval ashtray base.
Coloured. 114mm.   85.00
Welsh Leek, can be found with
inscription: *King Henry V. The*
Welshmen did goot servace (at
Crecy) in a garden where Leeks did
grow. Shakespeare.
2 sizes: 76mm.   6.00
     98mm.   6.50
Welsh Tea Party, 3 Welsh ladies
taking tea, can be found with hats
and cloaks coloured.
2 sizes: 50mm.   40.00
     95mm.   50.00
Welsh Tea Party, as above, on oval
base. 100mn.   58.00
Welsh Tea Party, as above, on ashtray
base. 42mm.   55.00
Welsh Lady Tea Pot & Lid.
Coloured. 152mm.   35.00
Japanese Girl, Model of with fan and
parasol, No 250. 64mm.   47.00

Seaside Souvenirs
Bathing Machine. *Morning Dip 7am.*
4 sizes: 50mm.   16.00
     55mm.   16.00
     65mm.   18.00
     85mm this size has No.32
     over the door.   22.00
Lifebelt. 80mm dia.   12.50
Lifeboat with yellow and blue rope.
110mm long.   20.50
Can be found inscribed with any
of the following names: *Brother &*
Sister; Bob Newson; Charles Arkcoll;
Charles Medland; Charles Susanna
Stephens; The Charlie and Adrian;
Co-operator No 2 also Co-operative
No 2; Eliza Aveus; Elizabeth
Simpson; George Leicester; James
Stevens No 5; James Stevens No 10;
Kentwell; Lady Hamar Hoyl: Louisa
Heartwell; Colonel Stock; Civil Service
No. 1; Heyland, Selina; Mark Lane;
Nancy Lucy; Richard Coleman; The
William Earle. Add £15.00

Liner, 4 funnels. RNS Lusitania,
unmarked, 180mm long.   80.00
Paddlesteamer, can be found
inscribed *Staithes captain Cook*
Discoverer of Australia, lived here
1742. 160mm long.   95.00
Rowing Boat. 83mm long.   12.50
Trawler. 125mm long.   30.00
Yacht. 125mm long.   22.50
Lifeboatman, bust.
3 sizes: 65mm.   17.50
     70mm.   20.00
     85mm.   40.00
Fishing Basket, found inscribed:
A good catch. 50mm.   14.50
Fisherman's Creel, with separate
lid. No. 18. 60mm.   12.50
Fisherman's Creel with fixed lid.
50mm.   10.50
Lighthouse *Sailor Beware* pierced
windows. 131mm.   16.00
Lighthouse.
2 sizes: 106mm.   8.50
     145mm.   14.00
Beachy Head Lighthouse,
with black band. Add £2.00.
2 sizes: 102mm.   10.50
     140mm.   14.50
Bell Rock. Lighthouse. No. 14.
108mm.   30.00
Cove Sea Lighthouse. 136mm.   34.50
Eddystone Lighthouse, smaller sizes
unnamed.
3 sizes: 70mm.   7.00
     105mm.   8.50
     140mm. No. 10, named.   13.00
Flamborough Head Lighthouse
3 sizes: 105mm.   25.00
     130mm.   25.00
     145mm.   35.00
Girdleness Lighthouse, Aberdeen.
106mm.   40.00
Kinnaird Lighthouse. 145mm.   35.00
Longships Lighthouse, Lands End.
100mm, found as a pepper pot.   16.00
142mm.   24.00
Manghold Head Lighthouse.   65.00
Pharos Lighthouse, Fleetwood, Model
of. No. 255.
2 sizes: 100mm.   14.50
     140mm.   15.50
If named, with matching crest.   22.00
Smaller size (fully inscribed) has
been found as pepper pot.

Scurdyness Lighthouse, Montrose.
Pepper pot 104mm. | 30 00
Spurn Head Lighthouse. 110mm. | 20.50
Winterton Lighthouse, Model of. 100mm. | 34.00
Withernsea Lighthouse. 105mm. | 22.00
Wolf Lighthouse. 105mm. | 35.00
Crab, very detailed. No. 6 or 9.
85mm long. | 17.00
Crab Ashtray. 90mm long. | 12.50
Oyster Shell dish. 72mm dia. | 5.00
Oyster Shell dish on 3 tiny feet.
90mm long. | 6.50
Nautilus shell on three 3 legs.
80mm long. | 22.00
Scallop Shell.
2 sizes: 70mm. | 5.00
92mm dia. | 6.00
Scallop Shell dish, very ornate.
83mm dia. | 6.00
Scallop Shell on rock, *Menu holder.*
58mm. | 10.50
Shell Ink Well, one open shell
inverted on another, usually
inscribed: *We are always glad to
hear from you.* Can also be found
inscribed: *We're aye prood to hear
fae ye* or *Pins.* 105mm. | 12.50
Whelk Shell, can be found
inscribed: *Listen to the sea* or *We
are always glad to hear from you.*
Size varies from
80mm-l00mm long. | 6.00
Punch and Judy Show. Rd. No. 37083.
90mm. | 55.00
Judy, bust, some colouring. 90mm. | 80.00
Punch, bust, some colouring.
Rd. No. 524786.
2 sizes: 65mm. | 75.00
80mm. | 55.00

**Bathing Beauties/Twenties
Flappers**
Bathing Belle on trinket box. 122mm
long. | 170.00
Can also be found in coloured
lustre finish.
Bathing Belle on ashtray Some
colouring inscribed: *cum fra dip.*
57mm. | 85.00
Bathing Belle dipping feet in pool,
with inscription: *Cumfradip.*
can be found with coloured figure.
98mm long. | 75.00

Flapper, sitting on bench - on oval
or heart-shaped tray, yellow hat
and dress, green shoes. 105mm. | 85.00
Plain white. | 70.00
Flapper in yellow dress and
headscarf reclining on
rectangular box and lid.
122mm long. | 125.00

Countryside
Acorn. 55m. | 7.50
Beehive on table. 78mm. | 17.00
Hay Stack, circular. 58mm. | 8.50
Hay Stack, rectangular. 50mm. | 6.50
Milk Churn. 60mm. | 6.00
Pinecone, curved. 88mm long. | 6.00
Tree Trunk vase. 70mm. | 6.50
Tree Trunk Hatpin Holder. 105mm. | 10.50

Animals
Small models of 'pets' were obviously
made in great numbers for many
years so the moulds do vary.
Large, more exotic animals were
much more expensive at the time
and so are consequently rare.
Bear and Ragged Staff. 80mm. | 45.00
Bear, polar. 96mm. | 50.00
Bear sitting. No. 2. 96mm. | 45.00
Bull, Highland. 130mm long. | 100.00
Calf, inscribed: *Why the Natives are
called Isle of Wight calves* with
cartoon.
100mm long. | 30.00
Camel, standing, 2 humps - Bactrian.
70mm. | 65.00
Cat, angry, standing with arched
back and green eyes, sometimes
inscribed: *My word if you're not off.*
63mm long, white. | 14.50
With colouring. | 17.00
Inscribed. | 20.50
Cat, climbing into boot, which has a
mouse peeping out of its toe.
100mm long. | 43.00
Cat, Cheshire. No bow round neck,
inscribed: *Keep smiling.*
2 sizes: 70mm (not inscribed). | 7.50
90mm(inscribed). | 14.50
Cat, The Cheshire. With orange or red
bow round neck, inscribed: *The
smile that won't come off.* 95mm. | 20.50
Cat, long necked and sitting. 108mm. | 12.50
Inscribed: *My word if you're not off.* | 17.00

Cat, Manx, furry.
3 sizes: 55mm long.	22.00
70mm long.	25.00
80mm long.	30.00

Can be found with coloured face.
Add £7.00
Cat, manx, painted, green eyes & red
mouth. 60mm long (tiny) 50.00
Cat with bow, sitting on plinth. Bow
sometimes coloured blue. 123mm. 35.00
- Cat sitting and smiling (grotesque,
rather similar to Cheshire Cat),
bow round neck, sometimes
coloured orange. No. 77. 68mm. 50.00
Cat sitting with bow round neck.
56mm. 16.00
Cat standing on hind legs, playing
flute. 80mm. 45.00
Cat standing playing piccolo. 77mm. 30.00

**Arcadian Black Cat
Registered Series**
No. 1 Black Cat on Jug. 60mm. 65.00
No. 2. Black Cat on vertical
horseshoe 76mm. 95.00
No. 3. Black Cat on pillar box
posting letter. 56mm. 75.00
This cat has also been found in
cobalt blue instead of black. 75.00
No. 4. Black Cat on telephone. 65mm. 115.00
 No. 5. Black Cat in canoe.
80mm long. 165.00
No. 6. Black Cat on wall. 70mm. 80.00
No. 6. Black Manx Cat on wall, cat
without tail. The model has a
matching Douglas Crest. 95.00
(A different mould to the above).
No. 7. Black Cat in boot. 61mm. 75.00
No. 8. Black Cat with bottle, bottle
can have solid or cork top, can be
inscribed: *Cheerio from...* (can be
found in lustre). 70mm. 75.00
No. 9. Black Cat on milk churn. *New
Milk* moulded on churn. (Can be
found in lustre). 70mm. 65.00
No. 10. Three Black Cats in bed.
65mm long. 95.00
No. 11. Black Cat on swing. 63mm. 75.00
No. 12. Black Cat in well. (Can be
found in lustre). 63mm. 65.00
No. 13. Black Cat operating radio.
63mm. Can also be found in Cobalt
Blue. 110.00
No. 14. Black Cat in Pram. (Can be
found in lustre). 70mm. 210.00

No. 15. Three Black Cats in basket,
and one on top. 70mm. 155.00
No. 16. Black Cat on scooter. (Can be
found in lustre.). 70mm. 210.00
No. 17. Black Cat with umbrella.
65mm. 165.00
No. 18. Black Cat on bicycle.
80mm long. 210.00
No. 19. Black Cat in yacht.
96mm long. 165.00
No. 20. Black Cat playing double
bass. 70mm. 210.00
No. 21. Two Black Cats on seesaw.
85mm long. 210.00
No. 22. Five Black Cats on a house,
their tails spell: *Good luck.* 65mm. 190.00
No. 23. Three Black Cats on sledge
(very rare). 210.00
No. 24. Black Cat playing piano.
52mm. 210.00
There are also very similar black
cats which are not part of the
Registered Series.
Black Cat, wearing kilt and
glengarry, playing golf standing
on golf ball. 70mm. 125.00
(This is from a Willow mould.)
Black Cat, standing alongside Welsh
leek wearing Welsh hat. 60mm. 105.00

Sitting Black Cats
Can be found on the following bases:
Armchair
2 sizes: 55mm.	38.50
90mm.	47.00

Ashtray, horseshoe shaped.
93mm long. 47.00
Ashtray, diamond shaped. *Good Luck
Ash Tray.* 69mm high, 120mm long. 47.00
Ashtray, octagonal shaped. 100mm. 30.00
Pouffe, inscribed: *Good luck.*
2 sizes: 80mm.	30.00
95mm.	35.00

Trinket box, horseshoe shaped.
70mm. 35.00
(All of these cats have blue/green
eyes and usually red bows, but
yellow bows are sometimes found.)

Animals Continued
Chimpanzee, sitting. 70mm . 32.00
Cougar (or Panther).
102mm long (rare). 82.50

Cow, Jersey. 125mm long.	65.00
Cow, some colour, sitting on lid of butter dish, inscribed: *Butter.*	
115mm dia.	30.00
Crocodile (or alligator).	
125mm long.	80.00
(Can be found with blue lustre finish.)	
Bill Sykes Dog, Model of sitting. Staffordshire Bulldog No. 300.	
103mm.	25.00
Sometimes inscribed: *My word it you're not off.* Add £10.00	
Bill Sykes Dog. Model of standing. Sometimes inscribed: *My word if you're not off.* Add £10.00	
4 sizes: 88mm.	17.00
102mm.	22.50
118mm long.	25.00
126mm long.	25.00
Bulldog, black, emerging from kennel inscribed: *The Black Watch.*	
2 sizes: 56mm dog half out of kennel.	22.00
96mm only face & front legs out of kennel.	22.50
Bulldog, sitting, very thin face.	
52mm.	40.00
Bulldog, standing. No. 301.	
Sometimes inscribed: *Who said Germans.* Add £20.00	
2 sizes: 125mm long.	22.50
130mm long.	24.50
Dog, Collie, lying down.	
78mm long.	30.00
Dog, Collie, standing. Sometimes inscribed: *Shetland Collie.* Add £4.00 or *Sheep Dog.* Add £8.00	
2 sizes: 60mm.	16.00
95mm long.	17.50
Dog, Dachshund. 90mm long.	38.00
Dog, King Charles Spaniel, begging on cushion.	
2 sizes: 68mm.	12.00
95mm.	17.50
Dog, Labrador Puppy, sitting, with back feet between front legs, sometimes inscribed: *Daddy wouldn't buy me a bow wow* or *My word, if you're not off.* Add £7.50	
2 sizes: 65mm.	20.00
75mm.	25.00
Dog, Puppy, head on one side.	
115mm.	10.50

Dog (Pup), sitting with one ear raised. 68mm.	14.00
Dog, Scottie, standing.	
2 sizes: 60mm high.	20.00
68mm high. 88mm long, Inscribed: *Scotch Terrier*	27.50
Dog, Scottie, sitting wearing blue glengarry. 60mm.	14.50
Dog, Scottie sitting wearing Tam o'Shanter. Hat can be found coloured blue. 85mm.	12.50
If with coloured hat.	16.00
Dog, Scottish Terrier, standing. Can be found inscribed: *Scotch Terrier.* Add £6.50 *As old Mrs Terrier said to her pup, in all lifes adventures keep your tail up.* Add £8.00	
2 sizes: 66mm long.	16.00
85mm long.	23.00
Dog, standing, facing sideways, curly tail and blue collar.	
80mm long.	30.00
Dog in Top Hat, sitting on back legs.	
115mm.	30.00
Dog, Staffordshire Bull Terrier.	
2 sizes: 70mm	12.50
80mm.	17.00
Dog, Staffordshire Bull Terrier, sitting, looking left. Inscribed: *Model of Bill Sykes Dog* on base and *My word if you're not off* on rear. Brown eyes. 104mm.	22.00
Dog, model of Bill Syke's Dog No. 300, second variation. 103mm.	25.00
Dog, walking, blue collar. with *Old Mrs Terrier* inscription. 90mm long.	19.50
Dog, Terrier looking out of kennel. Inscribed: *Beware of the Dog.*	20.00
Dog posy holder, some colouring.	
103mm long.	16.50
Donkey (matching crest Clovelly)	
4 sizes: 80mm long.	40.00
96mm long.	50.00
with saddle, 112mm long.	50.00
125mm long *Hee Haw.*	55.00
Smaller size has saddle. Large size can have inscription: *Hee-haw!.* Add £10.00	
Elephant, Indian, trunk attached to body	
2 sizes: 55mm.	30.00
67mm.	30.00
Elephant, Indian, trunk over head.	
67mm.	35.00

Elephant, Indian, trunk modelled
free from body, sometimes
inscribed: *Baby Jumbo*. Add £10.00
55mm. 30.00
Fawn, sitting. 50mm high, 80mm long. 40.00
Fawn, standing on oval base.
88mm. high, 65mm long. 45.00
Fish, fat. 98mm long. 5.50
Fish, open mouthed.
2 sizes: 80mm. 5.00
108mm. 6.50
Fish, lying on its right side.
122mm long. 8.50
Fish, curled body 110mm long. 11.50
Fish ashtray in shape of plaice,
usually inscribed: A *pla(i)ce for
ashes*, but can be inscribed:
Caught at... or *A plaice for everything*
125mm long. 14.50
Fox. walking, bushy tail. 108mm long. 80.00
Fox on square plinth. 114mm. 80.00
Frog, closed mouth. 45mm. 40.00
Frog, open mouthed and green eyes,
larger sizes inscribed: *Always
croaking.*
4 sizes: 60mm - no inscription.
but with green eyes. 18.00
70mm. 18.00
80mm. 25.00
100mm long. 25.00
Goat, mountain, *Yr Afr Gynreig.*
82mm long. 75.00
Hare.
2 sizes: 73mm long. 16.00
80mm long. 20.00
Kangaroo. 75mm. 80.00
Hippopotamus. 88mm long. 65.00
Lion, roaring. 85mm long. 23.00
Lion, walking.
3 sizes: 85mm long. 30.00
112mm long. 25.00
140mm long. 55.00
Smallest sizes can be found
inscribed: *King of the forest*, for
which add £10.00
Monkey, wearing coat, sitting
hand to mouth.
2 sizes: 65mm. 22.00
78mm. 22.00
Monkey, sitting holding coconut.
No. 34. 85mm. 22.00
Monkeys, three wise, sitting on wall
*I see no evil, I speak no evil, I
hear no evil.* 76mm. 15.00
Mouse, holding acorn. 60mm. 50.00

Otter, holding fish in mouth.
120mm long. 65.00
Pig, smiling and sitting. 63mm long. 23.00
Pig, short and standing, inscribed:
I won't be druv. 63mm long. 20.00
Pig, tall and standing, inscribed:
*You can push or you can shuv but
I'm hanged if I'll be druv.*
78mm high, 63mm long. 22.50
Hampshire Hog. Model of, sitting.
No. 148C. 70mm long. 25.50
Hampshire Hog. Model of, standing
inscribed: *Wunt be druv* and verse
No. 145.105mm long. 25.00
Irish Pig. 90mm long. 25.00
Sussex Pig, Model of. sitting,
inscribed: *Wunt be druv* or *You
can push.* No. 148. 88mm long. 30.00
Sussex Pig, Model of standing fat 22.50
Pig, can be found inscribed:
Mochyn bad with Welsh crest.
No. 148. 80mm long, if named 30.00
Sussex Pig, No. 148. Fat standing
pig, with verse. 48mm high,
95mm long. 17.00
Sussex Pig, Model of, standing thin
pig, inscribed: You *can push or you
can shuv but I'm hanged if I'll be
druv* or *Won't be druv* No. 148.
2 sizes: 78mm long. 20.00
85mm long. 22.00
Wiltshire Pig, Model of, sitting up on
haunches, alert ears. No. 148.
60mm. 30.00
Wiltshire Pig, Model of, standing fat
pig with double chin, inscribed:
Wunt be druv. No. 148. 85mm long. 22.00
Piglet, kneeling. 70mm long. 20.00
Polar Bear.
2 sizes: 100mm long. 75.00
135mm long. Inscribed:
Polar Bear. 80.00
Pony, New Forest, can be found
unnamed. 100mm long. 25.00
Pony, Shetland, often found
unnamed.
3 sizes: 93mm long. 25.00
110mm long. 25.00
120mm long. 40.00
Rabbit, ears lying along back. Found
numbered 22 and 23. sizes vary
between 60-80mm long. 10.00
Rabbit sitting, ears apart. No. 13.
Sizes vary between 50-68mm. 10.50

Rhinoceros. Can be found with one
or two ears. 90mm long. 95.00
Russian Bear, inscribed *War Edition*
and carries Russian Imperial
crest. 70mm. 100.00
Seal. 102mm long. 22.50
Squirrel, holding nut.
65mm. 30.00
Squirrel Jug. 80mm. 17.00
Teddy Bear, sitting.
2 sizes: 60mm. 24.50
90mm. 30.00
Smaller size is not found
inscribed.
Tortoise. 72mm long. 12.00
Tortoise, standing upright, wearing
blue or orange policeman's
helmet. 65mm. 80.00
Welsh Goat, Model of, inscribed: *Yr
Afr Cymreig.* 100mm long. 55.00
Wembley Lion. 100m long. (stylised
symbol of the B.E.E.). 26.00
Isn't this Rabbit a Duck. On its base a
rabbit, turned on its side a duck.
(Can be found in lustre.) 75mm. 30.00

Birds (including Eggs)
Chick, breaking out of egg.
3 sizes: 63mm long. 9.00
72mm long. 10.00
86mm long. 12.00
Larger size can be found
inscribed: *Easter egg* 17.50
Chick in Egg pepper or salt pot.
2 sizes: 58mm. 7.00
68mm. 7.50
Can have yellow head. Add £5.00
Chick, very tiny and completely
yellow, sitting on a white egg,
inscribed: *Every little helps mother
will be pleased.* 50mm long. 30.00
Egg salt and pepper pots. 58mm. Each 4.00
Eggshell, broken open. 39mm. 10.00
Egg with flat base, can be found
inscribed: *Sparrows egg.* 44mm. 13.50
Cockerel, standing, legs modelled
separately, sometimes inscribed:
Cock o' th' North or *Cock o' th'
South.* Some colouring to head.
100mm. 20.00
If named. 23.00
Can be found inscribed: *Chantelle.* 26.00
Cockerel, standing, legs modelled
together. Some colouring to head.
85mm. 25.00

Hen, standing, some colouring.
80mm (matches above). 25.00
Hen, roosting. 54mm. 8.50
Heron, on circular base. 83mm. 25.00
Bird perched on circular base.
Possibly the Royston Crow. 68mm. 30.00
Bird, perched on tree trunk, wings
extended. (Very impressive).
2 sizes: 125mm. 37.00
162mm (lustre). 40.00
Bird salt and pepper pots. 70mm.
Each 7.50
Dove, Fantail on square base. 70mm. 20.00
Goose. 86mm. 38.00
Manx Warbler 125mm. 20.00
Norwich Canary. 100mm. 10.00
If coloured yellow. 17.00
Norwich Warbler. Canary on rock,
with whistle and bubble blower
base. Named. Add £20.00
126mm. 22.50
Can be found on tree stump base
without blower. 125mm. 17.00
Owl, baby. 40mm. 16.00
Owl, Barn Plump. 63mm. 22.50
Owl, Horned (long eared).
2 sizes: 74mm. 15.50
95mm. 30.00
Owl (wise), one eye closed, with
verse. 98mm. 22.50
Parakeet.
2 sizes: 60mm. 14.50
83mm. 17.50
If inscribed: *Pretty Polly.* 12.50
Parrot sometimes inscribed: *Pretty
Polly,* for which add £5.00. Well
detailed, No. 252 or
No. 751. 70mm. 15.00
Peacock, yellow beak and coloured
plume. Rd. 120mm. 47.50
Peacock on ashtray. (Can be found
in lustre.) 80mm long. 22.00
Peahen. 72mm. 35.00
Pelican, giant beak with verse.
80mm long, 50mm high. 55.00
Pelican. 70mm. 35.00
Penguin. No details of size. 47.00
Pigeon on square base. 75mm. 30.00
Royston Crow on circular base. 65mm. 30.00
Royston Crow, perched on tree
trunk. 123mm. 40.00
Seagull. 76mm. 35.00
Seagull, sitting, blue colouring to tip
of wings and tail with yellow beak.
105mm long. 65.00

Stork. 80mm.	35.00
Swan, detailed plumage.	
2 sizes: 50mm long.	8.50
70mm long.	8 50
Swan posy bowl. 88mm.	8.50
Thrush on tree trunk. 125mm.	40.00
Turkey, on round base.	
2 sizes: 60 mm.	30.00
75 mm.	30.00
Turkey, on round lustre base.	
78mm.	30.00

Great War

Many of these models are found with the inscription *War Edition AD 1914* and a crest of 'one of the allied countries', (add £5.00 for this). Some of the soldiers, although sold separately, were based on the same design idea and form a set. They are therefore grouped together in the listings.

British Soldier, Model of, more often than not unnamed. 135mm. Two versions exist. The later mould has the rifle touching the hat, and rifle butt turned sideways.	175.00
Colonial Soldier, Model of. 135mm.	215.00
French Soldier, Model of. 135mm.	215.00
Scotch Soldier, Model of. 135mm.	215.00
Bugler Boy, Model of, in busby. 135mm.	215.00
Drummer Boy, Model of, in busby. 135mm.	215.00
Sailor, standing with hands on hips 132mm.	115.00
(All the above figures are standing to attention on an oval domed base.)	
British Cavalry Soldier, Model of, on horseback. 122mm.	235.00
Russian Cossack, Model of, on horseback. 122mm.	250.00
Despatch Rider, Model of, on motorbike. (Can be found in lustre). 120mm long.	95.00
Nurse and Wounded Tommy, Model of. 108mm long.	190.00
Nurse, inscribed: *Soldier's friend.* Red cross on chest. 132mm.	80.00
Sailor, bust, with hatband impressed *HMS Queen Elizabeth,* hat tilted down to left. 92mm.	47.50

Sailor, bust, found with hatband and scarf. Hat tilted down to right. Inscribed: *The Handyman, HMS Dreadnought.* 92mm.	47.50
Can be found inscribed *"Sailor Beware"*	55.00
Usually found with *Hearts of Oak are our ships.* Some colouring. Can be found with hat coloured blue but this is rare.	80.00
Sailor Winding Capstan, Model of. 105mm.	125.00
Soldier, bust, inscribed: *Tommy Atkins,* or *Territorial,* either found with verse 'It's the Soldiers of the King my lads'. Some colouring. 90mm.	40.00
with verse	50.00
Soldier with Respirator, bust, inscribed: *Model of new gas mask.* 95mm. (rare)	250.00
Tommy driving a Steam Roller over the Kaiser, inscribed: *To Berlin.* 120mm. (very rare).	500.00
Tommy in Bayonet Attack, Model of. 130mm.	170.00
Tommy and his Machine Gun, Model of. 72mm.	55.00
Tommy on Sentry Duty. Model of, in sentry box. 110mm.	85.00
Tommy throwing Hand Grenade, Model of, 130mm.	170.00
New Aeroplane, Model of. Biplane with fixed prop, and roundels in relief. 120mm long.	170.00
New Aeroplane, Model of. Monoplane with revolving propeller. 135mm long.	75.00
New Aeroplane, Model of. Monoplane with fixed propeller. 147mm long.	75.00
Monoplane, movable prop. 149mm long.	75.00
Monoplane, V winged, with fixed prop. & detailed surface. Propeller can be found with 2 or 3 blades.	
2 sizes: 118mm long. 2-bladed.	150.00
118mm long. 3-bladed.	165.50
140mm long. 2-bladed.	170.00
140mm long. 3-bladed.	190.00
(This model has a circular portion added for no other reason than to carry the crest.)	
Aeroplane Propeller. 150mm long.	30.00
RAF/RFC crest.	40.00
Rarely factory marked.	

British Airship, Model of, with
suspended engine. 120mm long.   125.00
British Airship on stand.
128mm long.   35.00
Observer or Sausage Balloon, Model of.
84mm.   75.00
Super Zeppelin, Model of. 127mm long.   60.00
Battleship: *HMS Queen Elizabeth.*
160mm long.   40.00
Battleship. 160mm long. *HMS Queen
Mary* (inscribed on deck). Rare.   150.00
Battleship, 3 funnels and tiny gun
fore and aft. 120mm long.   30.00
Minesweeper, not found named.
126mm long.   80.00
RMS Lusitania, not found named.
180mm long.   80.00
Torpedo Boat Destroyer, Model of.
115mm long. (Can be found in
lustre).   30.00
Submarine, inscribed: *E4.*
95mm long.   27.00
New submarine, Model of, inscribed:
E5. 126mm long.   30.00
Armoured Car, Model of. 95mm long.   50.00
Red Cross Van, red cross on each
side and rear. 'EH 139' printed on
radiator.
3 sizes: 78mm long.   40.00
85mm long.   40.00
160mm long.   700.00
The large size was made for shop
window display and is extremely
rare.
Tank, Model of; (without wheels).
5 sizes: 100mm long.   85.00
110mm long.   25.00
115mm long.   40.00
160mm long.   40.00
325mm long.   450.00
115mm size can be found inscribed:
Original made in Lincoln. Add £15.00
Also found inscribed *285.*
The two largest sizes also exist
with green/brown camouflage
markings. The smallest size is
quite rare and the largest size
is very rare, being so enormous
that it must have been made
for shop display. It can also
be found in orange lustre, for
which deduct £100.00.
Tank, Model of, with inset wheels.
115mm long.   25.00
Can be found inscribed: *Original
made in Lincoln.*   40.00

Tank, Model of, with trailing steering
wheels. 144mm long.   40.00
Tank, Model of, exactly as above but
with one trailing wheel. 144mm
long. (Rare).   350.00
Tank, Model of, exactly as above but
with a second wheel attached to
the one-wheeled tank.   100.00
Whippet Tank, large hexagonal gun
turret at rear. 180mm long. (Rare).   450.00
Field Gun.
4 sizes: 120mm long.   22.50
140mm long.   25.50
150mm long.   30.00
175mm long.   40.00
*New Field Gun with Screen and Sight
Hole, Model of.* 105mm long.   34.00
German Howitzer, Model of.
3 sizes: 115mm long.   21.50
140mm long.   25.00
150mm long.   30.00
Trench Mortar, Model of. On four
wheels. Can be rarely found
inscribed: *Roaring Meg.*
75mm long.   21.50
If inscribed   35.00
Trench Mortar on square base. (Krupp).
70mm.   22.50
Russian Gun captured at San
Sebastapol. 50mm.   30.00
Revolver, Model of. 83mm long.   77.50
Anti-aircraft Shell, Model of. 98mm.   22.00
Cannon Shell.
3 sizes: 70mm.   5.50
90mm.   8.50
135mm. (giant sized)   30.00
The 90mm and 135mm sizes are
often inscribed: *Jack Johnson.*
Add £10.00
or sometimes: *Hartlepool's
Bombardment Dec 16th 1914.*
Add £20.00
Cannon Shell Salt and Pepper pots.
70mm. Each   7.50
Shell Case. 56mm.   8.50
Clip of Bullets, Model of. 57mm.   30.00
Trench Flying Pig, Model of, (Flying
pig is a nickname for a type of
Stokes bomb.) 95mm long. (Very
rare):   170.00
There are two different versions.
One has a tail at the back and the
factory mark is on the side which is
used as a stand - add £20.00. A later
version has no tail and a factory
mark on base which is its stand.

Bomb dropped from Zeppelin, Model of. Inscription sometimes reads: *German Zeppelin* or *on Bury St. Edmunds*. 75mm.	17.00
If inscribed and with matching crest.	22.00
Bomb dropped from Zeppelin upon Sheringham during first raid on England 8.30pm Jany, 18th 1915, Model of. With movable three bladed propeller. 115mm.	170.00
Also found with the following inscription: *First bomb dropped from Zeppelin at Loftus Sept 8th 1915 at 9.30* or *Model of first bomb dropped from Zeppelin on Skinningrove Ironworks Sept. 8th 1915 at 9.30pm*	215.00
British Aerial Bomb, Model of. 75mm.	55.00
Canister Bomb, Model of. 60mm.	20.00
Plum Pudding Bomb, Model of. Often found unnamed. 72mm. (Rare).	90.00
German Hand Grenade, Model of. 78mm. (Rare).	120.00
Hairbrush Grenade, Model of. 104mm long. (Rare).	160.00
Mills Hand Grenade, Model of. 2 sizes: 62mm.	27.50
92mm.	55.00
British Aerial Torpedo, Model of. 102mm long.	47.00
German Aerial Torpedo, Model of. 88mm long.	55.00
Bandsman's Drum. No. 226. 53mm.	12.50
Bandsman's Drum, burst base variation. 53mm.	20.00
Bell Tent. 64mm dia. Open flaps.	15.50
If inscribed: *Camping out.* Can be found with open or closed flaps.	22.00
Capstan. 56mm.	14.50
Gurkha Knife, Model of. 110mm long.	25.00
Pair of Field Glasses, Model of. Often found not named. 78mm long.	19.00
Sandbag, Model of. 73mm long.	25.50
Tommy's Hut, Model of. 105mm long.	50.00
Trench Dagger, Model of. 102mm long.	70.00
• *Trench Lamp, Model of.* 70mm.	21.00
Water Bottle, Model of. 65mm.	17.50
Colonial Hat, Model of, (rarely found inscribed: *Anzacs).* 88mm wide.	20.00
Inscribed.	25.00
Glengarry. 90mm long.	22.50
New Zealand Hat. 71mm dia.	27.50

Officer's Peaked Cap, white or more usually with coloured badge and hatband. 65mm dia. Can be found inscribed: *Territorials cap.*add	10.00
White hatband.	12.50
Coloured hatband.	19.50
Solar Topee (Pith helmet). 60mm.	34.50
Steel Helmet, sometimes inscribed: *Tommy's Steel Helmet.* 65mm dia.	
Named	42.00
Unnamed	34.00
Anti-Zeppelin Candle Holder. 65mm.	22.50
Fireplace inscribed: *We've kept the home fires burning.* 4 sizes: 60mm.	17.50
90mm.	20.50
110mm.	23.00
115mm.	25.50
Angel with raised arms, found with R.A.F crest (not named) but must be R.A.F Memorial. No details of size.	115.00
Bishop's Stortford *War Memorial.* 132mm.	125.00
Brora War Memorial. 155mm. (Rare).	155.00
Burford War Memorial, with inscription. 128mm. (Rare).	170.00
Burnham on Crouch *War Memorial.* 146mm. (Rare).	125.00
Carillon Tower, Loughborough. War Memorial. 155mm.	60.00
Cavell Statue, inscribed: *Nurse Cavell.* 3 sizes: 110mm.	19.50
147mm.	19.50
160mm.	22.00
Cavell *Memorial Statue, Norwich,* inscribed: *Edith Cavell - Nurse, Patriot and Martyr.* 175mm.	37.50
Cenotaph, Model of, with green wreaths. 4 sizes: 80mm.	8.00
100mm.	10.00
140mm.	12.50
180mm.	14.50
Three larger sizes with inscription. Cheltenham War Memorial. 2 sizes: 150mm.	105.00
185mm.	105.00
Chesham *War Memorial.* 159mm.	125.00
Coventry War Memorial. 140mm.	125.00
Dingwall *War Memorial,* soldier on wide plinth. 125mm.	125.00
Dover Patrol Memorial. 130mm.	45.00

Dover *War Memorial*. 140mm.   75.00
Dovercourt War Memorial.
  2 sizes: 120mm.   110.00
       137mm.   110.00
East Dereham War Memorial, with
  inscription (rare).132mm.   160.00
Florence Nightingale Statue,
inscribed: *The Lady of the Lamp*.
  3 sizes: 125mm.   20.00
       147mm.   24.00
       170mm.   24.00
  (Different moulds)
Folkestone War Memorial inscribed:
May their deeds be held in reverence.
2 sizes:
  97mm wide at base, 125mm high   80.00
  150mm wide at base, 156mm high   80.00
Fryatt Memorial, with inscription
  (rare).   130.00
Great Yarmouth *War Memorial*, with
  inscription.
  2 sizes: 146mm.   75.00
       175mm.   55.00
Invergordon *War Memorial*. 148mm.
  (Rare).   125.00
Killin War Memorial. 150mm.   170.00
*Earl Kitchener Memorial, drowned off
Marwick Head, Orkney, 5th June
1916*. 110mm.   140.00
Lewisham War Memorial. 155mm.   80.00
Lockerbie War Memorial. 170mm.   140.00
Loughborough War Memorial,
  see *Carillon Tower*.
Margate *War Memorial*. 160mm.   135.00
March War Memorial. 160mm.   145.00
Moffat War Memorial with ram on a
  rock. (Rare). 165mm.   200.00
Newhaven Mercantile Memorial,
  with inscription. 155mm.   145.00
Norwich *War Memorial*.
  134mm long, 60mm high.   155.00
Plymouth War Memorial, with female
  figure. 120mm.   135.00
Plymouth *Naval War Memorial*, with
  inscription.
  3 sizes: 125mm.   55.00
       156mm.   60.00
       178mm.   65.00
Plymouth Royal Naval Memorial,
  on octagonal stepped base. 144mm.   75.00
Southsea *Naval War Memorial*.
2 sizes: 140mm.   65.00
       162mm.   75.00
Scarborough Lighthouse showing
  damage from enemy naval action.
  132mm.   105.00

Sheringham War Memorial, with
  inscription. 165mm.   125.00
Stowmarket Memorial Gates.
  110mm long.   115.00
Walsall War Memorial.   155.00
Warminster War Memorial. 150mm.   125.00
Woodhouse Eaves, War Memorial with
  inscription. 130mm.   160.00

Most war memorials are relatively
rare, possibly because they were
ordered in small numbers by
local shops, and were only made
for a relatively short period.

Home/Nostalgic

Anvil on tree trunk base, horseshoe,
  tongs etc. against base. 70mm.   7.50
Armchair 65mm.   9.00
Armchair, inscribed: *The old
armchair*, with verse. 90mm.   10.50
Ball of String, match holder and
  striker. 55mm.   20.00
Ball of String. 55mm.   22.00
Basket, straw, with twisted handle.
  73mm long.   6.00
  If inscribed: *Fruit Basket*   8.50
Basket of Milk, six bottles, tops gold
  or brown. 65mm.   24.50
Bell no clapper. 54mm.   7.50
Bellows. 95mm long.   14.50
Chair, highbacked. 90mm.   9.50
Coal Scuttle. 65mm.   6.00
  Sometimes found inscribed:
  Coal scuttle. 80mm.   9.50
Cradle. 48mm.   13.00
Dressing Table Swing Mirror, with
  drawer. 50mm.   19.50
Dust pan.
  3 sizes: 95mm long.   8.50
       105mm long.   10.00
       143mm long.   14.00
Firebucket. 55mm.   5.00
Fireplace, with teapot, cat etc. in
  bold relief. Inscribed: *There's no
place like home*. Some colouring.
  2 sizes: 90mm.   17.50
       112mm.   19.50
Fireplace, with cauldron, teapot, etc.
  moulded in slight relief.
  Inscribed: *There's no place like
home*. Some colouring.
  2 sizes: 65mm.   16.00
       110mm.   20.00
Flat Iron. 77mm long.   15.50

Frying Pan.
2 sizes: 114mm long. — 17.00
120mm long. — 17.00
Gladstone Bag. 82mm long. — 15.50
Grandfather Clock, narrow,
inscribed: *1:30.* or *2:30.*
2 sizes: 105mm. — 17.50
145mm. — 19.00
Grandfather Clock, Model of. Usually
inscribed: *Make use of time let not
advantage slip. Shakespeare.* Can be
found inscribed: *Top o' the morn.*
No. 209. 108mm. (Two moulds,
one with ornate moulding at top). — 20.00
Invalid Feeding Cup. 50mm. — 6.50
Jardiniere on fixed base. 95mm. — 6.00
Kennel, can be found inscribed:
Beware of the dog. 50mm. — 12.50
Lantern.
2 sizes: 70mm. — 8.50
90mm. — 12.50
Lantern, horn, not found named but
sometimes inscribed: *Watchman
what of the night.* 85mm. — 18.50
Lantern, with open sides. 125mm. — 24.00
Oil Lamp, flat. 92mm long. — 6.00
Pillar Box, with inscription: *If you
haven't time to post a line here's the
pillar box.* 63mm. — 14.00
Found marked *G.R.V.* — 16.00
70mm. *E.R. VII* — 17.00
Policeman's Lamp. 75mm. — 12.00
Potty. 36mm. — 6.00
Saucepan with handle and separate
lid. 45mm, 80mm long. — 15.00
Shaving Mug. 60mm. — 9.50
Spinning Wheel. 84mm. — 34.00
Stool, 3 legs. 40mm. — 9.50
Sundial, inscribed: *Life's but a
walking shadow.* Add £5 for
inscription.
2 sizes: No. 41. 86mm. — 8.50
115mm. — 10.50
Sundial on square base. 115m. — 8.50
Table, square with four legs. 40mm. — 7.50
Thimble. *Tak a Thimble Full.* 41mm. — 20.00
Umbrella, open. 50mm dia. (Usually
not factory marked.) — 17.50
Village Pump with trough. 90mm. — 16.50
Can be found inscribed. Add £5.00
Old Warming Pan, Model of, often
inscribed: *Polly warm the bed.*
No. 254. 125mm long. — 20.00
Old Warming Pan, Model of, with
ornate handle. No.251. 120mm long. — 17.50

Watering Can. No. 126. 74mm. — 10.00
Water Pitcher, inscribed: *Tak Hod
An' sup lad.* 60mm. — 8.50
Wheelbarrow. 100mm long. — 17.00

Comic/Novelty
Alarm Clock, inscribed: *Many are
called but few get up!*
2 sizes: 40mm. — 24.50
60mm. — 28.00
Billiken, often found not named.
63mm. — 7.50
Biscuit *Oval rich tea* beige, on white
base, 50mm. — 60.00
Biscuit *Oval rich tea* beige, on no
base, 80mm. — 60.00
Child (girl), yawning & stretching,
forming candle snuffer. 96mm. — 21.00
Child (boy), yawning & stretching,
forming candle snuffer. 95mm. — 21.00
Clown, bust. No inscription or
colouring. 65mm. — 14.50
Clown, bust, inscribed: *Put me
amongst the girls.* Some colouring.
Reg. No. 522477. 80mm. — 30.00
Clown, candlesnuffer, standing,
hands on hips, wearing baggy
suit. 104mm. — 47.50
Couple in Bed, inscribed: *John is
everything shut up for the night - All
but you darling.* Some colouring.
70mm long. — 75.00
Couple in Bed, man sitting up,
woman with all the blankets,
inscribed: *They don't need many
clothes in the daytime but they want
'em all at night.* 70mm long. — 75.00
Fat Lady on weighing scales, scale
registers 20 stone. Inscribed:
Adding weight. Blue or green
bonnet. 90mm. — 80.00
Jester, doubled faced bust, happy
with eyes open and sad with eyes
closed. Can be found inscribed:
Ye Jester awake. Ye Jester asleep.
Some colouring on larger size.
2 sizes: 70mm. — 14.50
90mm. — 20.00
inscribed — 27.00
Lavatory Pan with brown seat,
inscribed: Ashes. Not found
crested. 69mm. — 30.00
*Mister Gollywog, Now children when
I've tucked you safely in, just say Mr
Gollywog good-night.* Full figure,
standing. 118mm. — 400.00

Negro Minstrel, bust, verse by
Eugene Stratton. Some colouring.
100mm.   40.00
Petrol Pump Attendant, body is
pump. Inscribed: *Petrol Sir*. Can
be found with some colouring.
95mm. White   80.00
Coloured   95.00
Policeman, smiling, with arms
clasped behind back. 100mm.   47.50
Policeman, fat and jovial, with large
raised hand. Inscribed (on hand):
Stop. 94mm.   34.50
Policeman on point duty, with verse.
148mm.   55.50
Policeman, jovial holding large
truncheon. Uniform and helmet
blue. 106mm. (Rare).   105.00
Rabit/Duck *Isn't this Rabbit a Duck?*
50mm.   30.00
Robinson Crusoe standing figure
with gun. 122mm.   110.00
Sailor, standing, cap can be found
impressed: *HMS Lion*. Blue cap and
coloured face. 95mm.   65.00
Sailor Toby Jug, blue hat and coat.
60mm.   40.00
65mm (fatter) black face, white
jug, red hat.   47.50
108mm.   55.00
Sailor Vase, pink face and some
colouring. 103mm.   77.50
Sailor, negro features, Vase.
100mm.   70.00
(Late also found marked Goss
England)
Scottish Sailor Posy Vase, fully
coloured with green jacket & kilt
110mm.   65.00
Suffragette double sided bust front
sour old lady, inscribed: *Votes for
women*, back pretty young girl
inscribed: *This one shall have a
vote*. Coloured features.   65.00
A smaller version exists with no
colouring or inscriptions. 72mm.   30.00
Suffragette candle snuffer, double
faced as above. 72mm.   20.00
Suffragette hand bell, double faced
as above, with same inscription
and colouring. Also found
inscribed: *Nature has endowed
woman with so much power that the
law gives them very little. Dr Johnson*.
2 variations: curved bell. 110mm.   65.00
straight-sided bell. 100mm.   65.00
(All the suffragette items must be
considered scarce).

Teapot, comical, with eyes, mouth
and nose as spout. Reputedly Lady
Cadogan's Puzzle Tea Pot. Some
colouring.   65.00

Comic Ashtrays: Coloured figures
on white trays. (All are quite
rare).
Bird, possibly a crow, fully
coloured, dressed in top hat,
frock-coat, waistcoat and
trousers, carrying a black cane;
standing on pentagonal brown
base with a circular brown dish in
centre. 85mm.   80.00
Bookmaker, with greyhound and
hare on octagonal ashtray base.
Some colouring. 90mm long.   47.50
For Irish Colleen, Irishman and
Welsh Lady see: National
Souvenirs.
Golfer with golf club and ball
(matcholder and striker) on
ashtray base *Matches* outpressed
on ball. 103mm and 117mm long. 200.00
Golfer, standing on golf ball in
centre of hexagonal ashtray.
72mm.   125.00
Jester coloured, sitting on heart or spade
shaped tray, other card symbols
are on tray. 65mm.   85.00
Puppy with monocle, coloured with
hat, bow, cigar and beer! on
ashtray. (Can be found in brown
lustre). 90mm.   125.00
Scotsman, really grotesque, sitting
on bench on round tray. 95mm.   75.00
plain white   40.00
Woodpecker, red & blue, sitting on
round ashtray. 72mm.   40.00

Comic Cruet Sets: Rarely found as a
set. They are coloured.
Policeman salt pot. 80mm.   80.00
Regimental Sergeant Major pepper
pot.
80mm.   55.00
Naval Petty Officer pepper pot.
80mm.   47.50
Sailor, comic figure in blue with
green parrot on shoulder with
white mustard barrel with lid.
63mm.   65.00
Sailor pepper pot, standing, cap can
be found impressed *Lion*. Blue
cap and coloured face. 85mm.   55.00

Little birds: these are fully coloured heads popping out of white eggs. They do not seem to match any other series of models, the black boy's face is much more carefully detailed than the black boys listed below.
Flapper's coloured head hatching from egg inscribed: *A little bird from ....*

50mm long.	40.00
white head	20.00

Black Boy's head hatching from Egg, inscribed: *A blackbird from ....*
50mm long.   55.00

Black Boys - often found marked Rd. No. applied for. All the boys are fully coloured but sit on white boxes, baths and so on. Later models are very brightly and carefully coloured and lightly glazed. These are marked as late in the listing below. All these models, with the exception of A *Black Boy in a bath of ink,* are uncommon.

Black Boy standing with hands in pockets, also found as salt pot. 94mm. (Late).   155.00

Black Girl, yellow hat,standing with hands on hips, also found as pepper pot. (Pair with above). 94mm.   165.00

Black Boy playing banjo, boy can be wearing red, yellow or blue striped pyjamas. 85mm.   150.00

Black Boy in bath of ink, towel hanging at side, inscribed: *How ink is made* 110mm long. (Probably Willow Art mould).   115.00

Black Boy in hip bath holding yellow soap. 90mm (late).   155.00

Black Girl in hip bath holding yellow soap. 90mm.   155.00

Black Boy in bed with spider or black beetle, inscribed: *A little study in black and fright.* Boy can have red, yellow or blue striped pyjamas. 70mm long.   135.00

Black Boy in bed, face only peeping out from bedclothes, inscribed: *Just a little study in black and fright.*

70mm long.	105.00
No colouring.	40.00

Black Couple in bed, inscribed: *They don't need many...*71mm long.   145.00

Black Boy being chased up a tree by a crocodile. 80mm.   165.00

Black Boy Dish, lying on his back, hands around knees. 120mm long.   180.00

Black Boy eating slice of melon, sitting on a soapbox. 80mm. (late).   155.00

Black Boy eating melon slice, standing on corner of diamond shaped ashtray, inscribed: *I'se not melon-choly! (Rare)* 88mm.   155.00

Black Boy sitting at table eating a boiled egg which has a yellow chick popping out. 70mm.   135.00

Two Black Boys heads popping out of box, inscribed: *Box of chocolates.*

60mm.	75.00
Also found in white only.	30.00

Two Black Children, boy and girl sitting on a tree trunk. 80mm.   120.00

Black Boy holding giant pumpkin with lid. Pumpkin sometimes coloured green. 72mm.   155.00

Black Boy holding container for cigarettes, inscribed: *Cigarettes.* 100mm (late).   145.00

Black Boy holding container for matches. Inscribed: *Matches.* 100mm. (Late).   125.00
Also found with brown/blue marbelled finish.

Black Boy peering out of shower, coloured trousers hanging from top (rare) 67mm.   170.00

Children: very late models, beautifully coloured and detailed children on white armchairs, baths etc.. Usually found marked Rd. No. applied for. They are particularly appealing and unfortunately rare.

Girl and Boy sitting in armchair. Girl is wearing a frilly dress and has a large bow on her head; boy is dressed in top hat and tails. 60mm.   200.00

Girl and Boy sitting in armchair Boy wears black jacket and hat. 75mm.   215.00

Girl with pink dress and Boy with yellow trousers as above sitting on tree trunk. 87mm long.   150.00
plain white   50.00

Boy in nightgown, yawning and
stretching. Candle snuffer. 100mm.   25.00
Boy riding a Pig. Boy wearing a
coloured coat. 94mm long.   300.00
Girl standing by hip bath, wearing
towel. 75mm.   85.00
Girl, naked, blonde hair with red
bow, standing in circular bath,
draped in white and blue towel
and holding yellow sponge.
Registration applied for. 90mm.   120.00
Baby sitting in round Bath with a
coloured transfer of an insect
either a wasp or a fly).
80mm long.   50.00

Cartoon/Comedy Characters
Ally Sloper, bust, with inscription.
70mm.   30.00
85mm.   40.00
Baby, with arms outstretched,
inscribed: *Cheerio*. Some
colouring on face. 120mm.
(from Willow mould)   30.00
Bonzo dog sitting, hind legs
outstretched in front, name
impressed on collar. 68mm.   40.00
Bonzo, sitting on feeding bowl. 65mm. 40.00
Bonzo and Felix sitting on bench,
coloured and not named. 76mm.   125.00
Harry Lauder, bust. Inscribed: *Stop
ye're tickling Jock*. Often found not
named. Some colouring   17.00
83mm, named   30.00
98mm.   50.00
Mrs. Gummidge, standing figure
with inscription: A *lone lorn
creetur & everything goes contrairy
with her*. 112mm (rare).   55.00
Standing figure, probably a politician
(Lloyd George?) left hand in pocket,
right hand open and gesturing.
120mm.   50.00
Winkie the glad-eyed bird, not
named but can be found
inscribed: *Glad eyes*. 60mm.   22.00

Alcohol
GIN AND 'IT' Woman with gin
bottle, wearing black hat, blue top
and brown skirt, sitting on a bench
with a young lady dressed in a pale
green hat & dress. 65mm.   70.00

Series of late models of a fully
coloured comic man (looks rather
like Mr. Pickwick, bald with
spectacles, wearing a green suit,
but probably was a comedian or
comic character associated with
heavy drinking) on white
models.
Man, as above, blowing froth off
his beer tankard. 92mm. Can be
white, with silver tankard and
coloured face   65.00
or fully coloured.   82.50
Man, as above, holding tankard on
horseshoe ashtray, with
inscription: *The more we are
together the merrier we'll be*.
70mm.   65.00
White   30.00
Man, as above, clinging to neck of
bottle. Fully coloured, white
bottle.
2 sizes: 76mm.   55.00
95mm.   65.00
Man, as above, climbing into large
beaker. 75mm.   55.00
Beaker, fluted, with inscription:
*They speak o' my drinking, but they
dinna consider my drouth*, or *Ye
never ken the worth o' water till the
well not is dry*. 78mm.   7.50
Beer Barrel on stand, inscribed:
XXX on each end of barrel. 55mm.   6.50
Beer Bottle and tankard on
horseshoe ashtray, with
inscription: *The more we are
together the merrier we'll be*.   14.50
Beer Bottle and tankard on square
ashtray with inscription above.
90mm.   14.50
Bottle, syphon and glass on round
tray inscribed: *Irish and Soda*.
58mm.   15.50
Bottle, stout. No. 44. 63mm.   7.00
Bottle with cork. 76mm.   7.50
can be found inscribed: *Special
Scotch* or *One Special Irish*.   8.50
or more rarely *Lacon's fine ale*.   12.50
Carboy.
2 sizes: 55mm.   6.00
85mm.   6.00

Drunk leaning against a statue on
an ashtray. Inscribed: *How cold
you are tonight dear.* Coloured
figure on white tray.
100mm.   125.00
Monk, jovial, and holding glass
with verse: A *jovial monk am I
contented with my lot. The world
without this gate. If lout nor care for
it one jot.* Add £10.00 for black hat.
2 sizes: 70mm.   12.50
    120mm.   20.00
A Nap Hand, hand holding coloured
beer labels on heart shaped dish.
62mm long.   55.00
Silver Tankard. 85mm.   17.50
Soda Syphon. Can be found
inscribed: *Soda Water Syphon.*
No. 6. 100mm.   15.50
Tankard, foaming, with verse: 'The
more we are together'. 50mm.   8.50
Tankard, shaped. No. 41. 47mm.   5.00
Thistle Vase, with verse: '*Just a wee
deoch-an doris'.* 70mm.   5.00
Toby Jug, sometimes found with
verse: *No tongue can tell, No heart
can think, Oh how I love a drop of
drink.* 4 sizes:
    45mm. Smallest size   10.50
    can be found coloured   17.50
    65mm. Identical to Old Toby Jug.   16.00
    75mm.   16.50
    85mm.   16.50
Toby Jug, green coat, black bow tie,
white waistcoat with black stripes,
yellow trousers, black hat. 100mm.   75.00
Whiskey Bottle, can have solid or
cork top, inscribed: *One Special
Scotch* or *One Special Irish.* 100mm.   8.50
Whiskey Bottle and Soda Syphon on
tray, inscribed: *Scotch and Soda.*
88mm dia.   15.50

Sport/Pastimes
Billiard Table, cue and three balls.
100mm long.   125.00
Cricket Bag.
2 sizes: 80mm long.   16.50
    100mm long.   16.50
Cricket Bat. Can be found inscribed
Cricket Week Deal or *Cricket Week in
Birmingham.* 115mm long.   80.00
Curling Stone. 63mm dia.   30.00
Football. 50mm dia.   10.00

Footballer in green/yellow shirt,
blue shorts, black socks and brown
boots on ashtray base with hollow
ball inscribed: *MATCHES.* 107mm
high, 108mm long.   100.00
The F. A. Cup. 100mm.   18.50
    named.   30.00
Golf Ball, often inscribed: *The game
of golf was first played in the year
1448.* 42mm.   12.00
    if inscribed   16.50
Golf Club Head. 94mm long.   23.00
Golf Bag and Clubs. 105mm.   75.00
Caddy with clubs standing on golf
ball. 76mm.   40.00
Golfer wielding club next to ball,
opens as matches holder on
ashtray base. 110mm.   200.00
Golfer's Caddie holding golf bag.
Figure coloured. 116mm.   160.00
Golfer's Caddie, very tiny, holding
huge bag of clubs. 88mm.   85.00
Jockey on Racehorse, oval base,
some colouring, unglazed. 115mm. 95.00
Racehorse and jockey, some colouring,
on horseshoe ashtray. 100mm.   55.00
    Can be found inscribed: *Humorist
    Winner of the Derby 1922
    Donoghue Cup.* Add £20.00
Tennis Racquet. 95mm long.   16.50
Chess Set. Complete sets can be
found but these are very rare. It is
extremely difficult to collect a set
with the same crests although
Eastbourne and Hastings are
considered the most preferable.
Individual pieces are often
found however, the rook being
the most common, the pawn,
strangely, is quite rare.
King. 88mm.   35.00
Queen. 84mm.   35.00
    72mm.   25.00
Knight.
2 sizes: 55mm.   16.50
    63mm.   16.50
Bishop.
2 sizes: 60mm.   25.00
    70mm.   25.00
Rook. 55mm.   7.50
Pawn. 52mm.   30.00

Musical Instruments

Banjo.

2 sizes: 125mm long.	16.50
150mm long.	20.00
Double Bass. 153mm long.	40.00
Guitar. 153mm long.	19.50
Harp. 92mm.	80.00
Harp with green shamrocks. 104mm.	10.50
Piano, upright. 70mm long.	22.00
Tambourine. 50mm dia.	16.00
Violin with bow. 125mm long.	85.00

Transport

Car, open, Vauxhall. (Identical to Shelley No. 361). 135mm long.	140.00
Car, open tourer (2 seater) inscribed: *EH 139*; can be found also inscribed: *HELL*. 110mm long.	40.00
Car, saloon, inscribed: *EHI39*. 76mm long.	40.00
Car, open 2 seater, Morris, showing exhaust pipes, curved boot, etc. 105mm long.	95.00
Car, taxi, inscribed: *EHI39*. Front two seats open, hood over back two. 80mm long.	75.00
Charabanc,18 seater, inscribed: *7734 which upside down reads HELL.* 138mm long.	50.00
Can of Petrol, impressed: *Motor Spirit.* 55mm.	22.00
Omnibus, Double decker bus with stairs outside. 130mm long (rare).	190.00
A *Truck of coal from....*Wagon of black coal 80mm long.	30.00

Modern Equipment

Camera, folding. 60mm.	40.00
Gramophone in Cabinet, open top, black disc. 76mm long.	100.00
Horn Gramophone.	
2 sizes: 80mm.	40.00
112mm.	40.00
Radio Horn. 72mm. Inscribed: *Hello (town name) Calling*	35.00

Hats

Boy Scout's Hat. 73mm dia.	22.00
Luton Boater with coloured band usually unglazed.	
2 sizes: 94mm long.	22.50
100mm long.	22.50
These are usually found with no factory mark, presumably because this would detract from the piece.	
Bishop's Mitre. 53mm.	8.50

Bishop's Mitre. No.19.50mm long.	8.50
Mortar Board with moulded tassel.	
64mm wide.	40.00
Top Hat.40mm.	6.50
Top Hat, match striker and holder.	
45mm.	6.50

Footwear

High backed narrow Shoe.	
2 sizes: 90mm.	7.50
130mm long.	10.50
Hobnail Boot.	
2 sizes: 65mm long.	6.00
80mm long.	6.50
Ladies Ankle Boot. 70mm long.	6.00
Lancashire Clog. 94mm long.	6.50
Lancashire Clog, high narrow type.	
2 sizes: 95mm long.	7.50
135mm long.	11.00
Dutch Clog.102mm long.	5.50
Sabot, pointed toe. 60mm long.	6.00
Oriental Shoe.	
2 sizes: 85mm long.	6.00
105mm long.	7.50
Riding Boot.	
3 sizes: 73mm.	22.00
88mm.	25.00
105mm.	25.00
Shoe posy holder. l00mm long	8.50
Slipper.100mm long.	8.50
Slipper wall pocket.109mm long.	8.50
John Waterson's Clog	12.00

Miniature Domestic

These models can be found with crests, views, black cats and other transfer decorations.

Amphora Vase on three red balls. 90mm.	9.50
Bagware Cream Jug.	5.00
Beaker.40mm.	3.50
Beaker, fluted with inscription: *Ye never ken the worth of water till the well gangs dry.* 50mm.	7.50
Chamberpot. 98mm.	7.00
Cheese Dish, one piece, rectangular. 50mm.	10.50
Cheese Dish and cover with 'pinched in' sides, rectangular. 60mm.	10.50
Cheese Dish and cover, rectangular. 50mm high, 78mm long.	10.50
with *Stilton Cheese* inscription.	16.00
Cream Jug. 52mm.	3.50
Kettle. 55mm.	8.50
Milk Jug with crinkle top. 38mm.	3.50

Tea Cup and saucer. 40mm.	5.50
Teapot with lid, bagware with	
blue cord. 68mm.	17.00
Tea Pot with lid.	
2 sizes: 50mm.	7.50
60mm.	7.50
Tea Pot with lid, bulbous. 52mm.	7.50
Tea Pot with lid, wide base. 45mm.	7.50
Tea Pot, one piece. 48mm.	7.50
Vase with ram's head in relief.	
55mm.	6.00

Domestic

This is listed as it was made specifically to carry crests. Pieces can also be found with *Lucky Black Cat, Lucky White Heather* and other transfer decorations, but not usually views. Late pieces are found with the black cat *Arcadian* mark. Lettering is usually in blue.

Ashtrays, can be found inscribed: *Ashtray.* Various shapes: Club, diamond, heart and spade shaped with crinkle edges.	5.00
Club shaped tray with match box stand. 105mm wide.	15.00
Heart shaped bowl.	4.00
Horseshoe.	4.00
Octagonal.	4.00
Trefoil.	4.00
Round tray with match holder.	12.00
Bulb bowl, hexagonal.	4.00
Candle Snuffer, cone. No. 29. 63mm.	5.50
Candlesticks, various shapes:	
Column with ornate moulding.	6.00
Octagonal, fluted.	6.00
Short on fluted oblong base with handle. 156mm long.	12.00
Short on fluted leaf shaped base with handle.	6.00
Cup with the Wembley Lion moulded as the handle. 40mm dia.	22.50
Fern pots, fluted. 3 sizes:	10.00
Hexagonal. 3 sizes.	10.00
Flower bowl, octagonal.	7.00
Flower vase.	6.00
Hair pin box and lid, can be found inscribed: *Hairpins.* Fluted oblong or round.	8.50

Hair Tidy with lid, can be found inscribed: *Hair Tidy.*	
Various shapes:	
Curved sided. 60mm.	8.00
Hexagonal.	8.00
Octagonal with ornate moulding and blue bow.	10.00
Square, fluted. 65mm.	8.50
Hat Pin Holder, can be found inscribed: *Hat pins.* Various shapes:	
Octagonal.	17.00
Square fluted. 121mm.	17.00
Square with ornate moulding.	17.00
Fluted. 128mm.	17.00
Inkstand, with pen holder base. 150mm long.	10.00
Inkwell with lid. 68mm dia.	12.50
Match Holder, can be found outpressed: *Matches.* Various shapes:	
Hexagonal.	7.50
Round.	7.50
Oval Box and lid *Hair Pins.*	8.50
Pill Box and lid.	
2 sizes: 45mm dia.	6.50
50mm dia.	6.50
Pin Tray, can be found inscribed: *Pins.* Fluted round, diamond or oblong.	5.00
Pot Pourri, 2 shapes: Round vase shaped, lid with knob.	6.00
Round with domed lid (rather like a ginger jar).	6.00
Powder bowl, round.	4.00
Preserve jar with lid, round or tub shaped. 90mm.	7.50
Puff Box, can be found inscribed: *Puff box,* hexagonal or round.	8.50
Ring Stand, octagonal base. 55mm.	12.00
Rose Bowl. 86mm.	14.00
Rose Bowl, fluted with brass fittings.	16.00

Tableware

Cups and saucers, coffee cans and saucers, and plates are all found in classic and simple shapes.	Each 5.00
Also the following:	
Beakers, plain and fluted.	4.00
Butter Tub.	5.50
Butter Dish in carved wooden surround. 105mm diameter.	10.00

Cream jugs and sugar bowls
(matching) in various shapes:

Hexagonal	4.00
Octagonal	4.00
Round, plain	4.00
Round, fluted	4.00

These can occasionally be found
inscribed: *Elp yurzel to the craim* or
Be aisy wid the crame/sugar. Add
£6.00 with these inscriptions.

Egg Cup.	7.50

Jugs, in a variety of sizes, also

bagware.	4.00
Mugs. 2 sizes.	4.00

Mustard Pots. Various shapes:

Round with pointed lid.	4.50
Round, fluted and ornate.	4.50
Round with silver lid.	9.00
Round, tall, with silver lid.	9.00

Napkin Ring inscribed: *1* or *2* in

blue. 45mm.	12.50

Pepper & Salt Pots, various shapes:

Cone shaped, small.	5.50
Cone shaped, tall with silver lids.	12.00

Egg shaped with screw base. P

55mm.	4.00
Hexagonal.	4.00
Round, with silver plated lid.	9.00

If not hallmarked silver deduct
£5.00.

Plate, with thistles and leeks moulded in relief.	7.50
Sugar Basin on stand.	5.00
Sugar Castor.	7.50

Sugar Castor with EPNS top.

Inscribed: *Sugar.* 110mm.	8.00

Sweet Dishes, various shapes:

Octagonal.	4.00
Round, crinkle edges. 2 sizes.	4.00
Round, fluted,2 sizes.	4.00
Teapots. 1, 2 & 3 cup sizes.	10.00
Toast Rack. 120mm long.	13.00

Tobacco Jar with lid, inscribed:

Tobacco, with crossed pipes transfer.	20.00

Trinket Boxes, can be found
inscribed: *Trinkets*. Various
shapes:

Heart shaped. 4 sizes.	6.50
Heart shaped with moulded ribbon.	7.50
Hexagonal.	6.50
Horseshoe shaped.	6.50
Oblong.	6.50
Oval.	6.50

Round. 2 sizes.	6.50
Square.	6.50
Square with bevelled corners.	6.50
Square, fluted.	6.50
Thistle shaped. 75mm long.	8.00
Vases in a variety of sizes and shapes.	4.00 - 10.00
Wall Pocket, shield-shaped. 66mm.	6.50

Miscellaneous

Bagware Vase. No. 10. 50mm.	5.00

Dealer's change Tray, inscribed: *The
Collectors Favourite Arcadian China/
Finest Range of Novelties* (no crest)

195mm diameter.	200.00
Flower Bud Vase. 40mm.	5.00

Flower (Pansy?) shaped pin tray.

80mm dia.	5.00

Horse's Hoof as inkwell with lid.
Inscribed: *We're aye prood tae*

hear frae ye. 90mm.	12.50

Horse's Hoof on base No. 151.

30mm.	6.50
Horseshoe. 55mm long.	6.50
Horseshoe on stand.	6.50

Argonauta Porcelain

Argosy China

ARGONAUTA
PORCELAIN
ENGLISH MAKE
W͟M͟ WHITELEY L͟T͟D͟
BAYSWATER

Mark used for a London retailer.

Trademark used by James Macintyre & Co Ltd, Washington China Works, Burslem. This small firm were earthenware manufacturers and in the Pottery Gazette in 1913, advertised their firm as specialising in 'Arms Ware, School, College or Town Arms on Tobacco Jars, match pots and ashtrays'. This mark has so far only been found on 'smalls'. J. Macintyre and Co. pieces found tend to be rather heavy.

Argonauta Models
Ancient Artefacts
Mug, 1 handled, curved sides.
  No. 17. 35mm.   5.50
Salisbury Jack. 50mm. (With Trusty
  Servant motif and verse).   22.50

Miniature Domestic
Tea Pot and lid. 60mm.   15.00

Miscellaneous
Club shaped Dish. 75mm long.   5.00

Trademark used by Alfred B. Jones & Sons Ltd., Grafton China Works, Longton, Staffs, for a wholesaler or retailer in Southend-on-Sea. (Usual trademark Grafton). See Grafton China for further details. This may have been used as a reject outlet, as many pieces have firing flaws.

Most pieces found have been 'smalls' and many of them have carried Southend crests, so it is probable that the initials SEOS stand for Southend-on-Sea, and KB was a retailer. No device other than crests has been found on china with this mark. (A stock number has been recorded on one model and it is possible that many models carry such numbers).

Argosy Models
Seaside Souvenirs
Bathing Machine with large wooden
  wheels, and panelled body. 55mm. 16.00
Whelk Shell. 85mm.   5.00

Animals
Elephant, comic, standing with
  sandwich boards. 115mm.   100.00

Great War
Colonial Hat. 89mm long.   21.50

Home/Nostalgic
Baby's Rocking Cradle.
  62mm long.   14.00

Footwear
Boot with laces. No. 234.
  80mm long.   7.50
Sabot. 80mm long.   8.00

Miniature Domestic
Tea Pot with lid. 90mm long.   8.50

Arklow Pottery

We have no details of this trademark at present, and only one small piece has been found to date. It would appear to be a Republic of Ireland Pottery manufacturing for the local market.

Arklow Pottery Model
Irish Bronze Pot. 56mm. Inscribed:
a souvenir of Dublin on one side
and a colour transfer of The
Custom House, Dublin on the
other.   8.00

Asbury China

ASBURY
LONGTON

D.W.KEE
PEEL
Asbury China

Trademark thought to have been used by Hewitt and Leadbeater, Willow Potteries, Longton. (Usual trademark Willow Art). Pieces were probably bought in for re-sale by Edward Asbury & Co., Prince of Wales Works, Sutherland Road, Longton, and marked with an Asbury trademark.
Edward Asbury and Co. manufactured china and earthenwares from 1875 to 1925. In the early 1900's the firm was making transfer printed wares for the fancy goods trade including 'Charles Dickens' Ware – drawings by 'Phiz" on mugs, plates jugs and beakers. The company probably bought in its small range of crested items during the Great War. A Great War Commemorative is often found on 'smalls' and models, consisting of a transfer print of '5 Flags of the Allies' and inscribed: 1914. (No numbering system seems to have been used).

Asbury Models

Buildings - White
Cottage. 55mm long.   7.50

Historical/Folklore
Man in the Moon. 60mm.   30.00

Traditional/National Souvenirs
Welsh Hat. 57mm.   8.00

Countryside
Tree Trunk Flower Holder. 80mm.   8.50

Animals
Black Bulldog in kennel. 76mm long. 18.00
Bulldog, French, sitting. 110mm.   22.00
Cat in Boot. 68mm.   18.00
Dog, sitting, with bow. 75mm.   22.00
Pugdog, long neck, sitting. 115mm.   20.00
Dog, Scottie, wearing glengarry.
  88mm.   14.50
Elephant walking, trunk free from
  body. 75mm long.   20.00
Lion walking. 110mm long.   24.50
Pig. 81mm long.   22.00

Birds
Duck posy bowl. 70mm long.   12.50
Swan. 65mm long.   8.50

Great War
Monoplane, Bleriot type with
  movable prop. 147mm long.   75.00
HMS Lion. 142mm long.   47.00
Tank. 85mm long.   30.00
Kitchen Range, *Keep The Home Fires
Burning*, with pot on red fire.
  65mm high, 78mm long.   19.50

Home/Nostalgic
Anvil. 56mm.   7.50

Comic/Novelty
Billiken, flat grotesque type. 68mm. 7.50

Alcohol
Toby Jug. 75mm.   16.50

Footwear
Sabot.
  2 sizes: 60mm long.   5.00
           80mm long.   5.50

Miniature Domestic
Coffee Pot and Lid. 60mm.   10.00

Hats
Top Hat. 40mm.   6.50

Miscellaneous
Hammer Head. 82mm long.   20.00

Atlas China

Trademark used by Atlas China Co. Ltd., Atlas Works, Wolfe Street, Stoke. 1906-1910.

Mark used c. 1934-9.

This company formerly Chapman & Sons Ltd was not thought to manufacture heraldic china. Obviously they did so during the early years when Goss historical models were so popular. The company was later taken over by Grimwades Ltd.

Atlas Models
Ancient Artefacts
Newbury Leather Bottle, not
named. 67mm.   5.50

Domestic
Cup and Saucer. 80mm.   5.00
Sugar Bowl, late. 80mm.   4.00

Atlas Heraldic China

Mark can also be found with *'Made in England'* curved above the globe.

Trademark used by Taylor and Kent, Florence Works, Longton, for a wholesaler in Scotland. (Usual trademark Florentine). CR and Co. are not known to be china manufacturers (there was an Atlas china works in Stoke on Trent from 1889 to 1906 owned by Chapman and Sons, but they did not use this mark. From 1906 to 1919 the company was known as The Star China Co., and used a different mark together with the initials 'SCC').
All known models, except the thimble, are identical to Florentine models made by Taylor and Kent. (See Florentine China for details.) Taylor and Kent are known to have sold a great deal of china in Scotland so it is quite reasonable to suppose that they used this mark for a Scottish wholesaler.
All known models carry Scottish crests or Scottish colour transfer views, with the exception of a three-handled loving cup which has been found with a Blackpool crest. (Taylor and Kent did not use stock numbers) .

Atlas Heraldic Models
Ancient/Artefacts
Puzzle Jug. 68mm.	8.50
Salisbury Kettle, not named 100mm.	5.00
Three-handled loving cup. 40mm.	6.50

Monuments
Iona Cross. 108mm.	10.50
Statue: standing unglazed figure of possibly a Saxon or Viking Warrior with small oval shield in left hand. Square glazed base. 130mm. (The one model recorded has a Lanark Crest).	65.00

Traditional/National Souvenirs
Welsh Hat with blue cord and embossed tassels. 56mm.	10.00

Seaside Souvenirs
Whelk Shell. 100mm long.	7.00

Animals
Elephant, kneeling. 67mm.	20.00
Fish, open mouth. 120mm long.	5.00
Toad. 70mm long.	25.50

Birds
Kingfisher, with long beak. 80mm.	30.00
Pelican cream jug. 83mm long.	7.50
Swan posy holder. 80mm long.	6.00

Home/Nostalgic
Baby in Hip Bath. 100mm long.	14.50
Coal Scuttle. 62mm.	6.00
Iron. 75mm long.	14.50
Napkin Ring. 38mm.	8.50
The Old Armchair, with verse. 85mm.	9.50
Sofa. 82mm long.	12.50
Portmanteau. 80mm long.	6.00

Comic/Novelty
Boy on Scooter. 104mm.	24.00

Alcohol
Carboy. 76mm.	6.00

Sport/Pastimes
Cricket Bag. 110mm long.	16.50

Musical Instruments
Harp. 92mm.	9.50

Footwear
Babies Bootee. 98mm long.	25.00
Oriental Shoe with turned up toe. 95mm long.	5.50
Shoe, Ladies' 18th century. 95mm long.	7.50

Miniature Domestic
Cheese Dish and cover. 55mm.   8.50
Coffee Pot with lid. 63mm.   9.50
Cup and Saucer.
  2 sizes: 40mm.   5.00
          55mm.   5.00
Tea Pot with lid. 70mm.   9.50

Miscellaneous
Thimble. 40mm.   17.50

Aurelian China

Trademark used by Alfred B. Jones & Sons
Ltd (Usual trademark Grafton).
Only three pieces have been recorded so far.

Cup & Saucer. 47mm high, 110mm
  diameter (very fine).   7.00
Vase. 40mm.   4.00
Small Jug (Cheltenham crest).   4.00

Avon China

Mark used 1903-1906

Trademark used by Arkinstall & Son Ltd, Arcadian Works, Stoke-on-Trent. Arkinstall more usually used the trademark Arcadian China. (See under that heading for details of china and manufacturer). This mark is very like the earliest known Arcadian mark used by the firm. It is probable that Arkinstall tried out this trademark for a time when the firm was first established. (It is unlikely to be a retailer's mark as crests are found from places as far apart as Scotland and Wales.) A range of coloured transfers were made, identical to some with the Arcadian trademark.

Avon Models
Ancient Artefacts
Model of Loving Cup originated by
  Henry of Navarre, King of
  France, 3 handled. 39mm.   6.50
Roman Vase, Model of, No. 285.   5.50
York Roman Ewer, Model of   5.50

Traditional/National Souvenirs
John Bull, bust of. 85mm.   25.00

Seaside Souvenirs
Pharos Lighthouse 121mm.   15.00

Animals
Hare. 80mm long.   22.50
Pig, fat, standing. 90mm long.   20.00

Comic/Novelty
Suffragette Bust, double faced.
  89mm.   65.00

Sport/Pastimes
Golf Ball. 43mm.   14.50

Aynsley

AYNSLEY

AYNSLEY & SONS

Trademark used on china with military crests by John Aynsley and Sons, Portland Works, Longton. Aynsley models therefore almost always appear bearing military badges. Deduct £15 if no military badge.

John Aynsley and Sons are the well known firm that produce fine china today. The firm was established in 1864 to manufacture porcelain. In 1903 they advertised a 'number of fancy pieces, plain and white and enamelled in colours'. In 1904 they registered a number of designs of miniature military models as souvenirs of the South African war. These military items and 'smalls' are found with a series of military crests which pre-date the Great War. In 1908 with the introduction of the Haldane Act many of these Regiments disappeared. Obviously these models are of great interest to military model collectors and they are often found in Great War collections where unfortunately they have no business to be. Military crests found on Aynsley models are:

Alexandra Princess of Wales, Own Yorkshire Hussars - Leeds Squadron
Argyll & Sutherland Highlanders
Army Service Corps
Black Watch (RH)
Berkshire Regiment
The Cameronians
City of London V.A.D.
Coldstream Guards
Connaught Rangers 88th & 94th Foot

2nd Dragoon Guards (Royal Scots Greys)
3rd Dragoon Guards
4th Dragoon Guards
154th Dragoon Guards
Dublin Fusiliers 102nd & 103rd Foot
East Surrey Regiment
East Surrey Regiment Sutton Detachment
East Surrey Regiment 4th Battalion Wimbledon Detachment
Essex Regiment 3rd Volunteer Battalion
1st Essex Volunteer Artillery Eastern Div^n R.A.
Essex Regiment
Gordon Highlanders 75th & 92nd Foot
Grenadier Guards
1st Bn Grenadier Guards
Highland Light Infantry 71st & 74th Foot
13th Hussars
14th Hussars
3rd Irish Volunteers
Irish Guards
King's Dragoon Guards
King's Own Scottish Borderers
5th Lancers, Royal Irish
17th Lancers
21st Lancers
Leeds Company; RAMC Volunteers
1st Life Guards
2nd Life Guards
Lincolnshire Regiment
Liverpool Regiment
Liverpool Regiment 8th (Scottish) V.B.
1st London Royal Engineers Vols
3rd (City of) London Rifles
Lothians & Berwickshire
The Lothians & Berwickshire Yeomanry Cavalry
Manchester Artillery
2nd V.B. Manchester Regiment
1st Middlesex Victoria & St. George's Rifles
1st Middlesex Regiment Victoria and Albert's Rifles
4th Middlesex Regiment
4th Middlesex West London Rifles
7th Middlesex London Scottish Rifle Volunteers
13th Middlesex RV: (Queen's Westminsters)
18th Middlesex Regiment
20th Middlesex (Artists) Rifles Volunteers
Northumberland Fusiliers
Northumberland Hussars
Notts & Derby Regiment
Queen's Own Cameron Highlanders 79th Foot
The Queen's Surrey 4th Battalion Sutton Detachment
Queen's Westminsters

Royal Army Medical Corps
Royal Artillery
Royal Garrison Artillery - Southern Division
Royal Garrison Artillery - 1st North Division
Royal Horse Artillery
Royal Horse Guards
10th Royal Hussars
Royal Irish Rifles 83rd & 86th Foot
Royal Irish Fusiliers
Royal Marine Artillery
The Royal Munster Fusiliers 101st & 104th Foot
Royal Scots; 1st Foot
Royal Scots Fusiliers; 21st Foot
Royal Scots Greys
Royal Sussex Regiment
Royal Welsh Fusiliers; 23rd Foot
1st V.B. Queen's Royal West Surrey
2nd V.B. Queen's Royal West Surrey
Royal West Surrey Regiment (The Queen's)
Scottish Rifles 26th & 90th Foot
Scots Guards
Seaforth Highlanders (72nd & 78th Foot)
Sharp Shooters
South Notts Hussars
South Wales Borderers 24th Foot
Staffordshire Imperial Yeomanry
Staffs Imperial Yeomanry
Suffolk Regiment
Surrey Imperial Yeomanry
Sutton Detachment
Victoria & St. George's Rifles
The Welsh Regiment
West Yorkshire Regiment 14th Foot
Wiltshire Regiment

Aynsley produced only a few crests of towns and a range of Oxford and Cambridge colleges and do not appear to have made crested ware during the Great War. Some black monochrome transfer views can be found on domestic ware but as this firm made such a vast range of china this cannot be considered 'crested china' in the terms of this book.

£30.00 should be added for any Military badge on the following models.

Aynsley Models
South African War

Hand Grenade, with flames coming

from the top. 88mm.	40.00
Cannon Shell. 104mm.	30.00
Empty Shell Case.	40.00
Bandsman's Drum. 55mm.	35.00
High Boot. 118mm.	35.00

Bell Tent, with open flaps. 75mm.	35.00
Waterbottle.	
2 sizes: 80mm.	28.00
95mm.	28.00
Cap. 94mm long.	35.00
Colonial Soldier's Hat.	
2 sizes: 80mm long.	40.00
115mm long.	40.00
Forage Cap. 85mm long.	40.00
French Soldier's Cap. 75mm long.	
45mm high.	45.00
Glengarry. 90mm long.	40.00
Pickelhaube. 69mm long.	40.00
Pith Helmet. 68mm long.	40.00

Footwear

Boot. 60mm.	25.00
Ladies Shoe. 92mm long.	20.00

Domestic

Jug. No.26. 94mm.	10.00

Miscellaneous

Button, oval. 40mm.	15.00
Horse's Hoof. No.21.84mm long.	20.00
Circular Plaque.	
2 sizes: 58mm.	15.00
75mm dia.	15.50
Circular Plaque with silver rim.	
75m dia.	25.00
Loving Cup, 2 handles. 53mm.	12.50
Square Porcelain Plaque inset in lid	
of pewter box. 85mm sq.,	
40mm high.	20.00
Shield, with upright.	
2 sizes: 63mm. No.38	20.00
100mm.	20.00
Shield, no upright. 124mm long.	25.00
Trinket Box, heart shaped, with lid,	15.00
Vase. 58mm.	10.00

B

Balmoral China

BALMORAL CHINA

R & D
ENGLAND.

Trademark used by Blairs and Beaconsfield Pottery, Longton.

Blairs advertised 'Arms Ware' in 1902 but seem to have made very little. Only three models and several small vases have been recorded so one can only assume that they sold other models unmarked or used another trademark. Certainly crested ware was only a side line and the firm produced other decorative china, much of it at this time being very Art Nouveau in style. The firm was established in 1880 and was subsequently known as Blairs Ltd in 1911. This firm produced Great War Commemoratives. (See Blairs China.)

B Models
Animals
Pig, standing. 80mm long.   16.00

Home/Nostalgic
Suitcase, buff/brown. 80mm long.   5.00

Miniature Domestic
Cheese Dish, one piece. 50mm.   8.50
Vase, two-handled   5.00
Vase, shaded blue. 110mm.   5.00
Vase, shaded pink. 110mm.   5.00

Marks used 1909-1933.

Trademark used by Redfern and Drakeford (Ltd), Balmoral Works, Longton.

All china found with this mark, apart from the tankard below which has a Banff crest and the plate which has a Balmoral crest, has the British Empire Exhibition badge or an inscription *'Wembley 1925'* and was obviously made especially for this event. Some pieces have been seen overstamped with 'Willow Art' or 'Carlton' trademarks. The buildings are similar to Alexandra china.

Balmoral Models .
Buildings - White
The Marble Arch, unglazed top. 72mm. 30.00
Tower Bridge. 144mm long.   47.50

Monument
Big Ben. 143mm.   30.00

Bell China

Birds
Goose, standing and very fat, with
  long slender neck. 155mm.   47.50
Owl. 98mm.   12.00

Great War
Ad Astra Royal Air Force War
Memorial. Unveiled by HRH Prince
of Wales July 16th 1923 with gilded
eagle on brown orb. 173mm.   175.00
Cenotaph. 70mm.   20.00

Home/Nostalgic
Pillar Box. *GVR* in red and blue,
  open slit and verse to rear. 77mm.   22.50

Domestic
Tankard. 85mm.   5.50

This mark has been found on pieces of
domestic ware with EPNS tops. Taylor
and Kent specialised in producing china
for manufacturers to add metal lids etc. as
did many other potteries.

Bell Models
Domestic
Sugar Sifter with EPNS top.
  (Llandudno crest).160mm.   8.00
Bottle for ink or perfume, screw top
  made from an early version of
  plastic. 80mm. (Birmingham
  crest)   10.50
Salt Pot with EPNS top. 100mm.   7.50
Mustard Pot with hinged EPNS Lid
  221 impressed on base. 60mm.   7.50

Belleek

Mark used from 1891. The name of a retailer can replace 'Co Fermanagh Ireland'.
Trademark used by Belleek Pottery (David McBirney and Co.), Belleek, Co. Fermanagh, N. Ireland.
This well known Irish firm employed the noted Goss modeller William W. Gallimore for a short period, during which he imported to Belleek Ivory Porcelain production invented by WH Goss. The firm produced a range of crested domestic ware, 'smalls' and probably a few simple models although only two have been recorded. These were produced in 1900-1910, during the 2nd period of the factory.

Belleek Models
Ancient Artefacts

Chester Roman Vase.	85.00
Hastings Kettle. 53mm.	85.00
Irish Bronze Pot, not named, with yellow interior, handles and feet. (Ayr crest). 45mm.	85.00

Traditional/National Souvenirs

Shamrock shaped loving cup, 3 handles. 50mm.	85.00

Animals

Pig, sitting, decorated with green shamrocks. 55mm.	125.00
Terrier, standing. 88mm.	100.00
Tortoise. 70mm long.	100.00

Countryside

Milk Churn, with 2 handles. 60mm.	85.00

Alcohol

Barrel. 57mm.	85.00

Many very fine 'smalls' were produced by this Pottery often with the characteristic Belleek lustre finish. These are valued at £85.00 each. In the authors opinion they are somewhat overrated but they are scarce and collectable.

S. Bennion

Best English Make

For details of this china see VICTORIA ARMS CHINA.

Trademark used by A.B. Jones and Sons Ltd., Grafton China Works, Longton. (Usual trademark Grafton).

Best English Make Model
A 38mm bagware vase and several smalls have been recorded with this mark.   £5.00 each

Birks Crest China

Trademark used by Arkinstall & Son Ltd., Arcadian Works, Stoke-on-Trent. (Usual trademark Arcadian).

Birks Crest China Model Animals
Crocodile (or Alligator).
127mm long.   85.00

Birks China

Trademark used by Birks, Rawlins & Co. (Ltd.), Vine Pottery, Stoke, previously L.A. Birks & Co., established in 1885.
Birks Rawlins and Co. used the Trademark SAVOY CHINA. (See that entry for details of china and manufacturer.)
This trademark was obviously used in 1928 to trade on the old and respected name of Birks. We know the new company was already in financial trouble by this date. 1928 was rather late to introduce a range of crested ware and this venture did nothing to help the firm's sales. One colour transfer view of Hampton Court Palace has been recorded on a teaplate but known crests are from all over England. (Savoy china always carry stock numbers but these have not been recorded on Birks china.)

Birks Models
Traditional/National Souvenirs
Thistle vase. 52mm.   5.00

Animals
Three Wise Monkeys on diamond
   ashtray. 65mm.   22.00

Great War
Battleship with 3 funnels,
   inscribed: *HMS Tiger.*
   116mm long.   95.00
Cenotaph. 180mm.   12.50

Home/Nostalgic
Basket. 48mm.   6.00
Handbag. 88mm.   11.00

Comic/Novelty
Biscuit, impressed: *Huntley &
Palmers.* On stand.
Impressed: 399. 85mm.   60.00
With holes for hatpins.

Domestic
Tea Pot with lid. 110mm.   10.00

Birks, Rawlins & Co.

Trademark used by Birks, Rawlins and Co.
(Ltd.), Vine Pottery, Stoke. (Usual
trademark Savoy china).
All models and factory history will be found
under the Savoy entry.

Blairs China

Boots

BLAIRS
CHINA
ENGLAND

1914

Trademark used by Blairs Ltd, Beaconsfield
Pottery, Longton.

This firm used the trademark B
until 1911 and then used the
trademark 'Blairs China'. Using
the latter trademark they
produced a range of 'smalls' in
1914 with Great War inscriptions,
commemorative prints or cartoons.
They also used flags on a rope as
a decoration.(See B China.)   from £20.00

Trademark used for Boots The Chemist by
Arkinstall & Son Ltd, Arcadian Works,
Stoke-on-Trent.   (Usual   trademark
Arcadian).
Boots sold a range of crested 'smalls' in their
fancy goods departments. A transfer print
of Six Flags of the Allies is also found
inscribed: *In freedoms cause*. This
commemorative   often   occurs   on
unmarked wares; it was probably used by
one   of   the   known   crested   china
manufacturers who do not appear to have
marked their wares. (See Unmarked
Crested China.)

Boots Models
Ancient Artefacts
Glastonbury Abbot's Cup, not
named. No. 238. 48mm.   5.50

3-handled Loving Cup. 38mm.
    Bears the unusual combination of
    arms of City of London, Arms of
    Weymouth and Melcombe Regis
    and Dorchester.   7.00

Buildings Whole
Old Pete's Cottage. 75mm long.   30.00

Animal
Pig, standing, inscribed: *Wunt be*
    druv 85mm long.   16.00

Home/Nostalgic
Frying Pan. 108mm long.   17.00

Many 'smalls' were also produced
    not of very good quality. These
    often have Great War
    inscriptions.   £5 – £10
    For items with WWI flags add
    £5.00 - £8.00.

Botolph China

BOTOLPH
J. W. & Co

Marks used c1914-1926.

Trademark used by an unknown wholesaler.
    Originally, it was thought that J. W. & Co.
    referred to J. Wilson and Son, Park Works,
    Fenton, but I now believe Botolph to be the
    trademark applied to bought in pieces by
    an unknown wholesalers, possibly
    London based.
J. W. & Co. were supplied with Great War
    and Buildings by J.A. Robinson Ltd.
    (Usual mark Arcadian and later Willow)
    and Home/Nostalgic and Comic/
    Novelty by Taylor & Kent (usual
    trademark Florentine). Pieces in other
    headings listed are all from one of these
    two factories.
Botolph was made mostly for the London
    retail trade, many crests of the City of
    London are found and all known
    buildings, with the exception of Blackpool
    Tower, are found in London.
No other forms of decoration other than
    crests are found on Botolph models and no
    military or commemorative crests have
    been found. (No numbering system was
    used on models.)

Botolph Models

Ancient Artefacts

Puzzle Jug. 68mm.   7.00

Buildings - White

Big Ben.
  2 sizes: 92mm.   17.50
          130mm.   22.50
Blackpool Tower. 117mm.   10.00
Houses of Parliament. 53mm.   40.00
Marble Arch, Model of
  3 sizes; 48mm.   22.00
          66mm.   17.50
          80mm.   22.00
Nelson's Column. 124mm.   45.00
The Old Curiosity Shop, with
  inscription. 95mm long.   30.00
Old London Bridge, Ye. 86mm.   35.00
St. Pauls Cathedral.
  3 sizes; 76mm.   22.00
          90mm.   22.00
          127mm.   25.50
Temple Bar 96mm.   40.00
Tower Bridge.
  3 sizes: 76mm long.   30.00
          118mm long.   30.00
          133mm long.   40.00
Wembley Sports Stadium.
  1134mm long.   95.00
Westminster Abbey, West Front.
  3 sizes: 70mm (named).   25.00
          80mm.   25.00
          116mm.   28.50

Historical/Folklore

Man standing in Pillory. 105mm.   17.00
Mother Shipton. 73mm.   10.00

Traditional/National Souvenirs

John Bull, bust. 68mm.   14.50
Mr Punch, bust. 83mm.   40.00
Yarmouth Bloater. 100mm long.   8.50
Irish Harp with green shamrocks.
  106mm   9.50

Seaside Souvenirs

Bathing Machine. 70mm.   14.00
Bathing Machine with bather
  wearing towel in doorway.
  75mm.   16.50
Child sitting on rock, hand to mouth.
  108mm.   20.00
Houseboat, square. 90mm long.   10.00
Yacht. 125mm long.   14.50
Lifebelt. 85mm dia.   13.00

Fisherman's Creel, fixed lid. 60mm.   8.00
Lighthouse. 95mm.   5.00
'The Glad Sea Waves'. 48mm.   18.50
Whelk Shell. 98mm long.   6.50

Countryside

Haystack, circular. 55mm.   10.00
Haystack, rectangular. 56mm.   10.00

Animals

Camel. 90mm long.   16.00
Angry Cat, arched back, coloured
  features. 82mm.   14.50
Cat, long neck. 106mm.   12.00
Cat, sitting, looking left (ARC). 60mm. 12.00
Cheshire Cat. 90mm.   9.50
Dog, Bulldog. 57mm.   17.00
Dog, Labrador puppy with curly
  tail, sitting. 90mm.   16.50
Dog, King Charles Spaniel, begging
  on a cushion. 70mm.   14.50
Dog, Lying in cradle. 90mm long.   17.50
Dogs, King Charles Spaniels, two in
  Top Hat. 78mm.   20.00
Dolphin vase. 110mm.   8.50
Elephant, standing. 70mm.   30.00
Fish. 102mm long.   6.00
Hare. 93mm long.   16.00
Lion, walking. 120mm long.   25.00
Monkey, sitting, hands to mouth.
  65mm.   20.00
  90mm.   20.00
Mouse playing mandolin. 86mm.   30.00
Piglet, laying. 68mm long.   17.50
Pig, standing, can be found with
  inscription: *The Pig that won't go.*
  55mm.   17.50
Rabbit. 70mm long.   9.50
Rabbit, very fluffy. 100m long.   14.50
Seal with ball on nose. 75mm.   22.50
Tortoise. 70mm long.   10.00

Birds

Budgerigar. 100mm.   14.00
Canary on rock. 92mm.   12.50
Chicken in Egg. 63mm long.   8.00
Duck, comical, outstretched wings.
  66mm.   40.00
Hen, roosting. 52mm.   8.50
Kingfisher. 76mm.   30.00
Pelican Jug. 60mm.   7.50
Owl, baby. 70mm.   16.50
Swan. 63mm.   8.50
Swan posy holder. 90mm long.   6.50

Great War

Nurse, inscribed: A *Soldier's Friend*.	
125mm.	75.00
Sailor, bust of. 90mm.	40.00
Monoplane, with movable four	
bladed prop. 175mm long.	105.50
Observer Sausage Balloon. 80mm.	75.00
Zeppelin on stand. 130mm.	35.00
Battleship (HMS Queen Elizabeth).	
2 sizes: 115mm.	30.00
165mm long.	40.00
Larger size found with	
inscription: *Great War 1914-18. The*	
German Fleet surrendered 74	
warships Nov 21st 1918.	
Torpedo Boat Destroyer.	
110mm long.	27.50
Submarine, inscribed: *E4*.	
95mm long.	27.50
Submarine, inscribed: *E5*.	
127mm long.	27.00
Red Cross Van. *EH139*, with 3 red	
crosses. 88mm long.	40.00
Ambulance. 100mm long.	40.00
Armoured Car. 95mm long.	50.00
Tank, Model of, (without wheels)	
2 sizes: 100mm long.	85.00
155mm long.	40.00
Tank with small integral steering	
wheels. 115mm long.	25.00
Tank, Model of (without wheels),	
wide version. There are at least	
two different moulds, possibly	
three. One has the side guns	
moulded flat to walls of tank, and	
the other has forward facing guns	
protruding from side turrets	
standing proud of sides.	
125mm long.	33.00
Field Gun. 120mm long.	26.50
Howitzer. 135mm long.	26.00
Trench Mortar. 70mm.	22.50
Sandbag, model of. 72mm.	30.00
Cannon Shell, inscribed: *Jack*	
Johnson.	
2 sizes: 94mm.	10.50
135mm.	12.50
Shell, anti-aircraft. 96mm.	22.00
Clip of Bullets. 85mm.	30.00
Revolver. 83mm long.	75.00
Bandsman's Drum. 58mm dia.	10.00
Glengarry. 90mm long.	22.50
Water Bottle. 64mm.	19.00
New Zealand Hat. 73mm long.	20.00

Kitchen Range, black cat, brown	
teapot, orange flames, inscribed:	
We've kept the homefires burning.	20.00
Fireplace, inscribed: *We've kept the*	
homefires burning. 110mm.	22.50
Cavell Memorial, London,	
inscribed: *Nurse Cavell.*	
2 sizes: 115mm.	20.00
160mm.	22.00
Cenotaph, Whitehall London, Model of.	
With green wreaths and	
inscription.	
5 sizes: 80mm.	8.00
100mm.	10.00
120mm.	10.00
145mm.	12.50
180mm.	15.00

Home/Nostalgic

Armchair, inscribed: *The Old*	
Armchair and verse. 90mm.	9.50
Baby's Cradle. 45mm.	12.50
Baby in Hip Bath. 103mm long.	14.50
Coal Scuttle. 60mm.	6.50
Edwardian Boy and Girl cruet set.	
90mm.	Each 15.00
Flat Iron. 78mm long.	12.50
Garden Roller. 85mm long.	15.50
Grandfather Clock. 130mm.	17.50
Keys, on ring. 46mm.	25.00
Lantern. 70mm.	8.50
Pillar Box. 78mm.	12.50
Policeman's Lamp. 75mm.	10.00
Sofa. 80mm long.	12.50
Suitcase. 58mm.	6.00
Watering Can. 70mm.	9.50

Comic/Novelty

Boy on Scooter. 103mm.	20.00
Bust of smiling Boy, spill holder.	
71mm.	12.50
Bust of coloured gent in top hat	
(Eugene Stratton) 95mm	30.00
Jack in the Box. 95mm.	20.00
Screw, inscribed: *A big fat screw.*	
This refers to a wage rise.	
75mm.	30.00
Pierrot, sitting, playing banjo. Some	
colouring on hands and face.	
120mm.	35.00
Policeman with raised hand.	
Inscribed: *A Policeman's lot ....*	
140mm.	75.00
Suffragette candlesnuffer. 70mm.	30.00

Alcohol

Toby Jug. 65mm.	8.50

Champagne Bottle in Bucket,
inscribed: *Something Good a*

Bottle of the Boy.	15.00

Sport/Pastimes

Boxing Glove. 67mm long.	30.00

Cricket Bag,

2 sizes: 80mm long.	16.50
110mm long.	16.50

Golf Club Head.

2 sizes: 75mm.	25.00
95mm.	25.00

Snooker Table on 6 legs. With 3 balls
and cue resting on top.

100mm long.	125.00
Tennis Racquet. 97mm long.	17.50
Rook chess piece. 55mm.	9.50

Musical Instruments

Grand Piano. 85mm long.	20.00

Transport

Car Horn, inscribed: *Pip Pip.*

90mm long.	25.00

Charabanc, with driver.

115mm long.	40.00

Omnibus, double decker bus with

stairs outside. 130mm long.	190.00

Saloon Car, always found gilded on

one side only. 86mm long.	40.00

Modern Equipment

Gramophone, square. 60mm long.	25.00
Radio Horn. 96mm.	33.00

Hats

Bishop's Mitre. 55mm.	12.50
Boater, hat. 75mm long.	14.00

Footwear

High Boot. 90mm.	5.00
Lancashire Clog. 85mm long.	7.00

Oriental Shoe with pointed turned

up toe. 98mm long.	5.50

Shoe, Ladies,18th century

93mm long.	7.50

Thigh Boot, with scalloped rim.

100mm.	16.00

Miniature Domestic

Cheese Dish and sloped cover.

60mm.	10.00
Teapot with lid. 52mm.	9.50

Domestic

Flower Vase.

2 sizes: 95mm.	6.00
125mm.	9.50

Candlestick with snake around it.

100mm.	7.50

Miscellaneous

Horses Hoof vase. 64mm long.	5.00

Bow China

Trademark used by Birks, Rawlins & Co (Ltd.), Vine Pottery, Stoke (Usual trademark Savoy).
This firm usually used the trademark SAVOY CHINA (see under this heading for details of the firm's history and the china).
A small range of models with this mark has been recorded. They are mostly Great War miniatures but a few domestic items have also been found. Most have Scottish crests and firing flaws. It is probable that this mark was used for factory rejects. However, a number of perfect condition Ryde pieces have also been found with the above mark. Four military badges have been recorded, these being Army Service Corps, Gordon Highlanders, Royal Army Medical Corps and Seaforth Highlanders.
Numbering System. Stock numbers coincide with those listed on the same models with the Savoy trademark.

Bow Models
Ancient Artefacts
Carlisle Salt Pot (not named).
  60mm.   5.00
Celtic Vase in British Museum,
  Model of. No. 25. 45mm.   5.50
Greek Vase, inscribed: *Model of Greek*
  Vase from the collection of Sir Henry
  Englefield. No. 66. 72mm.   5.50
Lincoln Jack from original in museum.
  Model of. No. 39. 60mm.   5.50
Persian Vase. No.144. 75mm.   5.00

Seaside Souvenirs
Eddystone Lighthouse. No. 130.
  91mm.   9.00

Historic/Novelty
Model of Mary Queen of Scots chair
  Edinburgh Castle. 80mm.   10.00

Animals
Elephant and Howdah. No. 228.
  75mm long (Rare).   30.00

Great War
Battleship, 2 funnels, 4 guns fore
  and 4 guns aft, found inscribed
  with one of the following:
    HMS *Iron Duke*   125.00
    HMS *Lion*   115.00
    or HMS *Ramilies.*   125.00
  No. 524. 168mm long.
Submarine, inscribed: *E1,* usually
  found with inscription.
  150mm long.   85.00
Howitzer. 170mm long.   40.00
Cannon Shell, inscribed: *Iron rations*
  for Fritz. 115mm.   14.00
French Trench Helmet. 38mm.   30.00
Glengarry. 73mm.   30.00
New Zealand Hat, Model of.
  83mm long.   30.00

Home/Nostalgic
Fireplace. No.129. 90mm.   15.00

Hats
Balmoral Bonnet. No. 611. 74mm
  wide.   20.00
Top Hat. No.339. 44mm.   6.50

Bramwell China

British Manufacture

[BRITISH MANUFACTURE]

Trademark used by an Wiltshaw & Robinson Ltd., Carlton Works, Stoke-on-Trent (usual trademark Carlton) for a retailer probably in Sheffield.

Bramwell Models
Ancient Artefacts
Leather Jack, not named. No. 751.
62mm.   5.50
(This number does not occur for a
model like this in other ranges -
possibly the Stock No. should be
75 or 51. The other numeral being
a paintresses mark).

Seaside Souvenirs
Lighthouse Pepper Pot. 97mm.   8.00

Animals
Dog with raised ear. 80mm.   15.00

This mark is also found without the rectangular outline.

Some models are found with a simple British Manufacture stamp, rather than marked. These include arks, anvils, cottages, footballs, grandfather clocks, lighthouses, petrol cans, parian straw boaters, pillar boxes, propellers, puzzle jugs and top hats. These often have transfer views rather than crests. They are remarkably similar to the products of the Corona and Florentine factories which they probably are.

British Manufacture Models
Unglazed/Parian
Bust of *Burns*, beige. 162mm.   22.00

Ancient Artefacts
Puzzle Jug. 70mm.   8.50
Salisbury Kettle, unnamed.
100mm.   5.00
Southwold Jar. 87mm.   5.00

Buildings - White
Blackpool Tower. 122mm.   7.50
Brick Cottage, gilded features.
70mm long.   10.00
ClockTower, Skegness. 128mm.   15.00
Gateway. 170mm.   16.50

Historical/Folklore
Man standing in Pillory. 104mm.   16.00
Mary Queen of Scots' chair. 74mm.   10.00
Noah's Ark. (sometimes listed as a
houseboat) 90mm long.   10.00

Ye Olde Chertsey Bell, with coloured
wooden base. 88mm.   26.00
without base   17.50

Traditional/National Souvenirs
Cheddar Cheese, inscribed *Prime*
Cheddar Cheese, coloured yellow.
52mm.   12.00
Cheddar Cheese, model of, with verse
and flowers. 60mm dia.   12.00
Laxey Wheel. 84mm.   34.50
Welsh Hat, blue band. 58mm.   9.00

Seaside Souvenirs
Canoe. 110mm long.   9.00
Fish Basket, fitted lid. 63mm.   14.00
Yacht. 128mm.   14.50
Lighthouse. 100mm.   6.50
Whelk Shell. 84mm long.   6.00

Countryside
Milk Churn. 75mm.   6.00

Animals
Bull's head cream jug. 78mm.   8.50
Bulldog. 110mm long.   16.50
Camel. 96mm long.   16.00
Cat, angry with arched back,
coloured face. 70mm.   14.50
Cat, Cheshire Always Smiling.
85mm.   14.00
Cat with long neck. 112mm.   12.50
Cat sitting, bow on neck. 100mm.   17.00
Cat, Manx. 90mm long.   30.00
Cat in Boot. 85mm long.   16.50
Dog, Labrador, sitting. 85mm.   14.50
Dog in kennel. 68mm.   12.00
Elephant, standing, tiny. 44mm.   22.00
Dolphin vase. 112mm.   8.00
Fish vase, 2 openings. 90mm long.   5.00
Fish vase. 115mm.   12.00
Fox. 80mm.   30.00
Frog jug. 48mm.   8.50
Pig, hairy, standing with holes in
nostrils. Inscribed: *The pig that*
won't go. 85mm long.   16.00
Pig, standing, long snout.
90mm long.   16.00
Piglet, standing. 74mm long.   16.00
Rabbit, crouching. 65mm.   9.50
Rabbit fluffy. 110mm long.   16.50
Seal with ball on nose. 73mm.   19.50
Toad. 72mm long.   15.00
Tortoise. 70mm long.   10.00

Birds (including Eggs)
Egg. 65mm upright.   5.00
Giant Ostrich Egg. 100mm.   20.00
Fledgling cream jug. 64mm.   7.50
Brooding Hen. 65mm long.   8.50
Crested tit posy holder. 80mm long.   12.50
Owl. 2 sizes: 62mm.   16.50
          70mm.   16.50
Parrot. 95mm.   11.50

Great War
Monoplane with moveable
4-bladed propeller.
160mm long.   120.00
Tank, wide, large gun turrets.
126mm long. Impressed *B416.*   24.00
Guns modelled adjacent   35.00
Guns modelled proud   35.00
Cannon Shell. 100mm.   7.00
Propeller. 140mm long.   30.00
Rushden War Memorial. 164mm.   55.00
War Memorial. 152mm - Crest of
Weymouth.   90.00
Water Bottle. 88mm.   13.00

Home/Nostalgic
Anvil. 58mm.   7.50
Armchair with padded arms.
62mm.   16.50
Basket with coloured fruit.85mm.   22.00
Hip Bath.96mm long   12.50
Desk.35mm long.   12.00
Grandfather clock.129mm.   15.00
Old Armchair, The. 90mm.   8.00
Pillar Box. Can be found inscribed:
*I cant get...*70mm.   14.50
Policeman's Lamp. 70mm.   9.50
Shaving Mug. 37mm.   9.50
Settee. 82mm long.   13.00
Shaving Mug, angular handle.
44mm.   9.50
Shaving Mug. 55mm.   9.50
Suitcase, gilded straps. 57mm.   6.00
Tobacco Pouch. 75mm long.   7.00

Comic/Novelty
Baby in Bootee. 80mm long.   14.00
Jack in the Box with open lid.
92mm.   22.00
Man's Head jug. 75mm.   10.00
Pierot, coloured face. 125mm.
(Florentine).   45.00

Alcohol
Carboy. 74mm.   7.00

Sport/Pastimes

Cricket Bag. 110mm long.	16.00
Football. 55mm.	9.50
Golfball on tee. 63mm.	13.50
Bishop Chess Piece. 88mm.	30.00
Pawn Chess Piece. 60mm.	30.00

Musical Instruments

Double Bass	50.00
Harp. 92mm.	9.50

Transport

Petrol can impressed: *Motor Spirit.*	
67mm.	21.50

Modern Equipment

Gramophone, square. No horn.	
55mm.	25.00

Hats

Straw Boater, beige, unglazed.	
110mm long.	13.50
Top Hat. 45mm.	6.50

Footwear

Clog. 100mm long.	6.00
Lancashire Clog. 85mm long.	6.50
Sabot with turned up toe.	
93mm long.	6.00

Miniature Domestic

Candlestick, square. 80mm.	4.00
Kettle and lid. 80mm.	8.50
Cheese Dish and cover. 64mm long.	8.50
Cheese Dish and fixed cover.	
64mm long.	8.50
Cheese Dish and fixed cover.	
82mm long.	8.50
Cup and Saucer. 40mm.	5.00
Cup and Saucer. 45mm.	5.00
Jardiniere, one piece. 82mm.	5.00
Tea Pot and lid, ball-shaped.	
2 sizes: 70mm.	9.50
85mm.	8.50

Domestic

Dolphin vase. 114mm.	7.00
Matchbox holder. 23mm.	10.00
Pin Tray, in shape of clover leaf.	
70mm dia.	4.50

British Nautilus

For details of marks and manufacturer see Nautilus Porcelain.

Bronwen Treasure China   B.S. & Co.

No details of mark available.

Trademark used by unknown British manufacturer for a Welsh outlet, presumably in Bronwen. Only two pieces have been found so far.

Bronwen Treasure China Models
Highland Cuach, 76mm wide,
crest of Barry.   5.00

Pierrot playing Banjo, pink face &
hands, black pom-pom. 125mm.   45.00

Trademark used by unknown retailer, presumably in Prestatyn, as the only piece recorded is a small urn, 69mm decorated with a colour transfer of Prestatyn. Possibly manufactured by Birks, Rawlins & Co., Vine Pottery, Stoke (usual trademark Savoy China).

Burton

Bute China

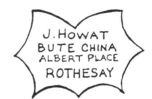

Burton may have been the name of the agent for this Austrian manufacturer.
Only one small vase has been recorded with the above factory mark, this bearing the crest of Falmouth.

4.00

Trademark used by a Scottish retailer on pieces supplied by Taylor and Kent (Ltd), Florence Works, Longton. (Usual trademark Florentine).

Bute Model
Miniature Domestic
Coffee Pot with lid. 63mm   9.50

Cable China

Caledonia China

Trademark used by a branch of J.A. Robinson & Sons, probably Willow Potteries Ltd. (Usual trademark Willow) or Taylor & Kent, Florence Works, Longton (usual trademark Florentine).

Cable Models
Seaside Souvenirs
Lighthouse, not named. 135mm.   7.00

Home/Nostalgic
Anvil. 56mm.   8.50
Book, closed. 60mm.   12.50
Coal Scuttle. 50mm.   7.00

Comic/Novelty
Minstrel bust, wearing Top Hat
no colouring. 90mm.   30.00

Footwear
Shoe with blue bow. 113mm long.   16.00

Miscellaneous
Hand holding Tulip. 81mm.   6.50

Trademark used by Taylor and Kent (Ltd), Florence Works, Longton and Birks, Rawlins & Co. for the Glasgow wholesaler CR and Co. (Usual trademarks Florentine and Savoy). (See also Atlas Heraldic China). For details of this china and manufacturers see Florentine China and Savoy China. Taylor and Kent used at least two different marks for this wholesaler, Atlas Heraldic China being the other known one. The Caledonia range mainly consists of small domestic ware and small pots and vases. All known crests are Scottish, and some transfer printed Scottish views can also be found on 'smalls'.

Caledonia (CR and Co.) China
Buildings - White.
Burns Cottage with inscription.
46mm high, 70mm long.   25.00

Seaside Souvenirs
Yacht in full sail. 127mm long.   14.50

Animals
Dog, Bulldog, standing with verse:
  Be Briton still to Britain true,
  Among ourselves united. For never
  by but British hands, Maun wrongs
  be righted. Burns. 130mm long.   30.00
Camel, kneeling. 95mm long.   16.00
Elephant with howdah. No. 288.
  76mm long.   30.00

Fish Head Jug. 70mm.	8.50
Manx Cat, wiry. 53mm.	30.00
Pig, standing. 80mm long.	16.50
Rabbit ears laid back. 105mm long.	9.50

Great War

Highland Infantryman with pack, rifle, on round plinth. 165mm.	190.00
Bust of Sailor, unglazed on glazed base, inscribed: *HMS Queen Elizabeth* on hat band. 140mm.	95.00
Monoplane. 127mm long.	115.00
Zeppelin destroyed by Lieutenant Robinson V.C. at Cuffley, Essex Sep 3rd 1916, with bladed prop. (Savoy). 174mm long.	215.00
Submarine, inscribed: *1*. 150mm long.	35.00
Torpedo Boat Destroyer. 140mm long.	170.00
Glengarry. 90mm long.	22.00

Home/Nostalgic

Kennel, inscribed: *Beware of the Dog*. 62mm long.	12.50
Policeman's Lamp. 70mm.	10.00
Shaving Mug. 55mm.	9.50
Sofa. 82mm long.	12.50

Comic/Novelty

Policeman, standing, hands behind back, appears to be holding shears. 105mm.	30.00

Modem Equipment

Box Gramophone. 55mm.	16.50

Alcohol

Barrel inscribed: *Real Scotch*. No. 405. 55mm.	7.50
Bottle inscribed: *Real Scotch*. 90mm.	7.50

Sport/Pastimes

Cricket Bag. 120mm long.	16.50
Curling Stone. 68mm wide.	20.00

Musical Instruments

Upright Piano, open keyboard. 70mm.	21.00
Bagpipes. 114mm long.	50.00

Footwear

Sabot. 90mm long.	5.50

Hats

Balmoral Bonnet, Model of. 71mm long. 30.00

Miniature Domestic

Cheese Dish and cover. 2 pieces.	8.50
Teapot and Lid. No. 418. 68mm.	10.00

Caledonia China

Trademark used by James Macintyre and Co Ltd, Washington China Works, Burslem, for sale in Scotland.
For details of this china and manufacturer see Argonauta Porcelain.
Models, 'smalls' and domestic ware found with this mark, all carry crests of Scottish towns.

Caledonia (Macintyre) Models
Unglazed/Parian
Bust, *John Travers Cornwall, the boy hero aged 16, Hero of Jutland Battle. Faithful unto death.* On glazed base. *HMS Chester* impressed on hat band. 115mm.   325.00

Buildings - White
Burn's Cottage. 70mm long.   20.00

Seaside Souvenirs
Lighthouse on rocks. 95mm.   10.00

Traditional/National
Welsh Hat. 56mm.   9.00

Animals
King Charles Spaniel begging on
   cushion. 70mm.   12.00
Two King Charles Spaniels sitting in
   top hat. 75mm.   16.00
Elephant posy bowl. 75mm.   9.50
Polar Bear, inscribed: *Sam.*
   88mm long.   50.00

Birds
Hen, roosting. 51mm.   9.50
Parrot. 92mm.   12.00

Great War
Red Cross Van. 87mm long.   35.00
Cenotaph inscribed: *The blood of
   heroes is the seed of freedom*
   140mm.   9.50

Home/Nostalgic
Policeman's lamp. 70mm.   10.00

Comic/Novelty
Screw inscribed *You could do with a
   big fat screw.* This means a wage
   rise. 75mm.   25.00

Transport
Motor Horn, outpressed *Pip Pip.*
   90mm long.   22.00

Footwear
Dutch Sabot. 70mm long.   6.00

Miniature Domestic
Coffee Pot and Lid. 65mm.   10.00

Caledonia Heraldic China

Trademark used by a Scottish wholesaler on crested china manufactured by leading arms ware firms including Birks, Rawlins and Co. (Savoy), Hewitt and Leadbeater (Willow Art), Wiltshaw and Robinson Ltd. (Carlton) and James Macintyre & Co. For details of china and manufacturers see Savoy China, Willow Art China, Carlton China and Argonauta and Macintyre. Most models carrying this mark are recognisably Savoy or Willow Art pieces but only one Carlton model has been recorded. The domestic ware is unlike that of the two firms and may well have been made in Scotland. All known china, with the exception of a Willow Art jug with the Huntingdon crest, and a vase with the Criccieth crest, has Scottish crests, no views or other transfer devices have been recorded.

Where models are known to be from Birks and Rawlins moulds they have, for the most part, the same stock numbers. However Birks and Rawlins use of stock numbers is at best perplexing (see Savoy China). Willow Art moulds always carry the same stock numbers when they are used.

Caledonia Heraldic Models
Parian/Unglazed

Bust of Admiral Sir David Beatty on circular plinth inscribed: *HMS Lion*. 150mm.	75.00
Burns at the Plough, standing on rectangular base with a red flower on ground. Inscribed: *Wee, modest, crimson tipped flower thou's met me in an evil hour*. Also inscribed: *Wee sleekit cowrin tim'rous Beastie...* 105mm.	75.00
Bust of Burns on square glazed base. 160mm.	40.00
Bust of Burns on round glazed base. 148mm.	30.00
Bust of Scott on square glazed base. 160mm.	35.00
Souter Johnny. 110mm.	30.00
Tom O'Shanter. 110mm.	30.00
The Sanctuary Knocker, Durham Cathedral, wall hanging plaque, decoration in relief. 110mm.	85.00

Ancient Artefacts

Lincoln Jack. No.34. 52mm.	5.50
Three handled Loving Cup. 48mm.	5.50

Buildings - Coloured

Model of House in Edinburgh where John Knox the Scottish Reformer died 24 Nov 1573. 93mm (Willow).	145.00

Buildings - White

Burns Cottage, Model of. 105mm long.	26.00
Carnegie's Birthplace. 70mm long.	65.00
Cottage, thatched. 60mm long.	10.00
Cottage, inscribed: *Tigh-na-gaat centre of Scotland*. 85mm.	30.00
First and Last House in England. 83mm long.	20.00
John Knox's House. 112mm.	50.00
Old Town House Dunbar, The. 135mm.	50.00
Windmill, movable sail. 86mm.	40.00

Monuments (including Crosses)

Old Town Cross in Dunbarton grey
  unglazed. 140mm.   150.00

Historical/Folklore

Grace Darlings Boat, Model of. Fully
  coloured boat on brown rocks.
  108mm long, unglazed.   55.00
James V Chair. Stirling Castle. 100mm.   12.50
Mary Queen of Scots Chair. 80mm.   9.50
Mons Meg, Edinburgh Castle.
  130mm long.   21.50

Traditional/National Souvenirs

Thistle vase. 78mm.   6.00
Welsh Hat. 54mm.   10.00

Seaside

Bathing Machine. 80mm.   14.00
Longship's Lighthouse, *Lands End.*
  118mm.   20.00
Lighthouse on rocky base. 115mm.   6.50

Animals

Angry Cat pincushion. 78mm.   10.50
Cheshire cat posy holder,
  2 sizes: 80mm long.   9.00
              90mm long.   10.00
Collie, standing. ll0mm long.   19.50
Dog, Bulldog, sitting. 55mm.   17.00
Fish. 130mm long.   6.00
Lion, standing, with verse: *Be Briton*
  Still... 130mm long.   30.00
Pig, lying down. 80mm long.   16.00
Pig, standing, fat with double chin.
  47mm high, 95mm long.   30.00
Pig, sitting. 100mm long.   20.00
Pig, sitting, inscribed: *You may push*
  me. No. 137. 75mm.   20.00
Pig, standing. 35mm.   16.00
Rabbit. 60mm long.   10.00
Seal with ball on nose. 75mm.   20.00

Birds

Clara Cluck candlesnuffer. (Savoy
  No.324) 70mm.   30.00
Swan, open wings. 57mm.   9.00

Great War

Scottish Soldier on circular base.
  160mm.   190.00
Monoplane with revolving prop.
  178mm long.   85.00
Airship, (Observation Balloon)
  inscribed: *Beta.* 80mm long.   95.00

Liner converted to a troop carrier
  inscribed: *HMS Lion.*
  140mm long.   105.00
Battleship impressed: *HMS Lion.*
  140mm long.   50.00
HMS Tiger, 3 funnels. No.525.
  167mm long.   115.00
Torpedo Boat *Destroyer, Model of*
  140mm long.   170.00
Red Cross Van. 87mm long.   40.00
Armoured Car (Reputedly a
  Talbot but not named).
  125mm long.   125.00
British Motor Searchlight, Model of.
  103mm long.   235.00
Tank with inset steering wheels,
  inscribed: *HMS Donner Blitzen*
  and *515* on side. 140mm long.   50.00
Tank, no steering wheels.
  Inscription exactly the same as
  above. 135mm long.   45.00
British Trench Mortar Gun.
  100mm long.   100.00
Field gun, Model of. 150mm long.   22.00
Limpet Mine. 57mm.   55.00
Shell, inscribed: *Iron rations for Fritz.*
  160mm.   10.50
Floating Mine. No. 429. 55mm.   65.00
French Trench Helmet. 82mm long.   50.00
Glengarry. 87mm long.   22.50
The Black Watch Memorial,
  Edinburgh. 127mm.   75.00
R.F.C. Cap. 80mm long.   70.00
Kitchen Range *Keep the Home Fires*
  Burning. 65mm.   16.00

Home/Nostalgic

Book. 60mm.   12.50
Suitcase, closed. 80mm long.   6.00

Alcohol

Thistle with inscription: *A wee deoch*
  an doris. 44mm.   6.00
Toby Jug. 62mm.   12.50

Musical Instruments

Bagpipes. 115mm long.   50.00
Upright Piano. 83mm long.   21.50

Transport

Charabanc. 125mm long.   47.00
Open Tourer. 112mm long.   40.00

Footwear

Oriental Slipper. 90mm long.   6.00

Hats
Top Hat. 44mm.   6.50

Miniature Domestic
Cheese Dish. 1 piece. 40mm.   9.00
Cheese Dish and cover. 50mm.   9.00

Cambrian China

Trademark used for a Welsh retailer by
Wiltshaw and Robinson Ltd, Carlton
Works, Stoke-on-Trent. (Usual trademark
Carlton).
For details of this manufacturer and china
see Carlton China. Only four models have
been recorded so far.

Cambrian Models
Traditional/National Souvenir
Welsh Hat, Model of, with longest
   Welsh place name round brim.
   No. 283. 56mm.   11.50

Animals
Pup with one ear raised. 79mm.   14.50

Great War
Armoured Car, inscribed: *R.N.A.S.*
   118mm long.   200.00
HMLS Creme-de-Menthe Tank with
   trailing wheels and combles
   inscription. 125mm long.   45.00

Carlton China

c1902-30.

Trademark used by Wiltshaw and Robinson Ltd, Carlton Works, Stoke-on-Trent. This mark can be found with 1., 2., 3. or 4. in the outer ring.

c1902-30.

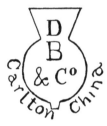

Trademark used for the Edinburgh retailer Duke Brown & Co. Only two Carlton models have been found with this mark, the usual Carlton mark having been sandpapered off and this applied on top. The mark is indicative of a Scottish thistle and the only pieces known bear the Edinburgh or Mary Queen of Scots arms.

Retailers mark post 1906.

CARLTON CHINA

Post 1930 mark.

CARLTON CHINA

Pre 1925 printed mark.

Carlton Ware

MADE IN ENGLAND

A few crested china items were made with this mark, none after 1940. Those that were, were often crazed. From 1928-1988, can also be marked 'Carlton China'.

Wiltshaw and Robinson started manufacturing in 1890 (a previous trademark used the same bird and initials W and R but did not use the name Carlton). A visitor to the works in 1902 reported that the firm specialised in making a large assortment of fancy goods and that they had been busy filling orders for the coronation. The firm was reported to make 'vases, teapots and waterjugs etc. Also pieces for silver mounting e.g. biscuit boxes'. It was also first in 1902 that Wiltshaw and Robinson 'the Manufacturers of Carlton Ware, Tinted Faience, etc.' advertised their 'latest speciality - Carlton Heraldic China' which could be seen at their London Agents, Messrs Green Bros, 47 Hatton Garden, E.C. This early advert would seem to indicate that Carlton was the first of the big Goss competitors to make heraldic china.

It is surprising that this company managed to remain independent of the Cauldon mergers that took place later on in Stoke, especially as Harold Taylor Robinson began his career as a traveller for the firm in 1899 when he was 22. By 1906 he had become a partner in Wiltshaw and Robinson, after having left this firm in 1903 to start his own company. (J.A. Robinson, the manufacturers of Arcadian). But somehow (not publicly disclosed) one of the original owners managed to buy him out, or at least break the partnership, and registered the firm as a private company in 1911. In an advert for Carlton Ware in the same year Mr J.F Wiltshaw proudly announced he was the sole proprietor of Wiltshaw and Robinson Ltd.

Mr Wiltshaw seems to have been determined to produce unique and novel designs, and his modellers (in fact the owners often designed their own models) were not influenced overmuch by the wares of the other potteries working in Stoke. They continued to produce very individual and (using a term much liked at the time) artistic models. The company seemed very concerned that only correct coats of arms should be used. I have been told that one customer designed a crest for his town and forwarded it to Carlton with an order for china. The order was filled but Carlton finding later that the crest was bogus asked for all the china to be destroyed (not all the models were destroyed however, and one lucky collector must have the only 'Ise Making Ink' with this Bawtry Crest).

By 1920 the Carlton speciality, lustre ware had been developed, the *Pottery Gazette* was full of praise for the lustre finishes the firm was using. After this date Wiltshaw and Robinson used lustre finishes on all their wares, including some heraldic china. This was obviously popular and although other firms later added lustre to their range it remained very much a hallmark of Carlton. A great number of heraldic models can be found in lustre, sometimes rather unsuitably on buildings and figures. By 1924 the firm had developed 'twelve very smart colours' in lustre (only five have been found used on crested pieces: mother of pearl, orange, tangerine, turquoise and black).

Throughout the period that Wiltshaw and Robinson produced heraldic china, they also made other decorative pottery. 'There are few factories in North Staffordshire that can claim to produce a bigger or more interesting range of earthenware fancies' *(Pottery Gazette)*. They also produced useful tableware but always in novel shapes or in 'lustrine' and decorated very much in the popular style of the time.

The firm exhibited goods of this kind at the 1924 British Empire Exhibition and appeared to be flourishing, but by 1931 Wiltshaw and Robinson Ltd was put into the hands of the Receiver. Presumably this firm, like many others, had found it difficult to overcome the Depression. Details of the firm's financial state were not made public and quite possibly the liquidation was voluntary, so that a new company could be formed. EW. Carder ceased to act as Receiver on March 7th 1932 and 'Wiltshaw and Robinson Ltd, Manufacturers of earthenware, etc' merged with 'Birks, Rawlins and Co Ltd', china manufacturers, previously of Vine Pottery, Stoke on Trent (makers of Savoy china). The merged company went on using the Savoy trademarks as well as Carlton for a few years.

Carlton Ware decorative and novelty items have continued to be produced. The ownership of the firm has changed and in 1957 the company became known as Carlton Ware Ltd. Representatives of the company claim that no records of the manufacture of heraldic china have been kept and that they know nothing of the early history of the firm. (In fact two of them did not know what crested or heraldic china was!) The firm went into liquidation in 1988. One can only hope that the growing interest in collecting Carlton Ware will prompt someone to search through whatever files remain and supply some information, trade catalogues, details of personal and other company trivia, which would be of enormous interest to collectors.

The firm must have survived all these years because of someone's ability to quickly change the style of its products to suit each new public whim and fancy. (The only plan for survival if one is in the fancy goods trade). This is most obvious when

surveying their range of crested china. The style of the Carlton models quite noticeably changed to exactly catch the mood of each period over the twenty odd years of production. The early ancient artefacts and historical models are properly labelled and have the right sober Victorian feel about them. The light hearted Edwardian holiday souvenirs are beautifully detailed and touched with colour. The Great War models are heavy with patriotism and yet the post war animals and novelty items are jolly and rather naive. Finally, no other company produced quite such vulgar lustre and coloured models to suit the taste of the late 1920s.

The quality of Carlton cannot be compared with the fine china made by Shelley and Grafton. They produced heavy models and the crests are not always painted carefully, although many examples of fine china and beautiful crests can be found. Carlton were competing for the same end of the market as Arcadian souvenir shops, bazaars and the cheaper china shops. However at its best Carlton can be very beautiful and the detail to be found on models throughout the range is quite extraordinary when one considers how cheaply they were sold.

Early decorations on small models normally found with crests include roses, green shamrocks and forget-me-nots (these can be found forming initials on beakers - a design also used by Goss). Wiltshaw and Robinson produced some view ware, but as they did not advertise this and there is relatively little around one can only assume that this was an unimportant line for them. (Possibly the production of view ware was only an early activity as these transfers are usually found on small domestic items and very rarely on named models.) This is a pity because the coloured transfer views used by this firm are excellent and compare well with Shelley (possibly the leader in the field). Other coloured transfers used are of a regional nature, such *Biddenden Maids*, *Welsh Teaparty*, *Grace Darling* and *The Trusty Servant*. These prints are found on all kinds of models, including buildings, sundials, hats and animals. One transfer view from New Zealand has been found.

Carlton produced a good range of Military badges:

Alexandra Princess of Wales Own Yorkshire Regiment 14th Foot
Army Service Corps
Canadian Forestry Battalion (224)
Coldstream Guards
Duke of Lancaster's Own (Blackpool Troop)
East Lancashire Regiment
Machine Gun Corps
New Zealand
RAF
RFC (Royal Flying Corps)
RNAS
Royal Naval Air Service
Royal Army Medical Corps
Royal Engineers
Royal Field Artillery
Royal Scots Greys
The Royal Scots
South Notts Hussars
Shropshire Light Infantry
Tank Corps (two versions)
Yorkshire Regiment

They also produced the following Naval badges:

HMAS Sydney
HMS Agincourt
HMS Andes
HMS Australia
HMS Bellerophon
HMS Birmingham
HMS Campania
HMS Caradoc
HMS Centurion
HMS Colossus
HMS Collingwood
HMS Conqueror
HMS Emperor of India
HMS Furious
HMS Hercules
HMS Indomitable
HMS Inflexible
HMS Iron Duke
HMS King George V
HMS Lion
HMS Marlborough
HMS New Zealand
HMS Queen Elizabeth
HMS Ramillies
HMS Renown
HMAS Sydney
HMS Temeraire
HMS Tyrant
HMS Thunderer
HMS Warspite
RMS Lusitania
RMS Duchess
Royal Naval Air Service
TTSS Royal Edward (transfer)

They also made an unusually large range of named battleships - one wonders if the firm had naval connections or whether this interest in the war at sea was due to the number of retail outlets in ports!

Some foreign crests have been found – Australian Towns, Tasmania, Bermuda and Hawaii - indicating some exporting, but it does not appear that Carlton ware was sold in allied countries during the Great War. There seem to be very few commemorative crests for the collector, only the BEE, Four Flags of the Allies, United we Stand and The Gloucester Historical Pageant 1907 are known. There is however, a commemorative transfer print of the Titanic with details of its sinking.

Wiltshaw and Robinson did produce a great number of models with the lucky white heather device rather than a crest. These are nearly always used on lustre pieces, some models, but more often vases, jugs and bowls. To a much lesser extent they also used Lucky Black Cat transfers, but the cats are usually part of a larger design incorporating horseshoes and four-leaf clovers and these again are often found on lustre models.

As Carlton manufactured coloured and non-crested animals, Toby jugs and ladies from 1925 onwards which are difficult to date these have not been listed here, although as they are often of a similar style to crested china they are frequently found in collections. There is also a range of model cars, made after the Second World War, which appeal to collectors but cannot be considered crested china. Anyone becoming addicted to Carlton might well look out for examples of all their products from 1890 to 1988. Early Art Nouveau and the later Deco style wares are already very expensive.

The factory closed in 1988 so any Carlton ware, and the variety of the range is vast, is worth collecting. Even modern items, such as teapots on legs, are worth looking for. Such a collection of items would almost certainly tell the story of 20th century popular taste.

Numbering system. Printed stock numbers appear on early models and can be taken as an indication that a model was made before 1914 at least. (Models that were originally numbered were made after this date but are found with no printed number.) Some early vases, mugs and trays have painted numbers, and these too are probably stock numbers. (Paintresses marks are usually small painted initials and cannot be confused with stock numbers.) Stock numbers are given where known in the following lists.

NB. Domestic ware and later gift items have impressed numbers (usually four numbers). By the 40's these reach the 1900's, so it is possible to find very late pieces impressed 1910, 1912, etc. Some misinformed stall holders will try to explain that this is the date of manufacture – do not be deceived!

Carlton Models

Parian/Unglazed

Unglazed models are mostly busts which are on circular glazed bases, normally carrying crests.

Bust of King Edward VII, later models inscribed. 135mm.	47.50
Bust of King Edward VII in trilby.	55.00
Bust of Queen Alexandra. 135mm.	47.50
Bust of King George V. 135mm.	47.50
Bust of Queen Mary. 135mm.	47.50
Bust of Burns, with verse by Wordsworth. 120mm.	30.00
Bust of *Sir Edward Carson KC, MP* with inscription: *Ulster will fight and Ulster will be right. Edward Carson.* 130mm.	75.00
Bust of Lloyd George. 115mm.	55.00
Bust of Dr Johnson, square base, no crest.	60.00
Bust of Lord Kitchener. Can be found inscribed: *In Memoriam Lord Kitchener of Khartoum went down in HMS Hampshire June 5th 1916 off the Orkney Islands. He did his duty.* 135mm.	75.00
Bust of John Ruskin. 2 sizes: 120mm.	40.00
135mm.	40.00
Bust of Scott, on glazed base. Impressed *Scott.* 126mm.	40.00
Bust of Shakespeare. 120mm.	17.50

Bust of Sydney, inscribed: *Sir Philip Sydney. Thy necessity is greater than mine.* 135mm.	45.00
Bust of *Wordsworth*, no base. 77mm.	19.50
Bust of Wordsworth, on glazed base, impressed: *Wordsworth.* 3 sizes: 115mm.	25.00
125mm.	25.00
135mm.	30.00

Ancient Artefacts

These models are often found not named, named models usually have a printed number and this is given where known. Most inscriptions begin: *Model of* so this will not be repeated throughout the list.

Ancient Lampfeeder found at St Mary's in a marsh near Hythe. 2 sizes: No.330. 46mm.	7.50
No. 829. 67mm.	7.50
Ancient Tyg, 1 handle. No.184. 66mm.	5.50
Ancient Tyg, 2 handles. No.245. 66mm.	5.50
Ancient Vase 1st Century AD, original in Wedgwood Museum, Burslem. No. 375. 60mm.	5.50
Ancient Roman Vase now in Wedgwood Museum, Burslem 1st Century AD. No.369. Rd. No.489060. 62mm.	5.50
No.378. 65mm.	5.50
Assyrian Vase, Model of old. No.258. 86mm.	5.00
Bournemouth *Ancient Bronze Urn in the Museum of the Royal Bath Hotel Bournemouth.* 50mm.	6.00
Brading Vase, inscribed: *Roman Vase found at Brading.* No.1. 35mm.	5.50
Cambridge Jug. No.332. 60mm.	5.50
Chester Ancient Vase.	5.50
Chester Roman Jug. No. 261. 70mm.	5.50
Chester Roman Vase. Found numbered 154, 286 and 288 (possibly different shapes). 60mm.	5.50
Christchurch Harvest Vase, inscribed: *Ancient Harvest Vase found at Christchurch, Hampshire.* No.407. 44mm.	5.50
Cobham Bottle, inscribed; *Model of Leather Bottle at Cobham, immortalised by Charles Dickens.* 60mm.	6.50

Colchester Ancient Vase,

4 models: No. 349. 50mm.	5.50	
No. 351. 66mm.	5.50	
No. 352. 55mm.	5.50	
No. 353. 68mm.	5.50	

Colchester Famous Vase. No. 80.
50mm. 5.50

Dartford Ewer, inscribed: *Roman
Ewer found in Dartford Museum.*
No.457. 76mm. 5.50

Dogger Bank Bottle. No. 251. 65mm. 5.50

Dorchester Jug, inscribed: *Old Jug
found in North Square, Dorchester.*
No.177. 52mm. 5.50

Dorchester Roman Jug found in Bath.
70mm. 5.50

Durham Abbey Sanctuary Knocker,
Wall Pocket. 84mm long. 12.50

Eddystone Jug. No.180. 58mm. 5.50

Elizabethan Jug or Stoup, inscribed:
*Model of the West Malling
Elizabethan Jug or stoup hallmarked
London 1581, sold for 1450 guineas.*

2 sizes: No.360. 74mm.	15.00
90mm.	15.00

Etruscan Vase, inscribed: *Model of
4th Century Etruscan Vase.*

2 models: No. 262. 89mm long.	5.50
No. 277. 45mm.	5.50

Fountains Abbey Cup. No.238. 50mm. 5.50

Glastonbury Bowl. No.172. 39mm. 5.50

Grecian Vase. N.257. 78mm. 5.50

Grecian Water Vessel, Ancient
No. 264. 85mm. 5.50

Hampshire Roman Vase. Inscribed:
*Model of Roman Vase found in the
New Forest, Hampshire.* No.247.
65mm. 5.50

Hanley Chinese Vase. No.263. 62mm. 5.50

Hanley Cyprus Vase. No. 374. 45mm. 5.50

Hanley Egyptian Vase.
2 different models:

No. 367. Rd. No. 489059. 64mm (2 large handles from neck to body).	5.50
No. 368. 63mm. (2 tiny handles on body only).	5.50

Hanley Roman Jug. No. 370. 55mm. 5.50

Hanley Roman Vase. 2 vases:

No. 372. 63mm.	5.50
No. 373. 50mm.	5.50

Hastings Kettle. No. 166. 60mm. 5.50

Heckmondwicke Saxon Jug.
No. 240. 80mm. 6.50

Hull Suffolk Palace Jug. No. 276.
62mm. 6.50

Hythe Ewer. No.339. 70mm. 5.50
(Ancient) Irish Bronze Pot. No. 183.
45mm. 5.50

Irish Kettle. No. 346. 65mm. 5.50

Jersey Milk Can, with lid. No.242.
70mm. 8.00

Lichfield Jug. No.181. 60mm. 5.50

*Lincoln Jack (from original in
museum).* No.156. 60mm. 5.50
Can be found with outpressed
Imp in relief. 17.00

Loving Cup. 2 handled. Not named.
No. 97. 38mm & 47mm. 6.50

Loving Cup. 3 handled. Not named.
53mm. 7.50

Merthyr Tydfil Roman Pottery.
Inscribed: *Model of Roman Pottery
excavated at Merthyr Tydfil.*

4 models: No. 288. 75mm.	5.50
No. 382. 50mm.	5.50
No. 383. 52mm.	5.50
No. 384. 42mm.	5.50

Newbury Leather Bottle. No. 229.
65mm. 5.50

*New Forest Roman vase found in
Hampshire.* No.243. 76mm. 5.50

Old Bronze Porridge Pot. No.221 5.50

Penmaenmawr Urn. No. 213. 50mm. 5.50

*Phoenician Vase (original in Hanley
Museum).*

2 sizes: No.274. 70mm.	5.50
No.259. 80mm.	5.50

Plymouth Jug. No.180. 58mm. 5.50

Pompeian Vessel, not named. 60mm. 5.00

*Portland Vase (now in British
Museum),* often found not named.

2 sizes: No.89. 58mm.	5.50
No.117. 80mm.	5.50

Puzzle Jug, can be found with verse.

2 sizes: 68mm.	6.50
90mm.	7.50

Larger size carries verse.

Puzzle Teapot with verse (one piece).
*This teapot pours but not until you
find out how the way to fill.* 60mm. 16.00

Roman Pottery, *1st century in
Wedgewood Museum, Burslem.*

3 models: No. 376. 65mm.	5.50
No. 377. 70mm.	5.50
No. 378. 68mm.	5.50

Roman Urn found at Milborne Port.
No. 265. 44mm and 50mm. 5.50

St. David's Vase. Inscribed: *Model of
Ancient Vase found at St. David's.*
No.249. 62mm. 5.50

Salisbury Kettle,	
2 models: No.188. 100mm.	5.50
No.281. 77mm.	5.50
Salopian Ewer. No. 75. 76mm.	5.50
Shakespeare's Jug. 70mm.	5.50
Silchester Urn. No. 193. 54mm.	5.50
Silchester Vase, inscribed: *Vase from Silchester in Reading Museum.* No. 171. 50mm.	5.50
Southampton Pipkin. No. 204. 54mm.	5.00
Spilsby Ancient Jug excavated 1887. At Spilsby. No. 299. 75mm.	6.00
Spinning wheel. *Exact Model of 4th Century Spinning Wheel.* 80mm.	13.00
Suffolk Jug. *Antique, Jug found on site of Suffolk Palace Hill now in museum.* 62mm.	5.50
(Old) Swedish Kettle. No. 344. Rd. No. 473069. 70mm.	5.50
Weston Super Mare Vase. No. 300. 80mm.	5.50
Winchelsea Vase. No. 87 also No. 211. 77mm.	5.50
Winchester Bushel. No. 323. 104mm wide.	30.00
Windsor Urn. No. 284. 50mm.	5.00
Wokingham Tankard, inscribed: *Model of old tankard jug found near Wokingham.* No.217. 78mmm.	6.00
York Roman Ewer, inscribed: *Roman Ewer from original in Hospitium at York.* No.178. 57mm.	5.50

Buildings - Coloured

Dove Cottage, the early home of Wordsworth, Model of. 50mm.	
Partly coloured	70.00
Fully coloured	100.00
Grasmere Church, Model of. 90mm.	110.00
(The) Transport and General Workers Union Convalescent Home, Littleport. 112mm long.	195.00
Hop Kiln. 98mm.	85.00

Buildings - White

Arundel Castle, The Keep. 120mm long.	115.00
Bandstand, inscribed: *O listen to the band.* 85mm.	39.50
Beach House, Canvey-on-Sea. 65mm.	110.00
Bishop's Tower Paignton. 80mm.	47.00
Blackpool Tower. 125mm.	10.50

Blackpool Tower with base.	
3 sizes: 100mm.	8.50
125mm.	10.50
164mm.	14.00
Blackpool Tower and Big Wheel on ashtray, inscribed: *Good old Blackpool.* (Can be found in lustre).	
2 sizes: 108mm.	40.00
130mm.	50.00
Burns Cottage, unnamed. 50mm. (Very delicate).	16.50
Burns Cottage, Ayr. 70mm long.	17.00
Carnarvon Castle, Eagle Tower. 100mm.	95.00
Birthplace of Andrew Carnegie. 67mm long.	40.00
Conway Castle. 130mm long.	125.00
Cottage with coloured doors, hedges and windows with a removable roof lid, and inscribed: *Ours is a nice house ours is,* or with verse *A little wife well willed, A little farm well tilled, A little mouse well filled and I am satisfied.* 70mm.	43.00
Deller's Cafe, Paignton. 62mm.	95.00
Douglas Jubilee Clock.	
2 sizes: 127mm.	75.00
132mm.	75.00
Douglas Tower of Refuge. (Lustre)	
2 sizes: 73mm.	40.00
88mm.	50.00
Dutch Cottage, Canvey Island, dated 1621. 75mm (scarce).	130.00
Fair Maid's House, Perth. 92mm. found with inscription: *Fair Maids House 1393* and verse "*loves darts cleaves hearts...*" Scott.	50.00
Farnham Castle, pearl lustre. 98mm.	55.00
Fire Engine House, Leatherhead. 115mm (uncommon).	125.00
Forth Bridge, with inscription. 166mm long. Also found in lustre.	40.00
God's Providence House Chester, inscribed: *Gods providence is mine inheritance.* Some colouring. 108mm.	35.00
Grasmere Church. 65mm high, 90mm long.	65.00
Grimsby Hydraulic Tower, with details. 165mm.	40.00
Guildford Castle. Ruins, with inscription. 75mm.	72.50

Harrogate *Pump House*. Inscribed:
*A nip and a smell from the old
sulphur well*. (Lustre) 75mm.   55.00
Hastings Castle Ruins. (Lustre) 88mm. 30.00
Hastings Clock Tower.
2 sizes: 127mm.   20.00
156mm.   22.00
Hop Kiln with coloured transfer of
hop. 96mm.   40.00
Irish Cabin found with coloured
shamrocks round base. Sometimes
inscribed: *There's a cabin in dear old
Ireland*. No.516. 75mm long.
Inscribed   26.00
No inscription.   16.00
Can be found all red. Add £10.00.
Irish Cabin, with woman and
spinning wheel outside, some
colouring. 82mm.   30.00
Irish Round Tower, found with
coloured shamrocks round base.
No.520. 126mm. Unnamed.   14.50
named   18.00
with Irish crest   22.00
Keswick Town Hall and Clock
Tower. 100mm.   125.00
King Charles Tower, Chester.
2 sizes: 85mm.   25.00
105mm.   30.50
Lincoln Cathedral. No.156. 60mm.   40.00
Marble Arch.
2 sizes: 90mm long.   17.50
127mm long.   20.00
Margate *Clock Tower*. 138mm.   20.00
Martello Tower, inscribed: *The Wish
Tower, Martello Tower erected in
1804, the date of Napoleons
threatened invasion* and verse.
67mm dia.   45.00
Martello Tower, as above as a trinket
box and lid. 67mm dia.   45.00
Moot Hall, Keswick. 102mm.   100.00
Morecambe Clock Tower. 127mm.   65.00
Old (Bishops) Tower, Paignton.
82mm.   55.00
Oldest chemyste shop in England, Ye.
Knaresborough. Coloured roof
and door. 80mm long.   65.00
Old Pete's Cottage, with detail of
origin of Old Pete. 72mm long.   35.00
Old Town House, Dunbar. House with
central tower & spire. 130mm.   72.00
Old Welsh Cottage, Model of No.400.
75mm long.   25.00
Pithead, Model of. 110mm (rare).   160.00

Rochester Castle Keep. 80mm.   50.00
Scarton Church. 90mm long.   55.00
St. *Leonards Tower, Newton Abbot*.
123mm.   85.00
St. Nicholas Church, Lantern Hill,
Ilfracombe. 98mm.   30.00
Also found with some colouring.   47.50
St. Pauls Cathedral. 112mm.   25.00
Scarborough Castle, Model of. 80mm.   80.00
Skegness Clock Tower. 124mm.   16.00
Smallest House in Wales at Conway.
115mm.   30.00
Tain Tower, Model of. Rare. 115mm.   110.00
Tintern Abbey Ruins, with green
moss on walls. 105mm long.   85.00
*Tom Tower, Christchurch, Oxford.
Contains great Tom Bell from
Osney Abbey 1683 A.D.* 127mm.   45.00
Tower Bridge, Model of. 88mm.   30.00
Trinity Castle Clock Gate. 90mm.   75.00
*Upleatham Old Church, the smallest
church in England*. 80mm.   55.00
Wallace Tower. 144mm.   82.50
Wembley Exhibition, British Hall.
(Lustre) 88mm long.   95.00
Wembley Stadium, inscribed: *Model
of British Stadium Wembley* and
details of cost and size.
110mm long.   95.00
Westminster Abbey, West Front.   25.00
Wimborne Minster.   65.00
Windmill with revolving sails can
be found inscribed: *The Sussex
Windmill*. Add £10.00. 103mm.   55.00
A Window in Thrums. 55mm.   40.00
Windsor Castle. 135mm long.   28.00
Windsor Round Tower. 95mm.   30.00
York, Bootham Bar. 114mm.   25.00
York, Cathedral, West Front. 112mm.   35.00
York, Micklegate Bar. 112mm.   35.00
York, Walmgate Bar. 95mm long.   90.00
Youghal Clock Gate, inscribed: *This
Clock Gate occupies the site of the
Ancient Trinity Castle Built in 1777*.
108mm   90.00

Monuments (including crosses)
Albert Memorial Tower, Belfast. 190mm. 150.00
Barrow Memorial, Ulverston,
inscribed: *Sailor Beware*. 135mm.   33.00
The Beacon, Alderley Edge 1799, with
inscription. 102mm.   100.00
Burns Statue, Burns holding a
crimson tipped daisy, with verse.
160mm (not often found).   45.00

Cairn on Culloden Battlefield 1746
with inscription. 65mm.   50.00
Caister on Sea, Lifeboat Memorial.
170mm.   28.00
Captain Cook's Monument on square
base unglazed. 145mm.   110.00
Cavell Memorial Statue. 165mm. See
Great War.
Celtic Cross. 142mm.   14.00
Colne Market Cross]822-1902.
125mm . (Rare).   75.00
Cross, thin, mounted on plinth.
144mm. Only known example has
a High Wycombe crest.   75.00
*Cumberland Stone on Culloden Moor
1746 (Model of).* Impressed on top
Cumberland Stone and inscribed
on side *The Battle of Culloden Moor
was fought April 16th 1746. The
Duke of Cumberland Directed the
operations of the English Army From
the Original Stone.* 90mm long,
40mm high.   42.50
Downham, The Clock. Presented to
the town by James Scott 1878. 155mm.   95.00
Flora MacDonald. Statue. 160mm.
(not common).   45.00
Florence Nightingale Memorial. See
Great War.
Garstang Market Cross, inscribed:
Model of Market Cross. 135mm.   45.00
Globe, Swanage, (Model of the)
Unglazed globe on glazed base.
86mm.   40.00
Tom Hughes, Monument. Rugby
School. Unglazed figure on
glazed base. 135mm.   30.00
Hull, *Fishermans Memorial,* with
inscription. l70mm.   20.00
Hull South African War Memorial
inscribed *Hull Soldiers War
Memorial.* 170mm.   25.00
Irish Cross. No.519,2 sizes:
115mm and 136mm.   17.50
Locke Tower, Barnsley, inscribed:
*This tower was erected in memory
of the donor of Locke Park by Phoebe,
widow of Joseph Locke MP, AD 1877.*
135mm.   140.00
Nelson's Column, not found
named. 163mm.   55.00
Queen Eleanor's Memorial Cross,
Northampton. 138mm.   80.00
Ripon Market Cross. 115mm.   18.00
Rufus Stone. 96mm.   7.50

Ruskin Cross, Model of, glazed or
unglazed cross on glazed base.
Rd No. 597960.
2 sizes: 122mm. White.   22.00
           122mm. Grey, unglazed.   70.00
           170mm. White.   23.00
St. Annes on the Sea Lifeboat
Memorial. 150mm.   25.00
Selby Market Cross. 130mm.   125.00
Battle of Stannard Hill Memorial.
116mm.   110.00
Toad Rock, Tunbridge Wells. 78mm.   25.00
Toad Rock, Near Hathersage, Model of.
100mm long.   75.00
Torquay Clock Tower. Inscribed:
*Model of Mallock Memorial,
Torquay.* 168mm .   30.00
Sir William *Wallace* Statue, Stirling,
with long inscription. *To Edward,
King of England.* 130mm.   50.00
Wilberforce Statue, Hull, with
inscription on base. 155mm.   35.00

Historical/Folklore
Bardic Chair, in lustre. 105mm.   30.00
Biddenden Maids, inscribed: *The
Biddenden Maids were born joined
together at hips and shoulders in
year 1100 and a 34Y in 1100.*
105mm.   80.00
Bonnie Prince Charles Chair. 1745.
110mm.   30.00
Caveman, standing figure holding
club. Brown hair and club. Can
have inscription: *Billie Bus, the
man who called for the empties BC
umpteen.* 113mm.   130.00
Crown of Scotland, inscribed: 'The
*Crown of Scotland. Robert Bruce
Crowned 1306, Buried Dunfermline
1329'.*68mm.   40.00
Dropping Well, Knaresborough,
sometimes found with coloured
details and water. 75mm.
Coloured   40.00
White   22.50
(The) Fiddler of York Minster. 135mm.   60.00
Font, not named. 133mm.   12.00
Fox's chair, inscribed: *Model of chair
of George Fox the Quaker, original at
Swarthmoor Hall Ulverston.* 96mm.   65.00
Rowing Boat, no seats, 125mm long
Model of Grace Darlings Boat.   47.00

Grace Darling's Boat, Model of, and
description. Boat in blue, white
on brown rocks. 108mm long.   55.00
Great Peter, Bell with clapper. *10 tons
15 cwts.* 55mm.   22.00
John Waterson's Clog. 100mm long.   35.00
Judge, bust, can be found inscribed:
*Defend the children of the poor,
Punish the wrongdoer (inscription
on New Bailey Courts London).*
70mm.   40.00
With inscription   add £10.00
Man in Pillory with some colouring,   50.00
can have inscription: *Ample time
for Reflection.* 108mm. If coloured
face, add £10.00.
Mary Queen of Scots Chair,
Edinburgh Castle. 80mm.   10.00
Mary Queen of Scots Bed, inscribed:
*The Bed of Mary Queen of Scots,
Holyrood Palace, Edinburgh.* Can
also be found inscribed: *Sure I
was born to everlasting cares like
hydra heads, one no sooner
disappears than another rises in its
room and drives me from repose,
Mary Stuart.* 90mm long.   165.00
Mother Shipton. 110mm. and 115mm.   17.00
Mother Shipton, coloured figure on
lustre oval base. 90mm.   30.00
Nose of Brasenose College Oxford.
94mm long.   16.00
Old Cromwell Cannon, also named
Mons Meg. 130mm long.   20.00
Ripon Hornblower.   16.00
*Scarborough Ducking Chair formerly
fixed on the Old Pier for the purpose
of ducking scolding women!! Last
used in ducking Mrs Gamble. New
in Museum. Period 1795.* 95mm.   75.00
Sedan Chair, inscribed: *Model of 17th
century Sedan Chair.* 70mm.   30.00
Ulphus Horn, The Famous. (York)
original in York Minster. 115mm
long (quite rare).
On base   40.00
Without base   45.00
(The) Wallace Sword, inscribed: *The
sword that seem'd fit for the
Archangel to wield was light in his
terrible hand.* 105mm long.   140.00
Watchman's Lamp, inscribed: *Model
of 16th century Watchman's Lamp
and Watchman what of the night.*
2 sizes: 80mm and 115mm.   10.50

Witch's Cauldron with Macbeth
verse *Double, double, toyle and
trouble, fyer burns and cauldron
bubble.* 45mm.   10.00
Ye Olde Spinning Wheel. 78mm   25.00
Cauldron, unglazed. 72mm.   5.00
*Xit, The Historical Dwarf. He is
said to have been born in the 16th
Century. He was under two feet
in height a brother of the Giants
Og, Gog, Magog. Xit was a noted
curiosity at the Tower of London
and was knighted Sir Napgissus
Le Grande. Model taken from a
statue formerly in an old garden
at Lewes.*   75.00

Traditional/National Souvenirs
John Bull, bust. 100mm.   25.00
John Bull with Bulldog, standing
figure on oval base. Union Jack
waistcoat and black hat, dog has
red, white and blue collar. 125mm. 165.00
Blackpool Big Wheel. Can be found
in pearl lustre.
2 sizes: 80mm.   20.00
                 100mm.   22.00
Bolton Trotter. 105mm long.   12.50
Bolton Trotter, hand holding a
trotter inscribed: *A good hold on a
Bolton Trotter.* 110mm long.   14.50
Pair of *Bowton Trotters.* 106mm long. 17.50
Cheddar Cheese, inscribed: *Prime
Cheddar Cheese.* Can be found in
dark yellow, both whole and with
slice out. 50mm.   12.00
with colour.   16.50
Cheshire Cheese, inscribed: *Prime
Cheshire Cheese,* with slice cut out.
53mm.   16.00
Cornish Pasty, inscribed: *This is a
Pasty don't 'ee see. Will 'ee have a
piece with me. There's more in the
kitchen.* 100mm long.   12.00
Cotton Shuttle, Model of. 93mm long.   65.00
Davy Lamp. See Miner's Lamp.
Laxey Wheel. 90mm.
Sometimes coloured   125.00
Ham, side of, pierced hole in
top for hanging. Inscribed: *A
Yorkshiremans advice to his son* etc.
60mm   18.00
Lincoln Imp moulded in relief on
Lincoln Jack, inscribed: *The Imp,
Lincoln Cathedral.* No.156. 60mm.   17.50

Kelly from the Isle of Man. 3 legged
man, holding Manx Kipper in
hand, fully coloured. 110mm.   150.00
Kelly from the Isle of Man. 3 legged
man, hands on hips, black cat
at feet. 110mm.   150.00
Kelly from the Isle of Man. 3 legged
man and large black manx cat all
on ashtray base. 89mm.   125.00
hand, fully coloured. 110mm.   150.00
Manx Legs on base (lustre). 95mm.   16.00
Miner's Lamp. Can be found
inscribed *Davy Lamp.* 110mm.   25.00
(The) *Ripon Horn* on rectangular
base, inscribed.
3 sizes: 67mm.   17.50
         80mm.   20.00
Ripon Hornblower, Model of with
verse. 120mm.   16.00
(The) Sheffield Grinding Stone.
80mm long (rare).   75.00
York Minster, The Fiddler of. 132mm.   80.00
Yorkshireman, standing figure
holding tankard - often found
not named. Found with
inscription: *Take hod and sup lad*
and verses. 126mm.   35.00
Irish Cabin Trunk, more often found
without this inscription. 58mm
long. Inscribed add £10.00.   10.50
Irish Colleen, on circular base with
shamrocks. Can have green cloak
and lustre base. 127mm.   100.00
Irishman, in black hat with yellow
pig, standing on rectangular base,
green edge, inscribed: *X miles to
Belfast and Don't be radin milestones
all the day Allana.* 90mm long.   300.00
Irishman, standing figure holding
shillelagh. 136mm.   75.00
Irishman's Hat, green band,
inscribed: *It's a long way to
Tipperary...* 45mm.   25.00
Irish Harp, with green shamrocks.
95mm.   12.00
Irish Harp, Model of surmounted by
crown. Decorated with shamrocks.
2 sizes: 95mm   16.00
         105mm.   16.00
Irish Jaunting Car, with horse and
driver, some colouring. 130mm
long (This is quite rare).   160.00
Irish Spinning Wheel. Irish lady
sitting by spinning wheel, partly
coloured with shamrocks. (Lustre.)
95mm.   65.00

Irish Spinning Wheel. (no lady). 78mm.   25.00
Saint Patrick's Mitre. 70mm.   30.00
Shamrock. 70mm.   7.00
*Gretna Green, Model of Blacksmiths
Anvil.* This anvil is often found
without inscription or verse.
70mm. With verse add £5.00.   7.50
Scotch Fisher Girl at Work, coloured
fish in barrel. 118mm.   55.00
Scotsman, standing figure, blue tam-
o'shanter with red bobble and
brown walking stick. With verse
Just a wee deoch and doris. 130mm.
Harry Lauder.   85.00
Tam-o'shanter (bonnet) with
coloured sprig of heather.
Inscribed: *Wha can sit on the
thistle noo.* 90mm dia.   24.50
Thistle hat pin holder. 80mm.   12.00
Thistle moulded Teapot with lid and
coloured thistle handle, can be
found in lustre. 85mm.   18.00
Thistle Vase, can be found with
verse.
2 sizes: 76mm and 115mm.   5.00
Prince of Wales Feathers. 95mm.   13.00
Pat's Hat and Dudeen, green ribbon
and black dudeen. With *Tipperary*
inscription on reverse. 45mm.   30.00
Welsh Hat, Model of, can be found
with longest Welsh place name
round brim. No. 283. for which
add £5.00. 56mm.   10.00
Welsh Hat, with orange band. Can
be found in lustre. 44mm.   10.00
Welsh Leek, Model of, can be found
with coloured leaves. 93mm.
white leaves   5.50
green leaves   8.50
black leaves   9.50
Jenny Jones. Two varieties Welsh
lady, standing figure with black
hat and red and green shawl.
125mm no basket   75.00
147mm with brown basket   40.00
Welsh Spinning Wheel, two Welsh
ladies with spinning wheel,
coloured hats and shawls. 95mm.   60.00
Welsh Tea Party, three Welsh ladies
taking tea, coloured hats and
shawls, etc. 90mm.   55.00
Bermuda Sailing Ship, can be found
with Bermuda crest. 127mm long.   30.00
Gondola. 127mm long.   22.50

Seaside Souvenirs

Bathing Machine, larger sizes found
inscribed: *Morning dip.* (Lustre)

4 sizes: 55mm.	14.50
65mm.	20.00
70mm.	22.00
77mm. 3 over door.	22.00

Bathing Machine with set of steps
each end. (Lustre). 85mm long.   25.00

Lifebelt. 105mm dia.   15.50

Lifeboat. Can be found inscribed:
Queensbury or *Alfred S Gerth, Port
Brancaster (Norfolk); Date: 1892-1916
Crew, Cox, 2nd Cox, Bowsman and 10
Oarsmen. Size: 34ft long by 8ft wide,*
for which £10.00 should be added.
113mm long.   24.50

Motor Boat with driver on waves
blue stripe. 120mm long.   27.50

Rowing Boat. 108mm long.   16.00

Trawler, inscribed on sail: *SM.*
115mm long.   70.00

Yacht with billowing sail.

120mm long, some colouring.	22.00
no colouring	17.50

If inscribed *Saucy Sue* add £10.00

Fisherman on Rock, holding brown
net, inscribed: *Son of the sea.*
117mm.   40.00

Fisherman's Creel. 70mm long.   7.50

Fisherman Bust. 90mm.   15.00

Fisherman on yacht pulling in net
on sea, black clothing. (Lustre).
105mm.   32.50

Lifeboatman, bust with colouring
on face. 80mm.   26.50

Lighthouse inscribed: *Sailor Beware,*
also found as hatpin holder.
140mm.   16.50

Barnsness Lighthouse, Dunbar 118mm.   75.00

Beachy Head Lighthouse, hatpin holder,
black top & band. 148mm.   13.00

Beachy Head Lighthouse, with
inscription, black top & black
band. Can be found inscribed:
*Beachy Head Lighthouse built in
1902. Contains 3,660 tons of Cornish
granite. Base diameter 50 feet Height
142 feet candle power 240,250. Light
visible 16 miles. One minute flashes.
Fog explosive every 5 minutes. 1/4 mile
from cliff.* 148mm.   17.00

Chapman Lighthouse. 103mm (rare).   47.50

Douglas Lighthouse. 128mm.   75.00

Eddystone Lighthouse, Model of.
138mm.   12.50

Flamborough Lighthouse, Model of.
Can be found as a hatpin holder.
115mm.   25.00

Flamborough Head Fog Siren Building.
87mm long.   60.00

Lighthouse Hatpin Holder
inscribed: *Girdleness.* 136mm.   30.00

*Mumbles Lighthouse and Telegraph
Office.* 127mm.   65.00

Mumbles Lighthouse, Model of Pepper
Pot. 102mm.   25.00

Pharos Lighthouse Fleetwood, Model of.
No. 409. 100mm (Identical model,
so named and with same stock
number can be found as a pepper
pot).   20.00

Portland Lighthouse Pepper Pot, with
orange band. l00mm.   22.50

Scarborough Lighthouse. 135mm.   65.00

Withernsea Lighthouse. 134mm.   17.00

Lighthouse Pepper Pot. l00mm.   12.00

Limpet Shell with 3 feet. 23mm.   6.00

Oyster Shell, found inscribed: *A
Whitstable native.* add £5.00. 70mm.   6.50

Scallop Shell on 3 tiny feet.
80mm long.   6.00

Shell Inkwell, inscribed: *We are
always glad to hear from you.*
95mm.   10.50

Whelk Shell, inscribed: *Listen to the
sea.* 100mm long.   6.00

Shell pin tray.   5.00

Bathing Beauty, reclining figure
with green or blue cap, hand
shielding eyes. 110mm long.   150.00

Bathing Beauty, fully coloured
figure, lying on edge of lustre
shell dish, bathing costume in
several colours. Inscribed: *Washed
up by the tide.* 115mm.

white	70.00
coloured	150.00

Bathing Belle, red, blue or yellow
bow to cap, sitting hands together
by face, legs stretched out. 77mm.   160.00

Boy on Donkey, can be found
inscribed: *Gee up Neddy* or more
occasionally: *This beats going to
school.* Can be found without
base. Sometimes partly coloured.
98mm long.

if inscribed: *Gee up Neddy.*	85.00
if inscribed: *This beats going to
school.*	120.00
white	75.00

Mr. *Punch*, bust. 82mm.   55.00
Punch and Judy Booth, with
   coloured Punch and Judy.
   Inscribed *Good Morning Mr*
   Punch. 133mm.   125.00
   Can be found uncoloured and
   without inscription for which
   deduct £50.00.

Countryside
Bee Hive on square stand, with
   coloured transfer of bee. 64mm.   17.50
Campfire, cauldron inside three
   upright poles on triangular base.
   122mm.   30.00
Campfire, (lustre).115mm.   30.00
Milk Can with lid. 55mm.   5.00
Pinecone, upright, closed. 79mm.   6.50
Tree Trunk candleholder. 113mm.   6.00
Tree Trunk vase, the Great Oak in
   Sherwood Forest, Nottingham.
   2 sizes: 65mm.   12.00
              120mm.   15.00

Animals
Ape (Orang-utan) holding orange,
   brown face, 58mm.   27.00
Bear, walking, looks like a Polar
   Bear, inscribed: *Russian Bear.*
   130mm long.   80.00
Bear and Ragged staff. 85mm.   40.00
Bear wearing glengarry with blue
   and orange stripes, sitting on
   base. 104mm.   55.00
Bull, inscribed: *King of the Herd*, or
   much more rarely: *The Ox of*
   Oxford. 103mm long.   85.00
Cat, angry, with back up, inscribed:
   My word if you're not off or *The*
   Midnight Rambler. add £10.00.
   80mm.   14.50
Cat, Cheshire, red bow and coloured
   face inscribed: *The Cheshire cat*, and
   The smile that won't come off.
   90mm.   12.50
Cheshire Cat, sitting, looking right,
   tail curled around to right, blue
   bow. 72mm.   12.50
Cat lying down, tail curled up
   behind. 84mm long.   40.00
Cat, on piano.95mm.   40.00
Cat (black), doing hand stand on
   oblong base, back legs up in the
   air. Inscribed: *Well what about it.*
   115mm (rare).   120.00

Cat, Manx. 75mm.   35.00
Manx Cat, back up, coloured face.
   Inscribed: *I am Rumpy* on
   forehead. 60mm.   75.00
Cat, long necked, coloured facial
   features. Inscribed: *My word* etc.
   ll0mm.   20.50
Cat sitting, chubby and kittenish.
   63mm.   14.50
Cat with blue bow sitting on square
   cushion, impressed: *Good Luck*
   in blue. 80mm.   16.00
Cat sitting, with red bow, salt pot or
   pepper pot. 70mm.   30.00
Cat sitting, wearing black topper
   with shamrock, bow tie can be
   found coloured red, blue, white
   or green. Also found in lustre.
   88mm.   30.00
Cat sitting, with blue bow (bow
   sometimes left uncoloured)
   56mm.   20.00
Cat sitting, with Greek Good Luck
   (Swastika) round neck. 59mm.   25.00
   This cat can also be found on a
   pouffe and inscribed: *Good Luck*.
   85mm.   22.50

Black Cat small.
Can be found with accompanying
   model coloured red or yellow, for
   which £20.00 should be added.
Found on the following:
Armchair (upholstered) with green
   swastika and red horseshoe on
   arms, (lustre), inscribed: *Jolly good*
   luck. 75mm.   45.00
   Can be found all in red, inscribed
   Good Luck.   65.00
(Old) Armchair with solid arms.
   90mm.   50.00
Ashtray, circular, can be found with
   transfer of cigarette, inscribed:
   Who burnt the cloth. 110mm dia.   45.00
Ashtray, club shaped, lustre.
   90mm long.   30.00
Ashtray, diamond shaped, lustre.
   95mm long (It seems very likely
   that small black cats will be
   found on heart and spade shaped
   ashtrays as well and that all four
   were made in white and lustre.   40.00
Ashtray, horseshoe-shaped.
   105mm long.   40.00
Candle holder, oval. 117mm long.   75.00

Chair. 90mm.	40.00
Dish, crinkle edge. 83mm dia.	40.00
Horseshoe ashtray, inscribed: *Jolly*	
good luck. 105mm long.	40.00
with Siamese black cat	55.50
with black kitten with red bow	50.00
Piano, open keyboard. 95mm.	75.00
Pillar Box, can be found red.	
Inscribed: *Good luck.* 110mm.	80.00
Rectangular Box and lid, inscribed:	
Good Luck or *Trinkets* (Lustre).	
90mm long.	35.00
Rocking Chair, lustre. 100mm.	45.00
Sofa. Inscribed: *Jolly good luck.*	
92mm long.	45.00
Trinket Box, inscribed: *Hairpins.*	
57mm long.	30.00

Black Cat, large:
Found on the following:

Armchair. *Jolly Good Luck.* 75mm.	45.00
Oval hatbox with coloured	
Swastika and horseshoe.	
Inscribed: *Good luck,* Base can be	
found in mother-of-pearl or blue	
lustre.	
2 sizes: 64mm.	30.00
85mm.	35.00
Pouffe, square the cat's bow is	
found blue instead of usual red.	
Inscribed: *Good luck.* 90mm.	30.00
Black Cat and Kitten on ashtray	
with match holder. Inscribed:	
Don't scratch me, scratch mother.	
Can be in maroon lustre. 70mm.	45.00
Black Cat on rectangular ashtray	
with match holder, 70mm high,	
100mm long.	60.00
Square Box and lid. 58mm long,	
63mm high.	35.00

Animals (cont.)

Chimpanzee. 84mm.	26.00
Doe on oval stand. 118mm.	80.00
Bulldog, sitting, inscribed: *Bill Sykes*	
dog. 95mm long.	25.00
Bulldog, sitting, thin faced.	25.00
Inscribed: *Model of Bill Sykes dog*	
and sometimes found also	
inscribed: *My word if you're not*	
off. 51mm.	25.00
Bulldog, standing, inscribed: *My*	
word if you're not off; can be found	
inscribed: *Slow to start, but what a*	
hold. Inscribed add £10.00.	
120mm long.	30.00

Dog (French Bulldog), sitting with	
pricked-up ears and blue eyes.	
57mm.	14.50
Dog, Staffordshire Bull Terrier,	
inscribed: *My word if you're not off.*	
100mm.	22.00
Dog, standing Collie. Inscribed:	
Scotch Collie. 110mm long.	40.00
Dog playing banjo, inscribed: *Some*	
Band. 83mm.	35.00
Bulldog looking out of kennel,	
inscribed: *The Black Watch.* Dog's	
head is coloured black. 90mm.	25.00
Dog (Puppy) in slipper. Puppy	
coloured brown. l00mm long.	80.00
Dog (Puppy) sitting with one ear	
raised. Can be found painted	
blue and in lustre, add £20.00.	
83mm.	13.00
With black spots.	17.00
This puppy can be found on a	
hand mirror (silvered) inscribed:	
Me twice. 105mm long.	55.00
Dog, Labrador Puppy. 65mm.	20.00
Dog, Scottie, begging, pink ears and	
red collar. Can be found coloured	
green or red, add £10.00, or in	
lustre. 74mm.	24.00
Dog, Scottie, begging, wearing a	
glengarry, some colouring.	
105mm.	14.50
Can be found on thistle base.	
105mm.	35.00
Dog, Scottie, sitting, wearing a	
blue or orange tam-o'shanter	
with orange bobble. Also found	
in lustre. Add £6 for coloured	
tam-o'shanter.	
2 sizes: 60mm.	12.00
80mm.	14.00
Dog, Black Scottie, wearing blue	
and orange tam-o'shanter on	
horseshoe tray inscribed *Jolly*	
Good Luck. 72mm high,	
110mm long.	55.00
Dog, Scottish Terrier, standing with	
tail in the air. May be found	
inscribed: *As old Mrs Terrier said to*	
her pup in all lifes adversities keep	
your tail up. Add £5.00. 92mm long	
77mm high.	22.50
Dog, *Scottish Terrier,* standing	
120mm long.	30.00

Dog, standing, impressed on collar: *Caesar* and inscribed: *I am the Kings dog.* Some colouring. 106mm long.   65.00

Terrier Dog, sitting one ear cocked. 87mm.   15.00

Donkey, inscribed: *Gee up Neddy* or *Flamborough Donkey* with orange and blue rosettes. 110mm long.   40.00

Elephant, walking. 58mm high, 75mm long.   30.00

Elephant with raised trunk. 51mm high, 80mm long.   35.00

Fawn. 70mm.   30.00

Field Mouse, on base. 54mm.   35.00
    Can be found fully coloured.   40.00

Fish (Salmon),112mm long.   10.50

Fish ashtray, inscribed: *A plaice for the ashes.* 120mm long.   12.50

Hare, with two long upright ears. 74mm.   15.00

Lion on ashtray base. 60mm.   18.00

Monkey, sitting hands to mouth. 90mm.   24.00

Monkey holding yellow coconut brown face. 58mm.   25.00

Monkeys - Three brown monkeys sitting on lustre ashtray base, *speak no evil, see no evil, hear no evil.* 52mm. 22.00

Monkeys - Three Wise Monkeys on wall. Inscribed: *Speak no evil, see no evil, hear no evil.* Lustre. 90mm.   14.00

Monkeys - Three Wise Monkeys, coloured brown, with red faces on rectangular base with the same inscription as above. 87mm long.   22.50

Pig sitting on haunches, inscribed: *Wunt be druv* or *You can push, you can shuv but I'm hanged if I'll be druv.* 60mm high, 92mm long.   22.50

Pig, standing, found inscribed: *W'ont be druv.* Also found entirely coloured blue. for which add £20.00. 65mm long.   17.50

Pig, very fat, standing, inscribed: *You can Push or You....* 85mm long.   22.00

Pig, fat and standing, found inscribed: *Wunt be druv.* Hairy skin 80mm long.   24.50

Pig, standing, fat found inscribed: *You can push, etc.* or *I'm the fellow who pays the rent.* for which add £10.00. 94mm long.   20.00

Pig, sitting, wearing coloured German Pickelhaube and with Iron Cross on left breast. Pepper Pot. Reg. No. 642626. White.   70.00
    90mm. Very rare. Colouring.   160.00

Piglet, standing. 70mm long.   17.00
    Inscribed: *Wont be druv.*   20.00

Rabbit, crouching with pricked ears. 65mm long.   12.50

Racehorse on oval base. 90mm high, 120mm long.   100.00

Shetland Pony.
2 sizes: 138mm long.   40.00
        150mm long.   40.00

Stag with large antlers on oval stand. 150mm. Two moulds exist, one looking left and one looking right, but less of them around, possibly because the antlers are fragile. Can be found in lustre.   110.00

Squirrel eating nut. 70mm.   30.00

Teddy Bear. 85mm.   24.50

Terrapin. 75mm long.   20.00

Welsh Goat on rocky base, inscribed: *Yr Afr Cymreig* (The Welsh Goat) or *Y-Machyn-Cymreig* No. 391. 96mm.   75.00

Wembley Lion on ashtray base, some colouring. 60mm (This was the stylised lion symbol of the British Empire Exhibition and is usually found with BEE crest).   55.00

Birds (including Eggs)
Bluebirds, two, coloured blue and yellow, on ashtray base. 88mm wide.   35.00

Egg, cracked open on top. 77mm long.   9.50

Hen roosting. 60mm long.   11.00

Hen and Cock, *salt, pepper* and *mustard* pots, some colouring - add £10.00 (Lustre) 70mm   each 15.00

Chicken hatching from egg. 64mm long.   10.00

Egg cracked open, lying on side. 74mm long.   10.00

Owl, baby. 66mm.   20.00

Owl, Barn, yellow/brown sitting on orange lustre ashtray. 68mm.   25.00

Owl, wearing black mortar board with red tassel (lustre). (Models with Irish crests can be found with red mortar boards.) 75mm.   25.00
    Models can also be found fully coloured blue or red.   40.00

Owl cream jug. 88mm.
Detailed feathers 22.50
Owl, pepper pot. 92mm. 22.00
Owl, fully coloured, on oval ashtray
base. 70mm. 30.00
Parrot, inscribed: *Pretty Polly.*
74mm. 16.50
Peacock. Can be found coloured
blue, add £10.00. 63mm. 24.00
Stork with pink beak, standing on
one leg. Can be found in lustre or
coloured. 110mm. 30.00
Swan
3 sizes: 55mm. 9.50
63mm. 9.50
76mm. 10.50
Smallest can be found coloured
red (add £10.00).
Swan pepper pot. 53mm. 10.00
Swan posy bowl. 78mm. 10.00
Woodpecker, comic, some colouring
on wings, beak and feet. 60mm. 55.00
Woodpecker, coloured on lustre
ashtray base. 84mm. 38.00
**Carlton made a series of 5 birds on
green bases and these are listed
below:**
Cock standing on green base, some
colouring to head. 85mm long. 40.00
Can be found coloured blue. 50.00
Goose standing on green base,
yellow beak. Also found in lustre.
72mm. 40.00
Duck standing up, rather comic, on
green base, yellow or orange beak.
105mm. 45.00
Duck airing wings, green base,
yellow beak. 80mm. Can be found 40.00
coloured blue with black trim.
Add £10.00.
Turkey on green base, coloured
beak and feet. Can also be found
in lustre and red or blue.
Add £10.00. 70mm. 40.00

Great War
Many Great War models are found
with the following Victory
inscriptions: *The Victory of Justice,
Armistice of the Great War signed
Nov 11th 1918 and Victory of Justice.
Peace signed at Versailles June 28th
1919.* These add interest but not
value.

Munitions Worker, inscribed: *Doing
her bit* and *Shells and more shells*
some colouring. 140mm. 190.00
Nurse with red cross, inscribed:
A friend in need. 150mm. 95.00
Old Bill, standing figure of Bruce
Bairnsfather's cartoon character.
Inscribed: *Yours to a cinder.*
138mm. 150.00
Can be found with facial
colouring and brown balaclava. 175.00
For Radio Operator see modern
equipment.
Sailor, bust. Inscribed: *The Handy
Man* and *HMS Dreadnought.*
85mm. 55.00
Somtimes found with Hearts of
Oak verse on back - add £10.00.
Sailor standing to attention with
blue trim. Inscribed: *Handy Man.*
135mm. 140.00
Scottish Soldier with rifle, wearing
glengarry, some colouring.
148mm. 190.00
Scottish Soldier with bagpipes,
wearing bearskin, some
colouring. Very rare. 148mm. 350.00
Scottish Soldier with rifle, wearing
bearskin (busby) Some colouring.
Very rare. 153mm. 250.00
Soldier standing to attention,
inscribed: *Are we downhearted No!*
and with verse *Its a long way to
Tipperary.* 153mm. 150.00
Soldier standing to attention with
ammunition belt worn over
shoulder. 125mm (rare). 150.00
Biplane with movable propellor.
145mm long, 95mm wide. 120.00
Can be found with coloured
roundel and tail or just coloured
tail. 145.00
Also found with coloured
roundel and tail with skids
instead of wheels. Very rare.
140mm long, 90mm wide. 300.00
Biplane, with coloured roundels
and tailplane with movable
propellor, can have two crests.
165mm long, 143mm wide. 400.00
Large and impressive.
Monoplane, rounded fuselage and
movable prop. 134mm long. 95.00

Monoplane, square fuselage and
movable prop. 140mm long.   95.00
Zeppelin or Airship with
moulded Iron Cross on side,
can be found with cross painted
black, or left white and coloured
roundels on nose.
118mm long.   70.00
with coloured RAF roundels.   80.00
or coloured French roundels.   85.00
British mine sweeper whose
splendid work will live forever
in the annals of British history.
115mm long.   65.00
Can be found inscribed: *HMS*
Gowan Lea,
HMS Peggy or
HMS Minesweeper.   100.00
Can be found with 'SH' or
'95' inscribed on sail.
A very rare version exists
inscribed: *HMD Indian Summer.*   125.00
Battleship. 125mm long, 38mm wide
in middle, 3 funnels, 2 guns fore,
2 guns aft.   55.00
Battleship. 34mm wide in middle.
No large guns. 110mm long.   50.00
Battleship, 2 funnels,4 guns fore,4
guns aft. 160mm long. Named:
HMS Canada,
HMS Australia,
HMS Marlborough   125.00
Battleship, 3 funnels, 4 guns fore, 2
guns aft. 160mm long. Named:
HMS Australia,
HMS Monarch
HMS Renown,
HMS Iron Duke,
HMS Princess Royal,
HMS Tyrant
HMS War Spite,
HMS Inflexible.   125.00
Not named.   75.00
Battleship, 3 funnels, 2 guns fore, 4
guns aft. 170mm long. Named:
HMS Lion,
HMS Tiger.   110.00
Battleship, 3 funnels, 4 guns fore,
2 guns midships, 2 guns aft.
167mm long. Named:
HMS Lion,
HMS Queen Elizabeth.   110.00

All the above can be found with
the following Victory inscription
only: *Great War l914-18. The*
German Fleet surrendered 74
warships Nov 21st 1918.
Battleship, 3 funnels. Both bow and
stern rolled inwards.
115mm long.   55.00
Battleship with high prow. 140mm
long. Inscribed: *HMS Humber,*
Model of British Monitor.   55.00
Has also been found with same
Victory inscription as above and
not named.   60.00
Named.   80.00
Battleship, two raised guns aft.
Named HMS Queen Elizabeth.   110.00
140mm long.
Battleship, with high prow, two
rear guns pointing upwards,
pinnacle with bulbous base
instead of funnel. 144mm long.
Scarce.   75.00
Can also be found with
transfer of 'HMS Lusitania' and
inscribed: *The Lusitania sunk*
by German submarine off the Irish
coast May 7th 1915. Lives lost 1275,
saved 703.   125.00
Battleship, wide with two funnels.
120mm long.   50.00
HMHS, Anglia, Model of, hospital ship,
rarely found named *HMMS Gowan*
Lea with 2 funnels, often found with
further detailed inscription:
Model of British Hospital Ship whose
voyage was disregarded on three
occasions by the German
Submarines. 165mm long. (Has
been found wrongly named as
HMS Tiger and as *RMS Lusitania).*   160.00
RMS Lusitania, 4 funnels. Found
with details of sinking: *The*
Lusitania was sunk by a German
Submarine May 7th 1915. Lives lost
1198, or the numerically incorrect
inscription: *Sunk by German*
Submarine off the Irish Coast, May
7th 1915. Lives lost 1275, Saved 703.
168mm long, also found inscribed
Remember the Lusitania   150.00
(Has been found wrongly named
as *HMHS Anglia*).

British Submarine, Model of, blunt nosed, often found without this inscription but with E9 on side. Submarines found unnamed are found with the following inscription: *Great War 1914-18. 150 German U Boats surrendered Nov 20th 1918.* With or without pinnacle. 140mm long.   65.00

Submarine, pointed nose and fish tail, inscribed: *E9.* 146mm long. (Slightly rarer than blunt nosed model).   70.00

British submarine, Model of, half-submerged, inscribed: *E9.* 124mm long.   80.00

Ambulance with 3 red crosses and WD on radiator. l00mm long.   45.00

Armoured Car with Rolls-Royce type front. 120mm long.   225.00
Difficult to find in perfect condition.

Armoured Car with 3 guns on turret, inscribed: *RNAS.* 116mm long.   210.00

British Anti-Aircraft Motor, Model of, inscribed: RNAS. 121mm long.   170.00

Tank with trailing steering wheels, inscribed: *HMLS Creme de Menthe.* 130mm long.   45.00
Also inscribed: *The British Tank successfully used against the Germans, Combles, Sept 1916.*   45.00

Tank with no steering wheels, inscribed: *HMLS.*
4 sizes: 80mm long found with
        Tank Corps crest.   130.00
        95mm long.   60.00
        134mm long.   45.00
        160mm long.   50.00
134mm & 160mm sizes are inscribed *HMLS Creme-de-Menthe* and *130* and can be found with *Victory* inscriptions. Also *The British Tank gave them hell at Marne 1918* and *Buy War Bonds. The British Tank successfully used against the Germans, Combles, Sept. 1916.*
The 134mm size can be found with Tank Corps and Fearnaught badges.   110.00

Tank Bank, as largest size tank above but with slot for coins. Two sizes of slot. Inscribed: *Buy War Bonds,* and can be found with *Combles* and *Marne* inscriptions. 156mm long.   100.00

HM Whippet Tank. 121mm long.   190.00

Italian Fiat Tank, not named. 100mm long. (Very rare). Looks rather like a dalek and usually has its fragile guns missing.   450.00

Vickers Tank, not named. 126mm long (rare). The latest model manufactured, approx. 1928-32.   260.00

British Machine Gun, Model of. MG ingreen wreaths on barrel. 2 moulds, one with open stand and one solid. 100mm long.   45.00

British Naval Gun, Model of. 88mm long (very rare).   215.00

British Trench Mortar, Model of. Mounted on steps and barrel at an angle. 66mm.   32.50

Trench Mortar, not named, with horizontal barrel. 60mm.   22.00

Field Gun, found inscribed: *French 75.*
3 sizes: 130mm long,
        outpressed *RFA.*   30.00
        148mm long.   30.00
        155mm long.   35.00
If named. Add £10.00.

Field Gun with screen and sight hole, inscribed: *French 75.*
2 sizes: 115mm long.   35.00
        145mm long.   45.00

British 15" Shell. Model of. 90mm.   17.00

Cannon Shell, Model of. No. 606. 75mm.   12.50

Bullet. 80mm.   7.00

German Incendiary Bomb, Model of. 75mm.   30.00

British Hand Grenade. 83mm.   30.00

Floating Mine. Model of. 83mm.   60.00

British Searchlight, Model of. Sometimes found inscribed: *The Zeppelin Finder.* 68mm. Inscribed   40.00
                                         50.00

Capstan, Model of, with brown rope. 70mm.   22.50

Bandsman's Drum, mustard pot found in lustre. 45mm.   12.50

Australian Hat. 75mm long. 20.00
  Inscribed: *Anzacs for ever* 25.00
Colonial Hat, often found unnamed.
  95mm dia. 19.50
  Can be found inscribed: *Anzacs*
  for ever. 25.00
  If inscribed: *Colonial Hat.* 30.00
Forage Cap. 80mm long. 22.50
Glengarry with coloured thistle.
  78mm long. 20.00
Glengarry with badge. 93mm long. 35.00
Officer's Peaked Cap, coloured
  band. 78mm long. 25.00
Territorials Hat, coloured hat band.
  85mm dia. 30.00
  Can be found with solid base. 40.00
Pair of folded blankets, orange &
  black border, or red and blue
  stripes can be found inscribed
  Let Dewsbury Blankets keep the
  world warm. 56mm long. 125.00
Kitbag, open neck, with verse.
  72mm. 25.00
Kitbag, closed neck, with verse.
  72mm. 25.00
Kitbag as Pepper Pot, with verse.
  72mm. 25.00
Bell Tent. 66mm. Can be found 16.00
  named *Tommies Bungalow.* 22.00
Blighty. Map of England and Wales,
  with verse *Take me back to dear Old*
  Blighty. 115mm. 75.00
Kitchen Range, with black kettle but
  no teapot. Inscribed: *Keep the*
  home fires burning till the boys come
  home. 70mm. 22.00
Kitchen Range with black kettle and
  brown teapot. Inscribed: *We've*
  kept the home fires burning till the
  boys came home or *Keep the home*
  fires burning till the boys come home.
  70mm. 22.00
Shrapnel Villa, Tommies Dugout
  somewhere in France. (From Bruce
  Bairnsfather's cartoons).
  83mm long. 65.00
Scarborough Lighthouse, Model of,
  with rectangular building showing
  shell holes from Great War. Can
  be found with blackened holes.
  98mm. (Rare). 115.00
Blackpool War Memorial. 130mm. 65.00

Brighton War Memorial. 105mm long.
  (Building, not a statue). 110.00
Cenotaph, inscribed: *The Glorious*
  Dead with 2 green wreaths.
  3 sizes: 105mm. 9.00
  110mm. 11.00
  146mm. 17.00
Clacton-on-Sea War Memorial.
  Unglazed angel on glazed base.
  148mm. 100.00
Cranbrook War Memorial. 140mm. 125.00
Douglas War Memorial. Can be
  found with lustre finish. 160mm. 85.00
Dunbar War Memorial. 123mm. 110.00
Edith Cavell, statue, inscribed:
  Brussels dawn October 12th 1915.
  Sacrifice. Humanity. (Lustre).
  2 sizes: 140mm. 20.00
  163mm. 23.00
Elgin War Memorial. 165mm. 160.00
Felixstowe War Memorial. 134mm. 200.00
Feltwell War Memorial. 140mm. 160.00
Florence Nightingale, 1820-1910 The
  Lady of the Lamp. Parian top.
  2 sizes: 140mm 30.00
  175mm 40.00
High Wycombe War Memorial, not
  named. 148mm. 160.00
Northallerton War Memorial.
  115mm. 85.00
Ripon War Memorial, found with
  Ripon Hornblower inscription.
  115mm. 80.00
Tunbridge Wells War Memorial,
  soldier, unglazed, on glazed plinth
  carrying a rifle with fixed
  bayonet. With inscription: *Our*
  Glorious Dead 1914-18. Honour,
  Gratitude, Praise. 170mm. 160.00
Ulverston War Memorial. 146mm. 190.00

Home/Nostalgic
Anvil on tree stump base. 76mm. 7.50
Baby lying on side holding paint
  pot with dirty cheeks. Sometimes
  inscribed: *Mother's Darling.* Some
  colouring. 125mm long. 135.00
Baby, similar to one above, with
  no paint pot, holding dress.
  Mother's Darling.
  136mm long. 145.00
Basket of coloured fruit. (Lustre).
  88mm. (Almost Art Deco). 22.00

Bellows. 95mm.	12.50
Book with lock. 66mm.	12.50
Cigarettes, matches and ash, container with cigarette on lid. 85mm long.	24.50
Cigarettes holder with lid & place for ashes, striker at rear. Most ornate ribbed design. Rare.	34.00
Candlesnuffer. Baby girl in bonnet and coat, blue buttons, blond hair. Arms outstretched. Standing on circular upright base. 128mm.	90.00
Clock, shaped, hands at 9.28. 83mm.	22.00
Coal Hod. 85mm.	6.00
Coal Hod, solid. 42mm.	12.50
Coal Scuttle. 60mm.	6.00
Coal Scuttle, helmet-shaped. 83mm.	10.00
Dog Kennel. 62mm.	12.50
Dust Pan. 94mm long.	15.00
Inscribed: Who said dust.	20.00
Fireplace, with a kettle and teapot in the hearth, green mantel cloth and dogs and clock on the mantelpiece. (Lustre). Found inscribed: By my Ain Fireside or East, West, Home is best. 85mm.	27.50
Fireplace with clock and dogs on mantelpiece, cauldron on fire and black cat by side. Inscribed as above or East or West, Home is Best (Lustre) or By my ain Fireside. 80mm.	30.00
Flat Iron, can be found in lustre. 2 sizes: 67mm.	16.50
77mm.	16.50
Frying Pan. Rd. No.537474. 110mm long.	17.00
Girl, Toddler, with outstretched arms on circular plinth, inscribed: Diddle'ums. Some colouring to face and bonnet. 130mm.	80.00
Grandfather Clock, Model of, inscribed: Make Use of Time... No. 389. 2 sizes: 105mm.	19.50
135mm.	22.00
Grandfather Clock, inscribed: Gude morn. 2 sizes: 105mm.	17.00
135mm.	22.00
Kettle, fixed lid, inscribed: Polly put the kettle on, we'll have some tea. 80mm.	22.00

(The) Old Armchair, solid arms, with verse or inscribed: Jolly Good Luck. (Lustre) 88mm.	14.50
(The) Old armchair, open 'barley twist' arms, with verse. 120mm.	15.50
Pillar Box GVR, found inscribed: If you haven't time to post a line here's the pillar box. 73mm.	13.50
Inscribed £20.00	
Pillar Box ER VII. 72mm.	24.00
Rocking Chair. 98mm.	22.50
Saucepan with lid. 100mm long.	19.50
Shaving Mug. 58mm.	9.50
Sofa, can be inscribed Jolly Good Luck 90mm long, 64mm high. (Lustre).	19.50
Spinning Wheel, found inscribed: Model of ye olde spinning wheel or more rarely: The exact model of 14th Century spinning wheel. 74mm.	20.00
Stool, three-legged. 40mm.	9.50
Sundial, shaped. 80mm.	7.50
Sundial, bulbous. 76mm.	9.50
Sundial, round, inscribed: Model of ye olde English sundial, and What' o'clock. lifes but a walking shadow. No. 525.	
3 sizes: 120mm.	14.50
330mm	14.00
140mm.	14.00
Sundial, square. Inscribed: Let others tell of storms & showers, I'll only count the sunny hours. 86mm.	12.50
Time Glass Egg Timer. 60mm.	22.00
Thimble. 40mm.	25.00
Trug or wooden basket. 78mm long.	12.50
Valise (or travelling case) with 2 straps. 55mm long.	10.00
Village Water Pump, 3 varieties:	
Round. 88mm.	16.00
Square. 100mm.	16.00
with trough. 115mm.	20.00
Warming Pan, model of can be inscribed: Sally warm the bed. No.392. 127mm long.	15.00
Wheelbarrow, high sides. 95mm long.	20.00

Comic/Novelty

Altar Inkwell with two orange and black candle holders and Buddha-like figure as cover for inkwell. Rare complete. Can be found inscribed: So Y Kik the god of luck and cheerfulness. Add £10.00 if so inscribed. (Lustre).90mm long.	60.00

Ashtray, with cigarette transfer
inscribed: *Who burnt the cloth?*
110mm dia.   23.00
Baby Girl Handbell, with clapper.
100mm.   27.50
Beaver, man with very long beard on
base, some colouring. 120mm.   145.00
Billiken, flat faced grotesque type.
63mm.   7.00
Billiken sitting on high backed chair
with thumbs raised, inscribed:
Thumbs up. 84mm.   12.00
Billiken without chair. 84mm.   7.50
Black Girl in hip bath, black water
and red bow inscribed: *I'se making
ink*. Can be lustre. 80mm long.   80.00
Black Girl in hip bath, different from
above, with high back, same
inscription. 85mm long.   80.00
White.   45.00
Choir Boy Handbell. 88mm.   24.50
Clown, bust, inscribed: *Put me
amongst the girls*. Some colouring.
75mm.   30.00
Humpty Dumpty: see sports.
I'm forever blowing bubbles. Pears
advert Blue Boy blowing bubbles.
Clothes blue, bubble and bowl
lustre. Can be found all in lustre.
110mm.   75.00
Ye Jester awake, Ye jester asleep double
faced bust.
2 sizes: 70mm.   22.50
            84mm.   25.00
(Only larger size found inscribed)
John Citizen, man carrying sack
inscribed: *Housing, unemployment,
taxes*. Hat and face coloured.
(Lustre)
95mm.   125.00
white.   70.00
Negro Minstrel, bust, verse by
Eugene Stratton. 85mm.
white.   70.00
coloured face.   90.00
Oval Rich Tea, brown biscuit on
white base.   50.00
Policeman hailing: *From...* 138mm. 65.00
Policeman with raised hand,
inscribed: *A policeman's lot is not a
happy one*. 140mm.   70.00
Sack of Meal with mouse peeping
out. Mouse can be coloured grey.
75mm.   22.00

Suffragette Handbell inscribed:
Votes for Women and *She shall have
Votes*. 100mm.   65.00
Tortoise, standing wearing a blue
policeman's helmet. 65mm.   60.00
Truck of Coal, *Black diamonds from*.
or *Black Diamonds* rarely
inscribed *Brought down from
Sunderland*, add £10.00. Can be
found in lustre. 2 sizes:
60mm long, 95mm long   40.00
Weighing Machine inscribed: *Try
your weight*. 120mm.   50.00
Yes we have no bananas, oval dish
with yellow bananas. 115mm.
Can be found in lustre.   17.00

Cartoon/Comedy Characters
Jackie Coogan, coloured or pearl
lustre figure of boy film star,
attached to white tree trunk,
ink well with lid. 73mm.   55.00
Harry Lauder, bust, with red bobble
on hat and coloured thistle.
80mm.   30.00
All white.   22.00
Ally Sloper, bust, inscribed: *Vote for
Sloper* etc. Some colouring.
2 sizes: 85mm.   40.00
            100mm.   55.00
Bonzo Dog, standing upright, not
named. Red tongue. 110mm.   30.00
Bonzo Dog, with pink & green bug
his tail. Inscribed: *When you are
on to a good thing stick to it*. Can
be found unnamed.   115.00
Felix the Cat on hat box or
rectangular base, inscribed:
Felix kept on walking.
Coloured Felix, swastika and
horseshoe on base (lustre base).
75mm.   250.00
Felix the Cat on lustre or rust
armchair, with Felix inscription.
Coloured Felix. 75mm.   125.00
White Felix.   85.00
Felix the Cat on ashtray:
Spade 95mm   100.00
Diamond   100.00
Felix the Cat on (lustre) pillar box,
with Felix inscription.
Coloured Felix.
115mm.   125.00

Felix the Cat on lustre sofa, with
Felix inscription. Coloured Felix.
90mm long.   125.00
Felix the Cat on *Hatpins* box and lid.
80mm long.   110.00
Felix the Cat on Trinket box, with
Felix inscription.
Coloured Felix. 93mm long.   110.00
White Felix.   85.00
Felix the Cat on rectangular base, a
much larger and well modelled
Felix than the above, with Felix
inscription. 82mm (very rare).
Coloured Felix.   300.00
White Felix.   125.00
Winkie the Gladeye Bird, some
colouring. 68mm.   23.00
Winkie the Gladeye Bird, red eyes,
one shut. 68mm.   23.00
Woody Woodpecker, fully coloured.
63mm.   50.00

Alcohol

Beaker, inscribed: *Tak a Thimblefull.*
No.153. 45mm.   7.00
Beer barrel on stilts. XXX in red on
sides. 57mm.   6.50
Bottle with solid top. 92mm.   7.50
Bottle with cork. 2 sizes:
70mm and 94mm.   7.50
Can be found with Bass sign on
reverse and *Bass & Co.'s. Pale Ale.*   13.00
Drunkard leaning on lamp-post,
fully coloured on ashtray.
Inscribed: *Show me the way to go
home* and *Swat a night Boys Hic,
Snow Usse Hic.* (Lustre.) 112mm.   75.00
Drunkard wearing top hat, sitting in
stocks. 80mm.   25.00
Gin bottle, inscribed: *Have a drop of
gin old dear.* 95mm.   22.00
Hand holding beaker of frothing ale
inscribed: *Good health.* Some
colouring. 88mm long.   14.50
Hip Flask.   10.00
Man sitting with beer barrel and
glass, some colouring. (Lustre).
Inscribed: *Beer Hic Beer Hic
Glorious Beer Hic.* 70mm.   55.00
Monk holding beaker, with verse: *A
Jovial Monk am 1.* 113mm.
Can be found with black cap, add
£10.00.   17.00

Mr. Pussyfoot, holding umbrella
with one foot on bottle of Scotch,
inscribed: *No home in Scotland.*
135mm coloured figure.   100.00
No colouring   65.00
(Mr. Pussyfoot was an American
Prohibitionist).
Soda Syphon. 100mm.   12.50
Thistle Vase. *Just a wee deoch and
doris, just a wee drap thats a'.*
50mm.   6.00
Toby Jug, with verse: *No tongue can
tell. No heart can sing How I love a
drop of drink.* Can be found
inscribed: *This jug is an exact copy
in miniature of the old Toby jug.*
No.413.
2 sizes: 68mm.   16.50
        75mm.   16.50
Can be found coloured.   22.00
Whisky Bowl, inscribed *Scuab* and
As'i coloured cross and thistles
on handles. 123mm dia.   7.50

Sport/Pastimes

Five pieces have been found
labelled British Sports Series. The
ashtrays labelled in this way have
been listed separately.

British Sports Series

Cricketer holding bat, with stumps
on ashtray base. Inscribed: *Play
M.C.C. The home of cricket formed
1787.* Coloured. Rd. No.685380.
105mm.   200.00
Goal with Keeper and Ball on ashtray,
inscribed: *League Football first
played 1888.* Some colouring.
Can also be found inscribed *Now
the Magpies,* with the goal keeper
in black and white strip.
100mm long.   160.00
Golfer standing with Club on ashtray.
94mm.   90.00
Coloured version.   150.00
Humpty, Dumpty sat on a Wall.
Humpty on wall on ashtray, some
colouring. With inkwell inset.
97mm.   150.00
Tennis player holding Racquet aloft
in front of net. Inscribed: *40 Love.*
Some colouring.
Regd. No. 684704. 83mm.   125.00

Other Sporting Items

Cricket Bag. 105mm long.	16.50
Cricket Bat. 118mm long.	80.00
Cricketer carrying bat, flat figurine on green base. Some colouring. 115mm (rare).	200.00
Curling stone, can be inscribed: *Soop-up.* 61mm dia.	24.50
Dice Pin Box and Lid, with black spots. 50mm square.	15.00
F.A. Cup., can be found in yellow. 100mm.	16.00
Inscribed *F A Cup*	30.00
Can be found inscribed: *The English cup won by Cardiff City 1927*	37.50
Footballer with football, arms outstretched, some colouring. 110mm.	100.00
Games Spinner and Match Holder on shield ashtray, inscribed: *Put and take: yer ash: a match.* 90mm long.	65.00
Golf Ball, can be found inscribed:	16.50
The ancient game of golf was first played in 1448. 50mm. Add £5.00.	
Golf Ball on Tee Salt Pot, coloured. 50mm.	17.00
Golf Club, can be found inscribed: *Fore,* or as above or both. 75mm.	26.00
Jockey standing on base, holding saddle and crop, silks can be blue/black, yellow/blue, red/black, green/black, orange/black or yellow/black. 121mm.	110.00
Jockey on Racehorse, rectangular base, silks can be blue/green, blue/brown, green/yellow red/black or red/yellow. Very occasionally the horse is found painted black. Can also be found with inscription: for example: *Ala Baculia: St Leger first run 1876.* 110mm long.	110.00
Jockey on Racehorse (comical) with real hair tail (often missing) on ashtray base, some colouring. Inscribed: *Horsey keep your tail up.* 102mm.	50.00
Jockey on racehorse wearing coloured silks on horseshoe base. Inscribed: *Humorist winner of the Derby 1881 Donoghue Cup.*	125.00

Racehorse on oval base.	
3 sizes: 118mm long.	115.00
125mm long.	115.00
140mm long.	115.00
Roller Skate. 120mm long.	45.00
Tennis Racquet. 140mm long.	19.50
Trophy with fixed lid. (Lustre).130mm.	17.50

Musical Instruments

Bagpipes. 114mm long.	50.00
Upright Piano, open coloured keyboard, Dolphin feet. 64mm high,90mm long.	
Marked keyboard.	25.00
Plain keyboard.	19.00

Transport

Charabanc, inscribed: *Over the hills and far away.* 'DN999' on radiator. 128mm long. Found in lustre.	47.50
Double Decker Bus, with driver and outside staircase, impressed: *Putney-Charing Cross: Globe Theatre John Bull Thursday: General.* 'DN999' on radiator. 126mm long.	215.00
Luggage Trolley, inscribed: *Luggage in Advance* and/or *LMS Rly to Timbucktoo.* Can be found in lustre. 80mm long.	45.00
Motorcycle and sidecar with rider. 112mm long.	100.00
Motorscooter on oval base. 115mm long.	55.00
Open Sports Car, 'DN999' on radiator. 106mm long.	50.00
Punt, with two women, some colouring. 113mm long.	75.00
Saloon Car, 'DN999' on radiator. 138mm long.	100.00
Stephenson Locomotive, with detailed inscription: *Locomotion 1825. This Engine was built by Geo. Stephenson and Son, and was used at the opening of the S. and D. Rly. Sept 27th 1825.* 88mm.	140.00
Locomotive. 120mm long.	160.00
For truck of Coal see Comic/Novelty	

Modern Equipment

Gramophone in Cabinet, black record on turntable, inscribed: *Music hath charms.* Found in lustre. 92mm. Can be found coloured blue, add £10.00.	75.00

Gramophone, square with Horn,
inscribed: *HMV* or *His Masters
Voice*, with transfer of 'HMV' dog
and notes of music. 96mm. 50.00

Gramophone with dog listening to
horn, on oval base. Inscribed: *His
Masters Voice*. Some colouring. 88mm
long. Very rarely found in lustre. 70.00

National cash register with '£.s.d.'
Found unnamed but with '£.s.d.'
(lustre). 70mm. 30.00
Plain. 20.00

Radio Operator, inscribed: *Listening
in.* Some colouring. 85mm. 140.00

Radio Operator with microphone,
inscribed: *Listening in.* Some
colouring. 85mm. 140.00

Radio Operator with horn,
inscribed: *Listening in.* Some
colouring. 85mm. 150.00

Telephone, stick type, inscribed:
Hello, Hello or rarely *All alone by
the telephone* for which add £10.00.
115mm. 30.00

Treadle sewing machine, rarely found
inscribed: *Singer*. 80mm. 30.00

Footwear

Boot.
3 sizes: 50mm. 6.50
72mm long 7.50
83mm long 12.50

Tall laced Boot. 85mm. Particularly
fine. 14.00

Lancashire Clog with verse: *There's
many a factory lass wi' clogs on her
feet*. 100mm long. 8.50

Riding Boot. 65mm. 16.00
Boot pin box. 10.00
Sabot. 100mm long. 8.50
Slipper wall pocket. 105mm long. 10.00
The Famous Thomas A Becket Shoe
105mm long. 35.00
John Watersons Clog.
2 sizes: 115mm long 22.00
160mm long 27.00

Hats
Bishop's Mitre. 70mm. 13.00
Straw Boater, red/black band.
104mm long. 19.00
Boy Scouts Hat. 95mm dia. 60.00
Top Hat. 40mm. 6.50

Miniature Domestic
Barrel Jug. 47mm. 5.00
Butter Dish & lid, buttercup knob.
55mm. 20.00

Cake Plate on stem. 50mm. 6.50
Cheese Dish (one piece). 45mm. 10.50
Cheese Dish, fluted with cover.
50mm. 10.50
Coffee Pot with lid. No.271. 78mm. 9.50
Dressing Table Set comprising 2
candlesticks, 2 pots with lids on
rectangular tray. 110mm long. 25.00
Kettle. Can be found inscribed:
Polly put the kettle on. Add £4.00.
60mm. 8.50
Saucepan. 38mm. 8.00
Tea set on tray. Tray 115mm long. 25.00
Teapot with lid. 40mm. 10.50
Teapot with lid. 50mm. 10.50
Teapot with lid. 65mm. 10.50
Teapot with swan-shaped lid. 70mm. 14.50
Can be found inscribed *Polly put
the kettle on*. 80mm (beige) 26.00
Thistle Tea Pot with lid, lustre.
76mm. 20.00

Carlton also made a whole range of
small vases, pin or ashtrays, pill
boxes and trinket boxes in club
diamond, heart and spade
shapes. They can be found with
crest or transfer views. Very few
articles for domestic use, plates,
cups etc. have been found but
this is probably because they
were used and broken.
Price range: 5.00 to 10.00

Domestic
Ashtray, circular with colour transfer
of cigarette and *who burnt the cloth*
Dia 110mm 20.00
Candleholder. 118mm. 6.00
Candlesnuffer. 65mm. 5.00
Hair Pins rectangular box and lid.
90mm long. 7.50
Hair Tidy and lid with *Pins* tray.
(Lustre). 85mm. 7.50
Hatpin Holder in shape of a thistle
on leaves. 80mm. 12.50
Hatpin Holder, square, scalloped
base. 97mm. 12.50
Horse's Hoof Inkwell with lid.
Rd. No.538564. 95mm long. 14.50
Horse's Hoof Pin Box and lid.
98mm long. 10.00
Mustard Pot, EPNS rim. 58mm. 6.50

Mustard Pot with lid. 60mm. 7.00
Preserve Pot with coloured pear
  and two leaves on lid. Inscribed:
  Preserve. (Lustre). 85mm. 12.50
Salt and pepper pots shaped. 55mm. 6.00
Sugar Sifter, EPNS rim,147mm. 8.50
Wall pocket, detailed embossing
  85mm. 8.00

Miscellaneous
Hand holding crinkle topped flower
  vase (not a tulip as usually
  found). 85mm. 8.50
  Fully coloured. 17.50
Hand holding a trotter. 98mm long. 17.00
Hand bell with porcelain clapper.
  100mm. 8.50
Horseshoe. 115mm. 5.00
Horseshoe photo frame. Inscribed:
  The Best of Luck. 125mm. 14.50
Jug. Inscribed: *Measure for Measure*.
  45mm. 8.50
Thimble. 39mm. 20.00

Carmen China

Trademark used for E.A. Green, Rugby by
J.A. Robinson & Sons Ltd, Arcadian
Works, Stoke-on-Trent (Usual trademark:
Arcadian).
For details of this china and manufacturer
see Arcadian China.
Although most models and 'smalls' found
with this mark have a Rugby crest, other
English crests are also discovered. E.G.
Green, whose name often appears below
the Carmen mark, was either a wholesaler,
or more probably J.A. Robinson used this
mark to supply other buyers.
All known models indicate that this mark
was not used after the Great War. No
devices other than crests have been
recorded. Stock numbers where used
would be the same as Arcadian models.

Carmen Models
Ancient Artefacts
Model of Old Butter Pot. 44mm. 5.50
Puzzle Jug. 65mm. 7.50
Model of Vase found near Winchelsea.
  75mm. 5.50

Monuments
*Tom Hughes Monument, Rugby
  School*. 140mm. 30.00

Historical/Folklore
Model of Old Warming Pan inscribed
  Polly Warm the Bed. 125mm long. 15.00

Seaside Souvenirs

Bathing Machine 'Morning Dip
7 a.m.'.65mm.   20.00
Eddystone Lighthouse. 125mm.   10.00
Lighthouse, *Sailor Beware.* 140mm.   12.50
Scallop Shell on 3 tiny feet.
90mm long.   5.50

Animals

Bulldog, sitting, *Bill Sykes dog.* 110mm   25.00
Bulldog, Standing, *My word if you're
not off.* 128mm.   25.00
Dog, Labrador Puppy, inscribed:
Daddy wouldn't buy me a bow-wow.
75mm.   25.00
Dog, Scottish Terrier. 66mm long.   17.00
Hare. 75mm long.   15.00
Shetland Pony. 125mm long.   40.00
Tortoise. 69mm long.   9.00

Birds (including Eggs)

Egg with flat base. 44mm.   8.00
Hen roosting. 54mm.   8.50

Great War

Model of Tommy on Sentry Duty.
105mm.   85.00
Standing Sailor, hands on hips.
125mm.   115.00
Standing Nurse *Soldiers Friend.*
126mm.   85.00
Monoplane. 114mm long.   85.00
Battleship, 3 funnels and tiny gun
fore and aft. 100mm long.   30.00
Torpedo Boat Destroyer, not named.
108mm long.   26.00
Jack Johnson. Shell. 90mm.   8.50
Tommy's Hut. 104mm long.   50.00
Bomb dropped from Zeppelin.
80mm.   17.00
Bandsman's Drum. 53mm.   12.50
Officers Peaked Cap with coloured
badge and hatband. 65mm dia.   20.00

Home/Nostalgic

Chair, high-backed. 90mm.   10.00
Grandfather Clock, with
inscription: *Make use of Time.*
110mm.   20.00

Comic/Novelty

Clown, bust, inscribed: *Put me
amongst the girls.* 90mm.   30.00
Monk, standing, black cap. 112mm.   20.00

Alcohol

Beer Barrel on stand. 60mm.   8.00

Sport/Pastimes

Golf Ball with inscription. 45mm.   14.50

Musical Instruments

Banjo. 150mm long.   20.00
Piano, upright. 60mm.   17.00

Footwear

Slipper. 105mm long.   7.50

Domestic

Candlesnuffer, conical. 65mm.   5.50
Circular Match Holder. 53mm.   7.50

Cascade China

Cauldon China

Trademark used for a Northern retailer on china manufactured by Hewitt & Leadbeater, Willow Potteries, Longton (usual trademark Willow Art).

Cascade Model
Home/Nostalgia
Book. No.72. 57mm.   12.50
Vase. 57mm. (Crest of Castleford).   5.00

BROWN · WESTHEAD'S
CAULDON CHINA
ENGLAND

'CAULDON IVORINE' or 'CAULDON PARIAN CHINA' may also be impressed or printed.

Trademark used by Cauldon Ltd (Brown, Westhead Moore & Co.), Stoke-on-Trent. For details of the history of this firm see Arcadian China. As Harold Taylor Robinson amalgamated most of his concerns and restyled them Cauldon Potteries Ltd in 1920, this mark can be found impressed or printed on china which also carries any other mark he was entitled to use, these include Arcadian, Goss and Willow. The Cauldon mark was mainly used on domestic china only one of which has been found with a crest, but plates, cups and saucers and other items were obviously overstamped with other marks and crests applied to fill orders from 1920 onwards.

One 'Cauldon' model with a crest has been recorded in several sizes. This is a model of the Queen's Doll's House, which is most appropriate as Cauldon had been commissioned to produce a miniature breakfast set for the house, each tiny piece having a royal monogram. The same model of the Doll's House can be found marked Arcadian.
Late transfer decorations found on china marked Arcadian can also be found on Cauldon domestic wares, which include small floral designs, coloured tropical birds and a Lucky Black Cat from the British Empire Exhibition, Wembley.

Cauldon Models
Buildings - White
Queen's Doll's House, found both
  glazed and unglazed.
  5 sizes: 75mm (also with lid).   40.00
          95mm (also with lid).   50.00
          118mm.   55.00
          125mm.   55.00
          146mm.   55.00
Full inscriptions can be found on
  the base of these models
  sometimes with Wembley arms
  outpressed.

Animals
Chick in Egg Pepper Pot, screwbase,
  yellow chick. 72mm.   12.00

Domestic
Posy Ring in beige. 115mm wide.   10.00
Tea Plate. 155mm dia.   5.00

Celtic Porcelain

Trademark used by the Nautilus Porcelain Co., Possil Pottery, Glasgow.
Only four pieces of china have been recorded carrying this mark and these have Scottish crests. Some form of numbering system appears on the base, but these could well be paintresses marks. (The log is marked '11'.) Nothing more can be recorded about this obscure mark until more items are found.

Celtic Models
Countryside
Log Vase. 32mm.   12.00

Alcohol
Carboy.   6.00

Footwear
Ladies heeled shoe. 86mm long.   10.00

Hats
Top Hat match holder & striker.   11.00

There is also a range of crested
  small vases.   5.00

Ceramic Art Co. Ltd.

Ceramic China

CERAMIC ART C° L°
STOKE ᴏɴ TRENT

Trademark used by the Ceramic Art Co. 1905, Crown Pottery, Stoke.

One small has been recorded with the commemorative decoration of Souvenir All Souls 1912 Bazaar, Heywood.
                                          15.00

Trademark used by an unknown British manufacturer, possibly the Ceramic Art Co. (1905) Ltd., Crown Pottery, Stoke. This manufacturer also produced a few items for a Chorley retailer, called Sandifords. (See Sandifords Ceramic China entry). The quality is similar to that of Royal Vale or Royal Ivory. Only a few smalls and the shoe below have been found so far, and these have the crests of St. Andrews, Dunkeld, Stornoway, Matheson of Lochalsh Ibo'ness and The Earl of Ancaster. See also Sandifords Ceramic China.
                                          £5.00 upwards

Ceramic China Model Shoes
Dutch Sabot. 95mm long.   7 00

Challenge China

Chelson China

Trademark used by Hewitt and Leadbeater for a retailer possibly in the
Birmingham area.

Only four pieces known
Jug. 83mm with Birmingham crest.   5.00
Lancashire Clog. 85mm long.   7.50

Challenge China Models
Home/Nostalgic
Kitchen Range No. 199, with
    Kidderminster crest   18.00

Sundial No. 205, with
    Kidderminster crest   10.00

1914191 9

Trademark used by New Chelsea Porcelain
Co. (Ltd), Bagnall Street, Longton.
This firm is not known to have produced
crested china as such, but they did
manufacture Great War commemoratives
on small domestic pieces and 'smalls'. The
commemoratives take the form of a black
transfer prints of *HMS Lion* and *HMS Iron
Duke*, with four coloured flags of the
Allies and inscribed: *For Honour and
Liberty*. The colour transfers are identical
to those used by Norfolk Crest China
produced for W H Smith by Hewitt &
Leadbeater, Willow Potteries. Some items
carry the further inscription: *God Save the
King*. Peace commemoratives were also
made. These have a transfer print of
Britannia, with the flags of the Allies and
the inscription: *Peace 1914-1919 Liberty
Truth Justice Honour*. Some bird transfers,
very similar to those used in the Arcadian
range, have been recorded.

Value from £5.00 upwards for smalls. War
commemoratives £20.00 upwards.

Christop China

Civic

No details of mark available.

Trademark used by an unknown manufacturer for a retailer in the Colonies. Manufacturer possibly Sampson Hancock (and Sons), Bridge Works, Stoke (usual mark Corona) as this firm used the circle and buckle device in several of its trademarks.

This mark has only been found on one small flat sided vase, inscribed: *Souvenir, settler's centenary. Grahamstown.* and with a crest of Cape of Good Hope.   15.00

Trademark used by Taylor and Kent (Ltd)., Florence Works, Longton. (Usual trademark Florentine). The products are very similar to IVORA WARE models.
For details of this manufacturer see Florentine China.

Civic Models
Ancient Artefacts
Chester Roman Vase (not named).
    62mm.   5.50

Seaside Souvenirs
Whelk Shell. 90mm long.   7.00

Traditional/National
Welsh Hat. 56mm.   8.00

Animals
Cat sitting with long neck. 105mm.
    (This is a model of a Destroyer's
    Ship's mascot which became
    popular during the Great War).   15.00
Elephant, kneeling. 60mm.   22.50
Manx Cat. 90mm.   35.00
Toad. 75mm long.   25.00

Great War
Bandsman's Drum. 55mm dia.   12.50

Home/Nostalgic
Watering Can. 75mm.   9.50

Sport
Cricket Bag. 110mm long.   16.50

Miniature Domestic
Tea Pot and lid. 68mm.   9.50

C.J.B. & Co

Clarence China

Mark used by Arkinstall & Son Ltd., Arcadian Works, Stoke on Trent. (Usual mark Arcadian).

Clarence Models
Ancient Artefacts
Model of Jug in Kendal Museum dated 1602.
No. 210. 74mm.   5.50

Animals
Pig. *Wunt be druv.* 70mm long.   20.00

Home/Nostalgic
Grandfather Clock. Inscribed: *The time o' day.*
110mm.   20.00

Comic/Novelty
Bust of Negro with Eugene Stratton verse.
Black face, some colouring. 95mm.   40.00

Trademark used by Sampson Hancock and Sons, Bridge Works, Stoke and later at the Gardon Works, Hanley, (Usual trademark Corona), for an unknown retailer.
One piece revealed has a Wembley UDC crest.
The majority of pieces recorded are small vases.

CJB & Co. Models
Great War
Airship. 130mm.   35.00
Field Gun. 130mm long.   25.00
Ghurka Knife, 140mm long   22.00
Red Cross Van. 98mm long.   40.00

Home/Nostalgic
Gas Stove. 67mm.   10.00

Clarence Crest China

c1914-c1925.

Trademark used by Beresford Bros., Clarence Works, High Street Longton. The models either bear a close resemblance to H & L (Willow Art) models or are the same. There must have been some connection between these two firms, both working in Longton. In addition a club trump has been found with both Arcadian and Clarence Crest factory marks. It is common to find firing flaws in this china.
This firm was established in 1900 to produce china and fancy goods. Very little is known about the firm, no mark was registered and the first reference found in the *Pottery Gazette* is an advertisement in 1920. In 1921 a further advertisement announces Beresford Bros as makers of 'View Ware. "A present from . . . ", also Crest Ware'. there is no reference to this firm after 1921 and the Clarence Works belonged to Crown Clarence Porcelain Co. after 1932. One can only assume that Beresford Bros became bankrupt as so many other firms did in the thirties, or that the firm changed its name to Crown Clarence.
This mark is most often found on small vases and domestic ware. The very small range of models bore a close resemblance to those being made by other Longton firms most notably Hewitt and Leadbeater (H and L or Willow Art

China). It is possible that some of these models were purchased from H and L before being decorated and glazed but none has actually been found impressed H and L so it is more likely that designs for models were copied or bought from a freelance modeller.
A commemorative saucer has been found with a transfer print of The Four Flags of the Allies with the inscription: 'For right and freedom' and one suspects that Beresford Bros made a range of such domestic items. Only one transfer print has been recorded, a coloured Kingfisher with the inscription: *Happy Days at . . . .* The two-handled vase with this inscription and blue edging can be found on Willow Art 'smalls', and again leads one to look for a connection between Beresford Bros and Hewitt and Leadbeater, but apart from both firms working in Longton no other evidence of such a connection can be found.
No numbering systems appear to have been used.

Clarence Crest Models
Ancient Artefacts
Canterbury Vase, *Model of Roman Vase found near Canterbury original in Canterbury Museum*. No. 285.
66mm.   5.50
Highland Whisky Bowl. Model of.
90mm long.   6.00
Loving cup, 3 handled. 40mm.   6.00

Buildings - White
The old home of the Rt. Hon. D.
    Lloyd George Esq. MP.
    Llanystymdwy near Criccieth.
    70mm high, 78mm wide.   40.00
Windmill. 85mm.   40.00

Monuments (including Crosses)
Baron Burton statue. 130mm.   30.00

Historical/Folklore
James V chair. 100mm.   11.50
Man in the Moon. 55mm.   20.00

Traditional/National Souvenirs
Welsh Hat with blue band. 55mm.   10.00

Animals

Cat sitting. 78mm.	12.50
Dog, Dachsund, sitting. 75mm long.	50.00
Elephant, standing. 78mm long.	20.00
Hare. 67mm long.	16.50
Highland Bull Inscribed: *King of The Herd.* 120mm long.	70.00
Pig, standing. 95mm long.	22.50
Piglet, standing. Inscribed: *Wunt be druv.* 73mm.	22.00

Birds

Canary on rock. 100mm.	13.00
Swan. 57mm.	9.50

Great War

Soldier standing to attention, inscribed: *Our Brave Defender.* 130mm.	55.00
Nurse, inscribed: *A friend in need.* 130mm	80.00
Monoplane with revolving prop. 150mm long.	75.00
Tank with trailing wheels. 130mm long.	25.00
Field gun with screen. 114mm long.	35.00
Bandsman's Drum. 58mm.	12.50
Kit Bag, with inscription: *Pack up your troubles in your old kit bag.* 70mm.	24.50
Tommy's Steel Helmet. 76mm long.	40.00
Kitchen Range, with pot on fire inscribed: *Keep the home fires burning.* No.199. 78mm long.	20.00

Comic/Novelty

A Truck of Coal from. . Wagon of black coal. 70mm.	40.00

Sport/Pastimes

Trump indicator (2 piece). 110mm dia.	30.00
Club trump. 65mm.	7.00

Alcohol

Barrel on stand. 59mm.	10.00
One Special Scotch, Bottle. 88mm.	8.50

Transport

Open Top Sports Car. 115mm long.	45.00

Footwear

Ladies heeled Shoe, blue bow. 115mm long.	16.50

A small range of domestic china was produced bearing colour transfers of good quality.   £6.00 upwards

Clays

CLAYS ENGLAND

Trademark used on crested china manufactured by Hewitt Bros. (Usual trademark Willow Art).

For details of Hewitt Bros china see Willow Art China.

This trademark is very perplexing, a very similar mark having been used by another Longton firm - Green and Clay, Staff Street, Longton. This firm went out of business in 1891. Almost all the models found with the Clays mark as above are made by Hewitt Bros and some have been found impressed 'H Bros. Willow'. One can only guess that there must be some family connection between the two firms indicating that the mark was inherited. Another alternative thought is that Harold Taylor Robinson inherited the mark during his Empire Building days (see Arcadian). Later when Hewitt Bros sold out to him he could have used the Clays mark on some unprinted but impressed Willow Wares. This obviously needs much more research as it is one of the fascinating mysteries which make crested china marks so interesting.

One transfer print has been recorded, being of a blue kingfisher with the inscription: *Happy days at . . .* Exactly similar prints can be found marked Willow Art and Clarence (see Clarence Crest China). Stock numbers are given where known.

Clays Models
Buildings - White
Chesterfield Parish Church.
  110mm long.   50.00

Seaside Souvenirs
Lighthouse. 110mm.   10.00

Historical/Folklore
Bell inscribed: *Curfew must not ring*
  tonight. 72mm.   10.00
Burns Chair, Dumfries as corner
  seat. 77mm.   15.00
James the Fifth Chair. 104mm.   12.50
Sir Walter Scott's Chair, Abbotsford.
  80mm.   12.50

Animals
Cow, kneeling. 115mm long.   60.00
Dog, Terrier, standing. 95mm long.   24.50
Elephant, walking. 70mm long.   20.00
Lion, crouching on base, roaring at a
  tiny mouse. 110mm long.   40.00
Lion, walking, open mouth.
  121mm long.   24.00
Pig, standing No. 54. 96mm long.   25.00

Birds
Wise Owl, with verse. 98mm.   24.50

Great War
Soldier, with rifle, inscribed: *Our*
  brave defender. 132mm.   55.00
Battleship, impressed: *HMS Lion.*
  140mm long.   45.00
Submarine, impressed: *E4.*
  116mm long.   30.00
British Tank, Model of, with trailing
  wheels. No.107. 125mm long.   25.00
Field Gun & Screen. 110mm long.   35.00
Red Cross Vase No. 218. 85mm long.   40.00
Officers Peaked Cap. No.100.
  75mm dia.   12.00
Kitbag, with inscription 69mm.   30.00

Home/Nostalgic
Pillar Box. *GVR.* 76mm.   17.00
Watering Can. 73mm.   10.00

Cartoon/Comedy Characters
Baby, with arms outstretched,
  inscribed: *Cheerio.* Some
  colouring on face. 125mm. (Great
  War cartoon character, could be
  'Pooksie'.)   30.00

Sports/Pastimes
Golfball. 47mm.   12.50

Alcohol
Barrel, on stand. 52mm long.   10.00
Thistle Vase *Just a wee dock and*
  doris. 64mm.

Clifton

Trademark used by a branch of J.A. Robinson Ltd, Stoke-on-Trent. Subsequently Cauldon Ltd. (Usual mark Arcadian).
This trademark was not registered, but the china was produced in the Arcadian Works at the same time as Arcadian and Swan models (Clifton pieces have been found with badly obliterated 'Arcadian' marks.) The few Clifton models which cannot be recognised as Arcadian are invariably found in the Swan range. A three-handled loving cup with crests of Edward VII and Queen Alexandra and details of their lives, reign and the 1901 census has been found with the Clifton mark. This is very much in the early Swan style and exactly the same loving cup has been found marked Swan. One could therefore suspect that this mark was offered by the firm of C. Ford (the makers of Swan China) instead of the usual Swan. Clifton is uniformly finer than Arcadian or Swan China and it obviously was a higher class range. The crests are painted with much more care as are the coloured models. Very few late models are found and it likely that the mark was not used after 1920. (There is one exception listed here, *A Box of Chocolates* is from a Willow mould and this would not have been used in the Arcadian Works until the mid-twenties; why this piece was marked Clifton will remain a mystery.)

Some view ware has been found and also these Military badges:
Royal Berkshire Regt. 49th and 66th Foot.
Royal Military College, Camberley
Royal Staff College, Camberley
Coldstream Guards
Oxford & Bucks Light Infantry
Lincolnshire Regiment
Notts & Derby Regt.
Royal Air Force
Royal Field Artillery
2nd Life Guards.
Otherwise all recorded models carry crests.
Numbering System Many of the Clifton models are numbered. Printed or painted stock numbers can be found, and these numbers are listed where known. The stock numbers occasionally correspond with the numbers found on similar Arcadian or Swan models, but this range seems to have been stocked separately. Paintresses' marks are initials painted on the base, where the stock number is also painted, the initial being placed at the end of the numbers. (Beware of the initials O and 1.)

Clifton Models
Parian/Unglazed
Bust of Edward VII with inscription. Wearing suit, no hat. 128mm.   50.00
Bust of King George V, glazed circular base, with inscription: *King George V born June 3rd 1865, ascended the throne May 6th 1910.* 135mm.   50.00
Bust of Queen Mary, glazed circular base, with inscription: *Queen Mary born May 26th 1867.* 135mm. 50.00
Bust of *HRH Prince of Wales*, unglazed on circular glazed base. Midshipmans uniform. 132mm.   85.00
Bust of Napoleon on glazed square base. 136mm.   80.00

Ancient Artefacts
Most inscriptions begin: *Model of, so* this will not be repeated throughout the list.
Ancient Tyg. No. 58. 70mm.   5.50
Ashbourne Bushel, inscribed: *His Majesty King Charles 2nd's Royal Standard Bushel fastened to the Market Cross in the year 1677.* 95mm across.   10.00

British Bronze Pot, Ancient. 71mm. 5.00
Cambridge Jug, inscribed: *Model of
Roman Jug found at Cambridge.* 60mm. 5.50
Canterbury Roman Vase, 2 shapes:
No.22. 63mm (with handle); 5.50
No.29. 60mm (no handle). 5.50
Carlisle Salt Pot. No.110. 40mm. 5.50
Chester Roman Vase. No.131. 60mm. 5.50
*Chinese Vase originally in Hanley
Museum.* 58mm. 5.50
Derby Roman Vase, inscribed:
*Roman Vase found at Little Chester,
Derby.* No.26. 63mm. 5.50
Dorchester Jug, inscribed: *Old Jug
found in North Street, Dorchester.*
No.17. 55mm. 5.50
Egyptian Vase, Ancient, about 230BC.
No.155. 45mm. 5.50
Exeter Vase. 65mm. 5.50
Fountains Abbey Cup. No. 94. 50mm. 5.50
Glastonbury Bowl. No. 65. 40mm. 5.50
Glastonbury Vase. No. 642. 55mm. 5.50
Hastings Kettle. N8. 237. 62mm. 5.50
Irish Bronze Pot. No. 62 50mm. 5.50
*Loving Cup originated by Henry of
Navarre King of France.* 3 handled.
2 sizes: 40mm. 6.50
50mm. 7.50
Newbury Leather Bottle, inscribed:
*Leather bottle found on battlefield of
Newbury 1644 now in museum.*
No. 83. 65mm. 5.50
New Forest Roman Jug, not named.
No.174. 67mm. 4.00
Nose of Brasenose College, Oxford
(not found numbered). 103mm long. 12.50
Pompeian Vessel, not found named.
43mm. 4.00
Portland Vase in British Museum.
No.57. 60mm. 4.00
*Puzzle Jug, original in South
Kensington Museum* with usual
verse. No.147. 70mm. 7.50
*Roman Salopian Ewer found at
Uriconium, now in Shrewsbury
Museum.* 75mm. 5.50
Silchester Reading Vase. 50mm. 5.50
Southwold Jar, (not found
numbered). 95mm. 5.50
Wedgewood Vase inscribed: *Ancient
Roman Vase in the Wedgewood
Museum.* 65mm. 5.50
Winchelsea Roman Cup (3 handles). 5.50
West Malling Stoup, Elizabethan.
74mm. 10.00

Buildings - White
Highland Cottage, Model of. 60mm. 25.00

Monuments (included Crosses)
Baron Burton monument. Inscribed:
Michael Arthur first Baron Burton.
2 sizes: 130mm: 30.00
160mm. 35.00

Historical/Folklore
Ancient Coaching Hat, Model of.
No. 687. 68mm long. 10.00
Jenny Geddes Stool, not named.
42mm. 9.50
Ripon Hornblower. 130mm. 20.00
Witches Cauldron with verse.
47mm. 5.50

Traditional/National Souvenirs
John Bull bust, eyes and mouth
coloured. 100mm. 30.00
Melton Mowbray Pie, The, pie with
moulded pastry adornments,
with verse. 50mm. 25.00
Scotsman, bust in Tam O'Shanter,
black pom-pom and coloured
thistle with verse: *Will you stop
your tickling Jock* .... 95mm long. 30.00
Thistle Vase. 93mm. 5.50
Ladies of Llangollen. 115mm. 120.00
Welsh Lady, bust, with inscription:
*Wales! Wales! My Mother's sweet
home in Wales* etc. With black
welsh Hat, with longest place name
and coloured chequered shawl.
80mm. 25.00
Welsh Leek. 95mm. 5.50
Welsh Tea Party,
2 sizes: 55mm. 40.00
95mm. 50.00

Seaside Souvenirs
Lifeboat inscribed: *Margate Lifeboat,
friend to all nations.* 118mm long. 20.00
Clam shell menu holder. 62mm. 10.50
Mr. Punch, bust, some colouring
red hearts on cheeks.
Rd. No. 524786 80mm. 50.00
Scallop shell inkwell *We're aye prood
tae hear from ye.* 93mm. 10.00

Countryside
Acorn. 42mm. 6.50
Haystack, circular. 58mm. 8.50

Animals

Bear and Ragged Staff, impressed:
WARWICK on base. No. 339.
85mm. — 50.00

Cat, angry, standing with arched
back, green eyes. 62mm. — 14.50

Cat The Cheshire inscribed: *The smile
that won't come off.* 95mm. — 12.00

Cat, long necked and sitting, can be
inscribed: *My word if you're not off.*
108mm. — 14.00

Bill Sykes Dog, brown eyes, inscribed:
My word if you're not off. 105mm. — 25.00

Elephant walking. Can be found
inscribed: *Baby Jumbo.* No. 237.
70mm. — 30.00

Frog, open mouth and green eyes,
inscribed: *Always croaking.* 80mm. — 25.00

Hare. No.10. 73mm high, 80mm long. — 16.00

Lion, walking. Inscribed: *King of the
Forest.* 110mm long. — 26.00

Sussex Pig, Model of, standing
inscribed: *You can push or you can
shuv but I'm hanged if I'll be druv.*
No.148.

2 sizes: 78mm long. — 20.00

94mm long (fat). — 22.50

Polar Bear, standing. 135mm long. — 80.00

Pony, Shetland.

2 sizes: 105mm long. — 40.00

120mm long. — 40.00

Teddy Bear, sitting. 90mm. — 26.50

Birds (including Eggs)

Chick emerging from egg.
72mm long. — 11.00

Cockerel, standing. Inscribed: *Cock
O'th'North* 100mm. — 20.00

Egg. 44mm. — 8.00

Owl. 69mm. — 20.00

Great War

Despatch rider, Model of, on
motorbike. 120mm long. — 95.00

Sailor, bust, inscribed: *HMS
Dreadnought* and *The handy man.*
95mm. — 47.50

With verse: *Hearts of Oak.* — 55.00

Sailor, bust impressed: *HMS Queen
Elizabeth.* 92mm. — 47.50

Soldier standing to attention with
rifle over shoulder. 137mm. — 200.00

Soldier, bust inscribed: *Territorial*
with verse *'It's the Soldiers of the
King'.* 95mm. — 50.00

Monoplane, movable prop.
155mm long. — 80.00

Battleship, impressed *HMS Lion.*
140mm long. — 47.50

British tank model of with trailing
wheels. 125mm long. — 30.00

Tank, Model of. 116mm. — 25.00

Tank with inset wheels.
127mm long. — 19.50

Red Cross Van. 90mm long. — 40.00

Howitzer (not found named).
115mm long. — 22.00

Field Gun with Screen. 112mm long. — 35.00

Trench Mortar. 70mm long. — 22.50

Bomb dropped from Zeppelin, Model of.
80mm. — 17.00

Canister Bomb, Model of. 60mm. — 22.50

Colonial Hat, Model of. 88mm wide. — 20.00

Glengarry. 95mm long. — 22.50

Officers Peaked Cap. 65mm long. — 22.50

Kitbag with verse: *Pack up your
troubles.* 75mm. — 25.00

Anti Zeppelin Candle holder 62mm. — 22.50

Sandbag. 73mm long. — 26.50

Trench Lamp. 67mm. — 21.00

Home/Nostalgic

Anvil on circular base. No. 25.
68mm. — 7.50

Bellows. 95mm long. — 14.50

Bucket. No. 92. 75mm. — 6.50

Dustpan. 110mm long. — 10.50

Flat Iron Stand. 70mm. — 8.00

Grandfather clock inscribed: *Top O'
th' morn.* 100mm. — 20.00

Grandfather Clock, Model of a,
inscribed: *Make use of time let not
advantage slip. Shakespeare.*
No. 209. 108mm. — 20.00

Pillar Box, inscribed: *G V R if you
haven't time to post a line here's the
pillar box.* 60mm. — 18.00

Saucepan and lid. 73mm long. — 8.00

Comic/Novelty

2 Black boys heads popping out of
box, inscribed: *Box of chocolates.*
Some colouring. 60mm. — 55.00

Clown figure candlesnuffer, baggy
suit, hands in pockets. 102mm. — 47.50

Clown, standing, hands on hips,
wearing baggy suit. 104mm. — 47.50

Clown, bust, inscribed: *Put me
amongst the girls.* Some colouring.
No. 12. 80mm. — 15.00

Jester, double-faced bust inscribed:
Ye jester awake and *ye jester asleep*   15.00
Policeman on duty, with verse.
148mm.   65.00
Suffragette Handbell. Inscribed:
*Votes for Women. This one shall
have a vote.* 105mm.   65.00

Cartoon/Comedy Characters
Ally Sloper, bust. Inscribed: *Good
Health Old Man.* 90mm.   40.00

Alcohol
Barrel on stilts. 60mm.   7.50
Monk, holding glass with verse.
112mm.   19.50

Sport/Pastimes
Football. 50mm dia.   9.50
Rook chess piece. 55mm.   7.00

Musical Instruments
Banjo. 152mm long.   20.00
Lute,162mm long.   40.00

Transport
4 Seater Open Car, folded down
hood. 140mm long.   50.00

Hats
Luton Boater, coloured ribbon.
95mm long.   22.50
Straw Boater, not found named.
78mm dia.   12.50

Footwear
Ankle Boot. No. 251. 85mm long.   6.50
Oriental Slipper. No.352.
105mm long.   7.50

Miniature Domestic
Cheese Dish and lid, inscribed:
Cheddar Cheese. 50mm.   22.00
Teapot and lid, whorl rim. 65mm.   00.00
Thimble *Tak a Thimble full.* 43mm.   20.00

Domestic
Cone candlesnuffer. 68mm.   5.50
Hair pins box with domed lid,
rectangular. 100mm long.   8.00
Napkin ring *I.* 38mm.   7.00

Recorded Numbered Ornamental Wares
No.16. Globe Vase. 46mm.   4.00
No. 37. Vase, wide mouth. 50mm.   4.00
No. 40. Trinket Box and lid,
horseshoe shaped. 65mm long.   6.00
No. 45. Trinket Box and lid, spade
shaped. 40mm.   6.00
No. 63. Pot on 3 small feet. 41mm.   4.00
No. 72. Jug. 60mm.   4.00
No. 74. Jug. 82mm.   4.00
No. 88. Jug with banded neck. 75mm.   4.00
No.100. Vase. 53mm.   4.00
No. 141. Vase. 47mm.   4.00
No.144. Vase. 50mm.   4.00
No.145. Vase. 53mm.   4.00
No.146. Vase. 50mm.   4.00
No.215. Vase. 60mm.   4.00
No. 216. Vase. 60mm.   4.00
No. 217. Vase. flat bottomed. 37mm.   4.00
No. 303. Vase. 52mm.   4.00
No. 305. Beaker. 34mm.   4.00
No. 532. Jug. 70mm.   4.00
No. 579. Loving Cup.   6.00
No. 587. Taper Vase. 60mm.   4.00
No. 666. Crinkle topped vase. 40mm.   4.00
Found not numbered. Trinket Box
and lid, heart shaped. 40mm.   6.00

Clifton China

1908-27 (with slight variation).

Trademark used by Wildblood, Heath and Sons (Ltd), Peel Works, Longton. The models show great resemblance to those of H & L - Willow Art, also working in Longton and later wares are identical to Arcadian models. Wildblood, Heath and Sons (Ltd) made china, mostly hotel and badge ware from 1899 to 1927. Crested china was produced from around 1907 when they first advertised Arms Ware. The production of arms ware seems to have been a small sideline for this firm as few models are found with this mark. Early wares tend to be domestic but in 1920 the firm were advertising china miniatures with crests and most of the named models were made at that date. Many of these models resemble Willow Art China made by Hewitt and Leadbeater also in Longton. There is no known connection between the two firms. so one can only speculate whether designs for moulds were bought sold or borrowed! For the most part the china is heavy and the crests are crudely coloured.

A few pieces of view ware have been recorded, including a nice *Cat and Fiddle, Buxton* inn sign. These are usually domestic items but transfer prints can be found on other models. Great War inscriptions and commemorative transfers are not found, but one interesting Military crest, *Royal Field Artillery* has been recorded.

Numbering system. Hand painted stock numbers are found on models and these are given where known. Paintressses' marks are usually initials painted underneath the stock number.

Clifton China Models

Parian/Unglazed
Bust of Queen Alexandra on round base. 137mm.	47.50

Ancient Artefacts
Loving Cup. 39mm.	5.00
Egyptian Urn, Model of. No. 130. 48mm.	5.50

Buildings - White
Wainhouse Tower. 135mm.	120.00

Monuments (including Crosses)
Burns, Statue on square base. 177mm.	30.00
Burton Statue, Burton on Trent. Inscribed: *Michael Arthur first Baron Burton, born 1837. Died 1909.*	
2 sizes: 130mm.	30.00
158mm.	35.00

Historical/Folklore
Burns chair, Model of. No. 49. 90mm.	9.50
Mons Meg Cannon. 135mm long.	22.50

Traditional/National Souvenirs
John Bull, bust of. 90mm.	25.00

Seaside Souvenirs
Lighthouse. 110mm.	7.00

Animals
Cat in Boot. No. 65. 68mm.	22.50
Cat, angry, standing with arched back. 63mm.	16.00
Cheshire Cat, still smiling, green right eye. 80mm.	9.50
Donkey. *Hee-Haw.* 120mm long.	65.00
Elephant, walking. 75mm long.	20.00
Hare. 70mm long.	13.00
Lion, crouching. 82mm long.	20.00
Lion, standing. 112mm long.	24.50
Pig, smiling and sitting on haunches inscribed: *You may push....* 72mm.	20.00
Shetland Pony. Inscribed: *A Native of Shetland.* 110mm long.	40.00
Tortoise, realistic. 93mm long.	35.00

Birds
Canary on Rock, unnamed Norwich
    Warbler. No.23. 98mm.   13.00

Great War
Airman standing to attention.
    140mm.   235.00
Sailor, standing at attention.
    Inscribed: *Our Brave Defender.*
    130mm.   55.00
Monoplane with movable prop.
    155mm long.   75.00
Beta Airship. 55mm.   115.00
Battleship, impressed: HMS Lion.
    140mm long.   50.00
Liner converted to Troop Ship, not
    named. 135mm long.   120.00
British Tank, Model of. 140mm long.   40.00
British Tank, Model of, with trailing
    steering wheels. No.120.
    130mm long.   30.00
Field Gun with Screen. No.214.
    115mm long.   35.00
Shell. No.114. 70mm.   6.00
Shell *Salt* Pot. 85mm.   6.00
Kit Bag with verse: *Pack up your*
    troubles. 72mm.   25.00
Bugle. 72mm long.   26.50
Drum. 65mm dia.   12.50
Tommy's Steel Helmet. 75mm long.   40.00
Military Dress Hat (Pickelhaube),
    with spike. 52mm high,
    62mm wide.   40.00
Edith Cavell memorial. 116mm.   20.00

Home/Nostalgic
Anvil. 88m long.   7.50
Shaving Mug. 65mm.   8.50
Watering Can. No.126. 75mm.   9.50

Comic/Novelty
Billiken, The god of luck. 75mm.   9.00
    Inscribed   11.50

Cartoon/Comedy Characters
Standing Baby inscribed:
    One of the B'Hoys. Saluting,
    coloured face, 160mm.
    Refers to the Alsager B'Hoys,
    Gentleman's Club.   30.00

Alcohol
Barrel on legs. No.85. 60mm.   6.00
Barrel on stand. No. 83.
    63mm long.   6.50

Musical Instruments
Bagpipes No. 138. 117mm long.   50.00
Lute. 160mm long.   35.00

Miniature Domestic
Cream jug. 74mm.   4.50
Cheese dish and lid, two-piece.
    60mm long.   9.00

Modern Equipment
Horn gramophone square base.
    No.27. 103mm.   25.00

Domestic Wares
Hexagonal and octagonal salt pots
    can be found inscribed: *Salt.* Jugs,
    beakers and small vases can also
    be found.   from £4.50
Menu holder, scallop shell on coral
    base. 63mm.   8.00

Miscellaneous
Bell. No.12. 55mm.   5.50
Hand holding Tulip. 80mm.   6.00

Colleen China

Collingwood

Trademark unidentified but could possibly be Belleek. It is similar to Shamrock China.

Colleen China Models
National Souvenirs
Bust of *John Redmond MP 1914*. (The bust is hollow and has a Wexford crest).137mm.   65.00

Domestic
Water Cooler. 63mm.   5.00

1924-30.

Trademark used by Collingwood Bros (Ltd.), St. George's Works, Longton.
Collingwood Bros manufactured china from 1887 to 1957. The firm produced very little crested ware, but they did make 'smalls' with the Wembley Lion symbol to celebrate the Wembley British Empire Exhibition 1924. Such souvenirs are very popular not only with crested china collectors but collectors of British Empire Exhibition memorabilia. Only one cup and saucer with the arms of Dublin has been recorded.
from £7.50

Columbian China

Coral Porcelain

Trademark used by the Coral Porcelain Co. also known as the Scottish Porcelain Co. This would appear to be a Scottish manufacturer producing for the Scottish market.

A range of 'smalls' with Scottish crests was produced, in addition to the models below.

£4.00 upwards

Coral Porcelain Models
Home/Nostalgic
Cradle on Rockers. 60mm long.
(Similar to Nautilus).   9.50

Traditional/National Souvenirs
Thistle Vase. 55mm.   6.00

Trademark used by an English manufacturer for export to British Columbia. A range of small vases bearing the crest of British Columbia were produced. Any of the firms known to have made crested china for the Colonies could have produced this china.

Columbian China Models
Vase. 60mm.   5.00

Home/Nostalgic
Match striker. 45mm.   7.00

The Corona China

Mark used between c1910-1937. The mark is sometimes found without the manufacturers name but with the addition at the base of the initials RBW - These may possibly be retailers initials.

Trademark used by Sampson Hancock (& Sons), Bridge Works, Stoke and later at the Garden Works, Hanley (renamed Corona Pottery).

Sampson Hancock and Sons was an old established firm of earthenware manufacturers, founded in 1858. On May 9th, 1900 Mr Sampson Hancock a prominent Wesleyan died, and the business was then carried on by his sons. The firm made domestic pottery of all kinds and later introduced high class semi-porcelain and ivory ware to their range, producing an extensive range of decorated dinner ware, toilet ware, flower pots, vases and jugs for the home, Australian and colonial markets. Before the Great War they were represented in London by M.V.V. Adams and had showrooms at 9 Charterhouse Street, Holborn Circus. Hancocks seem to have produced crest china in quantity as an emergency measure to see them through the war years when skilled labour was unavailable. Unlike other established potters they do not appear to have advertised this line, although as early as 1906 they announced that they made 'Art Trinket Wares'. Hancocks exhibited their 'Corona Ware' at the 1920 British Industries Fair but there is no indication that crested china formed a large part of the display. In 1924 the firm brought out a parian statuette of *Our Prince*, in civilian clothes complete with walking stick, modelled by P. Bryant Baker. The statuette came in three sizes and was specially designed to be sold to visitors to England for the British Empire Exhibition. (No record can be found of the firm actually exhibiting at Wembley in 1924 or 1925.) As yet no parian or unglazed models marked Corona have been recorded including *Our Prince*, although a glazed model of the Prince of Wales at his Investiture exists marked *Duchess*, which was another trademark used by the firm (see DUCHESS CHINA).

S. Hancock and Sons (Potters Ltd), Hanley, a title used from 1935, was put into the hands of the Receiver, R.E. Clark on 23rd March, 1937 - yet another victim of the Depression.

The company C. J. Bisson & Co. of 83 Liverpool Rd, Stoke-on-Trent were featured in *The Pottery Gazette & Glass Review* on 1st June 1920 as having been specialising in heraldic china for some years. An accompanying photograph shows a selection of their wares, which appear to be from the Corona range.

The Corona models are not very original, showing the usual range of animals, Great War and miscellaneous souvenirs in reasonably fine china with pleasant crests. It seems likely that the firm stopped making china miniatures in the early twenties as models have not been found decorated with other devices. There are a few pieces bearing coloured views but these are small pots and jugs and would have been made before the War. Hancocks did make a large number of Great War commemoratives: usually four flags of the Allies and inscribed: *European War 1914*. These have an unusual border of European flag bunting around the necks of vases and jugs. Also transfer prints of Generals decorated in the same way have been found and probably other Great War leaders were commemorated similarly.

The following WWI transfers/badges have been found with Corona or Duchess marks:

1st Life Guards
Black Watch
12th Lancers
Royal Berkshire Regiment
Royal Irish
Royal Engineers (2 types, one with 1 figure, another with 3 figures)
Union Jack (with Jellicoe inset)
Waiting (sailor and ship)
5th North Staffs
The Man in Khaki
The King's Own Yorkshire Light Infantry
The 13th County of London Regt
Princess of Wales Yorkshire Regiment
The Royal Standard (2 types with General French or Kitchener inset)
The 1st Grenadier Guards
Numbering system. Early crested models and Great War commemoratives can be found with gold or black painted stock numbers. These are recorded where known in the following lists. Paintresses' marks are a series of coloured dots or squiggles found near the trademark.

Corona Models
Ancient Artefacts
Aberdeen Bronze Pot. 58mm.	5.50
Canterbury Leather Bottle. No.156.	5.50
Chichester Ewer. 60mm.	5.50
Glastonbury Bowl. 42mm.	5.50
Hastings Kettle. 57mm.	5.50
Lincoln Jack. No.123. 57mm.	5.50
Loving Cup, 3 handled. 70mm.	6.00
Newbury Leather Bottle, not named. 72mm.	5.50
Puzzle Jug. No.148. 70mm.	6.50
Salisbury Kettle. No.222. 104mm.	5.50
Shrewsbury Roman Salopian Ewer. 60mm.	5.50

Buildings - White
Ann Hathaway's Cottage. 95mm long.	14.00
Blackpool Tower. 139mm.	9.50
Bottle Oven (inside of). 82mm.	16.50
Bridge, with grassy banks. 134mm long.	20.00
Canterbury Cathedral, West Front. 137mm.	40.00
Clifton Suspension Bridge. 115mm long.	75.00
Cottage. 60mm long. (This is identical to the model usually found marked British Manufacture.)	10.00
Crosthwaite Church, Keswick. 110mm long.	65.00
St. Osyth Priory, unnamed. 75mm.	50.00
York Cathedral, West Front. 115mm.	25.00

Monuments (including Crosses)
Bunyan's Statue. 165mm.	20.00
Tom Hughes Monument, Rugby. 136mm.	30.00
John Ruskin Memorial. 105mm.	17.50

Historical/Folklore
Mary Queen of Scots Chair Edinburgh Castle. 80mm.	9.50
Noah's Ark. 95mm long.	10.00

Traditional/National Souvenirs
Laxey Wheel. 80mm.	35.00
Medieval Queen in Cloak. 140mm.	35.00
Welsh Harp. 90mm.	9.50
Welsh Hat, can be found with longest place name round brim. 45mm.	10.00
With wording	13.50

Seaside Souvenirs
Bathing Machine. 71mm.	14.50
Canoe. 102mm long.	9.50
Lighthouse, not named. 105mm.	6.50
Lighthouse, with steps. 115mm.	8.50
Beachy Head Lighthouse, black band. 150mm.	12.50

Animals
Camel, 1 hump, kneeling. 114mm long.	16.00
Cat sitting, looking to dexter, No. 344. 57mm.	12.00
Cat sitting with ruff around neck. 105mm.	30.00

Cat, sitting, bow around neck, some
colour. 100mm.   17.00
Cheshire Cat. 95mm.   7.50
Manx Cat. 60mm.   30.00
Bulldog, standing. 112mm and
120mm long.   18.00
Bulldog, standing, with black collar
and Union Jack on back. (Very
rare).130mm long.   170.00
Cow Creamer. 133mm long.   20.00
Dog, King Charles Spaniel, begging.
69mm.   12.50
Fish Vase. 60mm.   6.00
Lion, lying down. 150mm long.   24.00
Mouse, eating nut. 44mm.   25.00
Piglet, kneeling. 65mm long.   16.00
Pig, standing. 84mm long.   20.00
Pony, Shetland. 110mm long.   30.00
Rabbit with raised ears. No.166.
63mm long.   9.50
Teddy Bear, sitting, can be found
completely brown with no crest.
No.194. 85mm.   24.50
Brown   30 00
Tortoise. 72mm long.   10.00

Birds
Swan. 85mm.   6.50
Swan, posy holder. 87mm long.   6.00

Great War
Monoplane, Bleriot type with
movable prop. 145mm long.   75.00
British Airship on base.
135mm long.   35.00
Battleship. 120mm long.   30.00
Lusitania. 163mm long.   120.00
Submarine, inscribed: *E4.* 115mm long. 22.50
New submarine, Model of. 146mm
long. (This is the submarine
usually named E5 by other firms).   22.50
Red Cross Van. 98mm long.   40.00
Renault Tank. No. 272. 100mm long.   95.00
Tank with inset trailing wheels.
100mm long.   22.00
Field Gun.
3 sizes: 120mm long.   22.50
130mm long.   24.50
140mm long.   30.00
Field Gun with Screen. 120mm long.   35.00
Mills Hand Grenade. 69mm.   19.50
Cannon Shell. 100mm.   10.00
Cannon Shell Pepper Pot. 112mm.   8.50
Torpedo, Model of. No.285.
145mm long.   75.00

Bandsman's Drum. No. 208.
63mm dia.   10.00
Officers Peaked Cap. 60mm long.   12.50
Bell Tent, hexagonal tent with open
flaps. No.209. 85mm.   16.50
Gurkha Knife. 140mm long.   22.00
Flash Lamp. No.323. 88mm.   10.50
Water Bottle. 68mm.   13.00
Grandfather Clock, same mould as
usual Grandfather clock but
clockface transfer at 3.25,
inscribed: *World War 1914-1919.*
Peace signed 3.25pm June 28th 1919.
128mm.   70.00
Cenotaph. Whitehall. 145mm   16.50
Florence Nightingale statue. 145mm.   25.00
Romsey War Memorial. 160mm   150.00
Rushden War Memorial. 158mm.   125.00
A small series of vases with
portraits of General French,
Lord Kitchener and Admiral
Jellico set in the Union Jack
or Royal Standard flag marked
1914 are worth £30.00 - £50.00.
A similar series of transfer prints of
soldiers in regimental uniforms
marked *1914* are worth
£50.00 upwards.

Home/Nostalgic
Alarm Clock, with detailed face.
85mm   30.00
Armchair. 62mm.   12.50
Baby in Bootee. 80mm long.   14.00
Baby's Cradle. 80mm long: 12.00
Cigarette Case. 72mm long.   13.00
Flask, rectangular with sloping
shoulders. No. 242. 65mm.   8.00
Grandfather Clock. 120mm.   16.00
Hip Bath. 95mm long.   12.50
Jardiniere, on fixed stand.
2 sizes: 82mm.   6.00
97mm.   7.00
Pillar Box, with verse. No.171.
2 sizes: 60mm.   14.00
74mm.   16.50
Policeman's Lamp. 70mm.   10.00
Sofa, 3-seater. 95mm long.   14.50
Tobacco Pouch. 77mm wide.   9.50
Watering Can. 70mm.   9.50
Writing Slope/Desk top. No. 268.
53mm.   12.50

Comic/Novelty
Man's Head cream jug. 76mm.   10.50

Sport/Pastimes

Tennis Racquet. 132mm long.	17.00
Bishop chess piece.	
2 sizes: 61mm.	30.00
90mm.	30.00
King chess piece. 115mm.	35.00
Knight chess piece. 70mm.	16.00
Pawn chess piece.	
2 sizes: 61mm.	30.00
90mm.	30.00
Queen chess piece. 84mm.	35.00
Rook chess piece. 68mm.	9.00

Musical Instruments

Banjo. 140mm long.	17.00
Double Bass. 150mm long.	55.00
Harp. 92mm.	9.50
Upright Piano. 63mm.	20.00

Modern Equipment

Gas Stove. 70mm.	13.00
Gramophone, square with no horn, arm on middle of record. Crest is on the front edge. 57mm.	25.00

Footwear

Ladies Button Boot. No.149. 65mm.	9.50
Ladies 18th Century Shoe. No. 146.	
90mm long.	7.50
Lancashire Clog.	
2 sizes: 70mm long.	6.00
102mm long.	7.50
Lancashire Clog. Square toe and gilded buckle. 60mm long.	7.50

Hats

Top Hat. 45mm.	6.50

Miniature Domestic

Cheese Dish. 1 piece. 60mm x 80mm.	8.50
Cheese Dish and cover. 60mm.	8.50
Coffee Pot and lid. 75mm.	9.50
Cream Jug, ornate. 78mm.	5.00
Fluted Jug. 47mm.	4.00
Fluted Bowl. 65mm diameter.	4.00
Kettle with lid. 70mm & 87mm.	10.00
Tea Pot with lid, pattern in relief. No.122.	
2 sizes: 60mm.	9.50
65mm.	9.50

Domestic

Candlestick square top and base. 83mm.	4.00
Candlestick, square top and base. No. 311. 103mm.	5.00
Candlestick round top and base. 85mm.	5.00
Pepper Pot. 80mm.	6.50
Salt Pot.	
2 sizes: 84mm.	6.50
95mm.	6.50
Tea Caddy and lid. 92mm.	12.50

Miscellaneous

Horseshoe, on slope. 70mm long.	5.00
Horseshoe, wall plaque.	
60mm long.	5.00

Corona Ware

Coronet Ware

"CORONA WARE"
MANUFACTURED FOR
CROSS & C°
CHINA ROOMS
LOWESTOFT

Mark used by unknown British manufacturer, possibly Sampson Hancock (& Sons). Only one small jug has been seen with this mark.

Mark used c1910-1921 but without initials before 1917.

Mark used 1921-c1924

Originally it was thought that Coronet Ware was produced by Ford and Pointon Ltd, Norfolk Works, Hanley, who became a member of the J.A. Robinson and Sons Ltd group (see ARCADIAN) in 1919. However, further research into the ware has revealed that pieces have in every case originated either from Taylor and Kent (Florentine) or J.A. Robinson & Sons Ltd (Arcadian).

It is most probable that Coronet Ware is a trademark for a wholesaler 'F.P.. & S.', or possibly Ford & Pointon were the wholesalers. The firm of Pointon and Co

Ltd at the Norfolk Works was sold in 1917, and a new company, Ford and Pointon Ltd was formed. Pointon and Co Ltd were basically tableware manufacturers but along with practically every other firm of this kind had begun to make crested china miniatures sometime just before or during the Great War.

At Ford and Pointon Ltd crest china production would have continued along with other decorative items and tableware. In 1920 at the British Industries Fair, J.A. Robinson showed a 'New range of Coaching Scenes in the Ford and Pointon China'. When J.A. Robinson was amalgamated with Cauldon Potteries Ltd in 1920, Ford and Pointon was described as making 'Fords' china - useful and ornamental, and a selection of these wares were exhibited at the B.E.E. in 1924 as part of the Cauldon display. This mark was not used on arms ware for more than a year or two at the Cauldon Place Works. The firm seems to have ceased to exist after the Cauldon/Coalport merger in 1933.

Two early commemoratives have been recorded, *Festival of Empire, Crystal Palace 1911* and *Shakespearian Exhibition, Earls Court 1912*. Flags of the Allies Great War commemoratives are found inscribed: *War 1914*, and two military badges are known - *The Kings Own Yorkshire Light Infantry* and the *Australian Commonwealth*. There is no evidence of any other forms of decoration being used on models other than coloured views and these are rare. (No numbering system seems to have been used).

Coronet Ware Models
Ancient Artefacts

Eddystone Jug. 58mm.	5.50
Fountains Abbey Cup, not found named. 48mm.	5.50
Guernsey Milk Can. 100mm.	6.00
Loving cup, 3-handled, flared rim. 38mm.	6.00
Puzzle Jug. 70mm.	6.50
Roman Oil Lamp. 100mm long.	6.00
Salisbury Kettle. 95mm.	5.50
Shrewsbury Roman Salopian Ewer. 60mm.	5.50

Buildings - White

Cottage. 50mm.	10.00

Monuments (including Crosses)

Iona Cross, on square base. 108mm.	12.50
Irish Round Tower. 106mm.	14.00
Wallace Memorial at Stirling. 120mm.	40.00

Historical/Folklore

Coaching Hat. 40mm.	12.00
Executioner's Block and Axe. 50mm.	35.00
Judge, bust. 60mm.	20.00
Man in Pillory. 103mm.	22.00
Mother Shipton. 72mm.	10.00

Traditional/National Souvenirs

Welsh Hat. 57mm.	9.50
Welsh Hat with blue band & gold tassles. 80mm.	10.50
Welsh Lady bust. 63mm.	17.00

Seaside Souvenirs

Bathing Machine. 78mm.	16.00
Bathing Machine with figure in doorway. 75mm.	22.50
Beach Chair. 84mm.	15.50
Bermudan rigged Sailing Boat. 125mm.	22.00
Houseboat. 90mm long.	10.00
Lighthouse. No detailed size.	6.00
Punch and Judy Booth, with Punch and dog Toby. (rare)	
2 sizes: 90mm.	65.00
110mm.	90.00
Punch, bust with red nose. 83mm.	50.00
Whelk Shell. 95mm long.	6.00

Countryside

Milk Churn, 2 handles and lid. 70mm.	7.00
Pine Cone on side. 90mm long.	6.00

Animals

Camel with 1 hump, kneeling. 56mm.	25.00
Cat, large and furry, snarling. 93mm.	55.00
Cat, long necked. 103mm.	12.50
Cat, Manx. 64mm.	30.00
Cat, angry. 80mm.	16.50
Cat, sitting inscribed: *The Cheshire Cat, always smiling.* 88mm.	12.50
Cat sitting, bow round neck. 70mm.	12.00

Dog, Pekingese on cushion, begging.
93mm.   16.50
Dog, spaniel type, standing.
76mm long.   12.50
Dog, Staffordshire Bulldog. 100mm.   16.50
Dog, standing, looking left wearing
medallion. 85mm long.   25.00
Dolphin Vase. 102mm.   7.50
Donkey, walking, ears back.
90mm long.   35.00
Elephant, kneeling. 60mm.   20.00
Elephant standing, trunk curled
down. 55mm.   20.00
Elephant walking. 70mm,
116mm long.   20.00
Fish, open mouthed.
2 sizes: 102mm   6.00
120mm long.   7.00
Frog, open mouthed and green eyes.
60mm.   16.00
Frog Jug. 47mm.   12.50
Monkey, wearing coat, sitting.
75mm.   13.00
Mouse playing Mandolin, on base.
80mm.   24.50
Pig, standing, inscribed: *The pig
that won't go*. 84mm high,
94mm long.   19.50
Pig, standing. 95mm long.   15.00
Polar Bear, walking. Inscribed:)
SAM. 93mm long.   55.00
Pony, inscribed: *Shetland Pony*.
74mm.   40.00
Rabbit sitting, ears flat.
74mm long.   10.50
Rabbit, fluffy. Raised ears.
100mm long.   16.00
Seal,with ball on nose.
85mm long.   20.00
Teddy Bear. 96mm.   30.00
Toad with closed mouth. 50mm.   22.50
Tortoise. 72mm long.   10.00

Birds
Bird on rock. 90mm.   14.50
Budgerigar. 80mm.   13.50
Hen, roosting. 55mm   9.50
Kingfisher. 80mm.   35.00
Kingfisher cream jug. 60mm.   9.50
Owl. 70mm.   16.50
Parakeet. 75mm.   14.00
Pelican cream jug. 80mm.   8.50
Swan posy holder. 90mm long.   6.00
Swan. 75mm.   9.50

Great War
Bust of Sailor. 90mm.   45.00
Bust of Soldier. 90mm.   45.00
Tommy in Bayonet Attack. 130mm.   170.00
Sailor winding capstan. 113mm.   140.00
British Airship, on base.
130mm long.   35.00
Biplane,inscribed: *Model of New
Aeroplane.* 100mm long.   170.00
Monoplane with movable prop
and cross hatching.
145mm long.   75.00
Monoplane with movable prop
and no cross hatching.
170mm long.   75.00
Battleship. 115mm long.   25.00
Torpedo Boat Destroyer, Model of.
105mm long.   30.00
Submarine, inscribed: E5.
130mm long.   25.00
Armoured Car with turret. 95mm.   50.00
Red Cross Van. 90mm long.   40.00
Tank. 110mm long.   25.00
Tank. 115mm long.   40.00
Tank with large gun turrets.
120mm long.   25.00
Tank with inset steering wheels.
116mm long.   25.00
Field Gun. 115mm long.   25.00
Canister Bomb. 60mm.   21.00
German Aerial Torpedo.
80mm long.   55.00
Observer Sausage Balloon. 82mm.   47.50
Bury St. Edmunds Bomb. 83mm.   17.00
Cannon Shell. 76mm.   7.00
Zeppelin Bomb. 78mm.   17.00
Bandsman's Drum. 55mm dia.   12.00
Bell Tent. No. 204. 88mm.   16.50
Field Glasses. 64mm.   17.00
Ghurka Knife. 110mm long.   22.00
Hand Grenade. 60mm.   47.00
Glengarry. 90mm long.   22.00
Peaked Cap. 63mm long.   12.00
Sandbag. 70mm.   25.00
Solar Topee. 60mm.   30.00
Telescope, folded. 70mm.   17.00
Trench Lamp. 70mm.   22.00
Tommy's Hut, unnamed.
105mm long.   50.00
Shell. 130mm.   10.00
Water Bottle. 63mm.   17.00
Dartford War Memorial (rare).
163mm.   165.00
Cenotaph. 100mm.   10.00

Home/Nostalgic

Anvil on wooden stump. 66mm.	7.50
The Old Armchair, with verse. 86mm.	10.50
Broom head. 105mm long.	22.00
Coal Bucket. 63mm.	6.00
Coal Scuttle, ornate. 68mm.	7.50
Dustpan. 100mm long.	10.50
Flat Iron. 75mm long.	16.50
Frying Pan. 115mm long.	17.50
Garden Roller. 83mm long.	16.50
Grandfather Clock. 130mm.	17.50
Grandfather Clock. 103mm.	20.00
Kennel. 52mm.	12.50
Lantern. 86mm.	12.50
Oil Lamp. 86mm long.	8.00
Pillar Box.	
2 sizes: 60mm.	14.00
78mm.	17.00
Policeman's Lamp. 70mm.	10.00
Portmanteau. 80mm long.	6.00
Shaving Mug. 58mm.	7.50
Sofa. 82mm long.	14.50
Stool, 3 legged. 40mm.	9.50
Torch. 88mm.	10.50
Watering Can. 70mm.	9.50
Wicker Chair. 92mm.	12.50

Comic/Novelty

Baby in Hip Bath. 100mm long.	14.00
Billiken, sitting. 64mm.	7.50
Boy on Scooter. 95mm.	30.00
Bust of Mrs Gamp the suffragette double faced, smiling and fierce. 90mm.	65.00
Clown, bust. 65mm.	14.50
Truck of Coal. 90mm long.	35.00
Jack in the Box. 95mm.	28.00

Alcohol

Barrel on stand. 56mm.	5.50
Bottle of Champagne in Ice Bucket. 85mm.	12.50
Carboy. 75mm.	7.00
Drunkard, bust of (looks rather like Ally Sloper). 74mm.	22.50
Toby Jug. 63mm.	12.50

Sport/Pastimes

Cricket Bag. 110mm long.	16.00
Cricket Bat. 115mm long.	80.00
Football. 50mm.	9.50
Golf Ball. 42mm.	14.50
Golf Ball on Tee. 63mm.	14.50
Golf Club head. 90mm long.	22.50
Tennis Racquet. 95mm long.	16.50

Castle Chess Piece. 67mm.	9.00

Musical Instruments

Grand Piano. 82mm long.	22.00
Guitar. 152mm long.	20.00
Harp. 95mm.	9.50
Piano, upright. 65mm long.	19.50
Tambourine. 68mm dia.	16.50

Transport

Saloon Car. 85mm long.	40.00
Motor Horn: *Pip Pip.* 90mm long.	25.50

Modern Equipment

Cash register. 47mm.	25.00
Radio Horn. 93mm.	30.00
Square Gramophone. 55mm.	25.00

Footwear

Boot. 70mm.	6.00
Ladies Ankle Boot. 76mm long.	6.50
Ladies 18th Century Shoe. 95mm long.	7.50
Sabot with turned up toe. 90mm long.	6.00

Miniature Domestic

Cheese Dish. 2 pieces. 50mm.	8.50
Coffee Pot with lid. 80mm.	9.50
Cup and Saucer. 40mm.	5.00
Tea Pot with lid. 70mm.	9.50
Tea Pot with lid. 95mm.	9.50

Domestic

Oil Lamp.103mm long.	6.00
Salt Pot octagonal. 85mm.	5.00
Serviette ring.	10.00

C P & Co.

Craven China

Trademark used by an unknown wholesaler by Alfred B. Jones and Sons. Grafton China works, Longton, Staffs (usual trademark Grafton).
Only three models have been found so far, having the arms of Hobart and Tasmania and the third a South African badge.

Ancient Artefacts
Model of Roman Vase found at
Yaverland, (Isle of Wight).   5.50
Model of Drinking Mug, original in
Museum. No.187. 45mm.   ´   5.50

Trademark used by Wiltshaw and Robinson Ltd, Carlton Works, Stoke-on-Trent (usual trademark Carlton).
For details of this firm and the china manufactured see CARLTON CHINA.
Wiltshaw and Robinson Ltd seem to have only used this mark during the Great War and a few years afterwards. They do not seem to have used the mark for a specific retailer as crests recorded are from all over Britain but in particular Yorkshire. Great War models can be found with 'The Victory of Justice Armistice of the Great War signed Nov 11th 1918' inscription.

Craven China Models
Animals
Cat sitting, blue bow. 56mm.   20.00
Rabbit, crouching. 60mm long.   12.50

Great War
HMS Humber. 140mm long.   80.00
Cannon Shell. 75mm.   7.50
British Searchlight. 70mm.   40.00
Glengarry, with coloured thistle.
   78mm long.   22.00
Kitbag. 72mm.   24.50
Tommies Bungalow Bell Tent. 67mm.   17.00

Home/Nostalgic
Old Warming Pan. Inscribed: Sally
   Warm the Bed. 130mm long.   16.00
Sundial on circular base. Inscribed:
   What-o-clock. 127mm.   14.00
Water Pump. 100mm.   20.00

Musical Instruments
Lute. 158mm long.   30.00

Footwear
Ankle Boot laces undone.
  78mm long.   6.50
Shoe Posy Holder. 100mm long.   6.50

Domestic
Pepper Pot, owl. 96mm.   20.00
Pin Box & Lid, diamond shaped.
  100mm long.   8.00
Trinket Box, round with domed lid,
  60mm diameter.   8.00

Crescent

Trademark used by George Jones and Sons
Ltd, Crescent Pottery, Stoke.

Craven Model
Cicular Pin Tray.   5.00

Crown Chelsea China

MADE IN ENGLAND

No details of this firm are known. Only one small has been recorded, a Mug, 74mm with the Selsey Arms.

Crown China

Trademark used by Wiltshaw and Robinson Ltd, Carlton Works, Stoke-on-Trent (usual trademark Carlton).

For details of this firm and the china manufactured see CARLTON CHINA.

This mark seems to have been used up to the twenties as an alternative trademark to Carlton. No view ware or other transfer devices have been found on pieces marked Crown.

Crown China Models
Buildings - White

Cottage, two chimneys. 50mm.	10.50
Brick cottage, one chimney, on rectangular base. 48mm.	12.00

Traditional/National Souvenirs

Blackpool Big Wheel. 82mm.	20.00
Irish Harp, surmounted by crown, decorated with green shamrocks.	14.50
Jenny Jones, Welsh lady, standing figure with black hat, brown basket and red and green shawl. 147mm.	40.00
Welsh Hat, with orange or gilded band. 44mm.	9.00

Seaside Souvenirs

Bathing Machine. 70mm. *Morning dip 7.00 am*	18.00
Motorboat with driver on waves. 120mm long.	27.50
Lifeboat. 113mm long.	21.50

Countryside

Milk Churn. 62mm.	7.00

Animals

Black Cat on oval hat box. 85mm.	30.00
Cat, sitting with blue bow. 57mm.	18.00
Dog playing Banjo, inscribed: *Some band.* 83mm.	35.00
Dog (puppy), sitting with one ear raised. 83mm.	12.00
Dog, Scottie, wearing a Tam-o'shanter, some colouring. 82mm.	12.50
Pig, inscribed: You *can push...* 85mm long.	22.00
Welsh Goat on rocky base, inscribed: Y *afr Cymreig* 98mm.	75.00

Birds

Bird cream jug. 84mm.	7.50
Hen, brooding. 60mm long.	11.00
Owl, wearing black mortar board with red tassel. 75mm.	25.00

Great War

HM Hospital Ship Anglia, Model of with 2 funnels. 165mm long.	145.00
Minesweeper. *SH* and blue stripe. 115mm long.	65.00

Home/Nostalgic

Armchair, ornate with barley twist arms. 120mm.	14.50
Bellows, ornate. 93mm long.	14.50
Grandfather Clock inscribed: *Gude Morn.* 103mm.	20.00
Grandfather Clock, inscribed: *Make use of time. Let not advantage slip.* 135mm.	22.00
Portmanteau. 55mm long.	10.00
Rocking Chair. 96mm.	22.50
Sundial, square or bulbous, inscribed: *Let others tell of storms and showers I'll count the sunny hours.* 90mm.	12.50
Sundial, circular. 76mm.	12.50
Sundial, bulbous. *What O'Clock* and *Life's but a walking shadow.* 130mm.	14.00
Village Pump, round. 76mm.	17.50
Water Pump with trough. 75mm.	17.00

Comic/Novelty

I'm forever blowing bubbles. Pears advert Blue Boy blowing bubbles. Clothes blue, bubble and bowl lustre. 110mm.	75.00
Truck of Coal, *Black diamonds from* 95mm long.	25.00

Alcohol

Beer Barrel on stilts. XXX in red on sides. 57mm.	6.50
Bottle. 90mm.	7.50
Toby Jug, with verse. 79mm.	14.50

Sport/Pastimes
British Sports Series

Golf club head *FORE, The Ancient Game of Golf was first played in 1448.* 65mm.	26.00
Tennis Player holding Racquet in front of net, inscribed: *40 Love.* Some colouring. 83mm.	125.00
Can be found on ashtray base.	

Transport

Luggage Trolley inscribed: *Luggage in Advance,* etc. 80mm long.	45.00
Motorbike and Sidecar with rider. 102mm long.	100.00
Motorscooter on an oval base, 115mm long.	55.00
Open. Sports Car, inscribed: *DN999.* 105mm long.	50.00

Footwear

John Waterson's Clog. 100mm long.	24.50

Modern Equipment

Gramophone in Cabinet, black record on turntable, inscribed: *Music hath charms.* 92mm.	75.00
Gramophone with dog, inscribed: *His Masters Voice.* 90mm long.	50.00
Radio Operator with microphone, inscribed: *Listening in.* Some colouring. 84mm.	140.00
Telephone, stick type, inscribed: *Hello, hello.* 115mm.	30.00
Treadle Sewing Machine. 72mm.	30.00

Miniature Domestic

Tea Pot with lid. 90mm.	9.50

Domestic

Hair-pins, ornate box and lid. 100mm long.	7.50

Miscellaneous

Horseshoe. 105mm long.	5.00

Crown Derby

Trademark used by Crown Derby Porcelain
Company Ltd.

Crown Derby Models
Footwear
Lady's Slipper. 98mm long.   20.00

Crown Devon

Trademark used by S. Fielding and Co (Ltd),
Railway Pottery, Devon Pottery, Stoke.
This factory specialised in lustre ware
with a yellow sheen.
S. Fielding and Co established in 1879, are
earthenware manufacturers. The firm
were not kown to produce a range of
crested china and only a small number
of models, in earthenware, have been
recorded. They would all appear to be
souvenirs from the Isle of Man. The mark
above was registered in 1930 but was
probably used long before that.

Crown Devon Models
Buildings - White
Tower of Refuge, Douglas IOM,
  also found in lustre and
  always with a
  Douglas Crest. 68mm.   30.00

Traditional/National Souvenirs
Legs of Man, lustre. 101mm.   17.00

Animals
Cat, Manx. 78mm.   30.00

Home/Nostalgic
Shaving Mug. 90mm.   9.50

Transport
Racing car with driver and
  co-driver, coloured, inscribed:
  Manx International Motor Car Race.
  140mm long.   175.00

Domestic
Butter Pot. Lidded wooden tub,
inscribed *Manx Butter Pot* with
black manx cat as knob.
No. 695. 100mm.   17.00
Dish. 81mm dia.   5.00
Gravy boat with Legs of Man
  handle with matching saucer
  (pottery). 135mm long.   20.00
Pot and lid bearing a colour transfer.
  86mm.   10.00

The Crown Duchy English China

Trademark used for a Morecambe retailer
and wholesaler by Taylor and Kent (Ltd.),
Florence Works, Longton. (Usual trademark Florentine). A Hawes Crest has also
been found.

Crown Duchy Models
Ancient Artefacts
Loving Cup. 39mm.   6.00

Birds
Chicken. 63mm long.   9.00

Alcohol
Tankard. 74mm.   6.00

Miniature Domestic
Teapot and lid. 50mm.   9.50
Teapot and lid. 72mm.   9.50

A range of domestic ware all
  with Morecambe crests was
  produced.   4.00-10.00

C&SC

This mark can be found with *Heraldic* written below the shield.

C & S.C

Trademark used by Taylor and Kent (Ltd.), Florence Works, Longton. (Usual trademark Florentine), for agents Collins & Sons, Chelmsford.
See Florentine China for details of the firm.
The four crests recorded so far are of Durban, Chelmsford, Kelvedon and Saffron Walden. Saffron Walden and Kelvedon are close enough to Chelmsford for Collins & Sons to have stocked these crests, but it is a mystery as to why a model with a Durban crest was given the C & S.C. mark. Taylor and Kent were known to export arms ware, and possibly used this mark on an extra model to complete an order.

C and SC Models
Seaside Souvenirs
Yacht. 127mm.   14.50

Home/Nostalgic
Baby's Cradle. 73mm long.   12.50

Domestic
Oil Lamp with lid. 95mm long.
(arms of Chelmsford).   7.00

Crown Staffordshire

Trademark used by Crown Staffordshire Porcelain Co. Ltd, Minerva Works, Fenton. Subsequently Crown Staffordshire China Co. Ltd.
This very well known firm did not produce a range of crested china, but, like most famous firms, could not disregard the prevailing fashions. A miniature milk jug and sugar basin with crests have been recorded and this would seem to indicate that a little miniature domestic ware was made. Only one 'small' has been recorded, a tiny vase, 40mm with a colour transfer of a galleon and buoy on sea.

Crown Staffordshire Models
Miniature Domestic
Milk Jug.   5.00
Sugar Bowl.   5.00
Tankard. 61mm.   8.00

Curzon Art

CW and Co.

Trademark probably used for a retailer by Hewitt and Leadbeater, Willow Potteries, Longton (usual trademark Willow Art). This mark has been found on 'smalls' with World War I commemoratives and also on the model listed below, with a Blyth Crest.

Four flags of the Allies and the
inscription: *United we stand.*   from 15.00

Curzon Art Model
Ancient Artefacts
Wokingham Tankard. 66mm.   5.50

Trademark used by Charles Waine (and Co.), Derby Works, Longton (usual trademark Venetia China).
For further details see Venetia China and Kyle Series.

CW and Co. Models
This mark has been found on a crinkle top vase with the inscription: *Festival of Empire, Crystal Palace, 1911.* 72mm.   12.50

Animals
Polar Bear. 105mm long
   63mm high, rare.   50.00
Dog, sitting, left ear down, right
   ear up. 66mm.   14.00

Cyclone

CYCLONE
H. A. A. & S

C^YCLON_E
A.A.A.
L
$CHIN^A$

CYCLONE
A.A.A.

Three marks recorded may well have been used by different manufacturers.

Trademark used by a wholesaler of crested china manufactured by several well-known firms including Taylor and Kent and Wiltshaw and Robinson (usual trade-marks Florentine and Carlton). For details of the above manufacturers see Florentine China and Carlton China. The initials AAA L are most certainly those of a large wholesaler who could have been based in London but was more probably in the Potteries at Longton. Models have been recorded as being identical to several well known ranges but most seem to have been made by Taylor and Kent and Wiltshaw and Robinson. A great number of 'smalls' and some domestic ware have been recorded but no transfer devices other than crests have so far been report-ed, indicating the mark was not used after the early twenties.

Cyclone Models

Ancient Artefacts

Ancient Tyg, one handle, not named. 70mm.	5.50
Chester Roman Vase, not named. 2 sizes: 50mm and 68mm.	4.00
Irish Bronze Pot, not named. 50mm.	4.00
Loving Cup, 3 handled. 38mm.	5.00
Plymouth Jug. 57mm.	5.50
Puzzle Jug. 68mm.	7.00
Salisbury Kettle, not named. 100mm.	5.00

Buildings - White

Blackpool Tower. 117mm.	14.50
Cottage. 70mm long.	10.50
Crofter's Cottage. 77mm long.	12.00

Monuments (including Crosses)

Iona Cross, not named. 108mm.	12.50

Historical/Folklore

Man in Pillory. 105mm.	20.00
Man in Stocks. 103mm.	22.50
Mother Shipton. 73mm.	10.00

Traditional/National Souvenirs

Highland Cuach. 83mm dia.	6.00
Thistle Jug with pineapple moulding. 64mm.	8.00

Seaside Souvenirs

Bathing Machine. 76mm.	18.00
Bathing Machine with figure in doorway. 75mm.	22.50
Yacht, in full sail. 127mm.	20.50
Lighthouse. 100mm.	10.00
Whelk Shell. 100mm long.	7.00
Child sitting on Rock. 110mm.	20.00

Countryside

Milk Churn, 2 handles and lid. 70mm.	8.00

Animals

Cat very plump with open mouth. 88mm.	20.00
Cat smiling, could be an unnamed Cheshire cat. 76mm.	8.50
Manx Cat. 90mm.	30.00
Dog in Kennel. 85mm.	12.00
King Charles Spaniels, two in top hat. 70mm.	20.00
Elephant kneeling. 82mm long.	20.00

Monkey crouching, hands to mouth.	
90mm.	24.00
Pig, standing, inscribed: *The pig that*	
won't go. 85mm long.	20.00
Puppy sitting, looking to his master.	17.00
Rabbit. 70mm long.	12.00
Seal with ball on nose. 75mm.	30.00
Terrapin.	20.00
Toad, very flat. 72mm long.	
32mm high.	22.50
Tortoise. 75mm.	15.00

Birds

Brooding Hen, 90mm long.	10.00
Fledgling cream jug. 68mm.	8.50
Kingfisher. 80mm long.	30.00
Owl, standing. 70mm.	20.00
Pelican cream jug. 83mm long.	8.50
Swan.	9.50
Swan posy bowl. 75mm long.	9.00

Great War

Submarine, inscribed: *E9.* Blunt	
nosed. 146mm long.	50.00
HMS Queen Elizabeth 168mm long.	90.00
Armoured Car, with 3 guns on	
turret, inscribed: *RNAS.*	
116mm long.	200.00
Tank. 125mm long.	27.50
Drum. 32mm.	10.00
Shell. 75mm.	7.00
Telescope, folded. 70mm.	18.00
Cenotaph, inscribed: *The blood of*	
heroes is the seed of freedom.	
2 sizes: 100mm.	10.00
140mm.	14.50

Home/Nostalgic

Old Armchair. 87mm.	8.50
Baby in hip bath.	
2 sizes: 90mm long.	13.00
103mm long.	15.50
Coal Bucket. 60mm.	8.00
Cradle on rockers. 58mm long.	12.50
Lantern. 65mm.	9.50
Oil Lamp. 60mm.	9.00
Pillar Box, inscribed: *I can't get a*	
letter from you so send you the box.	
76mm.	20.00
Policeman's Bullseye Lantern. 70mm.	17.00
Sofa. 82mm long.	17.00
Shaving Mug. 55mm.	8.50
Suitcase, slightly open. 77mm long.	9.00
Watering Can. 70mm.	9.50

Comic/Novelty

Boy on Scooter. 106mm.	30.00
Jack in the Box. 90mm.	28.00

Alcohol

Toby Jug. 65mm.	9.50
Upright Barrel. 53mm.	8.00

Sport

Boxing Glove. 70mm long.	35.00
Cricket Bag. 110mm long.	16.50

Musical Instruments

Tambourine. 70mm dia.	12.50

Modern Equipment

Square Gramophone. No horn. Arm	
is on edge of record. Crest also on	
record. 53mm wide.	27.50
Radio Horn. 95mm.	40.00

Footwear

Lancashire Clog. 88mm long.	6.50
Oriental slipper. 100mm long.	7.00
Sabot. 95mm long.	6.00
Shoes, Ladies' 18th Century.	
95mm long.	8.50

Domestic

Hairbrush Trinket Box with lid.	
140mm long.	17.00

Miniature Domestic

Coffee Pot with lid. 65mm.	9.50
Teapot with lid. 75mm.	9.50

Dainty Crest China

The Dainty Ware

Trademark used for retailer W. H. Smith and Son of London by Hewitt & Leadbeater, subsequently Hewitt Bros. (usual trademark Willow).

Dainty Crest China Model
Animals
Fish, open mouthed. 105mm long.   8.00

Trademark used by a London wholesaler on crested china manufactured by a number of companies including Hewitt and Leadbeater (usual factory mark Willow Art) but mainly Taylor and Kent (usual trademark Florentine).

For details of Taylor and Kent see Florentine. EB and Co were almost certainly the initials of a London wholesaler. Although the majority of models marked The Dainty Ware were definitely made by Taylor and Kent, others seem to have been made by a number of other manufacturers. A 'Japan' crest has been found on a model of a mouse. The crests of the Allies were reproduced during the Great War by J.A. Robinson Ltd but any other manufacturer could have produced them if requested. Several B.E.E. 1924 and 1925 crests have been recorded with this mark, but they are unlikely to have been made by Taylor and Kent. Quite a number of 'smalls' have been recorded but there are no clues as to their manufacturer. For the most part wares with The Dainty Ware mark are rather crude and were obviously sold very cheaply.

Dainty Ware Models
Ancient Artefacts
Bronze Pot. 56mm.	5.50
Carlisle Salt Pot, not named. 62mm.	4.00
Chester Vase. 62mm.	5.50
Puzzle Jug. 60mm.	5.50
Salisbury Kettle. 100mm.	5.50
Three-handled Loving Cup. 38mm.	6.00

Buildings
Blackpool Tower. 117mm.	17.00

Historical/Folklore
Man in Pillory. 104mm.	20.00

Traditional/National Souvenirs
Welsh Harp. 97mm.	12.00

Seaside Souvenirs
Bathing Machine. 71mm.	18.00
Bathing Machine with figure on steps. 75mm.	22.50
Rowing Boat. 100mm long.	12.50
Yacht in full sail. 127mm.	22.50
Lighthouse on rocks. 95mm.	12.50
Whelk Shell. 98mm long.	7.00
Child sitting on rock. 110mm.	20.00

Countryside
Tree trunk section, hollow. 73mm long.	16.50

Animals
Bulldog in Kennel. 68mm.	16.50
Cat, Cheshire, inscribed: *Always smiling*. 90mm.	14.00
Cat, sitting long neck. 115mm.	12.00
Dogs, two King Charles Spaniels in a Top Hat. 70mm.	20.00
Dog, sitting, head on one side, blue eyes, bow to neck. 69mm.	16.50
Pup, sitting, red eyes, bow around neck. 77mm.	16.50
Elephant, kneeling. 82mm long.	20.00
Fish, open mouth. 110mm long.	7.00
Mouse. 63mm long.	20.00
Pig, sitting. 63mm long.	19.50
Seal, with ball. 72mm.	27.50

Birds
Baby Bird cream jug.	
2 sizes: 48mm.	7.50
68mm.	8.50
Duck posy holder, yellow beak.	
80mm long.	12.50
Hen, roosting.	
2 sizes: 63mm long.	9.50
85mm long.	9.50
Kingfisher, with long beak. 80mm.	30.00
Parakeet. 75mm.	10.50
Swan posy holder. 88mm long.	9.00

Great War
Tommy and his Machine Gun. 75mm.	65.00
Tank. 164mm long.	29.50
Wide Tank. 120mm long.	35.00
Red Cross Van inscribed: *EH139*. 90mm.	40.00
Battleship. 110mm long.	30.00
Drum. 30mm.	10.00
Pickelhaube or spiked military helmet.	30.00
Cenotaph. 142mm.	12.50

Home/Nostalgic
Baby in hip bath. 103mm long.	16.50
Book. 57mm.	12.00
Coal Scuttle. No. 165. 70mm.	7.00
Cradle on rocker. 58mm long.	12.00
Flat Iron. 77mm long.	14.50
Grandfather Clock. 130mm.	18.50
Invalid Feeder. 85mm long.	9.00
Lantern. 70mm.	10.50
Oil Lamp. 60mm.	10.00
Old Armchair, with usual verse. 85mm.	9.50
Pillar Box. 76mm.	27.50
Portmanteau. 78mm.	10.00
Shaving Mug. 56mm.	12.50
Sofa. 80mm long.	12.50

Comic/Novelty
Boy on Scooter. 106mm.	27.00
Jack-in-a-Box. 91mm.	25.00
Monk, jovial and plump. 90mm.	25.00

Alcohol
Champagne bottle in ice bucket. *Something good. A bottle of the "boy"*. 85mm.	17.50

Sport/Pastimes

Boxing Glove. 65mm long.	35.00
Cricket Bag. 110mm long.	16.50
Cricket Cap. 65mm.	50.00

Musical Instruments

Grand Piano. 86mm long.	25.00
Tambourine. 70mm dia.	12.50

Transport

Charabanc with driver. 118mm long.	40.00

Modern Equipment

Bundle of keys, upright on circular base. 50mm.	20.00
Radio Horn. 95mm.	30.00
Square Gramophone with arm on edge of record. Crest also on the record. 57mm wide.	27.50

Footwear

Ladies Shoe with high heel and fluted tongue - 18th Century shoe. No. 187. 90mm long.	9.50
Lancashire Clog. 88mm long.	6.50
Sabot. 70mm long.	6.00

Miniature Domestic

Cheese Dish and cover. 75mm long.	10.00
Coffee Pot with lid. 63mm.	9.50
Kettle with lid. 80mm.	9.50
Tea Pot with lid, bagware. 68mm.	14.00
Tea Pot with lid, ribbed sides. 85mm long.	9.50
Tea Pot with lid, shaped body. 56mm high,95mm long.	12.50

Domestic

Cake slice pin box and lid. 140mm long.	17.00
Hair Tidy & Lid. 75mm.	8.00
Lily flower Vase. 120mm.	8.50

Delphine Crown China

Trademark used by J.H. Middleton & Co. Longton. Staffs. 1889-1941.
A small jug has been recorded with this manufacturers mark and the retailers mark of Rito China Services Ltd of Weston-Super-Mare with a City of Wells crest.

5.00

Derwent China

Desrosier & Cie

Trademark used for J.M. White, retailer in Matlock Bath by an unknown English china manufacturer.

Derwent Models
Ancient Artefacts
Fountains Abbey Cup. 60mm.   5.50
Loving Cup, 3 handled. 36mm.   5.50

Animals
Cheshire Cat. 88mm.   12.00

Miniature Domestic
Beaker. 40mm.   4.00

Only one 67mm vase has been found with this mark, valued at £4.00 (Boulogne-sur-mer Crest).
Obviously they were a French company, but it is not known if they were manufacturers, wholesalers or retailers.

Devonia Art China

Trademark used by Hewitt and Leadbeater for a Devon wholesaler or agent (usual trademark Willow Art).
For details of this firm and the china see Willow Art China.
It is likely that WB was based in Plymouth, and that Hewitt and Leadbeater and subsequently Hewitt Bros made crested ware for them for some time and in some quantity. There are Great War souvenirs and memorials, and some later models such as Black Cats. 'Black Cat' transfers were also made for the firm. A range of smalls was produced with blue rims and coloured Kingfisher transfer, inscribed *Happy Days at ....* A great number of 'smalls' have been recorded. Crests from all over Devon can be found and occasionally other places.
A few models are from Shelley moulds, for example the Cycle Lamp.
Numbering System. Willow models often carry stock numbers and where these are known they are the same.

Devonia Art Models
Ancient Artefacts

Glastonbury Roman Ewer. 60mm.	5.50
Irish Bronze Pot. 65mm.	5.50
Loving Cup, 3 handled. 40mm.	6.00

Buildings - White

Citadel Gateway, Plymouth. 110mm.	30.00
Cottage, brick. 60mm long.	12.00
Derry's Clock Tower, Plymouth.	
3 sizes: 125mm.	16.00
134mm.	18.00
156mm.	20.00

Monuments (including Crosses)

Plymouth Armada Memorial. inscribed: *Plymouth War Memorial. He blew with his winds and they were scattered.*	
2 sizes: 170mm	34.50
190mm.	40.00
Drake Statue, Plymouth. 160mm.	16.50
Mayflower Stone, 1620, Model of. 90mm.	70.00

Historical/Folklore

Bell, inscribed: *Curfew must not ring tonight.* 70mm.	9.50

Traditional/National Souvenirs

A Cornish Pasty. 93mm long.	12.00
Bagpipes. 118 long.	50.00
Prime Cheddar Cheese round cheese, with half a slice missing. Most unusual. 63mm.	13.00
Welsh Hat. 58mm.	8.00

Seaside Souvenirs

Eddystone Lighthouse. 145mm.	10.00
Lighthouse, not named. 110mm.	7.00
Oyster Shell. 75mm.	8.00
Scallop shell on coral hatpin holder. 80mm.	10.50

Animals

Bear Polar, standing on hind legs. 82mm.	50.00
Boar, standing on rocky base. 95mm long.	70.00
Black Cat, sitting on diamond shaped astray, inscribed: *Good luck* and *Ashtray.* Impressed No. 1016. 120mm long.	30.00
Bulldog sitting. 55mm.	25.00
Cat in Boot, with bow. 94mm long.	22.00
Cat, fluffy sitting. 75mm.	22.00
Cat standing with shield around neck. 75mm.	19.50
Cat, sitting, long-necked, one green eye, one red. Inscribed *Luck.* 130mm.	18.00
Cheshire Cat Still Smiling. 80mm.	12.00
Dog, Bulldog sitting. 55mm.	17.00
Dog, Bulldog, walking. 90mm long.	13.00
Dog, Bulldog, emerging from kennel, inscribed: *The Black Watch.* 70mm long.	25.00
Dog, Collie, sitting, bow round neck. 66mm.	12.50
Dog, Collie, standing with shield around neck. 60mm.	19.50
Dog, Scottie, sitting, blue glengarry. 57mm.	0.00

Dog, Labrador. 90mm long. 24.50
Dog, Scottish Terrier, standing.
88mm long. 24.50
Elephant, walking. 52mm. 20.00
Elephant Jug. 70mm. 14.50
Lion, walking.
2 sizes: 120mm long. 25.00
150mm long. 25.00
Pig, fat, sitting. No. 137. 25.00
Pig, standing. No. 60. 85mm long. 20.00
Pig, fat, standing. 95mm long. 22.00
Pony, inscribed: *A native of Shetland.*
110mm long. 45.00
Rabbit, sitting, with alert ears.
60mm long. 9.50
Teddy Bear, sitting. 76mm. 24.50

Birds
Canary on rock. 98mm. 20.00
Chicken. No. 911. 40mm. 12.50
Swan posy bowl. 35mm. 7.00

Great War
Soldier, inscribed: *Our Brave*
Defender. 130mm. 65.00
Standing Nurse inscribed: *A Friend*
in need. 135mm. 65.00
Monoplane with revolving prop.
150mm long. 85.00
Airship, inscribed: *Beta.* 75mm long. 90.00
Battleship. 116mm long. 30.00
Battleship, impressed. *HMS Lion.*
140mm long. 50.00
Battleship, inscribed: *HMS Tiger*
160mm long. 125.00
Submarine *E4* No. 215. 125mm long. 25.00
Troop Carrier, Liner converted.
No. 213. 140mm long. 95.00
Tank, inscribed: *HMS Whippet Tank.*
120mm long. 100.00
Tank with inscriptions: *HMLS Creme*
de Menthe, Victory of Justice... &
British Tank successfully....
130mm long. 50.00
Tank with trailing wheels.
125mm long. 22.50
Field Gun with screen. 115mm. 35.00
Trench Mortar Gun. 100mm. 55.00
Officer's Peaked Cap. 80mm long. 16.50
Fireplace, inscribed: *Keep the home*
fires burning. Some colouring.
100mm long. 20.00
Drum. 56mm dia. 12.50
Cheddar War Memorial, with
inscription: *Praise God and*
remember the men of Cheddar who
died for their country in the Great
War 1914-1919. 148mm. 170.00

Plymouth War Memorial with angel
holding wreath in front of column.
120mm, 145mm. 125.00
Plymouth Naval War Memorial.
2 sizes which are slightly
different models:
140mm octagonal stepped base. 75.00
160mm 4 columns at base. 75.00

Home/Nostalgic
Bucket, rope handle. 63mm. 6.00
Coal scuttle, helmet shaped. No. 101.
53mm. 7.00
Shaving Mug. 63mm. 9.50
Sundial on circular base, with
inscription: *'I mark not the hours'.*
118mm. 10.50
Sundial on square base. 84mm. 7.50
Wheelbarrow. 118mm long. 17.00

Comic/Novelty
Billiken. 60mm. 7.50
Sack of Meal with Mouse, inscribed:
May the mouse ne'er leave yer meal
poke wi' a tear drop in its eye. 63mm. 16.50

Alcohol
Barrel. 50mm. 6.00
Barrel on stand. 59mm. 6.50
Whiskey Bottle. No. 134. 63mm. 8.50
Whiskey Bottle, inscribed: *One*
Special Scotch. 88mm. 9.50

Transport
Cycle Lamp. 83mm. 70.00
Open Tourer, 4-seater. 112mm long. 50.00

Musical Instruments
Harp. 88mm. 9.50

Modern Equipment
Horn Gramophone. 105mm. 40.00

Sport/Pastimes
Spade Trump Indicator. 66mm. 6.00

Footwear
Lancashire Clog. 88mm long. 7.00

Miniature Domestic
Cheese Dish,1 piece. 68mm long. 9.50
Cup and Saucer. 35mm. 5.50

Domestic
Pepper Pot, octagonal. 95mm. 5.00

Diamond China

Trademark used by a London wholesaler, the china being manufactured by several leading crested ware specialists, including Birks, Rawlins and Co., Hewitt and Leadbeater and A.B. Jones and Sons Ltd. (usual trademarks Savoy, Willow Art and Grafton).

The tradename Diamond China was registered by the Blyth Porcelain Co., Blyth Works, High Street, Longton. However, this firm used the initials B.P. Co. Ltd., and printed the diamond the other way up. So I think we can discount this manufacturer who never actually advertised crested wares.

H.M. and Co. Ltd. was in all probability a London wholesaler. Why the mark sometimes carries the initial W is rather a mystery. (It is just possibly the manufacturer's initial, see W.)

Some models with this mark are recognisably made by Birks, Rawlins and

Co. (see Savoy China). All pieces from this factory are rejects, usually having bad firing flaws, in which event the value of such a piece will be reduced by 25%. Minor flaws can be discounted. Others are definitely made by Hewitt and Leadbeater (see Willow Art). Although the majority of known models and 'smalls' in this range were made by these two firms, there are a few models which were not. One model, a man with his feet and head protruding from a barrel looks very like a model made by A.B. Jones and Sons Ltd. (see Grafton China). Probably many firms supplied this wholesaler.

Crests are from all parts of the British Isles, but only early models and Great War souvenirs seemed to have been made, indicating that the mark was not used on crested china after the War. However, a Ladies Night Masonic commemorative from 1922 has been found.

One piece of view ware has been recorded which could have been produced by any of the potters mentioned above. A Great War commemorative is found with this mark, taking the form of a transfer of Four Flags of the Allies and inscribed: *United we stand*. This device was used by Willow Art. Stock numbers are given where known.

Diamond Models

Ancient Artefacts

Puzzle Jug. No. 98B. 66mm.		7.50

Historical/Folklore

Bunyan's Chair, Model of. No. 42. 90mm.		19.00
Mons Meg, Edinburgh Castle, Model of. 130mm long.		21.00

Traditional/National Souvenirs

Dutch Boy. 78mm.		12.50

Seaside Souvenirs

Bathing Machine. 60mm.		16.00
Lighthouse, on rocky circular base. 110mm.		9.50
Fisherman leaning into barrel. No. 395. 70mm.		35.00
Oyster Shell on shell base. 80mm long.		6.00
Scallop Shell. 76mm.		6.00

Animals

Cat in Boot, blue collar. 92mm long.		29.50
Collie dog standing. 84mm.		20.00

Dog in kennel. No. 654. 82mm long.   14.00
Dog, Spaniel, sitting up and begging.
  67mm.   16.00
Elephant, walking. 52mm.   20.00
Elephant with howdah. No. 228.
  78mm long.   30.00
Grotesque animal. 100mm.   12.00
Lion, walking. No. 228. 136mm long.   20.00
Mouse, nose to ground. 65mm long.   30.00
Pig, fat. 93mm long.   20.00
Pig, standing. 70mm long.   20.00
Rabbit, crouching. 89mm long.   12.50
Seal. 62mm long.   20.00

Birds
Canary. 100mm.   19.50
Duck, swimming. 67mm long.   16.50

Great War
Airship (observation Balloon),
  inscribed: *Beta*. 80mm long.   90.00
Battleship, impressed: *HMS Lion*.
  140mm long.   40.00
Armoured Car. 125mm long.   125.00
Red Cross Van with 'Rolls Royce'
  front. 110mm long.   70.00
British Motor Searchlight, Model of.
  103mm long.   225.00
  This model is prone to firing
  flaws or sinking in the middle
  which would reduce its value.
Field Gun with screen. 55mm.   30.00
Trench Mortar Gun. 98mm long.   55.00
Cannon Shell. 73mm.   8.00
Balmoral Bonnet. 73mm dia.   25.00
French Trench Helmet. 80mm long.   50.00
R.F.C. Cap. 76mm long.   80.00
Glengarry.
  2 sizes: 75mm long.   25.00
          100mm long.   25.00
New Zealand Hat. 80mm long.   25.00
Drum. 56mm dia.   12.00
Tent with open flaps. 70mm.   22.00

Home/Nostalgic
Anvil. 58mm.   7.00
Watering can. No. 455. 76mm.   15.00

Alcohol
Barrel. 52mm long.   5.50

Miniature Domestic
Cheese Dish. 1 piece. 45mm long.   9.50
Cheese Dish and cover. 45mm long.   9.50
Match Holder and striker, circular
  on coil of rope. 80mm.   10.00

Disa Art China

Trademark used by Valentine and Sons, Cape
Town. China manufactured by Hewitt
Bros. (usual trademark Willow Art).
For details of china see Willow Art China.

A range of 'smalls' usually with Cape Town
and area crests and two bowls with crests
of the Municipality of the City of East
London have been recorded in addition to
the models listed below. One small has
been found with Durban crest.

Disa Models
Traditional/National Souvenirs
Dutch Girl. 78mm.   12.50

Animals
Cheshire Cat, *Still Smiling*. 88mm.   16.50
Cat, chubby, arched back. 70mm.   16.00
Monkey holding nut. 85mm.   25.00

Birds
Wise Owl winking, with verse: *An
  aged owl sat in an oak*, etc. 93mm.   24.50

Great War
Liner Converted to Troop Carrier.
  140mm long.   95.00
Submarine. 118mm long.   25.00
Kitbag with verse: *Pack up your
  troubles*. 75mm.   24.50
Pickelhaube. 51mm.   30.00

Home/Nostalgic
Anvil. 57mm.   7.50
Coal Scuttle, helmet shaped. 50mm.   8.00

Alcohol
Barrel, on side. 44mm.   6.50

Miniature Domestic
Coffee Pot with lid. 70mm.   9.50

Do! Do! Crest China

Trademark used for a wholesaler, by Hewitt
and Leadbeater and Birks, Rawlins & Co.
(Usual trademarks Willow Art and
Savoy).
This wholesaler - LL and LD - also used
another mark (see Wy Not China) on
wares manufactured by Hewitt and
Leadbeater. The mouse found with the
Do! Do! mark is known to be a Hewitt and
Leadbeater mould. (See Willow Art
China.)
However the elephant recorded was made
by Birks, Rawlins and Co. (see Savoy
China), but does not carry their stock
number. It is quite possible that they used
this mark however, their numbering
system was nothing if not unreliable. Only
a Great War commemorative crest of flags
of the Allies and one Windermere crest
have been found on models with this
mark. This indicates that the mark was
only used for a short time.

Do! Do! Models
Animals
Elephant, sitting. 70mm.   25.00
Mouse. 64mm long.   25.00

Home/Nostalgic
James the Fifth Chair at Stirling Castle. 12.50

Dolphin

Doric Herald

Trademark used by Sampson Hancock (and Sons), Bridge Works, Stoke and later at Garden Works, Hanley (renamed Corona Pottery).
For details of this china and manufacturer see Corona China.

Dolphin Models
Miniature Domestic
Cheese Dish and cover, circular.
85mm dia.	9.50
Pot, No. 105. 52mm.	4.00

Trademark used by Taylor and Kent (Ltd), Florence Works, Longton for the Glasgow wholesaler CR & Co. Glasgow. See also Atlas Heraldic and Caledonia China. (Usual trademark Florentine).

This mark seems to have been used on domestic pieces only.
Value	4.00-10.00

Dougall's "Castle" Series   DRGM

DRGM

Trademark used for a Scottish retailer by Hewitt and Leadbeater. (usual mark Willow). Only one model known with Rothesay crest.

Dougall's Model
Monuments (including Crosses)
Highland Mary, statue on plinth.
150mm.   30.00

Impressed mark found on German china.

DRGM Model
Comic/Novelty
Locomotive and coaltruck,
   condiment set, lustre.
   130mm long.   22.00

The Duchess China

Can be found with H & CL under mark instead of S. Hancock & Sons above.

Trademark used by Sampson Hancock (and Sons), Bridge Works, Stoke and later at Garden Works, Hanley (renamed Corona Pottery). Many of its shapes carry the European War 1914 decoration with crossed flags and bunting to rim. Add £5 for pieces found with this decoration. (Usual trademark Corona).
For details of this firm and their products see The Corona China.
S. Hancock and Sons usually used the alternative mark Corona on crested ware, this mark having been registered as early as 1898. Most pieces recorded are 'smalls', decorative dishes and bagware and it would seem likely that the crests were added to pieces originally designed and marked to be sold plain. Although some English and Welsh crests are found, these pieces usually carry a Great War commemorative, four flags of the Allies with the inscription: *1914 European War*. Four interesting commemorative transfers have also been recorded: 'Royal Standard' with Kitchener inset, '5th North Staffs', 'Soldier of the 12th Lancers' and 'Royal Engineers'. These models do not appear to carry stock numbers. The Rd. No. found on models refers to the mark and not the model, it is Rd. No. 330440.

Duchess Models

Ancient Artefacts

Puzzle Jug with verse. 70mm.	6.50
Salisbury Kettle. 110mm.	5.50

Buildings - White

Bridge, with grassy banks. 134mm long.	20.00

Historical/Folklore

HRH Prince of Wales, future Edward VIII, in his investiture costume, standing on base. 88mm long,103mm high. (Very rare). 140.00

Traditional/National Souvenirs

A Cornish Pasty. 95mm long.	12.50
Welsh Hat. 55mm.	10.00

Seaside Souvenirs

Lighthouse. 110mm.	6.50

Countryside

Milk Churn with lid. 85mm.	6.00

Animals

Bear, Teddy, sitting.	
2 sizes: 75mm.	17.00
90mm.	18.00
Cat in boot, white bow.	
96mm long.	19.50
Elephant, walking. 74mm long.	20.00
Elephant Jug. 70mm.	14.50
Mouse. 61mm long.	25.00
Pig, standing, ears and feet pointing forward. 82mm long.	
No. 60.	20.00

Birds

Swan posy holder.	6.00

Great War

Battleship, four small twin funnels. 140mm long.	30.00
Picklehaube. 50mm.	30.00
Bell Tent. 70mm.	16.50

Home/Nostalgic

Hip Bath. 95mm long.	12.00
Shaving Mug. 55m.	9.50
Watering Can. 74mm.	9.50
Wooden Pail with rope handle. 64mm.	6.50

Comic/Novelty
Billiken, grotesque. 68mm.   8.00

Footwear
Lancashire Clog. 87mm long.   6.00
Miniature Domestic
Bagware Jug. 51mm.   4.00
Cheese Dish and cover. 65mm.   9.50
Cheese Dish and cover, circular.
   87mm dia.   8.50
Kettle with lid. 80mm.   10.00
Teapot with lid. 70mm.   9.00
Teapot with lid. No. 172.   9.00

Domestic
Inkwell with four grille holes.
   52mm.   12.50
Pepper Pot, octagonal. 94mm   7.50

Durbar

$\mathcal{D}ur\mathcal{b}ar$

Trademark used by C. Schmidt and Co.
Carlsbad, (Bohemia) on a wide range
of domestic shapes. For details see
Alexandra page 38.

E. B. & Co.

Echo China

For details of this china and manufacturers see Foley E. B. and Co.

Mark used by unknown British manufacturer for a Manchester retailer or wholesaler, F.B. & Co. Trevelyan China Manchester. See also Trevelyan China.

Echo China Models
Ancient Artefacts
Shrewsbury Romano - Salopian
Ewer. 65mm.   5.50

Animals
Pig, fat, standing, ears forward.
68mm long.   20.00

Eclipse China

Eglinton China

Produced for an unknown British whole-saler, possibly in the West Country as the coat of arms on the only known piece is Devizes. Manufactured by Wiltshaw & Robinson Ltd., Carlton Works, Stoke (agreed trademark Carlton).

Trademark used for a Scottish retailer by Hewitt & Leadbeater, Willow Potteries, Longton (usual trademark Willow Art).

Eclipse Model
Home/Nostalgic
Time Glass. 60mm.   18.00

Eglington China Models
Monuments (including crosses)
Burns Statue, with dog. 168mm.   20.00

Traditional/National Souvenirs
Thistle vase. 50mm.   8.00

Animals
Fish. 125mm long.   8.00

Domestic
Rectangular box and lid, ornately
    carved. 94mm long.   8.50

Elite

Elite H.M. & Co.

$e\backslash i t_e$

Trademark probably used by C. Schmidt and Co., Carlsbad (Bohemia). (Usual trademark Alexandra). For details of this china, see Alexandra.
One pot has been found with the above mark. The base is cream-coloured with gold flowers, whilst the lid has green trim, gold decoration and Chichester crest. No details of size available.

8.00

Trademark used for the wholesaler H.M. & Co. by A.B. Jones & Sons (usual trademark Grafton). Crests recorded with this mark are Weymouth and Melcombe Regis, Portsmouth, Dorking and Godalming.

Elite H.M. & Co. models
Ancient Artefacts
London vessel found during
excavations. 65mm.   5.50

Home/Nostalgic
Billiken, sitting. 43mm.   7.50
Cornish Pasty. 95mm long.   10.00

Footwear
Sabot. No. 212. 83mm long.   7.50

Miniature Domestic
Cup and Saucer. 35mm.   5.00

Domestic
Hair Tidy and Lid. No. 140. 77mm.   6.00

Elite China Series

Trademark used for the retailer David S.
Butler of Derby (Forerunner of the Butler
Group of Companies) by Hewitt and
Leadbeater, Willow Potteries, Longton.
(Usual trademark Willow Art).
For details of china and manufacturers see
Willow Art China.
All crests found are Derby or its environs,
and pieces are often found impressed: H
AND L WILLOW ENGLAND.
Stock numbers where recorded are the same
as those found on Willow Art models.

Elite China Series Models
Monuments (including Crosses)
Baron Burton Statue. 70mm.   30.00

Historical/Folklore
Bunyan's Chair. 92mm.   14.00
James V Chair.   12.50
Mary Queen of Scots Chair. 85mm.   9.50

Traditional/National Souvenirs
Cornish Pasty. 100mm long.   12.50

Animals
Cat, walking, with blue bow, fat
  and angry, tail in air. 80mm.   20.00
Lion, walking. 110mm long.   24.50
Pig, sitting. Inscribed: *You may*
  push.... 77mm.   20.00
Rabbit. 57mm long.   9.50

Great War
Soldier with rifle, inscribed: *Our*
  Brave Defender. Always found
  with gun broken off at top, but
  classed as perfect. 132mm.   65.00
Nurse, with red cross on apron,
  inscribed: *A Friend in Need.*
  133mm.   90.00
Red Cross Van, red cross on side.
  No. 218. 84mm long.   40.00
Florence Nightingale Statue, Model of.
  No. 225. 185mm.   22.00
Crich Stand War Memorial. 102mm. 160.00
Mickleover War Memorial inscribed
  with 26 names of the fallen and *To*
  the glorious dead of Mickleover
  1914-1919. No crest. 135mm.   160.00

Home/Nostalgic
Grandfather Clock, inscribed. 112m.   16.50

Cartoon/Comedy
Baby with arms outstretched,
  inscribed: Cheerio. Some
  colouring on face. 125mm.   30.00
Billiken the God of Luck. 102mm.   10.50

Musical Instruments
Bagpipes. 118mm long.   50.00

Miscellaneous
Hand holding Tulip. 80mm.   7.00

Miniature Domestic
Cup and Saucer. 35mm.   5.00

Emblematic T

Empire

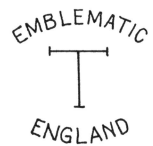

Mark used by an unknown manufacturer, and found on Goss pieces. How this came about is a mystery still waiting to be solved.

Trademark used by C. Schmidt & Co., Carlsbad (Bohemia).

The usual Schmidt range of ornately decorated hard paste porcelain wares can be found with this trademark. See Empire, Gem and Alexandra.

Empire China

Empire Gem

Trademark used for the retailer and whole-saler William Richie & Son Ltd. 24, 26 and 28 Elder Street, Edinburgh by Birks, Rawlins & Co. (Ltd), Vine Pottery, Stoke (usual trademark Savoy). All pieces recorded have Northern English crests.

Trademark used by Schmidt and Co., Carlsbad (Bohemia) For further details of this china see Gemma and Alexandra.

A range of domestic and miniature ware was produced.
Price £4.00-10.00

Empire China Models
Ancient Artefacts
Loving Cup, 2 handled. No. 47.
41mm.   6.00

Seaside Souvenirs
Bathing Machine. 65mm.   16.00
Boat. 130mm long.   14.50
Whelk Shell. No. 451. 80mm long. 6.00

Animals
Pig, standing, long ears pointing
forward. No. 199. 66mm long.   30.00

Great War
Bell Tent. 67mm.   22.00

Hats
Top Hat. 44mm.   7.50

Footwear
Lancashire Clog. No. 403. 82mm long. 7.00

Miniature Domestic
Cheese Dish and cover. 46mm.   9.50
Trinket Box, hexagonal, and lid.
36mm.   6.00

Empire Gem Models
Miniature Domestic
Cheese Dish with curved lid.
80mm long.   9.50

Puff box, beige with maroon
trim and coloured flowers,
68mm diameter.   10.00

Empress China

EMPRESS CHINA

Trademark used by Taylor and Kent (Ltd.), Florence works, Longton (usual trademark Florentine).

Empress Models
Ancient Artefacts
Chester Roman Vase, not named.
58mm.   5.50
Chichester Ewer. 60mm.   5.50

Buildings
Old Pete's Cottage, near Ramsey.
72mm long.   25.00

Seaside Souvenirs
Child sitting on rock, hand to
mouth. 108mm.   18.00

Animals
The Cheshire Cat. 90mm.   12.50

Cartoon/Comedy Characters
Ally Sloper bust, not named, with
red spotted nose, mouth and eye.
85mm.   30.00

Endor China

Trademark used for a retailer by J.A. Robinson & Sons. (usual trademark arcadian) and possibly Birks, Rawlins and Co (Ltd), Vine Pottery, Stoke. (Usual trademark Savoy).

Endor Models
Ancient Artefacts
Loving Cup, 3 handled. 41mm.   6.00

Traditional/National Souvenirs
Welsh Leek Vase. 90mm.   8.50

Seaside Souvenirs
Lighthouse. 107mm.   8.00

Animals
Cat in Boot, with mouse at the toe.
104mm long.   40.00

Footwear
Old Boot . 85mm long.   6.00

Alcohol
Barrel on Stand. 60mm.   8.00

Domestic
Bagware Jug. 50mm.   4.00

England

English China

MADE IN ENGLAND

$\nwarrow GLISH CHINA \nearrow$

MADE IN ENGLAND

Mark used by an unknown manufacturer. One small has been recorded, earthenware not porcelain, with the Arms of Colwyn Bay.

5.00

MADE IN ENGLAND

Trademark used by unknown British manufacturers.

England Models
Ancient Artefacts
Puzzle Jug. Old English. 70mm.   9.00

Seaside Souvenirs
Bathing Hut. 56mm. (Grafton)   12.00

Miscellaneous
Hand holding a tulip.   7.00

English China

English Emporium China

ENGLISH
EMPORIUM CHINA
F. PHILLIPS

Trademarks used by Alfred B. Jones & Sons Ltd., Grafton China Works, Longton, Staffs. (Usual trademark Grafton).

A large range of different shapes of small vase have been seen all with Grafton numbers and bearing the Franco-British Exhibition 1908 motif.   Each 15.00

English China Models
Seaside Souvenirs
Whelk Shell. 95mm long.   6.00

Animals
Elephant, large & comical with open back as posy holder, yellow trunk, black eyes. 110mm long.   50.00

Home/Nostalgic
Coal Scuttle. 65mm.   6.50

Domestic
Scent bottle, rectangular ribbed back.   6.50
Knave Candlesnuffer. 93mm.   35.00

Mark can also be found without the rectangular outline.

Trademark used by F Phillips, Bazaar owner, china thought to have been manufactured by James Reeves, Victoria Works, Fenton. (Usual mark Victoria China).
For details of china and manufacturer see Victoria China.
Much crested ware was advertised as being suitable for the Emporium or Bazaar Trade, so it is rather appropriate that this mark was used. The china is exactly the same as that marked VICTORIA CHINA which was thought to have been made by James Reeves. Very few pieces have so been recorded and it is very likely that this type of china was usually sold unmarked.

English Emporium Models
National Souvenirs
Welsh Hat. 62mm.   8.00

Animals
Cat, long necked. 110mm.   10.00
Teddy Bear. 98mm.   20.00
Toad. 70mm.   18.00

Birds (including Eggs)
Bird Jug. 70mm.   8.50

Home/Nostalgic
Baby's Cradle. 60mm long.   18.00

Comic/Novelty
Suffragette Handbell, double-sided
  with clapper. 110mm.   50.00

Domestic
Candlestick with handle. 80mm   9.00
diameter.

English Herald China

Trademark used for the Southend/Westcliffe
on Sea agent by Alfred B. Jones and Son
Ltd., Grafton China Works, Longton.
(Usual trademark Grafton). A number of
small shapes were made.

English Herald China Models
Ancient Artefacts
Aberdeen Bronze Pot, not named.
  60mm.   5.50

Seaside Souvenirs
Bathing Machine. No. 256.
  55mm long.   16.00

Animals
Cat, Cheshire. Inscribed: *Always*
  Smiling. 85mm.   12.00
Pig, sitting. Inscribed: *Wunt be druv.*
  90mm long.   20.00
Shetland Pony. No. 493.
  103mm long.   35.00
Squirrel. 70mm.   30.00

Traditional/National Souvenirs
Dutchman, sitting cross legged
  holding cheese. 85mm.   30.00

Domestic
Diamond pintray. 120mm long.   5.00

English Manufacture

Musical Instruments

Grand Piano 81mm long.	18.00

Miniature Domestic

Teapot and Lid. 55mm.	9.50
Kettle and Lid, gilded handle. 80mm.	9.00

ENGLISH MANUFACTURE

Trademark used by an unknown English manufacturer but probably Hewitt and leadbeater (usual trademark Willow Art) or Taylor and Kent (usual trademark Florentine). However, one dog has been noted which is from the Grafton factory.

In addition to the models listed below several smalls have been found, including one with the Bournemouth Centenary Crest and a Hull transfer.

English Manufacture Models
Ancient Artefacts

Puzzle Jug. 66mm.	6.00

Seaside

Fish, straight, *caught at Avonmouth* or *Bridlington*. 120mm long.	12.00

Countryside

Milk Churn. 70mm.	6.00

Animals

Cat Cheshire. Always Smiling. 88mm.	10.00
Dog, kneeling wearing a cap, with container for matches. Brown ears (GRAFTON), 85mm.	40.00

Home/Nostalgic

Coal Scuttle, helmet-shaped. 80mm long.	8.00

English Souvenir China

E.P. Co.

EMPIRE WORKS
STOKE-on-TRENT
ENGLAND

Trademark used for The Golden West Exhibition, 1909, by Taylor & Kent Ltd., Florence Works, Longton (usual trademark Florentine). All carry the Golden West Exhibition crest, or the Imperial International Exhibition crest, used by Florentine. Add £15 for these crests.

English Souvenir China Models
Seaside Souvenirs
Whelk Shell. 95mm long.   7.50

Animals
Camel, with 1 hump, sitting. 110mm.   18.00
Cheshire Cat always smiling. 91mm.   10.50
Elephant, kneeling. 95mm.   20.00
Fish, with open mouth. 118mm long.   8.50

Home/Nostalgic
Anvil.   8.50

Cartoon/Comedy Characters
Ally Sloper, bust, not named. 85mm.   30.00

Musical Instruments
Tambourine. 68mm dia.   8.50

Miniature Domestic
Cup and saucer. 38mm.   5.00
Mug. 47mm.   4.50

Trademark used by an unknown manufacturer.
The only piece found to date with this mark is a 115mm diameter earthenware sugar bowl with an Ipswich crest.
                                        5.00

Erin China

Esbeco

Trademark used for an Irish wholesaler by a British manufacturer.

Erin Models
Ancient Artefacts
Carlisle Salt Pot. 65mm.   5.50
Fountain Abbey Abbot's Cup,
    not named. 49mm.   4.00

Trademark used for the retailer S.B. & Co. possibly by Willow Art.
SB and Co. are not the initials of any china or earthenware manufacturer who are recorded as having made crested ware. The mark is probably that of a Scottish wholesaler. The models below may have been supplied by Hewitt and Leadbeater. (See Willow Art China).

Esbeco Models
Great War
Monoplane with movable prop.
    67mm.   75.00
British Tank, Model of, with inset
    wheels. 95mm long.   22.00
HMS Lion, impressed battleship.
    No. 213.   40.00
Red Cross Van. No. 216H.   40.00
Edith Cavell statue with
    inscriptions. 110mm.   20.00
Florence Nightingale statue. 120mm.   22.00

Home/Nostalgic
Anvil. 57mm.   6.50

Cartoon/Comedy
Baby with arms outstretched.
    Coloured face. Similar to Cheerio
    Baby 122mm.   40.00

Miniature Domestic
Shaving Mug. 55mm.   9.00

Domestic
Trefoil Cruet Set.   6.50

Etruscan China

Exceller

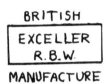

Trademark used for a retailer or wholesaler AD, probably manufactured by Charles Waine, Longton. (Usual trademark Venetia).
This mark has not been found on crested ware but black transfer prints of HMS Achilles and HM Torpedo Boat have been found on a 63mm vase and a 40mm loving cup, with this trademark. No known china manufacturer used the initials A.D. so these models could have been made by almost any firm for a wholesaler or retailer, with these initials. They are more aptly described as earthenware rather than china and are very similar to the colour transfer ware made by Charles Waine, the mark too being remarkably similar to the 'Venetia' mark this firm used on miniatures and 'smalls' (see Venetia China).

Etruscan Models
Three-handled loving cup with
  black transfer *HM Torpedo Boat*.
  34'. 40mm.   40.00
Vase with black transfer of *HMS*
  Achilles. 63mm.   40.00

Trademark used for a-retailer in the south of England, especially Worthing, by Sampson Hancock (and Sons). (Usual trademark Corona).
For details of this china see The Corona China. It is possible that R.B.W. owned a chain of souvenir shops in southern towns. Crests so far recorded are Worthing, Lancing, Littlehampton, Brighton, Haywards Heath and Lewes.

Exceller Models
Ancient Artefacts
Canterbury Leather Bottle. 47mm.   5.50

Traditional/National Souvenirs
Laxey Wheel. 80mm.   40.00

Seaside Souvenirs
Lighthouse on rocks. 150mm.   10.00

Animals
Tortoise. 70mm long.   12.50

Birds (including Eggs)
Swan Posy holder. 80mm.   8.00

Great War
Flash Lamp. 90mm.   18.00
Ghurka Knife. 140mm long.   30.00
Field Gun. 130mm.   30.00

Home/Nostalgic
Armchair. 60mm.   12.50
Cradle on rockers, wicker. 80mm long.   14.50
Tobacco Pouch. 75mm long.   12.50
Pawn Chess piece. 60mm.   20.00

Musical Instruments
Gramophone, square. 55mm.   30.00

Modern Equipment
Gas Cooker. 70mm.   10.00

Footwear
Lancashire Clog. 80mm long.   6.50

Miniature Domestic
Teapot with Lid. 60mm.   9.00

Excelsior

MADE IN ENGLAND

Trademark used by Taylor and Kent (Ltd), Florence Works, Longton (usual trademark Florentine) or Arkinstall & Son (usual trademark Arcadian).
This mark looks very like a retailers mark and not one used by a manufacturer. No known manufacturer used the initials W.P. and S.L. The mark seems to have been used only during the Great War as most of the 'smalls' found have the commemorative: Four flags of the Allies.

A range of 'smalls' with commemorative Four Flags of the Allies was produced.
Value   from £8.00

Excelsior Models
Buildings - White
Laxey Wheel.   40.00

Animals
Pig, standing. 70mm long.   20.00

Home/Nostalgic
Grandfather Clock. 100mm.   12.00
Horn Lantern. 85mm.   8.50

Sport/Pastimes
Cricket Bat. 113mm long.   80.00
Trophy Cup. 70mm.   12.00

Fairy Ware

An exceptionally wide mark used to over-stamp GEMMA marks.

Trademark used by Schmidt and Co., Carlsbad (Bohemia). (Usual trademark Gemma). These marks appear in blue, red, green or black.
For further details of this china see Gemma. Schmidt and Co. used this mark as an alternative to the Gemma mark. A great number of small domestic items such as bowls, cups and saucers, vases and ink wells are found with the mark. The china is often very decoratively moulded. Models are often identical to those marked Gemma and pieces have been found with both marks. As Fairy Ware is stamped over Gemma it seems that the latter was an early mark, the models recorded also indicating that the mark was not used after the War.

Fairy Ware Models
Ancient Artefacts

Irish Bronze Pot. 43mm.	4.00
Loving Cup, 3 handled. 39mm.	5.00
Puzzle Jug. 65mm.	6.50

Historical/Folklore

Coronation Chair. 100mm.	6.00

Seaside Souvenirs

Lighthouse on rocks. 105mm.	7.50

Animals

Cat, sitting, looking to sinister. 66mm.	14.00
Cow cream jug. 103mm long. (Probably a reproduction in miniature of an early Staffordshire 'creamer'.)	20.00
Dog, pug, lying, paws forward. 95mm.	22.00
Dog, puppy, sitting with one ear raised. 78mm.	12.00
Dog, puppy sitting cross-eyed looking at fly on his nose. 74mm.	20.00
Tortoise dish with lid. 80mm long.	12.50

Birds (including eggs)

Chicken and basket. 88mm long.	12.00

Home/Nostalgic

Bucket with rope handle. 83mm.	6.00
Cabin Trunk and Lid. 60mm long.	12.00
Grandfather Clock, with arabic numerals. 105mm.	16.50
Grandmother Clock, with arabic numerals. 85mm.	16.50
Kettle, very ornate. 71mm.	8.50

Pillar Box. 70mm.   18.00
Pillar Box, oval. 87mm.   19.50
Pipe, brown, on dish. 72mm long.   16.50
Shaving Mug, rope handle. 55mm.   9.50
Stool, 4 legs. 44mm.   6.00
Watering Can. 65mm.   16.50

Hats
Top Hat. 43mm.   7.50

Footwear
Ladies frilled shoe. 90mm long.   7.00
Sabot. 90mm long.   7.00

Miniature Domestic
Cheese Dish and cover. 55mm.   9.50
Cheese Dish and cover, two piece.   9.50
Cup and Saucer. 45mm.   5.00
Milk Jug. 40mm.   4.00
Teapot with lid, oval, ribbed sides.
  48mm.   9.50
Teapot with lid. 60mm.   9.50
Teapot with lid. 85mm.   9.50

Domestic
Teapot, oval. 130mm long.   12.50

Miscellaneous
Cup with 2 large silvered handles.
  50mm.   7.00
Mustard Pot and Lid on 4 gold feet.
  64mm.   5.50
Winged Sphinx Jug. 85mm.   15.00

Famous Henley China

Trademark used by the retailer Hawkins, Henley-on-Thames, manufactured by Hewitt and Leadbeater, Willow Potteries Ltd. Longton. (Usual trademark Willow Art).

Famous Henley China Models
Seaside Souvenirs
Eddystone Lighthouse, not named.
  No. 135. 110mm.   8.00
Rowing Boat, four seats. 103mm long.   20.00

Animals
Dog, Collie, standing, detailed fur.
  105mm long.   23.00
Pig, standing.
  2 sizes: 80mm.   20.00
            94mm long.   22.50
Elephant, walking. 52mm.   20.00

Great War
Standing Soldier with rifle,
  inscribed: *Our Brave Defender.*
  130mm.   50.00

Home/Nostalgic
Watering Can. No. 126. 75mm.   8.50

Alcohol
Barrel. No. 100. 35mm long.   8.00

Shoes
Clog. No.33. 72mm long.   6.00

Miniature Domestic
Cheese Dish and cover. 50mm.   9.50

FCCH

For details of this wholesaler, see Waterfall Heraldic China or Cascade China.

Fenton China

Mark used 1905-1912.

1900-1905.

Trademark used by E. Hughes and Co., Opal Works, Fenton.

E. Hughes and Co. was established in 1889 and were noted for their 'badge ware suitable for hotels, ships, clubs, schools and public institutions generally'. It is not therefore surprising that a firm making such wares would turn to the production of view and arms ware as soon as it became fashionable. The firm started producing 'Arms' ware in white china and in celadon well before 1900. In 1907 they began advertising Fenton China Arms Ware and offered to supply the arms of any town, city, county or college. During these years the firm produced a quantity of arms ware, mostly domestic items such as beakers, mugs, vases and shell trays. In 1908, Mr Edward Hughes died and although the firm went on advertising 'correct Heraldic china' for at least the next year they did not specialise in the production of these lines after that date, concentrating rather on tea sets and breakfast ware.

A considerable quantity of crested ware is found with the Fenton China mark but for the most part they are small vases, inkwells, dishes and jugs. Such items are very ornately moulded and look rather Victorian. Although the firm advertised view ware, few have as yet been recorded. (This is probably because such domestic pieces were used and have therefore not survived.) Fenton China was exported and vases with Canadian and Montreal crests have been found.

Fenton Models
Ancient Artefacts
Chester Roman Vase. No. 480.
  55mm.   5.50
Leather Bottle. 55mm.   5.50
Loving Cup. 39mm.   6.00
Loving Cup, 3 handles. 50mm.   6.00

Great War
Bell tent, open flap. 74mm.   17.00

Home/Nostalgic
Iron Trivet. 70mm.   9.00

Miniature Domestic
Cheese Dish and cover. 55mm.   9.50
Cup and Saucer. 35mm.   5.50

Domestic
Inkwell, square, with lid.
  50mm wide.   12.50

A range of useful domestic items
  such as egg cups and sealing wax
  holders was produced.
  Value   5.00-10.00

Filey China

Trademark used on wares made for a Filey retailer by Taylor and Kent (Ltd), Florence Works, Longton. (Usual trademark Florentine).

Filey China Model
Ancient Artefacts
Loving Cup, 3 handled. 39mm.   6.00

F.L.

Florentine China

Trademark used for a retailer on wares made by Sampson Hancock (& Sons), Bridge Works, Stoke and later at the Garden Works, Hanley. (Usual mark Corona) and Arkinstall & Son (usual trademark Arcadian).

F.L Models
Great War
Nurse, Standing. Inscribed:
Soldiers Friend. 132mm.   80.00
Tommy on Sentry Duty, model of
110mm.   85.00
Battleship. 120mm long.   30.00

Birds (including Eggs)
Chick hatching from egg.
60mm long.   9.00

Can often be found without 'Made in England'.

Trademark used by Taylor and. Kent (Ltd), Florence Works, Longton.
Taylor and Kent, a well known firm which survived the Depression, specialised in producing tableware, toy tea sets, commemoratives and while the craze lasted 'coat of arms ware', at reasonable prices. In 1911 the firm made front page news in the Potteries by persuading the Wallasey Coronation Committee to cancel an order for coronation mugs from a German firm and to fill the order themselves. They gained a great deal of kudos from this order. The firm could hardly have been aware of the longer struggle against Germany in which the whole country was about to embark. A sad sequence of events unfolds in the Pottery Gazette of the next few years. In 1914, Mr John Kent, the traveller for Taylor and Kent in the North of England and Scotland was called up for service. With the rank of Major he commanded the 1st Battery of the 2nd North Midland Division RFA. The company requested and encouraged customers to send their orders directly to the works. Major John Kent was regrettably killed in action in 1916, his death recorded with many others in the Gazette of that year (yet another victim of that pointless war). By 1913, Taylor and Kent were making 'Coat of Arms ware and View china' as well as

'Tea sets, Breakfast sets and Domestic China'. A year later large extensions were made to the Florentine Works because of the extra orders the firm were receiving. The new oven could accommodate some 5,000 dozen of porcelain miniatures at each firing. The firm obviously specialised in heraldic, commemorative and view wares throughout the war years and continued into the early twenties. They were recognised as one of the leading Staffordshire firms for souvenir china and one of the biggest suppliers. By 1925, however, Taylor and Kent had recognised the need to emphasise other products and were advertising their 'excellent china tea and breakfast ware suitable alike for home and export trades'.

Florentine china is not particularly fine and was produced as cheaply as possible, often marked with the name or trademark of the wholesaler. The range of models is not particularly original and most of the novelty items are to be found in other manufacturers' lists. (There is a similarity to models made by J. Reeves (Victoria China). The firm supplied wares under a large number of trademarks, the most common including Caledonia, Coronet and Cyclone, which cannot be explained by any known connection between the firms.)

Florentine does present, however, a very representative selection of models but a surprisingly small number of Great War miniatures.

Taylor and Kent made a great amount of crested domestic ware including some early items to which pewter lids and tops were added. View ware made by the firm is pleasant but unmemorable and they also produced a range of transfer prints of a regional nature including 'Welsh costumes' (also found on models marked Victoria China). An Australian transfer view of Tweed River Murwillumbah has been found, and also the crest of Toowoomba.

Commemorative transfers of the Great War are often found on 'smalls' and models including the Triple Entente (Flags of Great Britain, France and Russia in shields). The only military badge recorded is RMC Camberley. There is also an interesting commemorative of the War Museum Exhibition, Crystal Palace.

Many models and 'smalls' are found with 'Lucky Black Cat' transfers but no 'Lucky White Heather' devices have been recorded.

A scent bottle has been found bearing the inscriptions *White Rose, Breidenbach & Co. London* and *This article is British Made by British Labour. The Proprietor and Employees being British without exception. Breidenbach & Co. London. Eng.*

Taylor and Kent produced small china figures and other novelties which were not crested before 1900 and after 1925, although many of these would be of interest to some collectors, they have not been listed here as they cannot be considered crested china. (No numbering system was used on Florentine china).

Florentine Models
Ancient Artefacts

Aberdeen Bronze Pot, not named.	
58mm.	5.50
Chester Roman Vase, not named.	
62mm.	4.00
Fountain's Abbey Cup. 50mm.	5.50
Guernsey Milk Can. 105mm.	5.50
Irish Bronze Pot, not named.	
52mm.	4.00
Loving Cup, not named. 39mm.	6.00
Puzzle Jug. 67mm.	7.50
Roman Lamp.	
2 sizes: 62mm.	5.50
100mm.	7.00
Salisbury Kettle, not named.	
100mm.	5.00
Southwold Jar, not named.	
100mm.	4.00
Windsor Urn, not named.	
50mm.	4.00

Buildings - White

Blackpool Tower. 117mm.	12.00
Crofters Cottage. 70mm long.	17.00
London Bridge. 88mm long.	22.00
Marble Arch, not named. 50mm.	14.00
Old Pete's Cottage, near Ramsey.	
75mm long.	25.00
St. Paul's Cathedral.	
2 sizes: 93mm.	22.50
130mm.	22.00
Tower Bridge. 105mm long.	25.00
Westminster Abbey, West Front.	
85mm.	15.00

Monuments (including Crosses)

Caister-on-Sea, Lifeboat Memorial,
impressed: *1903*. 150mm.   25.00
Glastonbury Tor. 90mm.   40.00
Great Rock of Ages, Model of.
135mm.   18.00
Iona Cross. 108mm.   12.50
Nelson's Column. 121mm.   47.50

Historical/Folklore

Brussels Boy,120mm. Impressed:
Mannekin pis.   85.00
Judge, bust of. 77mm.   20.00
Man standing in Pillory. 105mm.   20.00
Man standing in Stocks. 105mm.   19.00
Mother Shipton 72mm.   10.00

Traditional/National Souvenirs

Blackpool Wheel. 110mm.   12.00
Laxey Wheel, Isle of Man, not
named. 85mm.   40.00
Legs of Man in Lifebelt. 95mm.   16.00
Lincoln Imp on pedestal. 106mm.   12.50
Thistle Jug. 63mm.   5.00
Welsh Bardic Chair 88mm.   22.50
Welsh Dragon Water Jug, with lid.
120mm.   16.00
Welsh Harp. 100mm.   10.00
Welsh Hat. 57mm.   10.00
inscribed with longest town name.   11.50
Irish paddy in front of cottage,
shamrock on base rear of cottage
acts as match holder, fully coloured.
No. 20707. 55mm.   30.00
Indian Canoe. 110mm long.   9.00

Seaside Souvenirs

Child sitting on Rock, hand to
mouth. 110mm.   18.00
Basket Beach Chair.
2 sizes: 85mm.   12.00
100mm.   14.00
Bathing Machine. 76mm.   14.00
Bathing Machine with figure on
steps. 75mm.   22.50
Fisherman, bust. 84mm.   25.00
Fishing basket, fitted lid. 58mm.   10.00
Fishing basket, separate lid.
65mm.   12.00
Houseboat. 57mm.   10.00
Houseboat, square. 90mm long.   12.00
Sea Waves on base. 57mm.   20.00
Lighthouse, not named. 90mm.   7.00
Whelk Shell. 100mm long.   7.00
Yacht, in full sail. 127mm.   18.50

Countryside

Milk Churn and lid. 72mm.   6.00

Animals

Bear, Polar inscribed: *SAM.*
95mm long.   35.00
Camel, kneeling.
2 sizes: 55mm long   16.50
95mm long.   19.00
Cat, inscribed *Manx Cat.* 61mm.   30.00
Cat, sitting.
2 sizes: 62mm.   12.00
112mm.   14.50
Cat, sitting, detailed fur. 90mm.   30.00
Cat, with long neck, sitting. 115mm.   12.00
Cheshire cat, The, inscribed: *Always*
smiling.
2 sizes: 90mm   14.00
115mm.   16.50
Cat with bandaged face. 88mm.   25.00
Cat in Top Hat. 65mm.   30.00
Dog, with bandaged face. 90mm.   25.00
Dog, Bulldog looking out of kennel.
If with black face add £10.00.
73mm.   17.50
Dog, Bulldog, sitting. 56mm.   20.00
Dog, King Charles Spaniel, sitting,
begging on cushion.
2 sizes: 70mm.   12.50
85mm.   14.00
Dog, lying in cradle. 90mm long.   17.50
Dog, puppy, sitting. 92mm.   12.50
Dogs, two King Charles Spaniels in
a Top Hat. 65mm.   17.00
Dolphin Vase. 102mm.   7.50
Donkey, walking. 90mm long.   25.00
Elephant, kneeling.
2 sizes: 82mm long.   20.00
95mm long.   23.00
Elephant standing. 75mm.   20.00
Fish, inscribed: *Caught at*
120mm long.   6.50
Fish, open mouthed. 115mm long.   7.00
Fish vase. 115mm.   6.50
Frog cream jug. 45mm.   12.00
Monkey, sitting, hands to mouth.
90mm.   20.00
Mouse, playing mandolin, on
circular base. 90mm.   25.00
Pig, lying down, alert ears.
80mm long.   19.50
Pig, standing.
2 sizes: 80mm.   19.50
95mm long.   22.50
Larger size found inscribed: *The*
pig that won't go.

Piglet, kneeling. 70mm long.	16.50
Pony, Shetland. 115mm long.	25.00
Rabbit, fluffy, ears up. 98mm long.	16.50
Seal, with ball. 72mm.	21.50
Toad, flat. 74mm long.	22.50
Tortoise. 74mm long.	11.00

Birds (including Eggs)

Baby Bird cream jug. 65mm.	7.50
Chicken, hatching from egg.	
63mm long.	9.00
Hen roosting.	
2 sizes: 60mm long.	8.50
90mm long.	11.00
Kingfisher with long beak. 80mm.	30.00
Owl. 75mm.	18.50
Parakeet. 75mm.	12.50
Parrot. 94mm.	14.50
Pelican cream jug. 83mm long.	7.50
Songbird on rock. 95mm.	12.00
Sparrow. 63mm.	22.50
Swan.	
2 sizes: 65mm.	7.50
80mm.	9.50
Swan posy holder. 88mm long.	7.00

Great War

Monoplane with 4 bladed movable	
prop. 175mm long.	110.00
Battleship. 175mm long.	50.00
Red Cross Van. 88mm long.	40.00
Tank with trailing wheels.	
127mm long.	30 00
Tank. 125mm long. (wide version).	35.00
Shell. 75mm.	6.00
Telescope, folded. 70mm.	13.00
Cenotaph, inscribed: *The blood of*	
heroes is the seed of freedom.	
140mm.	10.50
Gravesend War Memorial.	
140mm.	120.00
Great Yarmouth War Memorial,	
with inscription on all four sides.	
2 sizes: 145mm.	26.00
175mm.	30.00
Matlock Bath Memorial, some	
colouring, 155mm, found without	
factory mark.	125.00

Home/Nostalgic

Baby in Bootee. 95mm long.	14.50
Baby in Hip Bath. 100mm long.	16.50
Baby, left hand to mouth, sitting	
on rock.	18.00
Bellows. 107mm long.	14.50

Broom Head. 107mm long.	19.00
Case, Attache. 60mm long.	9.50
Chamber Pot. 40mm.	5.00
Coal Bucket. 60mm.	6.00
Cradle on rockers.	12.00
Dolly Tub with two pegs and	
clothes protruding. 82mm.	26.00
Flat Iron. 76mm.	14.50
Garden Roller. 85mm long.	16.50
Grandfather Clock.	
2 sizes: 95mm.	14.00
135mm.	16.50
Keys on Ring. 46mm.	25.00
Lantern. 65mm.	9.50
Man Standing in stocks. 105mm.	20.00
Old Armchair, The. 85mm.	12.50
Oriental Lamp (Aladdin's Lamp),	
with lid.	
2 sizes: 100mm long.	7.00
198mm long.	14.00
Pillar Box, inscribed: *I can't get a*	
letter from you so send you the box.	
76mm.	14.50
Policeman's Lamp. 70mm.	10.00
Portmanteau. 77mm long.	7.00
Shaving Mug. 55mm.	9.50
Sofa, 3 seater. 82mm long.	12.50
Travel bag, with moulded decoration.	
145mm long.	13.50
Watering Can. 68mm.	9.50

Comic/Novelty

Boy's head on container base, two	
side holes could be used for	
matches? 75mm long.	10.50
Boy on Scooter. 106mm.	30.00
Boy Pepper Pot. 90mm.	10.00
Girl in Bonnet Salt Pot. 90mm.	10.00
Jack in the Box. 90mm.	28.00
Man, comic character standing with	
hands raised in front of him.	
Wearing straw boater, barrel	
body, solemn expression. 130mm.	60.00
Monk Standing. 90mm.	15.00
Negro Minstrel, bust. 100mm.	30.00
Pekingese in Cradle. 70mm long.	16.50
Pierrot, hands and face flesh	
coloured, black pompoms on hat	
and costume. 125mm.	30.00
Pixie sitting on Flower Pot	
candlesnuffer. 180mm.	30.00
Pixie sitting on Thimble. 115mm.	30.00
Screw, inscribed: You *could do with*	
a big fat screw. (Wage rise). 75mm.	25.00
Suffragette Handbell, some	
colouring. *Votes for Women.* 108mm.	60.00

Cartoon/Comedy Characters
Ally Sloper, bust. Not named.
83mm.   25.00

Alcohol
Bottle of Champagne in Ice Bucket,
inscribed: *Something good a bottle*
of the boy or *A Bottle of the Best*
from... 85mm.   16.00
Carboy 76mm.   7.00
Toby Jug. 65mm.   10.50

Sport/Pastimes
Boxing Glove. 65mm long.   30.00
Cricket Bag. 110mm long.   16.50
Golf Ball vase on brown base.
55mm.   16.50
Also found as a scent bottle.   17.00
Football . 70mm.   9.50

Musical Instruments
Grand Piano. 85mm long.   20.00
Harp. 95mm.   10.00
Tambourine. 70mm.   7.50

Transport
Charabanc with driver. 115mm long.   40.00
Motor Horn, inscribed. *Pip Pip.*
88mm.   25.00
Saloon Car. 88mm long.   40.00

Modern Equipment
Gramophone, hexagonal, with horn.
90mm.   40.00
Gramophone, square, without horn.
53mm.   25.00
Radio Horn, plain or fluted.
2 sizes: 90mm.   30.00
96mm (fluted).   40.00
102mm.   40.00

Footwear
Bootee.   10.00
Lancashire Clog. No. 407.
88mm long.   6.50
Oriental Shoe with pointed turned
up toe. 95mm long.   6.00
Shoe, ladies,18th century.
95mm long.   6.50

Miniature Domestic
Bagware Vase. 50mm.   4.00
Cheese Dish, l piece. 45mm.   9.50
Cheese Dish and cover, 2 pieces.
45mm.   9.50

Coffee Pot and lid. 63mm.   9.50
Cup and Saucer. 40mm.   5.00
Jug and Bowl, ornate, tulip pattern
in relief. 55mm.   6.50
Kettle and lid. 85mm.   9.50
Tea Pot with lid. 3 sizes: 50mm,
60mm and 70mm. All sizes.   9.50
Tea Pot with lid, squat and wide.
88mm long.   12.50
Tea Pot, oval, with lid, ribbed sides.
80mm.   12.50

Domestic

Candlestick. 56mm.   5.00
Candlestick with Snake. 103mm.   7.50
Dragon Jug with lid. 120mm.   24.50
Hair Brush pin box and lid.
145mm long.   14.00
Jelly Mould bowl. 95mm long.   8.00
Jelly Mould Jug. 108mm long.   8.00
Lily Flower Vase. 120mm.   15.00
Napkin Ring. 40mm.   9.50
Scent Bottle (contained
'Wallflowers' scent) with
Breidenbach metal top which
unscrews. 93mm.
Many other varieties now found
including Lily of the Valley,
Opopanax and Violette de Palme.   17.50
Trowel pin box and lid. 140mm long. 14.00

Foley Bone China

Foley EB & Co.

MADE IN ENGLAND

EST. 1850

TRADE MARK
ENGLAND

Trademark used by an unknown Stoke-Upon-Trent manufacturer.
See Shelley China for discourse on the various uses of the Foley mark.

Trademark used by E. Brain & Co. of Stoke-on-Trent, established 1850.
Models bearing the arms of the City of London and several Australian crests have been found with the above factory mark which is not that of Wileman & Co., nor that of a London wholesaler of the same initials whose usual trademark is The Dainty Ware.

Foley EB & Co. Models
Flask, 58mm - City of Perth, plus 2
Australian crests have been found.   8.00

Ancient Artefacts
Model of Roman vase found at
   Yaverland I. of W.   5.50
Model of Bronze Bowl found at
   S. Canterbury. 55mm dia.   5.50

Great War
Pickelhaube. 50mm. (Westminster)   25.00

Footwear
Shoe, pointed toe. 100mm long.   7.00

The Foley China

Ford & Pointon

ENGLAND

1890-1910

ENGLAND

c1920-30

1890-1910

Trademark used by Wileman and Co., Foley Potteries, and Foley China Works, Fenton, Longton, subsequently renamed Shelleys Ltd.
For all details of manufacturer and models produced please see Shelley China.

In 1874, Charles Ford took over T & C Ford and produced Swan China at Cannon Street, Hanley. Ford also owned Ford & Pointon who produced Fords China at the Norfolk Works, Hanley. Both firms subsequently became branches of J.A. Robinson & Sons. (Usual trademark Arcadian). See also Coronet Ware.
This mark was mostly used on domestic ware only, and only one model has been recorded. Jugs, trinket dishes, cups and ashtrays are found with crests, transfer views and sometimes coloured transfers of tropical birds found on Arcadian pieces. The only known model is most definitely from an Arcadian mould.
The mark has also been noted overstamped by an Arcadian backstamp.

Ford & Pointon China Models
Alcohol
Soda Syphon. 100mm.   14.00

Great War
Officer's peaked cap, coloured
   barrel & badge, 70mm dia.   16.50

Miniature Domestic
Cup and Saucer, ornate. 60mm.   5.50

A range of domestic ware, trinket boxes,
   ashtrays, jugs etc.   5.00-10.00

Foreign/Germany

See also Saxony.

Germany

Foreign

Impressed marks.

Austria, Bavaria, Bohemia and Czech-oslovakia can also be found.

Many German firms manufactured crested china for the English souvenir market. German wares tend to be somewhat whiter and of poorer quality than British made wares. These firms include:
Max Emanuel, The Mosanic Pottery, Mitterteich, Bavaria. (Usual trademark Mosanic).
Moschendorf, Hof, Bayern. (Usual trademark PM and Rex).
Hutschenreuther, Probstzella, Thuringia. (Usual trademark P).
Klösterle, Carlsbad. (Usual trademark Union K).
Wilhelm Kutzscher & Co., Schwarzenberg, Saxony. (Sometimes used the trademark Princess China).
The models with impressed numbers would appear to be made by Max Emanuel. (Usual trademark Mosanic), as he was the only German manufacturer known to use stock numbers and registered numbers although pieces with improved stock-numbers were made by other German firms. Foreign, Austria or Czechoslovakia marks were incorrectly used after the Great War due to the unwillingness of the British to buy anything German. Nearly all of these models can be found in various shades of lustre, mostly yellow/brown, usually with the lucky white heather decoration or in full colour. They are often found with no coat of arms.

A range of coloured fairings were made, which although uncrested, are collected by some crested china collectors.   from 20.00

Germany/Foreign Models
Parian/Unglazed
Bust of General Booth, with beard. Inscribed: *The Salvation Army.* 86mm.   40 00
Bust of Carson, on blue glazed base. *Ulster will fight and Ulster will be right.* No.710. 105mm.   60.00
Bust of Mussolini, in uniform on rectangular base. 130mm. Rare.   70.00
Souter Johnny (impressed). Sitting coloured figure. No. 5140/A. 119mm.   30.00
Tam o'Shanter (impressed). Sitting coloured figure. No. 5140/B. Unglazed. 118mm.   30.00

Ancient Artefacts
Loving cup, 3 handled. 38mm.   4.00
Loving cup, 3 handled, with Nelson transfers in blue. 40mm.   20.00
Irish Bronze Pot. 50mm.   4.00
Plymouth Jug, not named. No. 4580. 60mm.   4.00
Portland Vase. No. 4684. 52mm.   6.00
Puzzle Jug. 68mm.   4.00
Southwold Jug. No. 4687. 40mm. (lustre).   4.00
Swindon Vase. No. 4557. Not named. 58mm.   4.00

Buildings - Coloured
Robert Burn's Cottage Nightlight. No. 5145. 130mm long.   30.00
Fairmaid's House Perth, Nightlight. 88mm.   65.00
Shakespeare's Cottage Nightlight. 112mm long.   29.50

Buildings - White
Bandstand. 2 sizes:
No. 3921. 75mm.   10.00
No. 3972. 90mm (lustre).   11.00
Birmingham Town Hall. 95mm long.   25.00
The Blackpool Tower and buildings. 122mm.   15.00
Blackpool Tower. No. 3484. 130mm.   8.50

Blackpool Tower cruet set (Tower is
salt pot, buildings either side
pepper and mustard - very
vulgar and therefore rather
appealing).135mm.   10.50
Boston Stump. No. 193. 128mm.   24.00
Clock Tower. No. 7727.   7.50
Cottage. No. 7208. 65mm long.
(lustre).   6.50
Cottage. No.6627. 60mm long.   8.00
Clock Tower Cruet comprising base,
central tower, two side towers all
with lids. 130mm.   20.00
Dunster Yarn Market. 24932.
95mm long.   30.00
Lantern Hill Chapel, Ilfracombe.   20.00
Margate Clock Tower. No. 7213.
153mm.7.50   7.50
Rye Medieval Gateway. No. 4412.
75mm.   40.00
Rye Medieval Gateway. No.4052.
67mm.   50.00
Scarborough Clock Tower. No. 3560.
138mm.   8.50
St. Winifred's Well, Holywell.
No. 4195. 60mm.   30.00
Windmill, fixed sails. No. 7223.
90mm.   14.50
Windmill, fixed sails, with hoist and
rope. No. 4167. 110mm.   14.50
Whitby Abbey, Ruin. No. 4169.
2 sizes: 75mm.   55.00
175mm.   65.00

Monuments (including Crosses)
Banbury Cross.
2 sizes: No. 6895. 135mm.   15.50
No. 3295. 150mm.   19.50
or No. 4245.
Margate Lifeboat Memorial. No.
3562 or No. 7200. 125mm.   12.50
Statue of Drake, wrongly named,
King Edward VII. 125mm.   20.00
Ripon Market Cross. No. 4197.
125mm.   13.00

Historical/Folklore
Alladin on lamp. Coloured.
110mm long.   20.00
Banbury Cross, lady on a horse.
No. 2445.
2 sizes: 97mm.   0.00
130mm.   17.00
Can be found coloured.
No. 2445. 97mm.   30.00

Cinderella's Coach. No. 5800.
96mm. (Lustre).   30.00
Mary Queen of Scot's Chair, not
named. No. 3604 or No. 3404.73mm.   5.50
Ripon Hornblower. No. 4196. with
inscription. 123mm.   11.00

Traditional/National Souvenirs
Blackpool Big Wheel.
2 sizes: No. 7534. 80mm.   10.50
No. 3561. 90mm.   10.50
John Bull, standing figure.   19.50
Burns Cottage, interior.   19.50
Coronation Chair. No. 2/21. 60mm.   5.00
Coronation Chair. No. 3583. 97mm.   5.00
Coronation Coach, (inkwell) with lid.
85mm.   27.50
Godiva, Lady, on horseback. 110mm.
No.4428.   20.00
Leaking Boot, Cleethorpes. (Statue
of boy holding boot, moulded to
chest). No. 4592. 130mm.   20.00
3 Legs of Man in Lifeboat - not
glazed.   14.00
Irish Colleen, standing by harp on
ashtray base. Coloured.
No. 20214. 80mm.   19.00
Irish Colleen with harp posy vase.
Coloured, no crest. No. 21585.
90mm.   19.00
Irish Colleen ashtray Coloured.
No. 21586. 86mm.   19.00
Irish Jaunting Car cruet, three-piece.
114mm long.   35.00
Irish Man, sat on stool ashtray,
playing bagpipes. Coloured.
No. 21587. 87mm.   19.00
Highland Mary Statue. 138mm.   20.00
Souter Johnny, unglazed, beige.
115mm.   30.00
Scots Lad spill holder, in kilt, shirt,
bonnet, belt, with big feet.
116mm.   35.00
Scots Girl playing bagpipes on
ashtray base. Coloured figure, no
crest. No. 21587. 85mm.   35.00
Sedan Chair. 122mm.   10.00
Welsh Tea Party. Three Welsh ladies
taking tea. Coloured. 96mm.   22.00
Welsh Lady, standing figure.
No. 8498. 140mm.   20.00
Dutch Boy holding Flag. Coloured.
No. 8912. 92mm.   22.00
Dutch Boy with Wheelbarrow.
No. 5803. 95mm.   23.00

Dutch Girl with Wheelbarrow.
No. 5803. 95mm. (Pair).   23.00
Dutch Girl, fully coloured. No. 3053.
110mm.   30.00
Dutch Girl with basket. Fully
coloured No. 3396. 86mm.   30.00
Dutch Boy holding fish and net.
No. 2555. 155mm.   27.50
Gondola. No. 5660. 132mm long.
Can appear coloured (add £6.00)
No. 3803.   22.00
Indian Canoe. 104mm long.   10.50

Seaside Souvenirs
Ark. No. 7193. 90mm.   7.00
Bathing Hut. No. 4433.(Lustre).64mm.   12.00
Bathing Hut with bather sitting
outside. No. 5668. 70mm long.   22.50
Bathing Hut. No. 6066. 60mm.   12.50
Bathing Hut Cruet Set. 4-piece.
Lustre. 85mm.   22.00
Deck Chair. 60mm.   12.00
Canoe, paddle and flag. No. 5175.
150mm long.   12.00
Canoe, Indian. 104mm long.   12.50
Coracle tied to Stump. No. 1284.
90mm.   6.50
Galleon with bird at front. Swan on
sea beside it. 83mm.   23.00
Galleon, in full sail. Coloured front.
No. 916. 205mm.   30.00
Liner on back of oval ashtray. No.
5808. 80mm. If coloured add
£8.00.   17.00
Ship with 3 masts on waves.
(Lustre).115mm.   22.00
Rowing Boat with rudder. No. 5176.
130mm long.   13.00
Steamboat Cruet Set. 4-piece. Some
colouring. 155mm long.   25.50
Yacht. Lustre. No. 1123. 115mm.   11.00
Yacht. No. 3482. 103mm.   12.50
Yacht. No. 4132. 113mm.   14.00
Yacht with waves, beige/rust.
No. 4422. 110mm.   11.00
Yacht, full sail on waves. No. 4438.
85mm.   10.50
Anchor, beige. 3 links of chain.
No. 5183. 75mm.   17.00
Lifebelt & Anchor, wall posy vase,
150mm.   14.00
Fisherman behind ship's wheel.
125mm. No. 2654.   24.00
118mm.   22.00

Fisherman holding fish, with net
match holder. No. 3397. 80mm.   18.00
Fishing boat with sails, net under
side on waves. No. 13364.
118mm long.   22.50
Fisherman's Creel. No. 7192. Fixed
lid. 60mm.   10.00
Fisherman's Wicker Basket with net
overflowing with fish, beige/
rust. No. 5186. 66mm.   21.00
Fish Basket with handle, draped in
net with 4 fish. 65mm.   16.00
Fisherman, Bust, holding ashtray,
fully coloured. No. 4282.   13.00
Lifeboatman, standing figure.
3 sizes: No. 6528. 115mm.   14.50
No. 7200. 128mm.   14.50
No. 3562. 122mm.   14.50
Lighthouse. No. 3585. 90mm.   6.00
Lighthouse. No. 1585. 80mm.   6.00
Lighthouse. No. 11223. 110mm.   6.00
Lighthouse on grassy base. No. 4418.
100mm.   10.00
Lighthouse. 150mm.   8.00
Beachy Head Lighthouse, black band.
3 sizes: 100mm.   9.50
118mm. No. 6723.   10.00
145mm.   12.50
Lighthouse (Beachy Head), yellow
rust lustre. No. 6474. 130mm.   10.50
Corbiere Jersey Lighthouse. No. 751.
100mm.   17.00
Shell dish, black edging.
145mm long.   3.50
Cockle shell dish. 115mm long.   4.00
Crab, Pin Box, in orange lustre.
No. 2191. 80mm long.   10.50
Boy or Oyster Catcher on Lobster.
No. 4426. 100mm long.   24.50
Boy in trunks on diving board.
Hand to face in trepidation.
No. 5799. 110mm.   26.50
Boy in skiff holding ice cream.
No. 4446.   20.00
Girl on rubber duck in sea. No. 5179.
85mm.   30.00
Black Boy on inflatable duck.
No. 5179. 78mm.   38.50
Girl sitting on boat holding lifebelt.
No. 3413. 118mm.   17.00
Girl wearing a hat on a donkey.
No. 4170. 110mm.   17.00
Girl riding a donkey. No. 4840.
115mm.   17.00
Boy riding a donkey No. 4840.
115mm. Pair with above.   17.00

Mermaid sitting in whelk.
No. 4430. 100mm long.   22.00
Girl in whelk, coloured.
No. 5334. 75mm.   25.00

Bathing Beauties/Twenties
Flappers
Found decorated in two styles –
white ware with clothes edged in
rust brown and the face and hair
coloured, or yellow / rust or other
shaded lustre. Value the same.
Bathing Beauty on ashtray. No.
4424. 95mm long (lustre).   26.00
Bathing Belles, two, on ashtray base
in relief in colour. Inscribed: *I'm*
letting myself go. People think I'm
potty but what do I care? 107mm.   35.00
Bathing Beauty on square ashtray.
110mm long.   22.00
Bathing Beauty on triangular
ashtray. No. 2578.
2 sizes: 75mm.   30.00
            90mm.   35.00
Bathing Beauty diving through
waves on lustre dish. 88mm long.   24.50
Bathing Beauty on oyster ashtray.
No. 4172. 75mm. (Lustre).   25.00
Bathing Beauty sitting up on lustre
shell, green costume. No. 4174.
70mm.   35.00
Bathing Beauty kneeling on pearl
lustre shell, green costume. 80mm
long, 60mm high.   35.00
Bathing Beauty reclining on shell,
orange costume. No. 4173.
90mm long. (Lustre).   35.00
Bathing Beauty reclining on tummy
on lustre shell, orange costume.
No. 4171. 100mm long.   35.00
Bathing Beauty reclining on oyster
ashtray, orange or purple
costume. No. 4027. 80mm long.   30.00
Bathing Belle, yellow costume,
reclining on lustre oyster shell.
80mm long, 58mm high.
No.4091.   35.00
Bathing Beauty sitting on oyster
shell. No. 4114. 80mm.   26.00
Bathing Beauty on slide - pair of
girls facing different ways both
with same No. 5801. Different
poses. 102mm. (Lustre).   each 30.00
Bathing Beauty sitting outside ridge
tent. 60mm.   20.00

Bathing Beauty peeping out of
Bathing Hut. Can be found with
right arm over head, or left arm
on shoulder No. 4421. 104mm.   30.00
Bathing Beauty on Turtle. No. 4451.
100mm long. (Lustre).   25.50
Bathing Beauty, coloured, orange
bikini and shoes, reclining on
inflated beige lustre fish. No. 11095.
75mm.   35.00
Bathing Beauty on Fish. No. 5796
(beige lustre). 103mm.   35.00
Bathing Beauty seated on breakwater
with waves on ashtray base, splashing
around with lifebelt around neck and
body. Inscribed: *The Buoy on the Girl*
at Bournemouth. No. 4890. 110mm.   65.00
Bathing Beauty paddling canoe,
with flag at back. No. 5174.
140mm long.   22.50
Bathing Beauty in canoe with
2-bladed paddle, no flag.
No. 5174. 140mm long.   22.50
Bathing Beauty in basket chair.
No. 2949. 100mm.   22.00
Bathing Belle on stylized donkey,
(Lucky White Heather). No. 5708.
95mm.   35.00
Flapper on Stool with Scottie dog.
No. 5672. 108mm. (Lustre).   25.00
Flapper Pin Cushion Girl, four holes
in base. Blue costume, pink hat.
No. 5717.   25.50
Girl in Basket Chair. No. 8902.
74mm. (Lustre).   17.50
Girl with parasol in Basket Chair.
2 sizes: No. 4165. 120mm.   30.00
         No. 4074. 104mm.   30.00
Sunbather with parasol, reclining.   35.00
Girl in slacks on beach ball. 115mm. 22.00
Girl in sleeveless dress on sea shell.
No. 4430. 85mm. (Lustre).   22.00
Girl sitting on a die, holding fan.
Colouring to hat, dress, shoes
& fan. No. 5971. 80mm.   35.00

Figures
Figures which are obviously seaside
souvenirs have been included in
that section. For Bathing Beauties
and Twenties flappers please see
'Bathing Beauties / Twenties
Flappers' heading. Some of the
figures below were obviously
made as a girl and boy pair.

Baby on Scottie Dog's back, holding
flag. No. 7148. Some colouring.
90mm long.   34.50
Bell Hop, holding basket of flowers
and letter with red seal. No. 6878.
110mm.   20.00
Bell Hop with 2 cases, telegram and
bouquet. Posy Vase. Coloured.
105mm.   20.00
Bell Hop, coloured, pushing
wheelbarrow. No. 5808. 96mm.   20.00
Boy dressed as Bell Hop with Globe.
No. 5197. 98mm.   20.00
Girl dressed as Bell Hop with Globe.
No. 5194. 98mm. (pair).   20.00
Boy dressed as Bell Hop, saluting,
sitting on suitcase. 75mm and
97mm. No. 5804   20.00
Girl dressed as Bell Hop, sitting on
suitcase holding flowers. No. 5804.
75mm long. (pair).   20.00
Boy leaning against wicker basket,
feeding birds, coloured. No. 2421.   20.00
Girl, pair to above, in same pose
looking to other direction.
No. 5671.   20.00
Child on red and white Scottie dog,
holding flag. No. 3148. 80mm.   35.00
Child in fez, riding elephant.
No. 7498. 80mm.   30.00
Two Children, skiing downhill on
slope. No. 5805. 95mm.   30.00
Child dressed in bobble hat and
sweater, holding ice skates.
No. 921. 110mm.   30.00
Two Children, on sledge on slope.
Two versions, looking left and
right. No. 5802. 95mm.   30.00
Two Children with a wheelbarrow
on slope. No. 6381. 90mm.   25.00
Boy on Swing, standing. No. 5809.
Some colouring. 110mm.   22.50
Girl on Swing, standing. No. 5808 or
5809. 110mm.   22.50
Boy Scout with dog. 100mm.   45.00
Girl Guide with cat. 103mm.   30.00
Boy with flag. No. 5798. 105mm.   22.00
Girl with flag. No. 5798. 105mm.   22.00
Boy, bathing dog in a tub, with
watering can and soap. 83mm.   25.00
Girl with pigtails, sitting on side of
oval wooden tub, holding two
kittens, with cat on other side.
Pair to the above.   25.00

Boy in black bowler hat and shoes,
polishing red heart and standing
beside basket of red hearts.
No. 3316. 86mm.   30.00
Girl in mob cap, blue dress and black
shoes, holding red heart and brush,
standing beside basket of red hearts.
No. 3316. 86mm.   30.00
Girl on open-mouthed fish. No. 5796.
100mm.   20.00
Girl in trousers and t-shirt leaning
against globe. No. 5797. 105mm.   25.00
Boy on square base, holding up
boat. 122mm.   25.00
Two boys boxing fully coloured, on
oval base. 108mm.   40.00
Boy carrying umbrella and satchel.
No. 21669. 85mm.   25.00
Boy with begging pug dog.
No. 7062. 75mm.   22.00
Boy feeding birds beside a basket.   22.00
Boy, standing, playing concertina,
fully coloured. No. 8527. 84mm.   25.00
Boy with hat, sitting on edge of
ashtray with dog and playing
concertina. Fully coloured.
No. 20835. 65mm.   25.00
Boy on bike with teddy bear on
pillion, wearing beret and gloves.
Fully coloured. No. 21691. 85mm.   30.00
Boy in top hat playing trombone, fully
coloured. No. 20884.   30.00
Boy on toy elephant on wheels,
coloured. No. 21686. 88mm.   25.00
Boy sailor, fully coloured, bell bottom
trousers, wearing cap, hands in
pockets. No. 10115. 95mm.   30.00
Girl Pin Box & Lid, holding fan and
wearing yellow & pink evening gown.
No. 4012. 70mm.   25.00
Girl, bow in hair, finger in mouth,
fully coloured. No. 11078. 115mm.   25.00
Boy, long trousers and braces, finger
in mouth. No. 11078. 115mm.   25.00
Girl, sitting with dogs, on a stand.
No. 7147. 85mm.   30.00
Girl with mandolin. No. 20396.
103mm.   24.00
Girl with banjo, seated, coloured.
No. 20884. 85mm.   24.00
Girl in coloured dress, wheeling
barrow. No. 3321. 110mm.   25.00
Girl with barrow, some colouring.
No. 4643. 100mm.   25.00

Girl sitting on chaise longue.
No. 5667. 95mm long.   30.00
Girl on blue seat, metal screw
stopper on head scent bottle.
No. 8596. 95mm.   22.00
Girl, kneeling, holding Camera, with
dog sat in front. No. 20883. 95mm.   30.00
Little girl tennis player, brown & green
dress, beige bonnet standing on oval
base with round brick posy holder.
No. 2916. 100mm.   40.00
Boy in bobbly jumper, holding toy.
No. 7255. 85mm.   25.00
Girl in bobbly jumper, holding toy.
No. 7255. 85mm.   25.00
Girl in brown dress with blue hat
playing with hoop next to posy
vase decorated with blue flowers.
No. 4189. 120mm.   30.00
Boy in blue trousers & blue hat to
match above. No. 4189. 120mm.   30.00
Edwardian lady holding cat and
basket. 100mm.   30.00
Girl in hat on donkey. No. 4428.
105mm.   16.50
Girl on donkey on oval base.
No. 4840.
2 sizes: 115mm.   16.50
             128mm.   16.50
Huntsman on horseback, coloured.
No. 2445. 100mm.   30.00
Huntsman, red coat, grey base,
chasing stag - green base. No. 8454.
100mm.   30.00
Gentleman wearing top hat,
carrying umbrella on green
ashtray base. No. 20036. 70mm.   23.00
Grapetreaders. Two in Basket. 110mm. 40.00
Country Gent on ashtray, coloured.
No. 20218. 83mm.   25.00
Gent on horse in huntsman's attire,
fully coloured. Spill holder.
No. 6880. 112mm.   25.00
Lady on horse, side saddle, in
hunting attire, fully coloured, spill
holder. 112mm. No. 6880.   25.00
Man & woman (lovers) on bench
within pillars, with steps leading
up to it. 65mm.   22.00
Princess, Arabian, riding camel. Fully
coloured. No. 909. 156mm.   25.00
Victorian gentleman and peasant girl
with pig on a rope. She is sheltering
him with her shawl from the wind
whilst he lights her match and holds
her rope. Inscribed: *The Last Match.*
No. 4018.   40.00

Woman with wickerwork basket of
fish on her back. 122mm.   40.00
Waiter in tailcoat, fully coloured, no
crest. No. 7061.   33.00
Welsh Lady, knitting, standing by
trunk with kitten playing with
wool. No. 7005. 95mm.   27.50

Countryside
Milkmaid holding churn. 124mm.   20.00
Pine Cone on side, lustre.
No. 7216. 90mm long.   7.00
Shepherd and Lamb by hollow tree
trunk. No. 846A. 75mm.   15.00
Shepherdess and Lamb by hollow
tree trunk. No. 846B. 75mm.   15.00
Stile with milestone, with heart and
initials. 100mm.   9.50

Animals
Bear, Polar, No. 4439. 90mm.   35.00
Bears, three on oval base. No. 4505.
73mm.   0.00
Butterfly vase. 45mm.   7.00
Butterfly on Vase. 98mm.   10.00
Cats, two hugging in Bath chair.
No. 5686. 68mm.   50.00
Cat in bandages, sitting. 90mm.   30.00
Cat, black on ashtray. No. 5002.
92mm long.   25.00
Cat, black, arched back standing on
green armchair. No. 1925. 57mm.   25.00
Cat, black, seated on orange armchair
washing paw. No. 3767. 78mm.   25.00
Cat, black standing four feet together
on orange armchair. No. 1925. 70mm. 25.00
Cat, Cheshire. No. 6622. 70mm.   7.50
Cat, Cheshire, with arched back.
No. 3922 (rust). 65mm.   9.50
Cat and chimney pot. No. 7582.
52mm.   10.00
Cat, sitting. No. 6623. 55mm.   9.00
Cat, standing on hind legs, comical.
85mm.   40.00
Cat in long skirt and blouse with tie,
carrying tennis racquet at waist
level. 100mm. Rare.   65.00
Cat in long skirt holding tennis
racquet down. 100mm.   65.00
Cat in long skirt holding tennis
racquet up. 100mm.   65.00
Cat on trinket box. No. 5678, No.
5679 & No. 5819. Can be found in
lemon/rust lustre. 88mm long.   16.50

Cats, one large and one small either side of a cauldron. No. 4721. 105mm long.   20.00

Cat, fat and miserable with bandage over eye and bow on head. No. 930. 80mm.   30.00

Cats, three in a laundry basket, or possibly one kitten and two pups. 65mm.   30.00

Cat posy bowl, detailed fur. No. 4394. 115mm.   15.00

Cat, grotesque with long neck, outpressed; *Luck* in orange. No. 3402. 132mm.   7.00

Cat, sitting, bow around neck. Lemon/rust. 60mm.   11.50

Cat, singing, holding song sheet, left paw on top of music. 65mm.   22.50

Cat and Rabbit in high boot. 95mm.   22.00

Cat and Rabbit in pair of boots. 83mm.   22.00

Cat with paw on rat. 73mm.   35.00

Cat peeping out of old boot. No. 6568. 98mm long.   19.50

Cat on back of boot, mouse on toe. No. 4720. 110mm long.   24.50

Cat on thermometer on upright column. No. 8876. 105mm.   28.00

Cat, black ears, sitting, in lustre slipper. No. 6980. 95mm long.   17.50

Black Cat with grey bow, on orange, green, purple, red or blue chair. No. 1925 or Nos. 3768, 7287 or 7887. *Good luck* in relief. 68mm.   25.00

Black Cat on sofa. No. 3767. 76mm.   25.00

Black Cat on orange chair, arched back. No. 8767. 50mm.   25.00

Black Cat in orange basket. No. 6231. 69mm.   22.00

Cow Creamer. No. 4394. 118mm long.   19.00

Cow's head cream jug. 80mm.   7.00

Cow, walking. 102mm long.   40.00

Dog, Pointer with coiled spring metal tail. 135mm long.   30.00

Dog, Pointer. 120mm long.   26.00

Dog in kennel. No. 3479. 70mm.   12.50

Dog in bandages, sitting. 90mm.   30.00

Dog in boot. No. 6568. 114mm long.   16.50

Dog, sitting, Spaniel. 67mm   12.50

Dog, Scottie, wearing Tam o'shanter. 74mm.   12.50

Dog, Terrier, standing. No. 6630. 74mm long.   14.50

Dog, Pug, lying down. 112mm long.   15.00

Dog, Pug sitting with top hat matchholder. No. 3417. 78mm.   11.50

Dog, Scottie in blue trousers, standing playing red concertina, with red top hat, standing beside match holder. 66mm.   22.00

Dog, black on ashtray base. No. 1971. 100mm long.   25.00

Dog's head spill holder. 46mm.   9.50

Dog with dead hare in mouth, on rocky base, plaque. 140mm.   30.00

Dog, King Charles Spaniel, head to one side, holding red flower on leaf base. No. 11447. 82mm.   10.00

Dog with paw on rat. 72mm.   35.00

Dog, puppy sitting. 70mm.   15.00

Dog, puppy on chaise-longue. No. 5894. 84mm long.   26.50

Dog, orange Scottie, sitting on purple lustre shoe. No. 349. 105mm long.   12.00

Dogs, mother and puppy on oval base. 80mm.   20.00

Dog standing, Chauffeur, smoking pipe wearing hat with glasses and long overcoat. 85mm.   55.00

Dog, possibly female, standing, dressed in long travelling coat and flat cap, tied with scarf under chin. 82mm. (Possibly a pair to the chauffeur above).   55.00

Dog, sitting with arms folded, with left eye blackened and cauliflower right ear, wearing battered top hat, on lustre ashtray base. Fully coloured. No. 7018. 75mm.   25.00

Dog Mustard Pot and Spoon. 80mm.   12.50

Dogs, two Bull Terriers sitting together. 80mm wide.   22.00

Dog, Black on pink padded French Chair. No. 6590. 65mm.   22.00

Dog, puppy, on a shoe. No. 6980. 100mm long.   12.50

Dog, Spaniel as Radio Operator. No. 3317. 77mm.   30.00

Donkey barometer string tail (orange lustre) No. 1897. 80mm long.   12.00

Donkey in harness with tree on oval base. Impressed *24*. 55mm.   15.00

Donkey, ears laid back, standing on oval base, in harness. No. 3486. 88mm long.   12.50

Donkey in Harness. No. 6102.
93mm long. 12.50
Donkey. 90mm long. 16.50
Donkey, standing inscribed:
Carisbrooke Donkey. 94mm long. 30.00
Donkey with saddle, standing,
88mm long. 12.50
Elephant sitting, posy holder.
No. 4391. 120mm long. 8.50
Elephant standing, posy holder.
No. 4508. 8.50
Elephant with foot on ball. No. 3682.
95mm long. 40.00
Elephant with howdah. 70mm. 40.00
Elephant with howdah cruet set.
70mm. 20.00
Elephant standing, trunk raised.
No. 6629. 75mm, 85mm long. 20.00
Elephant, ridden by circus monkey.
Raised trunk. No. 6388. 93mm. 40.00
Fish, very ornate. 110mm long. 8.00
Fish. No. 6476. 180mm long. 8.50
Fish. No. 5011. 125mm long. 8.00
Fish, box & lid. No. 2051. 128mm long. 8.00
Fish, open mouthed. No. 6475.
143mm long. 8.00
Fish Pepper Pot, black facial
features. 110mm long. 8.50
Fish on ashtray base, coloured.
No. 11560. 83mm. 10.00
Frog, yellow/green on white oval
base. 60mm. 19.50
Frog on shell, the frog is usually
brown or green on a lustre shell.
No. 4450. 110mm long. 15.00
Two Goats standing by open tree
trunks. 50mm. 16.50
Hare, sitting. 74mm. 9.50
Horse, standing in sleigh. 20.00
Jaguar, open mouthed, crouching on
oval base. No. 934. 125mm long. 40.00
The Jersey Cow lying down, gilded
horns. 118mm long. 25.00
Lion on base. Left and right facing
found. Obviously sold as a pair
as they have the same No. 4166,
(lustre). 90mm, 115mm long. 10.00
Lion Posy Holder, lying down.
No. 4392. 125mm long. 10.00
Lion & Lioness on base, lemon/rust
No. 4454. 240mm long. 16.00
Lion & Lioness on base, running,
lemon/rust. No. 4856. 230mm long. 16.00
Lobster Trinket Box & lid, orange.
130mm long. 8.00

Monkey, sitting. No. 7198. 82mm. 17.50
Mouse, sitting, large ears. 70mm. 20.00
Three Wise Monkeys on wall.
No. 7195. 80mm. 12.00
Pig, standing. No. 3566. 98mm long,
53mm high. 22.50
Pig, standing, posy holder, pink.
No. 4865. 135mm long. 18.00
Pig, sitting on haunches. Pepper
Pot. 70mm. 18.50
Pig, sitting up with front trotters on
hips! Pink snout. 87mm. 40.00
Pig, gilded, peering over rim of cup.
2 sizes: 55mm. 12.50
75mm. 14.00
Pig, sitting, heavy china. 66mm. 7.00
Pig, standing. 98mm long. 22.50
Pig, lustre, in boat. 115mm long. 14.00
Rabbit/Duck. Inscribed: *Isn't this
rabbit a duck?* 75mm. 25.00
Rabbit, sitting upright. 85mm. 15.00
Rabbit in clothes on sledge.
90mm long. (Saxony). 30.00
Seal on rectangular base. No. 4452.
Base can be found in lustre.
127mm long. 16.50
Sheep with silver lambs on oval
base. No. 8031. 90mm long. 16.00
Shetland Pony. 100mm long. 20.00
Snail. No. 5178. 112mm long.
(Lustre). 17.00
Snail. No. 7187. 92mm long. 17.50
Tortoise trinket box and lid.
2 sizes: No. 402. 78mm long. 12.50
No. 6625. 85mm long. 14.50
Turtle Pin Box and lid. 128mm long. 16.00
Wild Boar, charging. Pepper Pot.
No. 9279. 85mm long. 19.50

Birds (including Eggs)
Egg Shell, empty. 60mm long. 7.00
Bird on branch, oval base. No. 3816.
60mm. 12.00
Bird, possibly Pelican with large open
beak forming pepper pot. No. 9280.
62mm. 10.00
Bird on edge of nest pin tray. 3 eggs.
No. 312. 58mm. 22.00
Bird on rock, head looking right.
80mm. 13.00
Can be found fully coloured. 22.00
Bird on rock, head looking left.
Coloured. 118mm. 22.00
Bird on rock, looking left, black
edging to wings. No. 6483. 106mm. 14.00

Chicken, red comb. No. 6621.
80mm. 12.50
Chickens, two with flowers on vase.
Can be found with a lustre finish
or with chickens, flowers and
ladybird coloured on white
ground. No. 5806. 120mm. 8.50
Chick Pepper Pot. 67mm. 9.50
Chicks, two, yellow, on vase,
squawking at each other.
120mm. 17.00
Cockerell and two chickens on slope.
No. 5807. Some colouring.
95mm long. 30.00
Cockerel Pepper Pot. 74mm. 9.50
Duck, fully coloured, on lemon lustre
trinket box and lid.
75mm long. 14.50
Duck Jug. 130mm long. 7.00
Duck Ashtray. No. 5695.
110mm long. 9.50
Duck, Indian Runner, long neck and
two ducklings, oval base.
No. 7873. 106mm. 14.00
Cockatoo with 2 fledglings on nest,
purple with red crest on head and
green nest. No. 7141. 16.00
Duckling Pepper Pot, can be found
coloured. 80mm.
Coloured. 14.50
White 9.50
Duckling wearing hat, carrying
umbrella, on leaf shaped base.
Yellow lustre on mauve base.
No. 11448. 85mm. 10.00
Fledgling, blue with orange beak on
ashtray base. 10.00
Goldfinch on rock. Coloured.
No. 877. 97mm. 23.50
Heron Posy Holder, No. 4445.
120mm long. 9.50
Kiwi, fully coloured, glazed,
outpressed *Kiwi NZ*. No. 6527.
72mm. 40.00
Owl on three books. No. 937.
100mm. 20.00
Owl on tree stump, with inscription.
115mm. 12.50
Parrot and cockatoo squawking,
facing one another. No. 5812.
100mm long, 85mm high. 29.50
Parrot. No. 6626. 64mm high,
75mm long. 8.50
Peacock on oval ashtray. No. 4934.
80mm long. 15.00

Pelican, drooping beak. 92mm. 12.50
Penguin Pepper Pot. 82mm. 14.50
Pheasant, blue on yellow/brown
ashtray. No. 4934. 60mm. 13.00
Seagull, posy bowl. No. 4445.
125mm long. 8.00
Seagull, flying. Posy holder.
No. 5903. 66mm. 22.00
Swan on blue water, brown beak.
No. 4169. 85mm. 14.50
Swan posy bowl, yellow beak.
93mm. 6.00
Swan posy bowl. No. 3486.
81mm long. 6.00
Turkey posy holder. No. 1361.
90mm. 9.00

Great War
French Soldier, kneeling. No. 1809.
94mm. 70.00
Monoplane, with hole in body,
could be posy holder or pin
cushion. Lustre. 77mm long. 15.00
Monoplane with egg timer
propellor. No. 8488. 112mm long. 15.00
Monoplane with pilot. No. 7207.
100mm long. 25.00
Monoplane with gold fixed prop.
No. 4437. 76mm long. 29.50
Monoplane Cruet. 155mm long. 16.00
Monoplane in orange lustre.
130mm long. 15.00
Air Ship, open top, posy holder.
131mm long. 25.00
Airship Cruet set. 192mm long. 40.00
Ambulance, Red Crosses on sides.
No. 854 or 3916. 80mm long. 28.50
Tank with forward facing guns and
curved exhaust pipe on roof. No.
8424 and No. 854. 110mm long. 40.00
Tank, small, no wheels. 20.00
Bomb on 4 feet. 85mm. 7.00
Bucket Helmet. 55mm. 40.00
Field Glasses. No. 5187. 73mm. 15.00
Pith Helmet. 57mm long. 25.00
French Soldier's Cap. 60mm long. 30.00
Mess Pot. 55mm. 25.00
Cenotaph with inscription.
2 sizes: No. 6725. 110mm. 6.50
No. 6726. 148mm. 7.50
Clacton on Sea War Memorial.
No. 6999. 125mm. 22.50
Great Yarmouth War Memorial.
110mm. 16.00
130mm. 22.00

Matlock Bath War Memorial,
often poor quality

4 sizes: No. 6655. 120mm.	12.00
No. 4194. 140mm.	14.00
No. 3924. 155mm.	16.50
197mm.	18.00

Southsea War Memorial. No. 6660.

2 sizes: 120mm.	20.00
160mm.	30 00

Worthing War Memorial. No. 6776.

3 sizes: 108mm.	14.00
155mm.	16.50
166mm.	20.00

Home/Nostalgic

Anvil. No. 6618.

2 sizes: 60mm.	6.00
85mm.	6.50
Armchair, padded arms. No. 3404.	
78mm.	7.00
Armchair, upholstered. No. 6812.	
74mm.	14.50
Basket, tiny. 40mm.	6.00
Basket, blue bow and red roses on handle. No. 4714. 75mm.	6.00
Basket of coloured Fruit. No. 3918. 85mm.	13.00
Bath on four splayed feet. No. 5188. 115mm long.	13.50
Bellows Pin Box and lid. No. 2001.	6.50
Book, brass bound and open. No. 8470. 52mm.	12.50
Book, open, with heart in relief on front cover. 50mm. No. 8470.	12.50
Box Iron. No. 5671. 90mm long, 62mm high.	12.50
Carpet Bag, open top. 86mm.	6.00
Coffee Table, central stem. 60mm.	6.00
Chair, ornate. No. 3567. 105mm.	12.50
Chair, Lloyd Loom. 62mm.	12.00
Chair, padded high back. No. 6095. 70mm.	9.50
Coal Scuttle. No. 6813. 55mm.	6.50
Clock with rope columns.	6.50
Easel on stand with brushes. No. 5448. 112mm.	8.00
Fireplace, *There's No Place Like Home.* No. 2275. 65mm.	10.00
Flat Iron (rust lemon). No. 5671. 80mm long.	17.00
Grandfather Clock. No. 22. 95mm.	7.00
Grandfather Clock, inscription. *Make use of Time.* No. 3401. 140mm.	10.00
Grandmother Clock. 88mm.	7.50
Jardiniere fixed base. 88mm.	6.00

Mantle Clock, ornate. 85mm.	7.50
Mantle Clock with side wings. No. 4729. 72mm.	7.00
Mantle Clock, time - 11·12 or 9·26. No. 4810. 100mm long.	7.00
Pail with handle down. No. 5185. 65mm.	6.50
Pedestal. No. 6905. 83mm.	2.00
Pipe, gold on orange dish. 85mm dia.	8.50
Pocket Watch. No. 5184. 70mm.	24.50
Policeman's Lamp. 70mm.	6.50
Post Box. No. 6496. 75mm.	12.50
Post Box, oval, inscribed: *Letters.* No. 3483. 88mm.	15.00
Sack of Meal. No. 1645. 80mm.	12.00
Shaving Mug.	
2 sizes: 30mm.	7.50
40mm.	7.50
Sofa, ornate. 70mm long.	10.50
Stool, blue lustre. 53mm.	7.00
Suitcase, re-inforced corners. No. 6814. 76mm long.	7.00
Umbrella, coloured. 70mm.	12.00
Watering Can, no rose. 50mm.	11.00
Watering Can, heavily gilded. 103mm.	11.00
Watering Can, rust coloured. No. 1423. 87mm.	11.00
Watering Can. No. 4427. 90mm.	11.00
Watering Can, deep blue with transfer scene. 120mm.	12.00
Wheelbarrow. No. 51277. 135mm long.	10.00

Comic/Novelty

Black boy sitting on toilet pan in lavatory. Door half open. Another black boy peeking in. Inscribed: *Shut the D... door* and *Engaged* and *My resting place in Perth* on plinth. No. 5660. 67mm.	20.00
Black boys, three as musicians (Banjo, Saxophone, Drums) in Blue jackets (Salt, Pepper, Mustard) on oval tray. No. 9002. Tray 150mm long.	60.00
Black *Momma* candlestick, coloured. *A present from...* 100mm long.	24.50
Bride and Groom in large Shell. No. 5795. 105mm.	24.50
Coronation coach ink well.	30.00
Cupid with wings standing at curtained window, his and her shoes on ledge. No. 753. 90mm.	19.50

Egg as house with rabbit peering
out of barred window in egg.
With standing rabbit in tailcoat
alongside and a snail in front.
65mm.   40.00
Egg supporting tiny chick and hare.
Blue ribbon, green base.
No. 6893. 75mm.   0.00
Gnome matchholder, fully coloured,
with white beard, carrying sack.
No. 5270. 100mm.   50.00
Jester. 75mm.   6.50
Pierrette standing by open bag.
No. 3315. 90mm. (pair).   12.50
Pierrette reclining on trinket box.
No. 3498. 110mm.   17.50
Pierrot Mustard Pot, head as lid.
No. 9301. 100mm.   30.00
Pierrot standing by open bag (Lustre).
No. 3315. 90mm.   12.50
Pierrot, fully coloured, sat on dice,
playing concertina, sack at back
as match holder. No. 5971. 80mm.   30.00
Pierrette, fully coloured, sat on dice
with fan. Sack at back as match
holder. No. 5971. 80mm.   30.00
Pixie on oval base. 60mm.   12.00
Policeman, fully coloured at front.
No. 7083. 84mm.   27.00
Sack of Money, with figure 500,000
impressed in seal. No. 1645.   13.00
Sailor, comical, smoking pipe. Some
colouring. No. 8959. 132mm.   30.00
Sultan sitting on bowl. No. 4834.
100mm.   18.00

Cartoon/Comedy Characters
Bonzo salt pot, inscribed: *I'm Salt,*
some colouring and in lustre.
80mm.   17.00
(This is a very true likeness of
Bonzo, exactly like the drawings
of him).
Felix the Cat, standing in front of
match holder and striker,
coloured. 84mm.   100.00

Alcohol
Champagne Bottle in Ice Bucket.
82mm.   7.00
Toby Jug. No. 6608. 63mm.   9.50

Sport/Pastimes
Boy, footballer spill holder, fully
coloured. No. 3476. 80mm.   35.00

Boy footballer match holder, ball at
feet, fully coloured.
No. 6114. 85mm.   35.00
Boy, tennis player match holder,
partly coloured. No. 3414. 80mm.   30.00
Girl tennis player match holder, racket
in left hand, ball in right hand,
fully coloured. No. 3872. 85mm.   30.00
Footballer, blue shirt and socks,
white shorts, ball at feet and hands
on hips. Goggle-eyed. No. 4055.
132mm.   30.00
Tennis Player, long flannels, ball in
right hand, racket in left. Fully
coloured. No. 5312. 142mm.   30.00
Tennis Player, lady with racket,
standing by net. No. 3414. 85mm.   30.00
Trophy and lid. 105mm.   12.00
Artist's Easel and brushes. No. 4841.
65mm.   4.00
Club card suit indicator. No. 3919.
80mm.   12.50

Musical Instruments
Accordian. No. 5661. 90mm long.   10.00
Grand Piano. No. 4168. 85mm long.   14.50
Guitar. 136mm long.   16.50
Upright Piano. No. 7134. (lustre).
70mm.   14.50

Transport
Coal Truck. No. 3915. 75mm.   14.50
Coal Truck. No. 3916. 65mm long.   14.50
Girl in Car. No. 5774. 100mm long.
(lustre).   30.00
Girl driving a car with gladstone
bag and bundle on top. No. 5794.
85mm long.   30.00
Hot Air Balloon, square basket.
2 sizes: 65mm.   40.00
90mm.   55.00
Locomotive. No. 8427. 120mm long.   35.00
Locomotive 2-4-4. Cruet set with
black coal. No. 69627/34.
135mm long.   35.00
Motor Car, open top (lustre).
150mm long.   25.00
Motor Car, open top. No. 3917.
75mm long. (lustre).   15.00
Motor Car, open tourer. No. 1912.
chauffeured. 92mm long.   20.00
Motor Car Cuet Set. 120mm long.   22.00
Luggage Trolley, loaded.
80mm long. No. 4425.   30.00
Ornate Sleigh. No. 7952.   35.00
Petrol Can, impressed: *Motor Spirit.*
No. 7214. 67mm.   16.00

Modern Equipment

Binoculars. No. 5187.	
2 sizes: 60mm.	12.50
75mm.	12.50
Cruet Set Binoculars, in lustre.	
70mm.	10.00
Folding Camera. No. 5182. 75mm.	24.00
Horn Gramophone. No. 7196.	
42mm.	17.50
Horn Gramophone. No. 3563. 70mm	
long, 80mm high.	22.50
Dog listening by gramophone on	
beige oval ashtray. 115mm long.	30.00
Radio with horn. No. 5180. 70mm.	40.00
Treadle Sewing Machine. No 5439.	
72mm.	17.50

Hats

Boater, lustre. No. 4429. 97mm long.	8.50
Helmet with plumage. 48mm.	13.00
Jockey's cap. 70mm.	15.00
Top Hat Match Striker. 42mm.	6.50
Top Hat with brown umbrella on	
top. 60mm.	9.50

Footwear

Ankle Boot, open top and eyelets.	
2 sizes: 135mm long. No. 3586.	8.50
105mm long.	6.50
Baby's Bootee, quilted, threaded	
with real ribbon. 52mm.	12.50
Boot, Ladies. No. 1835. 70mm.	6.50
Boot, open. 48mm.	8.00
Dutch Clog. No. 2079. 70mm long.	5.00
Ladies Slipper. 150mm long.	7.50
Ladies 18th Century Shoe. 84mm long.	7.50
Lancashire Clog. No. 3587.	
2 sizes: 125mm long.	5.00
180mm long.	7.50
Oriental Slipper. No. 5428.	
95mm long.	6.50
Ornate Ladies Shoe. No. 3322.	
115mm long.10.50	14.50
Sabot, with orange lobster in relief	
on side. 105mm long.	7.50
Sabot, No. 1406A. 74mm long.	6.00

Miniature Domestic

Bowl. 40mm.	4.00
Cheese Dish and cover, ornate	
shape. No. 33/68. 80mm long.	8.00
Cheese Dish and cover, flat sloping	
top. No. 3043. 70mm long.	7.50
Cheese Dish and cover, shield	
shaped base, some colour.	
85mm long.	8.50

Cheese Dish and lid, one-piece. No.	
6114. 65mm long.	6.50
Cheese Dish and cover, handle on	
curved face. No. 6632. Lustre.	
76mm.	7.50
Coffee Pot and lid. No. 3442. 65mm.	8.50
Jug, fluted. 60mm.	3.00
Jug. No. 2753 pink with gold handle,	
and mask as extended neck. 78mm.	4.00
Jug. No. 4683. 60mm.	3.00
Kettle and lid. (Lustre). No. 1226.	
78mm.	8.50
Mug, two-handled. 38mm.	3.00
Tea Pot and Lid, wide base. 45mm.	8.50
Tea Pot and Lid, square base.	
No. 973. 120mm.	9.50
Tea Pot and Lid. No. 4866. 65mm.	8.50
Tea Pot and Lid. No. 9084. 65mm.	8.50
Tea Pot and Lid. No. 4809. 60mm.	8.50
Toast Rack. 74mm long.	8.50

Numbered Domestic Items

Candleholder. No.5605	5.00
Candlestick. No. 358. 80mm.	5.00
Cone Vase. No. 4539.	3.00
Chamberstick. No. 5486. 45mm.	4.00
Inkwell with stopper - bound with	
metal for thermometer. No. 02169.	
100mm long.	5.00
Heart shaped trinket box. No. 5098.	
70mm wide.	4.00
Two handled vase. No. 5682. 65mm.	3.00
Square Plate. No. 32. 145mm.	3.00
Trinket Box, horseshoe shaped,	
bright yellow. No. 2356.	
80mm long.	4.00
Pin Box and lid. No. 2001.	4.00
Vase, silver-rimmed, yellow body	
(Bavaria). 82mm.	9.00

Miscellaneous

Cow Bell, porcelain clapper. 80mm.	4.50
Egg cup. 50mm.	10.00
Horse's Head and Horseshoe on	
ashtray base. Some colouring.	
105mm wide.	
No. 3929. 44mm high	8.50
Ribbon Plates, various designs,	
175mm - 225 mm dia.	15.00

FP&S

Trademark used by Ford and Pointon Ltd. Norfolk Works, Hanley, subsequently a branch of J.A. Robinson and Sons, Ltd. and later Cauldon Ltd. (Usual trademark Coronet).

For details of this firm and the china produced see Coronet Ware and Ford & Pointon.

This mark was probably used by Ford and Pointon Ltd before the Great War. The mark is mostly found on small vases and miniature domestic pieces. No view ware or other transfer prints have been recorded.

FP and S Models
Ancient Artefacts
Loving Cup, 3 handles. No. 19.
38mm.   6.00
Whisky Quaich. Two handled.
Dia. 55mm.   7.00

Historical/Folklore
Miner's Lamp. 70mm.   16.00

Great War
Officers peaked cap. 60mm.   17.00

Animals
Pig, fat. 70mm long.   20.00

Home/Nostalgic
Baby's Cradle. 63mm long.   12.50
Dustpan. 53mm long.   9.50
Policeman's Lamp. 65mm.   12.00

Musical Instruments
Tambourine. 72mm long.   8.50

Footwear
Boot. 35mm.   6.00
Oriental Shoe, with pointed toe.
90mm long.   7.50

Miniature Domestic
Beaker. 39mm.   4.00
Cheese Dish and cover. 50mm.   9.50
Circular Trinket box and lid. 60mm.   6.00

Furstenberg

Trademark used by a German manufacturer for German Souvenir China.

This mark has only been found on a small 60mm vase with the crest Köln Rh. (Cologne).   5.00

G Bros

Trademark used by Grimwades Ltd. Winton, Upper Horley and Elgin Potteries, Stoke. See Grimwades.

Gaelic

The Garnion Ware

"Ⓞéaⳉcʌ Ṣ⅄⅁
ℭ-Ṣıopⴷıŋ"

THE
GARNION
WARE

Trademark used by a Japanese manu-facturer for the Irish market, this being gaelic for *Made in Japan*.

A pierced plate with the crest of Dublin and two 92mm vases have been found.   10.00
The porcelain is greyish in colour.

Gaelic Models
Footwear
Shoe, Ladies high heel.   7.00

Mark used by an unknown manufacturer, thought to be foreign.

Only one small vase with a Guernsey crest has been recorded.   4.00

Gemma

Often found without 'Czecho-Slovakia' under mark, or just with the latter.

Trademark used by Schmidt and Co., Carlsbad (Bohemia). Almost all models can sometimes be found with a lustre finish. Established in 1883, Schmidt and Co. were one of the biggest German exporters of crested china. Before the war AUSTRIA sometimes was printed under the mark but after the war it was more acceptable to print the name of the newly formed state of Czechoslovakia.

Schmidt and Co. used the Gemma mark mostly on miniatures, especially on domestic ones, but some useful domestic ware can be found with the mark including inkpots, pen stands, pill boxes, ribbon plates and salve pots. (One salve pot has been recorded with a silver rim with a Birmingham mark!). Some modern collectors look down upon the very white bodied German crested china that was popular in the period of its manufacture. This attitude is often unfair for, although much Gemma china is clumsy and cheap looking, there are some very delicate pieces especially in the miniature domestic range. Some of the coloured animals and lustre models are exceptionally appealing and inventive and should not be over-looked by collectors who like the later crested wares.

See also Fairy Ware, another Schmidt factory, the mark of which is occasionally found overprinted over the Gemma mark.

Gemma china sold very well in the twenties probably because it was so cheap, and so many of these coloured and lustre finish models are to be found. 'Black Cat' transfers were also used and there are a great number of items with 'Lucky White Heather' usually on lustre but sometimes on a white body. The firm specialised in a yellow shaded lustre, tints varying in depth, but usually shaded from pale lemon, through orange to almost rust. Many bathing beauties are found in this yellow/orange to lustre marked only Germany, but it seems probable that they were made by this firm (see unmarked). Other shades of lustre found on Gemma models include pink, blue, dull orange and mother-of-pearl.

Schmidt and Co. also produced a range of view ware, and coloured and mono-chrome (black only) views can be found on Gemma models and 'smalls'. Some interesting transfer prints can be found on late miniature models including flowers, crinoline ladies and twenties beauties. Two fully coloured Gemma pots have been found with battleship transfers. It is likely that a series of these was made.

Three interesting commemoratives have been recorded, Festival of Empire, Crystal Palace 1911; Imperial Service Exhibition, Earls Court 1913 and War Museum Crystal Palace. Obviously no Great War commemoratives are to be found, as it was illegal to import German china at the time, but crests of King George V appear and the badges of HMS Dreadnought and HMS Illustrious. (No numbering system was used on Gemma models.)

Gemma Models
Ancient Artefacts

Chester Roman Vase. 65mm.	4.00
Irish Bronze Pot. 43mm.	4.00
Loving Cup, 3 handled.	
3 sizes: 39mm.	4.00
50mm.	4.00
(can be found with	
silver rim).	9.50
68mm.	4.00
Puzzle Beaker with verse as below.	
64mm.	17.00

Puzzle Coffee Pot with long spout
and inscription:
*Try your skill, this pot to fill and not
to spill don't use the spout except to
pour out.* 64mm.   18.50
Puzzle Coffee Pot with short spout
and inscription: *Try your skill, this
jug to fill and not to spill don't use
the spout except to pour out.* 64mm.   22.50
Puzzle Cup and Saucer, actually a
beaker with a handle, with verse:
*Try how to drink and not to spill and
prove the utmost of thy skill,* or *Try
your skill this cup to fill but do not
spill. You must not give the problem
up till you succeed to Drain the cup.*
Two types - one with holes in
handle, one without. 55mm.   22.50
Puzzle Cream Jug.
   2 sizes: 42mm, with verse.   6.00
   45mm, holes in rim, no verse.   6.00
Puzzle Jug, with verse.
   3 sizes: 52mm   6.00
   70mm.   6.00
   80mm.   7.50
Puzzle Jug, sometimes with verse
impressed with a shell pattern,
lustre. 52mm.   10.50
Puzzle Loving Cup,1 or 3 handled
   3 sizes: 45mm, with verse.   17.00
   55mm (lustre).   17.00
   67mm, no verse.   10.00
Puzzle Mug, 2 types, with or
without holes in handle. 51mm.   16.00
Puzzle Sugar Bowl,2 handles. 42mm.   16.00
Puzzle Tea Pot. 45mm, with verse.   19.00
   and 62mm without verse.   16.00
Puzzle Teapot. 94mm long.   16.00
Puzzle Tankard, with verse. 50mm
   and 68mm.   10.50
Puzzle Watering Can, with verse.
   48mm.   20.00
Sedan Chair, green. 127mm.   30.00
Quite a number of 'smalls' have
been recorded, often in
Victorian / Gothic style and very
ornate, which may or may not be
ancient artefacts - but are
probably just ornamental!   4.00-6.00

Buildings - White
Blackpool Tower. 130mm.   8.50
First and Last Refreshment House,
not named. Also found in
yellow / orange lustre.
   72mm long.   10.50
Cottage. 72mm long.   8.50

Historical/Folklore
Coronation Chair. Can also be
found in yellow / orange lustre.
   98mm.   6.00
Coronation Coach Inkwell & Lid.
   115mm long, 70mm high.   20.00
Miners Lamp. 58mm.   16.00

Traditional/National Souvenirs
Kelly from the Isle of Man posy
holder, with cat. Inscribed: *A
present from the Isle of Man.*
   115mm.   50.00
Manx Cats as handles of Miniature
Domestic pieces: see 'Animals'.
Manx Legs inside lifebelt. 85mm.   15.00
Manx Man, standing, wearing top
hat. 124mm.   50.00
Welsh Candlestick, Welsh lady
handle. Black hat. 80mm dia.   20.00
Welsh Hat, often found with 'Welsh'
transfer print, add £5.00.
   75mm dia.   10.00
Welsh milk jug, Welsh Lady handle,
some colouring.
   2 sizes: 54mm.   24.50
   62mm.   26.00
Welsh Ladies' head cream jug.
   72mm.   22.00
Welsh Lady, coloured, as handle of
Cheese Dish and cover.
   74mm long.   26.50
Welsh Lady, coloured, as handle of
Tea Pot and lid. 68mm.   27.50
Welsh Lady, coloured, as handle of
Mug. 55mm.   20.00
Welsh Lady, coloured, as handle of
Watering Can. 65mm.   22.50
Welsh Lady, coloured, as handle of
Coffee Pot and lid. 54mm.   27.50
Welsh Lady, coloured, as handle of
Vase. 75mm. Also found with two
Welsh Lady handles.   30.00

Seaside Souvenirs
Bathing Machine money box. 83mm.   17.00
Yacht. 88mm high,102mm long.   17.00
Beachy Head Lighthouse. Black
band. 123mm.   12.50
Lighthouse. 95mm.   6.50
Lighthouse on Rock. 120mm.   7.50
Lobster Ashtray, red lobster
forming handle. 63mm long.   10.00
Horn shaped lustre Shell on shell
base. 80mm.   7.50

Countryside

Milk Churn with lid. 72mm.   5.00

Animals

Cat, sleeping, lying on side. Can be
found inscribed: *Stop Yer Tickling
Jock*, add £8.00.
83mm long.   24.50
Cat in Bowler Hat. Cat can be found
coloured, add £20.00. 63mm.   30.00
Cat, Cavalier style with bows on
boots, ruffles on trousers. 83mm.   50.00
Cat, Comical, standing hands on
hips, black features. 97mm.   25.00
Cat, Egyptian, lying down. 78mm.   24.00
Cat, sitting in Top Hat, pink ears.
70mm.   27.00
Cat, pink ears and nose, in saucepan
with black handle. 70mm long.   40.00
Cat, peeping out of frilled rim bowl.
Cat's face coloured. 60mm.   35.00
Cat, peeping out of plain rimmed
bowl. 58mm.   40.00
Cat, crouching, rarely has blue or
yellow bead eyes. 50mm.   25.00
Cat, lying down, ready to pounce.
Comical. 90mm long.   30.00
Cat, Manx standing on candle
holder. 80mm.   30.00
Cat, sitting in ladies shoe, with shoe
tongue flopping out. 80mm long.   35.00
Cat, sitting, paw on rat. 76mm.   45.00
Cat, sitting, black features. 73mm.   26.50
Cat sitting in bowl. 64mm.   35.00
Manx Cat, sitting. 74mm.   25.00
Manx Cat, standing stretched.
94mm long.   30.00
Manx Cat, down on front paws,
upright back paws. 98mm long.   35.00
Manx Cat handle on jug Cat
coloured. 80mm.   30 00
Manx Cat as handle on a cup. Cat
coloured. 48mm.   30.00
Manx Cat handle, coloured on
candlestick holder. 60mm.   30.00
Manx Cat handle, coloured, on
miniature Cheese Dish and cover.
76mm long.   32.00
Manx Cats, coloured, as two handles
on a vase. 73mm.   35.00
Cow cream jug, some colouring.
127mm long.   23.00
Dog, comical standing with hands
on hips, black features. 88mm.   38.00

Dog, cross-eyed, with fly on his
nose. Can be found with some
colouring. 76mm.   20.00
Dog, curled up on its side.
98mm long.   26.50
Can be found inscribed: *Stop Yer
Tackling jock.*   30.00
Dog, King Charles Spaniel, sitting.
83mm.   14.50
Dog, pug lying down. 92mm long.   22.00
Dog, pug sitting. 100mm long. Some
colouring to face.   25.00
Dog, possibly a retriever, sitting with
dead rat. 95mm long.   45.00
Dolphin Vase. 100mm.   9.00
Fish with open mouth. 140mm long.   7.00
Fish pin cushion holder.
106mm long.   7.00
Fish, pepper pot, black features.
110mm long.   7.00
Fish vase. 110mm long.   6.00
Frog Prince (Frog with crown on   45.00
head) with colouring. 90mm.   47.50
Pig in Top Hat, all white. Pig has
pink muzzle and ears.   25.00
Pig coloured pink. 60mm.   30.00
Pig as above but with Chef's Hat.
93mm.   50.00
Pig in saucepan with black handle.
Pig coloured pink. 57mm.   30.00
Pig, standing, hands on hips, pink
muzzle and ears. Can also be
found in yellow/orange lustre.
100mm.   35.00
Pig, sitting, can have pink muzzle
and ears. 100mm long.
With colouring.   19.50
Without colouring.   16.50
Pig, curled/lying, pink ears and
muzzle. 82mm long.   40.00
Pig, pink, lying on edge of
horseshoe ashtray. 65mm long.   22.00

Court Room Pigs, modelled from
T.S. Elliot's *The Hunting of
the Snark*
All coloured pink as follows:
Policeman, with black helmet with
yellow badge. 80mm.   150.00
Barrister, with monocle. 80mm.   125.00
Prisoner, trotters padlocked. 80mm.   150.00
Witnesses, female with balmoral
bonnet, male with bowler. 80mm.   160.00
Judge, robed. 80mm.   125.00
Jury Box of six Piglets. 120mm long. 170.00

Shetland Pony. 108mm long.　　30.00
Tortoise trinket box and lid.
　80mm long.　　　　　　　　13.50

Birds (including Eggs)
Cockatoo on branch, some
　colouring. 102mm.　　　　　30.00
Cock Salt Pot, coloured. 71mm.　17.00
Hen Egg Basket, 2 pieces, red comb.
　95mm long.　　　　　　　　25.00
Swan posy holder.
　2 sizes: 70mm long.　　　　　6.00
　　　　　90mm long.　　　　　6.00

Great War
Despatch Rider's Cap with Goggles.
　65mm dia.　　　　　　　　　25.00
　With colouring.　　　　　　　50.00

Home/Nostalgic
Armchair, straight backed. 50mm.　7.50
Bag, open on four feet.　　　　　6.00
Bag, carpet, open.　　　　　　　6.00
Basket, leaf-edged with handle. 34mm.　4.00
Basket. 60mm and 90mm.　　　　4.00
Basket, star-shaped. 65mm dia.　　4.00
Bucket with looped handle. 80mm.　5.00
Bucket with rope handle. 51mm.　　4.00
Chair, French style, straight-backed.
　No. 3567. 110mm.　　　　　　6.00
Clock, bracket. 76mm.　　　　　9.50
Clock, ornate. 85mm.　　　　　　9.00
Coal Bucket and lid, ornate. 55mm.　6.50
Coal Scuttle, cylinder shaped.
　65mm.　　　　　　　　　　　5.00
Coal Scuttle, box shaped. 50mm.　5.00
Coal Scuttle, helmet shaped. 70mm.　6.50
Coal Scuttle, ornate. 76mm long.　6.50
Cradle on rockers. 60mm long.　　10.00
Dressing Stool. 4 legged.
　62mm long.　　　　　　　　　5.50
Fireplace, inscribed: *There's no place
like home.* Some colouring. 68mm.　13.00
Flat Iron. 71mm long.　　　　　12.50
Garden Trug.80mm long.　　　　4.50
Grandmother Clock. Can be found
　in yellow/orange lustre. 88mm.　8.50
*Home Bank, you don't miss what goes
in - what comes out will surprise
you.* Oval box with handle and
　slit. 58mm.　　　　　　　　　10.50
　Not named.　　　　　　　　　7.50
Hot water jug. 60mm.　　　　　10.00
Jardiniere. 80mm.　　　　　　　5.00
Jardiniere and stand. 165mm.　　7.50

Jardiniere pot and stand. 121mm.　7.50
Mantel Clock, ornate. 85mm.　　10.50
Pillar Box, oval. Can be found
　inscribed: *Letters,* or *Letter Box*
　add £3.00. 90mm.　　　　　　14.50
Policeman's Lamp. 45mm.　　　10.00
Rocking Chair. 60mm.　　　　　12.50
Saucepan with silver lid and black
　handle. 70mm long.　　　　　12.50
Shaving Mug. 60mm.　　　　　　7.50
Shaving Mug, square handle. 40mm.　7.50
Shaving Mug, with raised shell
　pattern. 55mm.　　　　　　　9.50
Sofa, very ornate. 60mm.　　　　8.50
Sofa, straight-backed. 60mm.　　7.00
Stool, circular with 3 legs. 55mm.　7.00
Stool, rectangular with 4 legs. 55mm.　8.00
Table. 45mm.　　　　　　　　　7.50
Tobacco Jar with brown pipe on lid.
　70mm.　　　　　　　　　　　16.50
Trunk with separate lid. No. 351.
　60mm long.　　　　　　　　　6.50
Wash Bowl and Jug set. 58mm.　6.50
Washing Basket, with pierced sides.
　30mm.　　　　　　　　　　　4.00
Watering Can, also yellow/orange
　lustre. 70mm.　　　　　　　　8.50
Wheelbarrow, also in yellow/
　orange lustre.
　3 sizes: 45mm.　　　　　　　7.50
　　　　　63mm long.　　　　　7.50
　　　　　95mm long.　　　　　7.50

Comic/Novelty
Briar Pipe, brown on leaf tray.
　72mm long.　　　　　　　　　13.50
Whistle, shaped as ewer. 45mm.　4.00

Alcohol
Beer Mug. 47mm.　　　　　　　4.00

Sport/Pastimes
FA Cup, not named. 68mm.　　　8.00
FA Cup and lid. 110mm.　　　　10.00
Trophy, 2 handled with separate lid.
　150mm.　　　　　　　　　　13.00

Musical Instruments
Tambourine ashtray with gilded
　discs. 68mm long.　　　　　　6.50

Modern Equipment
Cash Register. 35mm.　　　　　16.00
My Little Typewriter. 44mm.　　17.00

Hats

Bowler Hat. 83mm long.	20.00
Fireman's Helmet. 74mm.	40.00
Peaked Cap, very large.	
118mm long. Unglazed.	10.50
Straw Boater. 75mm dia.	11.50
Top Hat, can be match striker. 45mm.	5.50
Top Hat. 60mm,110mm long.	5.50

Footwear

Boot, pierced eyelets.	
2 sizes: 88mm long.	5.50
135mm long.	7.50
Dinant Wooden Shoe. 80mm long.	7.50
Dutch Sabot. 88mm long.	5.00
Ladies Shoe with high heel and fluted tongue. Two different moulds. 75mm, 80mm and 90mm long.	7.50
Ladies Shoe with pronounced heel & instep. 58mm, 98mm long.	10.00
Clog with buckle. 125mm long.	6.50
Lancashire Clog. 125mm long.	6.50
Shoe with lace holes. 90mm long.	6.50

Miniature Domestic

Complete tea sets can be found on round or square trays. These usually consist of teapot, sugar bowl, milk jug and two cups and saucers. Usually, except saucers, each piece is crested but on really small sets only the tray carries a crest.	30.00
Cake Dish. Can also be found in yellow / orange lustre. 70mm dia.	4.00
Stilton Cheese Dish and cover, round. 45mm dia.	8.50
Cheese Dish and cover.	
2 sizes: 63mm.	8.50
76mm long.	8.50
Cheese Dish and Cover, moulded in shell form, scallop ribbing.	13.00
Cheese Dish and Cover, two piece in the shape of a Swan. 76mm long.	13.00
These can be found coloured, lustre, beige and with transfers as well as crested in the usual manner. The larger size is sometimes inscribed: *Cheshire Cheese* for which £8 should be added.	
Cheese Dish with large handle to cover. 77mm long.	14.00
Coffee Pot with lid, ribbed sides. 63mm.	8.50

Coffee Pot with lid with ornate handle. 78mm.	8.50
Cup and Saucer. 40mm.	5.00
Found yellow.	add £4.00
Cylinder Box and lid, moulded hinge, for cigarettes. Match striker base. No. 2065 $^1/_2$. 63mm.	9.50
Also found with fixed lid and money box slot.	12.00
Dish. 40mm.	4.00
Dressing Table Set, miniature. These usually comprise 1 tray, 2 candlesticks, 1 ring tree, 2 scent bottles with stoppers and 3 powder bowls with lids.	30.00
Kettle with lid, ornate. 66mm.	8.50
Kettle with lid, flat handle to use on range. 90mm.	12.00
Kettle with lid. 75mm.	7.50
Kettle with lid, with 2 spouts. 63mm.	6.00
Meat Dish and lid, oval. 76mm long.	5.50
Milk Jug, square. 44mm.	4.00
Moustache Cup, vertical ribbing. 47mm.	7.50
Mug. 50mm.	4.00
Photograph Frame, glazed, with cardboard backing. 94mm.	16.00
No backing.	7.00
Ribbon Plate, hexagonal. 78mm long.	12.00
Tea Pot, also found in yellow / orange lustre.	
4 sizes: 50mm.	8.50
60mm.	8.50
65mm.	8.50
70mm.	8.50
Tea Pot, square with lid. 64mm.	10.00
Tea Pot and lid, taper with square handle. 56mm.	10.00
Tea Pot and lid, pearl lustre, shell pattern. 82mm.	17.50
Tea Pot and lid, diamond shaped. 64mm.	14.00
Tea Pot and lid, with two spouts (left / right pourer) and silver handle. 67mm.	10.00
Tea Pot & Lid, heart-shaped with animal head spout. 65mm.	12.00

Domestic

Candlestick. 78mm dia.	5.00
Candlestick. 80mm.	5.00
Candleholder. 44mm.	5.00

Candleholder shaped match holder
with striking surface. 60mm.   6.00
Egg Cup, goblet-shaped. No.22. 66mm. 6.00
Gravy Boat. 100mm long. 40mm.   6.50
Hair Tidy. 63mm.   6.00
Inkwell and lid, with pen rest.
65mm long.   12.50
Inkwell/Striker, ball-haped. 40mm.   6.50
Match Holder, ball-shaped on
circular base with unglazed striking
surface. 55mm.   10.00
Mustard Pot and lid, on saucer base.
60mm.   5.00
Pepper Pot with ribbed sides.
83mm.   4.00
Ring Tree Candleholder. 70mm.   8.00
Tea Pot and lid, oval. 130mm long.   10.50
Toastrack. 39mm. 70mm long.   7.50
Trefoil, salt, pepper and mustard
dish. 40mm.   5.50
Trinket Box and lid. 45mm.   5.00

Germany

All details and listings of china marked
'Germany' will be found under 'Foreign/
Germany entry.

Gladstone China

Gladstone China

Trademark used by George Proctor & Co. (Ltd), Gladstone Pottery, Longton. 1924 - 1940.
A range of domestic ware was made of heavy quality.

Trademark used by Taylor and Kent (Ltd.), Florence Works, Longton (usual trademark Florentine).
For details of this manufacturer and china produced see Florentine China.
This mark was used mainly on domestic and miniature domestic items. No other decoration other than crests have been found on pieces with this mark.

Gladstone Models.
Miniature Domestic
Cheese Dish and cover. 50mm.   8.50
Mug, one handle. 35mm.   4.00
Hexagonal Vase. 77mm.   4.00
Ewer. 83mm.   4.00

Footwear
Ladies 18th century frilled shoe.
  90mm long.   8.50

W.H. Goss

1862-1930.

Printed mark used on small bases also found as impressed mark.

Used from 1930. Can also be found with the following added; *Hand Painted, Royal Buff,* and *Cottage Pottery.*

Trademark used by William Henry Goss (Ltd), Falcon Pottery, Stoke.
The prices and a full listing of every Goss piece known to the author will be found in the companion volume to this guide, *The*

Concise Encyclopaedia and Price Guide to Goss China by Nicholas Pine.
Values of the thousands of crests and decorations to be found on Goss china appear in *The Price Guide to Arms and Decorations on Goss China* by the same author. Full details of marks, including 42 illustrations, will be found in chapter 2 of the former book.
Many pieces appear bearing either Arcadian, Willow Art, W.H. Goss or W.H. Goss England marks, as the later period of crested china (1925-37) saw much merging of companies and liberal use of marks.
Any piece with the W.H. Goss or W.H. Goss England mark is worth a small premium over a similar piece not so marked and a priced list of Goss England, or Third Period items will be found in *The Concise Encyclopaedia and Price Guide to Goss China* previously referred to. New pieces are constantly coming to light however, and that list is by no means exhaustive.
The values of Arcadian and Willow Art models have increased rapidly over the past ten years and the differential between these and examples marketed by the Goss factory has narrowed considerably.
W.H. Goss Ltd. were the originators of heraldic porcelain. So well known were their products that the term Goss was used to describe any make of crested china. The products of the Falcon Works are so popular with collectors that several books have been written about the firm.
The early history and the lists of models and other wares made by Goss are well covered in these books and so will not be repeated here. But I do feel it necessary to say a few words in praise of Adolphus Goss and to explore the connection between Goss and Harold Taylor Robinson (see Arcadian China).
William Henry Goss was an important potter in his day, developing the ivory porcelain body used for heraldic china. He was an industrious and studious man, very much the Victorian. The real hero must be his son Adolphus Goss who joined the firm in 1883, it was he who saw the commercial possibilities of heraldic china. The Goss firm had for sometime been decorating small ivory pots with crests of University Colleges and public

schools for sale in local china shops and Adolphus rightly saw that these had much wider possibilities. The public interest in archaeology and heraldry could both be satisfied by producing for each town and city miniature historical shapes with applied local coats of arms. Adolphus not only searched the country's museums for suitable ancient artefacts to copy but also found local shops to act as agents. Each agent sold local souvenirs with the correct local crest, but could order other shapes if he so desired. (An exercise in massmarketing that was years before its time). He also wrote several of the verses to be applied to china. In addition, he sketched and coloured some 2,500 transfer printed views and 6,000 coats of arms, all of which were sent to the factory with the order by Adolphus.

These heraldic porcelain pieces became enormously popular not only in tourist areas, where they made the most perfect souvenir, but in towns and cities all over Britain. The Goss name became famous, but by 1906 many cheap pot versions were being made by other firms who didn't stop at ancient artefacts but applied crests to any other shape imaginable, some 10,000 in all which are listed in this book including, even comic miniatures.

W.H. Goss never forgave Adolphus for thus allowing the Goss name to be debased: he would have preferred to have been remembered for his parian wares. Without Adolphus however, the firm would not have prospered and in fact this became evident in 1906 when William Henry died he left the firm to Adolphus' young brothers Victor Henry and William Huntley, and the story from then on is one of gentle decline.

W.H. Goss left Adolphus £4,000 and commissions, which was dutifully paid, but this left the company very badly financed. With no Adolphus the firm seemed to lack the commercial drive necessary to survive. Goss produced very few miniatures to commemorate the Great War, and although they produced a range of exquisite military badges and crests and even tried making dolls' heads, this period was really the beginning of the end. The other major crested ware manufacturers were making exciting and popular models and the people buying them were not concerned with the beauty of the china. Goss hopelessly failed to catch the style of crested souvenirs popular in the twenties, and so by 1930 the firm was in such financial trouble that the Falcon Works had been foreclosed on by the bank. The trustees of William Huntley sold the business, but obviously not the property to Cauldon Ltd. whose managing director was Harold Taylor Robinson. Mr Robinson arranged the purchase of the business of W.H. Goss from Cauldon Ltd. for £2,500. He subsequently bought the Falcon Works from the mortgagee for £4,000. The bank lent him £6,000 to complete the purchase and he then formed W.H. Goss Ltd. The issued capital stood at £6,000 all in ordinary shares all allotted to Harold Taylor Robinson. He acted as director until May 1932 when the firm was put into the hand of the Receiver as the whole Taylor empire crashed. Of the 6,000 ordinary shares he gave 1,000 to his brother, 500 to his father, 500 to his wife, and 1,000 to a business friend. 2,000 shares were transferred to Royal Crown Derby Porcelain Co. Ltd. as part of some rather clever deal that Mr Robinson always seemed to be involved in. After 1930 the wares marked Goss cannot be considered to be really Goss, the china is not so fine and the moulds used could be from any firm in the Cauldon group. I have termed this the third period of Goss manufacture. For history of the firm after 1932 please see Arcadian China.

Gothic China

BRITISH
MANUFACTURE

Trademark used by James Reeves, Victoria
Works, Fenton (usual trademark Victoria).

Gothic China Model
Traditional/National Souvenirs
Welsh Hat, blue cord and gold
  tassels, longest place name round
  brim. 51mm.   11.00

Grafton China

1900-1915

1920's on domestic ware.

1915-1933
This mark can also be found with the word
  England above the shield instead of inside
  it.
It can also be found with Importe
  D'Angleterre written around the lower
  edge of shield.

Used after 1915 mainly on later domestic ware, in green or black.

NB Retailers name often appears above these marks for example MEW BROS, SANDOWN I.W.

This rather strange mark has been found on some small models. It could have been a mark used on small bases but as the initials ABJ and S are absent it is rather odd. The firm also used the simple mark: MADE IN ENGLAND.

Trademark used by Alfred B. Jones and Sons Ltd., Grafton China Works, Longton, Staffs.

NB. Although the Grafton stock numbering system is very reliable, several items have been found with the wrong numbers. The most usual number is given here. It is not unusual to find two models consistently given the same number.

A.B. Jones and Sons Ltd. are one of the firms that produced arms ware in any great quantity, to have survived the 1930's and

to be still in business today. (They are now trading as Crown Lynn Ceramics Ltd. and use the trademark Royal Grafton). Although Grafton China had a large share of the china souvenir market they always produced other domestic and ornamental lines and presumably they sold enough of these, especially abroad, to keep going through the Depression.

Alfred B. Jones of the Grafton China Works had taken his two sons, Messrs. N.B. and A.B. Jones, Jnr, into partnership on 1st January 1900, the firm was then known as A.B. Jones and Sons Ltd. At that time they announced 'The firm will still make tea and breakfast sets for the Home, Colonial and American Markets, their chief specialities'. They were, however, in 1900 already advertising 'Badge Ware and View Ware' and were obviously producing goods for the lower end of the market (hotel ware and small souvenir items).

By 1906 A.B. Jones and Sons were making a special line of 'Miniature ivory arms china with the arms of any County, City or Borough painted in correct heraldic colours'. The pieces included jugs, loving cups, trays, milk jugs and vases in innumerable shapes. They also supplied 'local views of any locality' and had introduced another interesting speciality the 'zoo' series, animals of all kinds in pure white china, but do not appear to have been applying arms to them at that time.

By 1909, Mr John Walker, their London Representative at the Showroom in Buchanan Buildings, Holborn, was able to display Grafton 'Transparent ivory arms ware' in several hundred different shapes 'antique, pleasing, artistic, useful, quaint and humourous'. So it seems that between 1906 and 1909 Grafton had begun applying arms to more interesting pieces than vases and milk jugs, presumably animals, ancient artefacts and other souvenir items.

As the craze for heraldic china grew, Grafton appeared to place greater emphasis on its production. In 1919 they introduced crested souvenirs of the Great War and a series of zoo-logical (sic) interest, including many attractive models of elephants, monkeys, mice and what not else, in all sort of postures!' By 1920 they advertised the firm to the trade as makers of 'heraldic and view wares, miniature mascots, grotesques' and only 'also tea and breakfast ware'.

A.B. Jones were present at the British Industries Fair in 1920 and at the British Empire Exhibition 1924, displaying 'Tea, Breakfast, Dessert, Dinner and Coffee Services and Fancy Goods - coloured, Heraldic and Model Reproductions'. The firm still produces much the same kind of ware today, with the exception of heraldic china which they last advertised in the 1920's. Unfortunately in 1946 there was a fire at the Grafton works and all the records of crested china production were lost, so even this manufacturer, who did not go bankrupt or merge, can offer no detailed information on wares made in the early part of this century. In 1909 A.B. Jones offered in the *Pottery Gazette* to send 'coloured sheets of illustrations of Grafton China to anyone in the trade writing for them'. Regrettably none of these tantalising sheets have so far been found.

Grafton was one of the major producers of good quality heraldic china, perhaps rivalling Shelley as the main Goss competitor for the better end of the souvenir market. Certainly Grafton models are in the main rather more imaginative and clever than Shelley, and the china tends to be finer, indeed Grafton is porcelain, not earthenware or 'pot' as it is termed in The Potteries, and A.B. Jones were the only major manufacturer apart from W.H. Goss to produce heraldic china in porcelain. The arms on Grafton models are very well produced and the colours are much more muted and subtle, and therefore rather more attractive than on other china.

Because this firm worked quite independently of any other arms ware manufacturer its wares have a style and character of their own. This is particularly noticeable in the Great War and animal models. The soldiers produced as souvenirs of the Great War are in action: *Over the Top* and *The Bomb Thrower* are unlike anything produced by most other firms as are the series of children playing on the beach. The range of white crested animals includes many more grotesque

and comical items than are usually found, and Grafton are the only manufacturers apart from Tuscan to add coloured glass bead eyes to their animals. Many amusing miniature coloured animals were made, but these are invariably made without a crest and so have not been listed here. The style is very obviously late 20's, when coloured china souvenirs became more popular. One can only assume that Grafton stopped using crests on such items earlier than the other major manufacturers who went on producing coloured pieces with crests long after the interest in heraldic devices had waned. (This is probably one of the reasons why A.B. Jones survived the Depression. Their souvenir ware must have looked very 'modern' in the 20's).

Only two military badges have been recorded – *The Gordon Highlanders* and *Tidworth Camp* but the following commemoratives are found: *Flags of Liberty; Franco-British Exhibition 1908; Latin-British Exhibition, Great White City 1912; British Empire Exhibition 1924/5*. Some foreign crests have been found and these are usually marked *Importe d'Angleterre*, and were made for export.

Grafton seem not to have used *Lucky Black Cat* and *Lucky White Heather* devices or any other form of decoration on their models, other than coloured transfer views and regional souvenirs such as the *Somerset Cuckoo*. (View ware too is well produced but the colours are much more vibrant than one would expect from this manufacturer). Black transfer prints are also found including two unusual portraits of the *Prince of Wales, President of B.E.E. 1924* and the *Duke of York President of B.E.E. 1925* which are really commemoratives.

Numbering system. The numbers sometimes appearing on the base of Grafton pieces are stock numbers that occur consistently on certain models. On early china numbers are printed but they are mostly found painted in black and for that reason are not always easy to read. The letter that follows the numbers is obviously the paintresses' mark. The highest number found is 737, but anyone making a numerical list of known models will find that many numbers are missing.

The models listed without numbers and domestic ware will account for many of the gaps but nothing has been found numbered 570-632 and one wonders if these were perhaps used on coloured models without crests. Stock numbers are given in the following lists.

Grafton Models
Parian/Unglazed

Bust of *Burns*, impressed, on round glazed base. 137mm.	25.00
Bust of John Peel, inscribed: *D'ye ken John Peel with his coat so grey.* 120mm.	80.00
Bust of Albert I of Belgium, wearing hat, on glazed base, inscribed: *Albert I.* 125mm	65.00
Bust of *Allenby*, impressed, square glazed base. 145mm.	80.00
Bust of George V, inscribed: *George V.* 125mm	55.00
Bust of David Lloyd George. No. 415. 135mm.	55.00
Bust of *Foch*, impressed. Square glazed base. 135mm.	55.00
Bust of Field Marshal, Sir John French. 140mm.	55.00
Bust of Admiral Sir John Jellicoe. 140mm.	55.00
Bust of General Joffre. 155mm.	50.00
Bust of Lord Kitchener, with inscription and impressed on back: *Kitchener.* No. 395 102mm Glazed.	40.00
125mm.	50.00
Bust of General Pershing on square glazed base. 148mm	105.00
Bust of Lord Roberts, impressed on back: *Roberts.* 135mm.	65.00
Bust of Sir *Walter Scott*, impressed: *Scott*, on circular glazed base. 120mm.	21.50
Bust of President Wilson. 140mm.	80.00

Ancient Artefacts

These models are often found not named and are quite often decorated with a coloured transfer view rather than a crest.

Ancient Kettle with 2 spouts, not found named. No. 325. 52mm.	5.50
Aberdeen Bronze Pot. No. 217 and No. 280.	
2 sizes: 56mm.	5.50
65mm.	5.50

Brading Roman Vase. 5 vases of different shapes:	
No. 135. 60mm.	5.50
No. 136. 62mm.	5.50
No. 137. 62mm.	5.50
No. 139. 35mm and 55mm.	5.50
No. 195. 30mm and 35mm.	5.50
Burial Urn, inscribed: *Ancient British Burial Urn excavated in Cornwall.* 64mm	6.00
British Vase. No. 17. 40mm.	5.50
Butter Pot. No. 185. 40mm.	6.00
Canterbury Pilgrim Bottle. Rd. No. 470749. No. 317. 48mm.	6.00
Carisbrooke Castle Font, inscribed: *Model of Jacobean Font in Carisbrooke Castle I.O.W.* 70mm.	0.00
Chester Roman Vase. No. 165. 60mm. This has been found inscribed wrongly: *Roman Lamp Pompeii 1st century AD.*	5.50
Chinese Jar of early Ming porcelain. No. 273. 70mm.	10.00
Chinese Pilgrim Bottle. No. 269. 88m.	7.50
Chinese Teapot and lid. 2 different models:	
No. 70. 54mm.	6.00
No. 77. 54mm.	6.00
Chinese Vase. 3 vases of different shapes:	
No. 276. 86mm.	5.50
No. 282. 85mm.	5.50
No. 282. 75mm.	5.50
Collingbourne Ducis, Medieval Pilgrim Bottle found at. No. 181. 53mm.	9.50
Cyprus Vase 900 BC to 355 AD. No. 120. 70mm.	5.50
Elizabethan Bushel, not named.	6.00
Ely Drinking Mug. 2 shapes:	
No. 186. 40mm.	6.00
No. 187. 39mm and 46mm.	6.00
English Wine Glass. 4 glasses of different shapes:	
No. 309. 75mm. (Comical)	7.50
No. 310. 75mm. (Straight sided)	7.50
No. 311. 70mm. (Goblet)	6.50
No. 312. 70mm. (Ovoid bowl)	6.50
Egyptian Pottery – these specimens were discovered by Doctor Flinders Petra (sic) in Egypt, manufactured about 4,000 BC.	
No. 155. 60mm.	6.00
No. 156. 50mm.	6.00
No. 157. 60mm.	6.00
No. 158. 61mm.	6.00
The following two models have this inscription and further inscriptions.	

Egyptian Bottle. No. 159. 57mm.	6.00
Egyptian Tear Bottle. No. 151. 42mm.	6.00
Egyptian Vase, *Model of Ancient.* No. 323. 45mm.	6.00
Guernsey Milk Can and lid. No. 478.	8.00
Hereford Kettle. This model has a separate lid. No. 179. 80mm. (Can be found wrongly numbered 174.)	11.50
Hythe Crowellian Mortar. 40mm.	5.50
Medieval Pilgrim Bottle. No. 181. 53mm.	5.50
London Vessel, inscribed: *Model of vessel found during excavations in London.* 7 different models:	
No. 201. 85mm.	5.50
No. 202. 82mm.	5.50
No. 204. 44mm.	5.50
No. 205. 48mm.	5.50
No. 206. 45mm.	5.50
No. 207. 48mm and 84mm.	5.50
No. 208. 70mm.	5.50
Norman Pot, inscribed: *Norman pot from original in Burley Hill Museum.* No. 182. 45mm.	5.50
Old Ale Pot. No. 176. 60mm.	5.50
Old English Wine Glass. No. 309. 73mm.	5.50
Oxford Jug. No. 179. 60mm.	6.50
Pompeian Roman Lamp 1st Century AD. No. 119. 59mm.	6.00
Pompeian Vase. No. 110. 35mm.	6.00
Pompeian 1st Century Lamp. No. 118. 75mm.	6.00
Portland Vases, not named. 50mm. No. 150 and No. 530.	4.50
Loving Cup, not found named. No. 145. 40mm.	6.00
Loving Cup, three handles early version. 99mm.	10.50
Reading Roman Vase. 50mm.	5.50
Roman Vase. No. 160. 48mm.	5.50
Romsey Bushel, Model of Ancient. No. 149. 53mm.	8.00
Salisbury Kettle.	
No. 173. 97mm.	5.50
No. 174 105mm.	5.50
(Can be found wrongly numbered No. 179.)	
Shakespeare's Jug. No. 124. 76mm.	6.00
Shrewsbury Roman Ewer, inscribed: *Roman Ewer found at Uriconium original now in Shrewsbury Museum.* No. 175. 76mm.	6.00

Shrewsbury Vase, inscribed *Ancient British Vase found in the 4th Century Uriconium Cemetary.* No. 179. 42mm.	5.50
Southwold Jar.	6.00
Swiss Urn, inscribed: *Urn from Swiss Tacustrine Habitation.* No. 184. 40mm.	5.50
Swiss Urn. No. 185. 44mm.	5.50
Yaverland I.W. Roman Vase. No. 125. 50mm.	7.00

Buildings - Coloured

Bell Hotel, Tewkesbury. 92mm long.	80.00
Captain Cook's house Great Ayton re-erected in Melbourne. 95mm long (rare)	150.00
Couch's House, Polperro, with arms of Polperro on roof. 62mm high, 90mm long.	190.00
House on the Props, Polperro. 100mm long.	125.00
Old Chapel, Lantern Hill, Ilfracombe. 72mm long.	65.00
Old Maids Cottage, Lee, Ilfracombe. 70mm long, 68mm high.	85.00
Old Toll Bar, Gretna Green. 125mm long.	175.00

Buildings - White

Bath Abbey, West front. 105mm.	45.00
Bargate, Southampton. No. 3. 90mm.	35.00
The Tower, Blackpool. No. 521	
3 sizes: 115mm.	14.50
120mm.	14.50
135mm.	15.50
Caernarvon Castle. 90mm.	75.00
Citadel Gateway, Plymouth.	
2 sizes: 105mm.	30.00
119mm.	40.00
Egyptian SPHINX head in rock. 67mm.	40.00
First and Last Refreshment House in England, Land's End, found numbered 469 and 627. 75mm long.	17.00
Gynn Inn, Blackpool, inscribed: *Model of Blackpools famous landmark, the old Gynn Inn demolished 1921.* No. 520. 125mm long.	140.00
Houses of Parliament. No. 424. 115mm.	42.50

Irish Round Tower (not named),
often has green shamrocks on
base. No. 417. 137mm.   13.00
with shamrocks and Irish crest   17.50
Lincoln Cathedral, West Front.
No. 368. 115mm.   34.00
Old Cornish Cottages. 125mm long. 100.00
Old Chapel, Lantern Hill, Ilfracombe.
75mm long.   25.00
Old Toll-Gate House, including path
with gate, inscribed: *Ye olde toll-*
gate house. No. 498. 130mm long.   65.00
Old Toll-Gate House, as above but
not on base with path and gate,
and not named. No. 502 and
No. 501. 63mm long.   40.00
Oldest Chemists Shop in England
established 1790, also can be found
inscribed: *Model of the oldest*
pharmacy in England
Knaresborough, Yorkshire.
Established in the reign of George 1st
1790, some colouring. 97mm long.   85.00
Plas Mawr, Conway. 93mm (rare).   125.00
St. Pauls Cathedral, London.
2 sizes: No. 423. 145mm.   34.00
No. 633. 115mm.   22.00
Scarborough Castle Ruins, not
named. White unglazed on
glazed base. 104mm.   100.00
Skegness Clock Tower, not named.
No. 443. 127mm.   16.00
Smallest House in Great Britain,
Conway. No. 560. 92mm.   25.00
Tonbridge Castle. 88mm long.   35.00
Westminster Abbey, front. No. 422.
121mm.   30.00

Monuments (including Crosses)
Banbury Cross. 141mm.   20.00
Irish Cross, not named, green
shamrocks on base. No. 419.
138mm.   23.00
Lloyd George Statue, Carnarvon.
150mm.   75.00
Margate Lifeboat Memorial. 140mm. 30.00
Ramsgate Lifeboat Memorial
(Statue of Lifeboatman), not
named but often found with the
inscription: *Souvenir from the*
Imperial Bazaar Albion Hill,
Ramsgate, which was twice wrecked
by Zeppelin bombs on May 17th 1915
and June 17th 1917 on base.
140mm.   30.00

Rufus Stone. 96mm.   6.50
(John) Ruskin Memorial Stone,
inscribed: *John Ruskin*
MDCCCXIX-MDCCC and
religious verse. No. 515. 120mm.   17.50
St. Anne's Lifeboat Monument erected in
honour of 13 brave men who lost their
lives while attempting to save the crew
of the German barque 'Mexico'
December 6th 1886. No. 495. 161mm. 30.00
Sandbach Crosses. 130mm.   75.00
Southport Lifeboat Memorial.
No. 497. 121mm.   25.00

Historical/Folklore
Antique Horn Workbox, Model of, plus
lid. No. 308. 70mm long.   16.00
Antique Bureau. 64mm.   20.00
Burn's Chair No. 667. 88mm.   17.00
Charles I bottle with removable
head lid, not named and thought
by some collectors to be Guy
Fawkes. No. 209. 96mm.   55.00
Coaching Hat, not named. No. 213.
60mm long.   7.50
Lady Warrior in duck boat, holding
shield & sword. 125mm.   120.00
Mephistopheles, standing figure of
devil in Elizabethan costume.
140mm.   200.00
President Wilson's Grandfather's Chair.
No. 491 and 492. 75mm.   19.00
Ride a cock horse to Banbury Cross
(lady on horse). No. 569.
106mm long.   75.00
Robin Hood. 135mm.   150.00
St. Thomas A Becket Dec. 29th 1170.
137mm.   145.00
Saint Wilfred of Ripon Patron Saint of
the City of Ripon. 136mm.   145.00
Ye Old Chertsey Bell. 57mm.   17.00
Winged Horse on base, possibly
Pegasus. 85mm.   75.00

Traditional/National Souvenirs
Blackpool Big Wheel, not named.
2 sizes: 78mm.   13.00
100mm.   17.00
Cornish Pasty. No. 340. 95mm.   10.00
A Cornish Pasty. No. 578 (*a 'fat' pasty*).
108mm long.   14.00
Anvil, inscribed: *Model of the famous*
Anvil at the old Blacksmiths shop
Gretna Green on front, and on back
Over the Anvil at the Famous Smithy
many romantic marriages have been
celebrated. No. 552. 67mm.   11.00

Prime Cheddar Cheese. 38mm.	12.50
Cheddar Cheese with floral	
decoration and verse. Never	
found factory marked. 60mm dia.	12.50
With *Cheddar* transfer.	12.50
John Peel, Bust. 72mm.	30.00
Leaking Boot, Cleethorpes, statue of	
boy, boot joined to hand by	
string. 156mm. Also marked on	
base WIL-WAT China.	90.00
Lincoln Imp on pedestal. 108mm.	14.00
Ripon Horn Blower, often found not	
named, inscribed: *The horn is*	
blown every night at 9. Formerly it	
denoted that the watch was set for	
the night. No. 304. 136mm.	17.50
Toby Jug, coloured. English. 80mm.	30.00
Toby Jug, coloured. Irish. 80mm.	80.00
Toby Jug, coloured. Scots. 80mm.	70.00
Toby Jug, coloured. Welsh Lady.	
76mm.	70.00
Irish Harp, green Shamrocks.	
No. 418. 85mm.	15.00
Welsh Harp. No. 418. 90mm.	12.00
Welsh Hat, with blue band and bow,	
can be found with longest Welsh	
place name printed round brim.	
No. 383. 50mm.	10.00
With longest place name	12.50
Welsh Milk Can with lid. No. 479.	
103mm.	7.00
Yarmouth Bloater. 115mm.	10.00
Dutchman, sitting cross legged and	
holding cheese. No. 230. 85mm.	20.00

Seaside Souvenirs

Bathing Machine. No. 256. With large	
or small wheels.	
2 sizes. 55mm long.	16.00
65mm long.	18.50
Boat with billowing sail, inscribed:	
Polly. No. 448. 115mm long.	32.50
Boat, flat bottomed with bird's head	
as figurehead. No. 442.	
80mm long.	8.00
Houseboat, rectangular. No. 401.	
73mm long.	14.00
Lifeboat, inscribed: *Saint Cybi,*	
Robin Hoods Bay or *Whitby.*	
No. 332. 110mm long.	15.00
Fisherman, bust on round, waisted	
plinth. No. 234. 116mm.	20.00
Lifeboatman, bust. No. 245. 109mm.	35.00
Rowing Boat, can be found	
inscribed: *Sant Cybi* (patron saint	
of Holyhead) on models with a	
Holyhead crest, *Robin Hoods Bay*	
and Whitby. No. 169. 130mm long.	12.00
Inscribed	18.00

Fisherman's Creel with lid. No. 292.	
72mm long.	10.00
Beachy Head Lighthouse, with black	
band. No. 3. 135mm.	14.50
Eddystone Lighthouse. No. 315.	
102mm.	10.00
Lighthouse, with steps on base and	
gilded windows. No. 47. 145mm.	10.00
Lighthouse, miniature	
candlesnuffer. No. 64. 71mm.	10.00
Lighthouse pepper pot. 108mm.	7.50
Conch Shell. 105mm long.	7.50
Shell dish. No. 533. 63mm long.	6.00
Shell with handle. No. 536. 54mm.	6.00
Oyster Shell, on coral legs. No. 496.	
51mm.	7.00
Shell dish with handle. No. 537.	
80mm.	6.00
Shell Jug. No. 524 on 3 tiny whelk	
shell feet. 76mm.	12.50
Shell Jug, with handle. No. 536.	
43mm high. 75mm long.	6.00
Whelk Shell,	
5 sizes: No. 57. 80mm long.	6.00
No. 65. 45mm long.	6.00
No. 65. 85mm long.	6.00
No. 428. 70mm long.	6.00
No. 528. 115mm long.	8.50
Bathing Beauty, reclining, wearing	
swimsuit and mob-cap, holding	
parasol. 135mm (uncommon).	150.00
Boy holding model yacht, on beach	
base, coloured hair and yacht.	
No. 563. 85mm.	125.00
Boy in swimsuit, swimming on a	
rectangular blue 'sea' base. Hair	
and eyes coloured. No. 565.	
120mm long.	100.00
Girl kneeling on 'beach' base with	
red bucket and spade, brown hair	
and red hat brim. No. 564. 75mm	
(563-565 are all quite rare).	
Coloured	135.00
White	82.50
Boy in Sailor Suit, holding hat, on	
Donkey. 85mm and 109mm.	90.00
Child on Donkey, some colouring	
square base. No. 570. 94mm.	90.00
Deep Sea Diver. No. 261. 105mm.	210.00

Countryside.

Axe in Tree Stump. No. 61. 80mm.	12.00
Milk Churn with handle. No. 625.	
53mm.	6.50
Milk Can and lid. No. 417. 106mm.	6.00
Milk Can and lid. No. 478. 72mm.	6.00
Pine Cone, partly closed. 77mm long.	8.50

Animals

Some Grafton animals were given tiny glass bead eyes, those without have small holes. Even without these beads the models remain very attractive, but obviously a complete model is more desirable and £10 should be added for models having glass eyes. The range of large comical cats with these coloured bead eyes and coloured bows are particularly appealing but are hard to find.

Bear, dressed as boy, standing on shell tray. 85mm.	50.00
Bear and Ragged Staff. No. 224	
2 sizes: 85mm.	40.00
100mm.	40.00
Both versions can have bead eyes.	
Water Buffalo, lying with head turned, curved horns. 110mm. (very rare).	110.00
Bull, yellow, flat on base. (Art Deco). 65mm.	50.00
Calf, not named, but mostly found with cartoon transfer of farmer and wife behind gate with calf on the other side (add £12.00). No. 287. 100mm long.	25.00
Camel, 2 humps. No. 242. 125mm long.	40.00
Cat, Black sitting on pouffe *Luck* in red lettering, ruff of fur around face. 76mm.	70.00
Cat, Cheshire, inscribed: *The Cheshire Cat* and *Always smiling.* can have red mouth and nose, one bead eye (green, yellow or red) and one eye closed, inscribed: *The Cheshire Cat.* Found with and without separate shield carrying crest.	
2 sizes: No. 228 or 288. 86mm.	12.00
No. 171. 100mm.	16.00
Cat, fat crouching and angry No. 211. 55mm.	30.00
Cat, crouching, angry with tail in the air. Found with bead eyes, green bow and decorated face. No. 303. 88mm long 98mm high.	30.00
Cat in Jar, inscribed: *From Chicago Perishable.* No. 277. 80mm.	55.00
Cat singing, red mouth and green bow. 75mm.	75.00

Cat Scent Bottle, sitting with removable head. No. 229. 93mm.	75.00
Cat, sitting and comical, green bow and tail at front can have bead eyes (blue or green). No. 319.	
2 sizes: 88mm.	25.00
103mm.	30.00
Cat, sitting and winking. No. 612.	
2 sizes: 80mm red or orange bow.	24.50
105mm green or yellow bow.	30.00
Cat, sitting, green bow, red tongue, surprised face, black features. 100mm.	70.00
Cat, black, on round trinket box.	80.00
Cat, blue or yellow with arched back, on roof of house with black chimney. *Music on the tiles,* unglazed, no crest. No. 471. Rd. No. 668183. 80mm.	100.00
Cat, sitting and comical, yellow bow. Found with verse: *As I was going to St.Ives.* No. 351. 94mm.	30.00
Cat, sitting and comical, green bow and tail at front, can have bead eyes. No. 339. 154mm.	55.00
Cat, sitting and comical, yellow bow and tail at back, with bead eyes. No. 344 or No. 420 (no colouring £30.00). 146mm.	65.00
Cat, sitting, winking with both thumbs in *Thumbs Up* position, Orange bow, thumbs painted black. 83mm.	100.00
Cat, sitting, tail at back, yellow bow. No. 320. 104mm.	30.00
Cat, standing, arched back and tail in the air with green bow. No. 303. 100mm.	35.00
Cat, standing, arched back, small tail, green bow. No. 527. 78mm.	30.00
Cat, standing and comical, blue bow and green eyes. 88mm long.	32.50
(Cat) Kitten. No. 211. 50mm.	27.50
Cat, oriental with huge orange bow and body shaped as a bowl. Painted facial features. 90mm.	67.50
Lady Cat, upright, wearing coat and bonnet and carrying handbag, bow to neck. 90mm.	160.00
Cat salt pot, red open mouth and green bow tied at back. No. 729. 92mm.	110.00
The Jersey Cow, often found not named. No. 545. 60mm.	50.00
Cow, long-horn, sitting down. No. 646. 150mm long.	77.50

Bulldog, British, inscribed: *Slow to start but what a hold.* 83mm.   35.00
Bulldog, standing with feet wide apart. No. 391. 51mm.   20.00
Bulldog, sitting, can have bead eyes (yellow, red or green). No. 250.
2 sizes: 88mm.   40.00
102mm.   45.00
Bulldog salt or pepper pot.
No. 250. 80mm.   30.00
Dog in boater and clothes.
No. 249. 88mm.   67.50
Dog in top hat and clothes. 95mm.   67.50
Dog, scent bottle with head lid.
No. 232. 100mm.   42.50
Dog, Greyhound, standing with front legs on small oval base.
No. 709. 102mm long.   100.00
Dog, with 2 heads, one head is smiling and the other is sad. Two varieties. Sometimes found with a paper tag around neck inscribed: *Two heads are better than one.*
No. 645. 38mm.   95.00
No. 646. 63mm long.   100.00
Dog, King Charles Spaniel, sitting.
No. 390. 53mm.   17.50
Dog, kneeling, having human body and wearing a green cap.
No. 488. Can be found coloured with match holder. 85mm.   75.00
White.   45.00
Dog salt pot, sitting, large head, blue stripes to ears, red nose.
75mm.   30.00
Dog, Labrador Pup, sitting looking right, with bead eyes (yellow or green). Larger size can be found painted yellow or blue. (Add £15.00)
No. 355.
2 sizes: 58mm.   35.00
85mm.   55.00
Dog, Puppy, sitting, one ear raised and scratching with back leg. (Often found coloured with no crest, add £15.00.) No. 410. 85mm.   17.50
Dog, running, with fly or bee on tail, some colouring. 95mm long.   50.00
A stylised version of this was made as a menu holder, coloured yellow and white. (late)
80mm long.   50.00
Dog, Scottie, standing. No. 432. Can be found with bead eyes.
105mm long.   27.50

Dog with ball between front paws.
114mm long.   75.00
Ten varieties of Bonzo dog, all white with black spots and ears, eyes closed and yellow collars and marked *Swains Studdy Series.* Rd No. 700156, are as follows:
Dog, yawning, on ashtray base, inscribed: *Tired Tim.* 105mm long.   70.00
Dog, with ball in mouth, inscribed: *The Ball Boy* on ashtray base.
105mm long.   75.00
Dog, begging with bowl in mouth on ashtray base, inscribed: *Oliver Twist.* 105mm long.   85.00
Dog walking on side of ashtray.
110mm long, 85mm wide.   75.00
Dog, yawning. 46mm.   65.00
Dog, crouching, playing with yellow ball.   70.00
Dog, with ball in mouth and ball between front paws. 46mm.   80.00
Dog with grey ball in mouth, and ball between front paws. 45mm.   40.00
Dog, talking to stick telephone on yellow ashtray base inscribed: *"Holborn 6633 (Four Lines)"* *"I'm not arguing, I'm telling you - give me Swains".* 75mm.   80.00
Dogs, three, captioned: *Ball Boy, Tired Tim, Oliver Twist.*   80.00
Elephant, circus, standing on forelegs on stool. No. 231. 105mm.   110.00
Elephant, sitting and comical.
No. 438. 127mm.   75.00
Found coloured purple or green.   85.00
Elephant, sitting with trunk raised, comical. No. 102. 75mm.   60.00
Elephant, walking. No. 426
No. 470 or No. 491.
3 sizes: 50mm.   42.50
65mm.   42.50
80mm.   42.50
Can be found coloured purple or red.
With colouring.   60.00
Elephant, African. No. 490. 55mm.   30.00
Elephant, with sandwich boards, crest one side and inscribed: *Turn me round* on the other. 102mm.   125.00
Elephant, large comical with open back as posy holder, yellow trunk, black eyes. No. 734. 110mm long, 76mm high. Rare.   75.00
Elephant, flat black body in art deco style. White face and trunk on rocky base. No. 475. 75mm.   40.00
Fawn, sitting. 64mm long.   38.50

Fish, twisted, open mouth. 98mm
long. No. 179. ... 11.00
Fish, curved vase. No. 196. 57mm. ... 5.50
Fish, curved tail and open mouth.
No. 392 or 451. 105mm long. ... 11.50
Fish, curved with bead eyes.
No. 196. 125mm long. ... 10.00
Fish, curved. No. 197. 70mm. ... 9.50
Fish, curved body and open mouth.
No. 393.
2 sizes: 80mm long. ... 12.00
110mm long. ... 14.00
Fish. No. 244. 110mm long. ... 7.50
Fish, straight and scaly. No. 247.
2 sizes: 88mm long. ... 5.50
115mm long. (bead eyes) ... 12.50
Fish, straight and fat with open
mouth. No. 341. 102mm long. ... 7.00
Fish, straight with open mouth.
No. 97. 100mm long. ... 8.50
Fish, straight and thin. No. 302.
2 sizes: 76mm long. ... 7.00
112mm long. ... 8.50
Large size can be found with
bead eyes.
Fish, twisted open mouth, red bead
eyes. No. 179. 98mm long. ... 11.00
Fox with bead eyes (yellow).
No. 462.
2 sizes: 80mm long. ... 60.00
140mm long. ... 65.00
Fox, without bead eyes (i.e. model
designed without them).
135mm long. ... 50.00
Can be found painted red.
Add £10.00.
Fox with pheasant on stand. No.
434. Can be found painted red.
139mm long (late). ... 65.00
Fox crouching. No. 467. 76mm long. ... 75.00
Frog, with closed mouth, hands on
chest, sitting on back legs. Can be
found with bead eyes. No. 204.
72mm. ... 35.00
Lion, standing. 105mm long. ... 23.00
Monkey, can be found with bead
eyes.
No. 242. 87mm. ... 15.00
No. 243. 60mm. ... 15.00
No. 286. 70mm. ... 15.00
Can be found painted yellow,
red, green or blue. ... 26.50
Monkey, sitting, wearing coat, hand
on chin. No. 245. 62mm. ... 15.00
Can be found painted yellow
Black or blue. ... 20.00

Monkey, wearing coat, hand on
foot. 68mm. ... 16.50
Mouse. No. 40. 46mm. ... 40.00
Mouse, sitting up. No. 210. 42mm. ... 25.00
Mouse, sitting up, holding nut,
yellow bead eyes. No. 243. 43mm, ... 25.00
Mouse. No. 222. 68mm.
(Candlesnuffer). ... 20.00
Mouse nibbling cheese. No. 439.
47mm. ... 25.00
Mouse on cheese, can be found
purple or blue with pink ears.
No. 459. 55mm (late). ... 37.50
Mouse, sitting, holding nut, green
eyes. No. 461. 40mm. ... 55.00
Mouse sitting on pudding. 66mm. ... 55.00
Pig, fat, lying asleep, inscribed:
Wunt be druv. No. 421. 83mm long. ... 75.00
Pig, running, red bead eyes. No. 416.
87mm. ... 95.00
Pig, sitting, long pointed nose and
long ears tilted forward. No. 203
or 263. 90mm long. ... 50.00
Pig, sitting with raised ears and
miserable expression. No. 203.
65mm. ... 55.00
Pig, sitting on haunches, alert ears
and grinning face. Blue bead eyes,
Wunt be druv. 66mm. ... 95.00
Pig, sitting and laughing, can have
bead eyes, inscribed: *Wunt be druv*.
No. 338. 65mm. ... 65.00
Pig, sitting, is much fatter than the
above, inscribed: *Wunt be druv*.
No. 176 or 341. 95mm long. ... 55.00
Pig, sitting up on hind legs, found
inscribed: *Wunt be druv* or *I won't
be drove*.
No. 417. 70mm. ... 35.00
No. 420. 80mm, one ear flat. ... 50.00
Pig, standing, inscribed: *Wunt be
druv*. 88mm long. ... 22.00
Pig, fat. 95mm long. ... 40.00
Piglet, standing, fat and inscribed:
Wunt be druv. No. 342.
98mm long. ... 30.00
Piglet, standing, can be found with no
inscription but normally found
inscribed: *Wunt be druv* or *I won't
be drove*. No. 343. 70mm long. ... 16.00
Polar Bear. No. 102.
105mm long, can be found
orange, add £15.00. ... 50.00
Polar Bear, standing on rocky base.
117mm long. ... 60.00

Polar Bear, baby, lying on its back
holding back foot, red eyes,
yellow lustre. 50mm wide,
60mm high.   75.00
Pony, Shetland. No. 493.
70mm, 105mm long.   35.00
Very rarely found inscribed:
New Forest Ponies.   50.00
Rabbit, Giant, sometimes with
yellow bead eyes. No. 240.
112mm long.   22.50
Can be found painted brown.
Rabbit, comical, crouching with
huge alert ears, yellow glass eyes.
No. 172. 74mm.   80.00
Rabbit trinket dish, pink eyes.
No. 734. 122mm long.   50.00
Rabbit, crouching, head tucked in.
No. 102. 30mm.   75.00
Rat, sitting up. Candle snuffer.
No. 210. 65mm.   30.00
Sea Lion. 75mm high, 77mm long.   25.00
Seal. No. 402. 75mm long. (This is a
very delicate model).   22.50
Snail. No. 328. 88mm long.   17.50
Squirrel holding nut, can be found
with bead eyes. No. 327. 75mm.   30.00
Terrapin. No. 253. Can be found
painted yellow, add £15.00.
92mm long.   16.00
Vole. No. 100. 55mm long.   55.00
Wallaby, 90mm.   85.00

Birds (including Eggs)
Bird / fledgling, some colouring.
(very plump and pretty).
2 sizes: 60mm. No. 434.   25.00
          65mm. No. 435.   25.00
Bird, match holder with orange
legs, and large beak (late). No. 737.
68mm.   30.00
Birds, two with long beaks and
spread wings in the form of a tall
taper vase. 145mm.   15.00
Chicken half out of egg, can be
found with bead eyes. No. 326.
73mm long.   19.00
Chick Ashtray with compartment to
hold matches, striker on tail.
No. 102. Some colour. 80mm.   40.00
Cockerel salt pot, inscribed: *SALT,*
some colouring. 62mm. No. 727.   34.00
Cock on circular base. No. 454.
100mm (pair with hen).   20.00

Grotesque Duck posy holder, open
beak, detailed feathers. No. 142.
100mm long.   35.00
Duck, swimming, occasionally
found inscribed: *Aylesbury duck.*
No. 377. 96mm long.   20.00
Inscribed.   27.50
Duck posy holder, comical, yellow
beak. No. 442. 80mm.   40.00
Duck posy or cigarette holder, some
colouring. No. 732 115mm long.   35.00
Duck match holder, striker and
ashtray. Some colouring. No. 735.
80mm.   35.00
Hen, on circular base, can also be
found in orange or purple. Add
£15.00 No. 453. 100mm (pair
with cock).   20.00
Hen, roosting on basket base.
82mm.   15.00
Kingfisher on base. No. 670. 62mm.   50.00
Owl on rocky base. No. 687. 132mm.   60.00
(very impressive model).
Penguin. No. 329. 88mm.   30.00
Royston Crow. 66mm. Coloured.   50.00
Swan, head under wing. No. 409.
85mm long.   22.50

Great War
Prince of Wales in uniform, one
hand in pocket, cigarette in other.   500.00
American Soldier (Doughboy),
squatting. No. 452. 80mm.   200.00
Two versions found fully
coloured.   Each 400.00
Also appears painted black
except for cigar. No. 85. 80mm.   250.00
British Territorial Bulldog, seated
figure of Tommy with bulldog
face, red and blue bands on hat.
No. 262. 90mm.   250.00
Cavalry officer, standing. No. 411A.
128mm. Very rare.   500.00
Cossack, standing knife in belt.
130mm.   300.00
Kitchener bust (glazed) on circular
base, inscribed: *Lord Kitchener of
Khartoum creator of British Army
1914/1918. Born June 24th 1850.
Died serving his country June 5th
1916 by the sinking of HMS
Hampshire off the Orkneys.* No. 395.
2 sizes: 100mm.   40.00
          130mm.   50.00
See also *Parian/Unglazed* Section.

German officer match holder,
caricature of head inside with
life-belt, some colouring. No. 214.
95mm dia.

Plain	40.00
Coloured	75.00

Or could it possibly be the
Kaiser?

Sailor, seated and holding a model
submarine, blue on hat band
impressed: *Victory.* Is often found
inscribed: *We've got 'U' well in
hand.* 74mm. — 110.00

White — 75.00

Can also be found fully coloured.
No. 452. 80mm. (very rare). — 200.00

Soldier leaving Trench, inscribed:
Over the top. No. 433. 118mm. — 175.00

Soldier throwing Hand Grenade,
inscribed: *The Bomb Thrower.*
No. 425. 140mm. — 175.00

Soldier throwing Hand Grenade,
without the ammunition box
which must have been added for
stability. A forerunner of above.
Two examples known. 140mm.
(Very rare). — 400.00

Biplane, fixed prop. No. 450. 145mm
long. (Very rare). 2 versions
open wing ends and closed
wing ends. — 250.00

Monoplane, fixed prop. No. 414.
135mm long. — 80.00

Dreadnought, battle ship with high
prow. No. 408. 142mm long. — 75.00
Same ship with same stock
number found inscribed:

HMS Gosport	100.00
HMS Victory.	90.00
No name.	70.00

HMS Iron Duke. No. 431.
155mm long. — 100.00

Submarine, inscribed:*E9.* No. 406.
145mm long. — 47.50

Motor Ambulance with curtains,
inscribed: *Motor ambulance car
given by Staffordshire china
operatives. British Red Cross
Society: St John Ambulance
Association. Load not to exceed 1
driver, 1 attendant and patients.*
With red, or rarely a blue cross.
No. 397. 98mm long. — 77.50

Tommy Driving a Motor Tractor,
inscribed: *Model of motor tractor
used on western front.*
No. 456. 80mm long. — 300.00

Renault Tank. 100mm long. — 75.00

Tank with steering wheels,
inscribed: *H M. Landship Creme de
Menthe.* No. 413. 118mm long. — 35.00

Tank, no steering wheels, inscribed:
H.M. Landship Creme de Menthe.
No. 413. 98mm long. — 35.00

Also found inscribed: *Model of
Whippet Tank.* 98mm long. (Rare). — 100.00

Whippet Tank, inscribed: *Model of
Whippet Tank.* No. 449. 115mm long. — 170.00

Alpine Gun with moving wheels,
inscribed: *Model of Alpine gun.*
No. 394. 105mm long. (Very rare). — 250.00

Desert Gun. No. 430. 155mm long. — 85.00

Field Gun on Sledge, inscribed:
French 75. No. 412. 160mm long. — 75.00

German Gun captured by British.
No. 403. 153mm long. — 70.00

Trench Howitzer (can be found with
Ramsgate Imperial Bazaar
inscription. See Monuments.
Ramsgate Lifeboat Memorial)
No. 404. 75mm long. — 20.00

Cannon Shell. No. 33. 108mm. — 12.50

Cannon Shell. No. 400. 76mm. — 8.50

Cannon Shell, inscribed: *Jack
Johnson.* No. 399. 90mm. — 12.50

Cannon Shell. No. 558. 106mm. — 12.50

German Incendiary Bomb. No. 405.
80mm. — 20.00

Mills Hand Grenade with removable
metal pin, often found without
inscription. No. 411 or No. 117.
83mm. — 30.00

Bandsman's Drum. No. 236. 45mm. — 12.50

Bell Tent with open flaps, with or
without base. No. 239. 65mm. — 22.50

Boot with Puttee. No. 389. 75mm. — 23.50

Anzac Hat with blue band.
110mm long. — 30.00

Colonial Soldier's Hat. No. 238.
89mm long. — 21.50

Pith Helmet. No. 36. 69mm long. — 20.00

Water Bottle. No. 234. 80mm. — 15.00

Cenotaph, inscribed: *MCMXIV
MCMXIX - The Glorious Dead* and
3 coloured flags on reverse.

2 sizes: 138mm.	17.50
(Flags add £15.00).	
155mm.	21.50
(Flags add £15.00).	

Glandford Brigg War Memorial.
  114mm.   125.00
Sphinx moulded with face of
  Kitchener. 67mm.   50.00

Home/Nostalgic
Anvil candlesnuffer, never found
  factory marked. 56mm.   8.50
Anvil on heavy base. No. 552. 70mm.   9.00
Armchair, winged. No. 389 or 395.
  76mm.   18.00
Baby crawling, brown hair, blue eyes,
  rectangular base. No. 544.
  112mm long.   95.00
Baby sitting up. No. 481. 63mm.   30.00
Baby's Rocking Cradle. No. 294.
  62mm long.   14.00
Basket with handle. No. 29. 52mm.   4.50
Cabin Trunk. 56mm long. No. 351.   14.00
Flat Iron. No. 162. 65mm long.   15.00
Flower Basket. No. 244. 65mm.   6.50
Grandfather Clock. No. 396. 110mm.   17.50
Handbell, with or without clapper.
  No. 15 or No. 153. 82mm.   8.50
Handbell, with clapper. No. 265.
  51mm.   7.50
Horn Lantern, inscribed. No. 306.
  76mm.   10.00
Laundry Basket. No. 534. 75mm long.   6.50
Pillar Box. No. 63. 68mm.   20.00
Rocking Horse. 125mm long.   47.50
Shaving Mug. 40mm.   10.00
Tub, hole in top. No. 149. 45mm.   5.00
Village Water Pump. No. 331. 80mm.   13.00
Watering Can.   8.50

Comic/Novelty
Billiken. No. 291. 44mm.   5.50
Boy, grotesque, sitting cross-legged,
  top of head on egg-cup. 62mm.   67.50
Boy Scout holding bugle. 133mm.   160.00
Boy Scout saluting.
  No. 304 and 355. 133mm.   140.00
Chinese Man Pepper Pot, some
  colouring. No. 722. 70mm. (There
  must be a matching Salt Pot).   35.00
Fu Hsing God of Happiness, Chinese
  Priest standing upright, holding
  baby, some colouring to headwear.
  No. 270. 115mm.   60.00
Gladiators Head, Candlesnuffer.
  No. 228.   55.00
Head, comic salt pot, miserable face
  and droopy bow tie. No. 255 or
  No. 250. 85mm (matches below).   15.00

Head, comic pepper pot, happy face
  and perky bow tie. No. 258.
  85mm. (matches above).   15.00
Knave Candlesnuffer. No. 101.
  90mm.   55.00
Lemon with lid, stalk handle.
  No. 62. 60mm.   19.00
Pierrot, sitting cross-legged on box
  playing banjo, can be found with
  some colouring. No. 566 or No. 561.
  103mm.   85.00
Policeman, cylindrical body
  covered by cape. No. 427. *Special
  Constable*. 115mm.   140.00
Teapot with face of General Kruger, on
  lid spout and handle form arms,
  some colouring. No. 264. 48mm.   100.00
Watch Stand, Father Time head with
  beard forming legs. No. 154. 110mm. 70.00

Cartoon/Comedy Characters
Bonzo Dog, pepper pot. 80mm.   70.00
Sunny Jim with red bow tie, red
  spotted nose and black topper.
  No. 130. 86mm.   70.00

Alcohol
Barrel, upright as pepper pot.
  No. 15. 69mm.   15.00
Bottle with cork. No. 715. 68mm.   8.00
Champagne Bottle. No. 221. 102mm.   10.00
Champagne Bottle pepper pot.
  No. 225. 102mm.   10.00
Man in Barrel, head and feet
  protruding, inscribed: *No beer*.
  No. 429. 115mm.   38.50
Soda Syphon. No. 313. 93mm.   13.00
Tankard. 80mm.   5.00
Toby Jug, red, staff in left hand.
  65mm.   30.00

Sport/Pastimes
Footballer with ball on small base.
  130mm.   95.00
Golfer holding bag of golf clubs,
  comic figure, inscribed: *The
  Colonel*. No. 352. Cigarette is often
  broken off. Can be found in green
  cap. 90mm.   55.00
  Can be found fully coloured.   75.00
Comical Golfer in baggy trousers,
  bent over ball with clubs, about
  to put, on tray base. 72mm.   225.00
Golf Ball salt pot. 52mm.   13.00
Golf Ball on tee pepper pot.
  No. 293. 52mm.   10.50

Tennis player, lady holding racquet
(reputedly Suzanne Lenglen).
133mm.   160.00
Tennis racquet. 118mm long.   22.00
Dice, Trump Indicator, heart,
diamond, club and spade and no
trump on five sides. 35mm.   30.00

Musical Instruments
Irish Harp, green shamrocks. 86mm.   10.00

Transport
Charabanc, with 5 rows of seats,
inscribed: *Dreadnought. No. 564.*
100mm long.   45.00
If inscribed   55.00
Mons Bleriot, bust, inscribed: *First
man to fly across the channel in an
aeroplane July 25th 1900.*
No. 252. 85mm.   85.00
Punt with two girls aboard with
wooden pole. 115mm long.   77.50

Modern Equipment
Horn Gramophone, square base.
No. 641. 92mm.   42.50

Hats
Bowler Hat. No. 410. 93mm long.   30.00
Coaching Hat. No. 213. 37mm.   7.00
Irish Top Hat. No. 239. 35mm.   12.50
Irish Hat. No. 121. 70mm long.   22.00
Top Hat. No. 189. 37mm.   58.50
Fireman's Helmet. No. 66. 65mm.   35.00

Footwear
Boot, laced. No. 237. 80mm long.   7.50
Lancashire Clog, sometimes found
inscribed: *Model of Lancashire
Clog.* No. 407. 90mm long.   6.50
If inscribed   7.50
Sabot. No. 212. 80mm long.   7.00
Also appears with manufactured
hole for wall hanging. Same
price.
Oriental Shoe, pointed. No. 170.
3 sizes: 80mm long.   6.00
95mm long.   6.00
104mm long.   7.50
Shoe, lady's 18th century. No. 50.
83mm long.   8.00
Slipper Wall Pocket. 100mm long.   10.00

Miniature Domestic
Beaker. No. 73. 52mm.   5.00
Candleholder, circular. No. 80.   5.00
Cheese Dish and cover (2 pieces)
No. 78. 65mm long.   12.00
Cup and Saucer, fancy. No. 107.
48mm.   5.00
Cup and Saucer, No. 108.
50mm high. 110mm dia.   5.00
Cup and Saucer. No. 122. 67mm dia.   5.00
Cup. No. 147. 39mm.   4.00
Milk Jug. No. 72. 40mm.   4.00
Mug with handle. No. 36. 48mm.   4.00
Mug with handle. No. 143. 41mm.   4.50
Shaving Mug. No. 290. 52mm.   10.00

**Numbered Domestic and Ornamental
Wares**
No. 1 Vase wide base, narrow top.
93mm.   4.00
No. 2. Vase. Ivy covered. 60mm.   4.00
No. 3. Jug, elongated spout. 80mm.   4.00
Also Vase. 88mm.   4.00
No. 4. Jug. 75mm.   4.00
No. 5. Vase. Bagware. 45mm.   4.00
No. 6. Cauldron. 41mm.   4.50
No. 8. Vase. 61mm.   4.00
No. 9. Vase, shaped edge. 62mm.   4.00
No. 10. Vase, shaped, with cruciform
top. Can be found coloured red.
70mm.   4.00
No. 11. Vase. 66mm.   4.00
No. 12. Jug, angular handle. 72mm.   4.00
No. 13. Jug. 67mm.   4.00
No. 14. Two handled vase. 66mm.   4.50
No. 15. Bell, no clapper. 86mm.   5.00
No. 16. Vase. 37mm   4.00
No. 17. Crinkle-top Jug. 30mm.   4.00
No. 18. Hexagonal Vase. 63mm.   4.00
No. 19. Vase, pinched top. 65mm.   4.00
No. 20. Vase, 2 handled. 68mm.   4.00
No. 21. Jug, ornate. 75mm.   4.50
No. 22. Vase, bulbous, with
ornamental shoulders. 50mm.   4.50
No. 23. Vase, with moulding. 60mm.   4.50
No. 25. Vase, 2 handles. 60mm.   4.00
No. 26. Wavy edged dish.
69mm diameter   5.00
No. 27. Vase, bulbous. 60mm.   4.00
No. 28. Ewer. 55mm.   4.00
No. 29. Churn. 52mm.   5.00
No. 30. Vase. 50mm.   4.00
No. 31. Beaker. 62mm.   4.00
No. 32. Beaker. 62mm.   4.00
No. 33. Trefoil Cruet Set.   8.50

No. 34.3-handled Loving Cup.
47mm. — 8.50
No. 36. Tankard Mug. 66mm. — 4.00
No. 37. 2-handled mug. 45mm. — 4.00
No. 38. 3-handled Loving Cup.
48mm. — 8.50
No. 44. Jug. 60mm. — 4.00
No. 45. Jug, crinkle top. 40mm. — 4.00
No. 46. Jug. 60mm. — 4.00
No. 52. Ewer. 80mm. — 4.00
No. 53. Ewer. 76mm. — 4.00
also Vase. 50mm. — 4.00
No. 55. Pot and lid, ribbed. 60mm. — 4.00
No. 57. Jug, fluted base. 68mm. — 4.00
No. 60. Vase, 2 handled. 38mm. — 4.00
No. 64. Vase. 60mm. — 4.00
No. 65. Posy Bowl. 68mm long. — 4.00
No. 66. Thistle. 53mm. — 13.00
No. 67. Tray, diamond shaped.
121mm long. — 5.00
No. 68. Tray, heart shaped.
100mm long. — 5.00
No. 69. Tray, shield-shaped. 80mm. — 5.00
No. 70. Oil Lamp & Lid. 93mm long. — 6.50
No. 71. Tray, club shaped.
100mm long. — 5.00
or Vase, 2 handles. 40mm. — 4.00
No. 72. Jug. 40mm. — 4.00
No. 73. Beaker. 33mm and 52mm. — 4.00
No. 74. Pot with 3 blunt feet. 47mm. — 4.00
No. 75. Jug. 39mm. — 4.00
No. 78. Miniature crinkle bowl.
48mm dia. — 5.00
No. 79. Coffee can. 58mm. — 4.00
No. 80. Miniature circular
Candleholder. — 5.00
No. 81. Vase. 60mm. — 4.00
No. 82. Diamond pin box and lid.
90mm long. — 6.50
No. 83. Heart shaped pin box and
lid. 63mm dia. — 6.50
No. 84. Spade or Heart shaped pin
box and lid. 68mm. — 6.50
No. 85. Club shaped pin box and
lid. 68mm. — 6.50
No. 86. Bowl. 48mm dia. — 4.00
No. 87. Vase, fluted and one
handled. 30mm. — 4.00
No. 88. Vase. 40mm. — 4.00
No. 89. Flat faced vase. 56mm. — 4.50
No. 90. Flat bottle vase. 57mm. — 4.50
No. 91. Vase. 39mm. — 4.00
No. 92. Tray, hexagonal. 69mm dia. — 4.00
No. 94. Vase. 44mm. — 4.00
No. 95. Vase, Globe with crinkle top.
43mm. — 4.00

No. 96. Vase, Taper. 45mm. — 4.00
No. 99. Dish, Trefoil. 80mm wide. — 6.00
No. 100. Tray, spade shaped.
78mm long. — 5.00
No. 102. Ewer (But Polar Bear found
with same No.) — 4.00
No. 103. Pitcher. 60mm. — 4.00
No. 104. Vase. 65mm. — 4.00
No. 105. Pitcher with high looped
handle. 64mm. — 4.00
No. 106. Jar. 60mm. — 4.00
No. 117. Giant ornate Jug. 146mm. — 8.00
No. 118. Wine Bottle. 72mm. — 4.00
No. 121. Vase, bulbous, 2 handles.
60mm. — 4.00
No. 125. Pot, round. 52mm. — 4.00
No. 127. Vase, long necked. 62mm. — 4.00
No. 128. Vase. 70mm. — 4.00
No. 129. Long narrow-necked Vase.
73mm. — 4.00
No. 130. Bowl with handle. — 4.00
No. 131. Basket, ornate. 123mm long. — 8.50
No. 140. *Hair Tidy* and lid. 90mm. — 9.50
No. 141. *Hair Pins*, oval box & lid.
120mm long. — 6.50
No. 143. 1-handled Mug. 40mm. — 4.00
No. 144. 2-handled Mug. 40mm. — 6.50
No. 145. 3-handled Loving Cup.
39mm. — 8.50
No. 149. Tobacco Jar with lid,
inscribed: *Tobacco* on lid.
120mm. — 14.00
No. 152. Vase with ornate heron
handles. 145mm. — 6.50
No. 154. Vase, narrow neck. 61mm. — 4.00
No. 155. Cylinder vase. 60mm. — 4.00
No. 156. Vase. 60mm. — 5.00
No. 157. Ribbed Jug. 70mm. — 4.00
No. 158. 60mm. — 6.00
No. 161. Fluted Jug. 62mm. — 7.50
No. 177. Vase, bulbous. 40mm. — 4.00
No. 191. Vase, wide body. 70mm. — 4.00
No. 205. Jug. 45mm. — 4.00
No. 212. Square-topped Vase. 68m. — 4.00
No. 236. Horse's Hoof. 44mm. — 7.00
No. 242. Stamp Box and lid.
47mm long. — 6.50
No. 260. Vase, 2 handles. 37mm. — 4.00
No. 263. Salve Pot and lid.
45mm dia. — 5.50
also Hexagonal Vase. 55mm. — 4.00
No. 267. Round Pot and lid.
45mm dia. — 5.50
No. 273. Vase, square neck. 78mm. — 4.00
No. 277. Star shaped box and lid. — 5.50

No. 278. Shaped Vase. 80mm.	4.00
No. 282. Four-sided Vase. 78mm.	4.00
No. 295. Rectangular box and lid. 47mm long.	5.50
No. 296. Circular Box and lid. 43mm dia.	5.50
No. 297. Pill Box and lid, oval. 45mm long.	5.50
No. 298. Pill Box and lid, rectangular. 45mm long.	5.50
No. 299. Pill Box and lid, 5 sided. 28mm.	5.50
No. 300. Stamp Box and lid, 5 sided. 50mm dia.	5.50
No. 301. Vase, bulbous. 50mm.	4.00
No. 302. Vase. 48mm.	4.00
No. 311. Jug. 65mm.	4.00
No. 314. Vase. 39mm.	4.00
No. 316. Triangular Chest and lid. 70mm long.	9.00
No. 318. Pill Box and lid, decorated with angel's heads. 63mm.	9.00
No. 323. Tall narrow Vase. 45mm.	4.00
No. 324. Tiny Urn. 46mm.	4.00
No. 325. Urn with spout, handle and lid. 48mm.	5.50
No. 339. Two-Handled sugar basin. 123mm long.	5.50
No. 341. Tall Vase, narrow neck, 2 bird handles. 155mm.	8.00
No. 348. Jug. 63mm.	4.00
No. 349. Jug, slim. 66mm.	4.00
No. 358. Sauce Boat. 105mm long.	6.50
No. 359. Sugar basin. 124mm long. 80mm.	4.00
No. 360. Pin Tray, triangular. 85mm long.	4.00
No. 367. Pin Box, oval. 90mm long.	5.50
No. 372. Jug, slim neck. 76mm.	4.00
No. 373. Jug, long necked. 75mm.	4.00
No. 374. Jug, fluted base. 73mm.	4.00
No. 375. Vase, double mouthed. 63mm.	4.00
No. 378. Sauce Boat. 120mm long.	6.50
No. 379. Jug with stem. 70mm.	4.00
No. 386. Ashtray, triangular on 3 feet. 75mm dia.	4.00
No. 387. Candlestick. 160mm.	7.50
No. 500. Casket with lid. 84mm long, lions head handles.	12.50
No. 502. Mustard Pot with lid and spoon. 70mm.	6.50
No. 504. Vase, octagonal. 60mm.	4.00
No. 505. Octagonal Vase. 56mm.	4.00
No. 506. Vase, octagonal. 54mm.	4.00

No. 507. Taper Vase, octagonal. 60mm.	4.00
No. 524. Whelk Shells Jug. 76mm.	6.00
No. 526. Bowl, 2 handled. 118mm wide.	7.50
No. 526. (Also). Decagon Jug (10 sided). 55mm high, 110mm long.	9.50
No. 529. Vase, with moulding. 45mm.	4.50
No. 530. Vase. 50mm.	4.00
No. 531. Vase, curious wedge shaped. 50mm.	4.00
No. 532. Beaker, ribbed. 53mm.	4.00
No. 533. Grain Scoop. 60mm long.	10.00
No. 534. Oval woven Basket without handle. 75mm long.	7.50
No. 535. Vase, shaped. 52mm.	4.00
No. 589. Vase. 112mm.	5.50
No. 590. Tray. 150mm long.	6.00
No. 594. Shallow Woven basket. 73mm long.	5.00
No. 614. Vase. 70mm.	4.00
No. 616. Cylinder lip salve pot and lid. 30mm.	5.50
No. 622. Vase. 121mm.	4.00
No. 634. Vase, wide top. 34mm.	4.00
No. 638. Tall Vase, narrow flared base, curved rim. 120mm.	14.00
No. 649. Vase, hexagonal wide top. 51mm.	4.00
No. 650. Goblet, hexagonal wide top. 55mm.	4.00
No. 651. Vase, octagonal. 58mm.	4.00
No. 652. Vase, hexagonal shaped top. 57mm.	4.00
No. 653. Vase, pentagonal tapered. 57mm.	4.00
No. 654. Bowl. 35mm.	4.00
No. 656. Vase, thin.	4.00
No. 657. Vase, bulbous hexagonal base. 44mm.	4.00
No. 658. Vase, octagonal. 50mm.	4.00
No. 659. Triangular Pot. 42mm.	4.00
No. 660. Vase. 52mm.	4.00
No. 663. Tall narrow Jug. 100mm.	5.50
No. 669. Font Vase. 83mm.	10.00
No. 671. *Salt* Pot. 82mm.	7.50
No. 672. *Pepper* Pot, shaped. 84mm.	7.50
No. 676. Cream Jug. 60mm.	4.50
No. 680. Tall 2-handled Vase. 122mm.	50.00
No. 681. Salt Pot, egg-shaped. 45mm.	5.50
No. 682. Pepper Pot. 45mm.	5.50
No. 695. Chalice. 75mm.	10.00
No. 712. Vase, shaped. 68mm.	4.00

No. 713. Hexagonal Vase. 70mm.   4.00
No. 714. Vase. 69mm.   4.00
No. 715. Narrow Vase. 68mm.   4.00
No. 726. Egg Cup, Goblet. 50mm.   10.00

Not numbered
Ashtray, bulbous. 94mm diameter.
  66mm high.   7.50
Candlesnuffer, Anvil, not factory
  marked. 56mm.   7.50
Cup & saucer, full size.   10.00
Egg Cup. 60mm.   6.50
Sauce Boat. 126mm long.   6.50
Pill Box, ivy leaf shaped.
  57mm long.   5.50
Pill Box & Lid, triangular with
  embossed sides & lid. 45mm.   5.50
Menu holder, shield shaped. 58mm.   20.00
Vase, wide body, narrow neck.
  148mm.   13.00

Granic China

Trademark used by an unknown manufacturer but possibly Sampson Hancock
(and Sons), Bridge Works, Stoke and later
at the Garden Works, Hanley (usual
trademark Corona).

Granic Models
Crinkle edged vase. No. 262. 55mm.   4.00

Footwear
Ladies high boot, ornate. 30mm.   13.50

Grays Sports China

Mark registered in 1911 but used at least as early as 1902.

is decorated with a transfer of a Portsmouth Footballer and the inscription to rear: *CHAMPIONS SOUTHERN LEAGUE 1901-2*. Each transfer design is registered, the earliest registration number being from 1907-8. However, the transfer designs were in use for some years before the numbers were properly registered.

from £50.00 each

One small has been found with a Blackpool crest and one with a Liverpool crest.

A.E.GRAY & Cº
GLEBE WORKS
HANLEY

A.E.GRAY & Cº. LTD
HANLEY
ENGLAND

Trademark used by A.E. Gray & Co., Glebe Works, Mayer Street, Hanley.

A.E. Gray and Co. were earthenware manufacturers - the company was renamed 'Portmeiron Potteries Ltd' in 1961.

The 'Sports China' series very much appeals to collectors of pre- Great War souvenir china. Vases, jugs and beakers are found with transfer prints of footballers in the colours of League teams. One such small

The Griffin China

Trademark used by the London wholesalers, Sanderson & Young, 21 Red Lion Square. Manufactured by several potteries, probably branches of J.A. Robinson & Sons (Coronet Ware), and Taylor and Kent (Florentine).
Sanderson & Young were quite well known wholesalers who could have sold wares produced by any English manufacturer, probably several manufacturers supplying models during the same period. Crests recorded indicate that the models were sold in the South of England, although a Norwich Crest has been found, and, judging by models recorded this mark was not used during and after the Great War. No view ware or other transfer devices have been found.

Griffin China Models
Ancient Artefacts
Fountains Abbey, Abbot's Cup, not
  named. 49mm.   4.50
Lichfield Jug. No. 60. 62mm.   5.50
Loving Cup, 3 handles. 39mm.   6.00
Irish Bronze Pot. 50mm.   5.50
Newbury Leather Bottle, inscribed:
  Leather bottle found at Newbury
  1644 on Battlefield now in Museum.
  No. 83. 65mm.   5.50
Salisbury Kettle. 100mm.   5.50
Scarborough Jug, inscribed: *Jug*
  about 600 years old found in the
  Ancient Moat of Scarborough.
  50mm.   5.50

Buildings - Coloured
Cottage. 95mm.   22.50

Monuments (including crosses)
Iona Cross. 110mm.   14.50
Sailor's Stone, Hindhead. 94mm.   16.50

Traditional/National Souvenirs
Welsh Hat, blue cord. 55mm.   8.00

Seaside Souvenirs
Lighthouse Candle-snuffer. 104mm.   10.00
Yacht, in full sail. 127mm.   22.50

Countryside
Milk Churn and lid. 85mm.   8.00

Animals
Cat, *The Cheshire Cat Always Smiling.*
  88mm.   11.50
Cat, furry, mouth open. 87mm.   12.00
Cat, Manx. 83mm long.   25.00
Camel, one hump. 88mm.   17.00
Dog, King Charles Spaniel, begging
  on cushion. 72mm.   15.00
Dog in wicker cradle. 90mm long.   22.00
Pig, standing. 90mm long.   20.00
Toad. 72mm long.   22.50

Birds (including Eggs)
Hen, roosting. 54mm.   8.50
Parrot. 78mm.   12.50
Swan. 75mm long.   9.00
Swan Posy holder. 80mm.   6.00
Baby Bird cream jug. 66mm.   8.50

Home/Nostalgic
Coal Scuttle. 75mm.   6.50
Coal Scuttle, helmet shaped. 60mm.   8.50
Policemans Lamp. 70mm.   12.50
Pillar Box. 75mm.   14.00
Shaving Mug. 55mm.   9.50
Suitcase, closed. 80mm long.   8.00
Telescope, folded. 70mm.   16.00
The Old Arm Chair with verse. 90mm.   12.00
Watering Can.   9.50

Comic/Novelty
Boy on Scooter. 115mm.   30.00

Sport
Cricket Bag. 115mm long.   16.00

Musical Instruments
Drum. 57mm dia.   12.00
Tambourine. 68mm dia.   8.50

Footwear
Lady's 18th Century Shoe.
  90mm long.   7.50
Oriental Slipper. 95mm long.   7.00

Miniature Domestic
Teapot and lid. 52mm.   9.50

Domestic
Candle Holder. 77mm dia.   7.00
Napkin ring.   7.00

Grimwades

Trademarks used by Grimwades Ltd. Winton,
  Upper Hanley and Elgin Potteries, Stoke.
Earthenware firm more noted for hotel and
  domestic ware. But also made a few
  pieces for export.

Grimwades Models
Ewer, 69mm crest of Dominion
  of Canada.   5.00
Jug. No. 1823. 69mm. Crest
  Dominion of Canada   5.50

Grimwades also produced a range of earthenware Great War domestic pieces of some
interest.
The War Time Butter Dish (for a family of ten),
inscribed: *Made by the girls of Staffordshire
during the winter of 1917/18. When the boys
were in the trenches, fighting for Liberty and
Civilisation. Special message from Rt. Hon.
D. Lloyd George, Prime Minister: 'I have no
hesitation in saying that economy in the
consumption and use of food in this country is
a matter of the greatest possible importance to
the Empire at the present time'.* 110mm dia.
The War Time Bread and Butter plate, similar
inscription. 200mm dia.
The Patriotic Sugar basin for a family of ten with
a message from Lloyd George. 40mm.
Approximate value of pieces in this
  range.   15.00-20.00
A Teapot of usable size has been
  seen with the above Staffordshire
  operatives inscriptions together
  with the coat of arms of
  Littlehampton.   50.00

Grimwades also produced a range of
  Victory & Peace commemoratives
  but is, perhaps best known for
  Bairnsfather Ware, a range of
  earthenware plates, mugs, bowls
  etc. all bearing transfer printed
  sepia views of Bruce Bairnsfather's
  WWI Cartoon Character, Old Bill.

Grosvenor China

Trademark used by Jackson & Gosling on a
95mm diameter fluted dish bearing the
Arms of Quebec.
                                                5.00

Grosvenor Series

Grosvenor Ware

Trademark used by Arkinstall & Son Ltd., Arcadian Works, Stoke on Trent. (Usual trademark Arcadian).

Trademark used by Arkinstall & Sons (usual trademark Arcadian).

Grosvenor Series Models
Ancient Artefacts
Egyptian Pottery Discovered by Dr Flinders. 50mm.   5.50

Seaside Souvenirs
Fish lying on side. 120mm long.   6.50

Animals
Black Cat Radio Operator. 70mm.   110.00
Black Cat playing double bass. 70mm. 210.00

Home/Nostalgic
Open Umbrella. 35mm.   17.00

Trademark used by Sampson Hancock (& Sons), Bridge Works, Stoke and later at the Garden Works, Hanley (renamed Corona Pottery. Usual trademark Corona).

For details of these marks and their manufacturers see The Corona China and Arcadian.

The second mark was used as an alternative to the Corona trademark; as crests are found from all over Britain it is unlikely to have been a mark specially used for any specific wholesaler or retailer. No commemorative crests, view ware or transfer devices have been found on models. The mark appears to have been only used during the Great War.

The first mark was used on pieces of Arcadian, particularly War Memorials and Black Cats.

Numbering System. Models can be found with gold or black painted stock numbers. These are recorded, where known, in the following lists:

Grosvenor Models
Ancient Artefacts
Canterbury Water Bottle. 50mm.	5.50
Guernsey Milk Can and lid.	
2 sizes: 68mm.	6.00
95mm.	8.00
Jersey Milk Can and lid. 53mm.	6.00
Leather Jack. 58mm.	5.50

Buildings - White
Blackpool Tower, on heavy detailed base. 127mm.	12.00
Building with arched doorway & crinolated roof, found with the Newbury coat of arms. 74mm.	15.00
Clifton Suspension Bridge. 120mm long.	75.00

Traditional/National Souvenirs
Laxey Wheel. 80mm.	40.00
Welsh Harp. 90mm.	9.50

Seaside
Lifeboat, solid interior. 130mm long.	50.00
Lighthouse on rocky base. 150mm.	22.00

Animals
Cat, sitting, large ruff of fur. 100mm.	22.50
Cat, black, on horseshoe (from Arcadian Registered Series mould). 74mm.	95.00
Cat, black in yacht (from Arcadian Registered Series) 75mm.	165.00
Cow Creamer. No. 376. 130mm long.	185.00
Fish. 88mm long.	6.50
Lion, lying down. No. 369. 150mm long.	35.00
Pig, standing. No. 158. 84mm long.	20.00
Tortoise. 70mm long.	12.00

Great War
Submarine, inscribed:*E4*.110mm long.	22.50
Renault Tank. 100mm long.	85.00
Torpedo, Model of. 150mm long.	95.00
Ghurka Knife. 140mm long.	25.00
Bell Tent. No. 209. 85mm.	16.50

Burford War Memorial.
In grateful memory of the men of Burford who fell in the war
of 1914-1918. 130mm.	170.00
Campden War Memorial. 146mm. Scarce	175.00
Newnham War Memorial. 140mm. (rare).	150.00

Home/Nostalgic
Baby in Bootee. 80mm long.	13.00
Cigarette Case. 70mm long.	15.00
Desk Top. 35mm.	16.50
Grandfather Clock. 123mm.	14.50
Hip Bath. 92mm long.	12.50
Jardinière on fixed stand. 92mm.	8.00
Tobacco Pouch. 75mm long.	12.50
Watering can. 72mm.	9.50
Post Box. 62mm. Inscribed *I can't get a letter...*	16.00

Sport/Pastimes
Tennis Racquet. 136mm long.	22.00
Castle Chess Piece. 65mm.	15.00
Knight Chess Piece. 72mm.	25.00
Pawn Chess Piece. 60mm.	20.00
Queen Chess Piece. 82mm.	45.00

Musical Instruments
Banjo. 145mm.	20.00
Piano with open lid. 60mm.	17.50

Modern Equipment
Gas Cooker with match striker top. 70mm.	12.00

Footwear
Ladies 18th Century Shoe. 90mm long.	7.50

Miniature Domestic
Column Candlestick. 100mm.	4.00

Miscellaneous
Horseshoe on slope. 70mm long.	4.00

Gwalia Ware

Oldbury, Knighton,
& Llandrindod Wells.

Trademark used for a Llandrindod Wells retailer by an unknown manufacturer. Only 2 pieces recorded, bearing Llandrindod Wells crests.

Gwalia Models
Ancient Artefacts
Chester Roman Kettle, not named. 4.00
Loving Cup, one handled. 40mm. 4.00

H&L

H & L

Impressed mark used 1905-1919.

Impressed mark used by Hewitt & Leadbeater, Willow Potteries, Longton. Usual trademark Willow Art, these impressed initials are often found on models that also carry the Willow Art mark.

For details of this firm see Willow Art and Willow China.

Early in its history this firm specialised in parian ware, which carried the impressed mark 'H & L'. Many busts also carry the printed trademark Willow Art China so they will be found listed under that heading. Several other models have been recorded with only this impressed mark but as they are normally found with the Willow Art mark they too will be found listed under that heading.

The models listed below have not been found with a printed mark and are not normally found with crests.

H & L Models
Parian/Unglazed
Bust of *Bourne*. 154mm. 65.00
Bust of *Clowes*. 150mm. 65.00
Bust of Albert King of the Belgians,
  Oct 29th square base, unglazed.
  172mm. 80.00
Bust of Sir John French. *Oct 2nd*
  168mm. 80.00
Bust of Field Marshall Lord
  Kitchener. Impressed *'C.S.*
  Chadwick copyright Sep 11th 1914.'
  170mm. 95.00

Bust of Jellicoe on square
  glazed or unglazed base.
  Oct 21st 170mm.   75.00
Bust of *Shakespeare* on square base.
13 sizes: 105mm.   17.50
         112mm.   17.50
         126mm.   40.00

Buildings - Coloured
Ann Hathaway's Cottage
  3 sizes: 60mm long.   18.00
         105mm long.   30.00
         125mm long.   40.00
*Mason Croft, Residence of Miss Marie
  Corelli.* 73mm.   150.00
Shakespeares House. 50mm long.   16.00

Historical/Folklore
*Font in which Shakespeare was
  baptized, Model of.* 95mm dia.   19.50
Lincoln Imp, not named. 130mm.   12.50

Cartoon/Comedy Characters
Dr Beetle and Sunny Jim, sitting on
  striped armchair with rose and
  brown colouring. 95mm.   175.00

H&S

H & S
P

Trademark used for a Plymouth retailer by
  Hewitt & Leadbeater, Willow Potteries,
  Longton (usual trademark Willow Art).
For details of this china and the manufacturer see Willow Art China.
As two of the models recorded are to be
  found in Plymouth it is almost certain
  that the 'P' in the 'H & S.P' stands for
  Plymouth. It is quite possible that H & S
  supplied a number of shops in English
  resorts, or that Hewitt & Leadbeater used
  pieces with this mark to complete other
  orders. The mark does not appear to have
  been used after the Great War and no
  transfer devices of any kind have been
  recorded.

H & S Models
Unglazed
Bust of Field Marshall Lord
  Kitchener on square base. 170mm. 95.00

Ancient Artefacts
Guernsey Milk Can and Lid.
  No. 172. 6.00

Buildings - White
Derry's Clock, Plymouth.
  2 sizes: 132mm. 18.00
       155mm. 20.00
Hastings Castle Ruins. 100mm. 30.00

Monuments (including Crosses)
Burns, statue on square base.
  170mm. 30.00
Drake, statue, Plymouth.
  160mm. 20.00
Highland Mary Statue, Dunoon,
  on plinth. 150mm. 35.00

Historical/Folklore
Church Bell, inscribed: *Curfew must*
not ring tonight. 70mm. 12.50

Seaside Souvenirs
Rowing Boat on rocky base. No. 164.
  113mm long. 17.00

Animals
Pig, sitting with inscription: You *may*
push... 75mm. 22.50

Great War
Battleship, impressed: *HMS Lion.*
  140mm long. 40.00
Submarine. 120mm long. 30.00
Tank. 125mm long. 22.50
Field Gun with screen. 117mm long. 35.00

Home/Nostalgic
Coal Scuttle. 53mm. 8.50
Garden Trug. 70mm. 8.50

Footwear
Sabot. 70mm long. 6.00

Hamilton China

Trademark used for H. Hamilton, Milton &
Amber, Saltburn, for products of J.A.
Robinson & Sons Ltd. (Arcadian).
These models are always found with the
Saltburn by the Sea crest and were sold in
that town by H. Hamilton whose trade-
mark they bear.

Hamilton Models
Ancient Artefacts
Puzzle Jugs. 67mm. 6.00

Seaside Souvenirs
Two curling waves on an octagonal
base, inscribed: *The glad sea waves.*
  50mm. 40.00

Animals
Kneeling Camel. 18.00

Birds (including Eggs)
Kingfisher. 77mm. 30.00

Home/Nostalgic
Policeman's Lamp. 73mm. 8.00

Comic/Novelty
Jack-in-the-Box. 90mm. 25.00

Miniature Domestic
Shaving Mug. 57mm. 9.50

Domestic
Sugar Basin. 53mm. 4.00

Hargreaves & Son Ltd

Hayter & Stickland

Hayter & Stickland

Mark used by an unknown British manufacturer for a Buxton, Derbyshire retailer.

Hargreaves Models
Ancient Artefacts
Chester Roman Vase. 55mm.   5.50

Comic/Novelty
Cat and Fiddle, Buxton. Grey Cat,
red eyes, nose and mouth sitting
on green cushioned chair playing
violin. No details of size
available.   70.00

Trademark used by a Winchester retailer of an unknown manufacturer.

Only one piece has been recorded to date although I suspect there are others. The piece is identical to the Goss original of which it is no doubt a copy, but whilst the Goss example has been produced in that firms usual parian ware, the version sold by Hayter and Stickland is typical English porcelain.

Hayter & Stickland Model
Ancient Artefacts
*Cardinal Beaufort's Salt Cellar
(1404-1447)* with *Arms of St. Cross
Hospital* and *Cardinal Beaufort's
White Hart.*   30.00

Heal English China

Heathcote China

No details of mark available.

Trademark used by an unknown English manufacturer. This is possibly a misspelling of Real English China. See P. 347.

The only model recorded so far is an anvil on a brick base with the crest of Southend-on-Sea. 60mm.   6.00

Trademark used by H.M. Williamson & Sons, Bridge Pottery, Longton.
Domestic manufacturer not known to have made crested souvenirs, only domestic wares found:

Heathcote China Models
Cup and saucer with Burgh of
  Stirling crest with early mark.   5.00
Cup and saucer with Troon crest
  with late mark.   5.00
Coffee Can and saucer, with the 4
  Flags of the Allies. 56mm.   15.00

Herald China

Herald Series

Trademark used for a wholesaler or retailer by Alfred B. Jones & Sons Ltd. Grafton China Works, Longton, Staffs. (Usual trademark Grafton).
See English Herald China.

Trademark used for William Holmes & Co, fancy goods importers, Glasgow, on china manufactured by Alfred B. Jones & Sons Ltd. Grafton China Works, Longton, Staffs. (Usual trademark Grafton).
For details of this china and the manufacturer see Grafton China.
Several models and some domestic ware are found with this printed mark, most have Scottish crests, but some have been found with N. Irish crests. One model has been found with a colour transfer view of Portaskaig, Islay.
Numbering System. Where stock numbers occur they are the same numbers as found on 'Grafton' models. Numbers where known are listed below.

Herald Series Models
Ancient Artefacts

Chester Roman Vase. 60mm.	5.50
Yaverland Roman Vase. No. 125. 50mm.	5.50

Seaside Souvenirs

Whelk Shell. 83mm long.	6.00

Animals
Cheshire Cat, The. Always Smiling.

One green glass eye. 86mm.	10.00
Bulldog, sitting. No. 250. 88mm.	40.00
Cock, circular base. No. 454. 95mm.	20.00
Dog, King Charles Spaniel, sitting. No. 390. 55mm.	17.50
Dog, Puppy, sitting with one ear up, scratching with back leg. No. 410. 85mm.	17.50

Frog, sitting upright, hands on
chest. No. 204. 74mm.   35.00
Monkey sitting wearing coat.
70mm.   18.00
Pig, sitting. No. 341. 90mm long.   35.00
Rabbit. No. 240. 112mm long.   19.50
Rabbit dish, coloured eye.
123mm long.   30.00
Shetland Pony, sometimes found
inscribed: *A Native of Shetland.*
105mm long. (This model can be
found with a crest of Shetland.)   35.00
Snail. No. 328. 88mm long.   17.50

Birds (including Eggs)
Duck, sitting. No. 47. 90mm long.   20.00

Great War
Tank, no steering wheels, inscribed:
HM Landship Creme-de-Menthe.
No. 413. Rd. No. 659588.
98mm long.   35.00
Desert Gun. 150mm long.   85.00
German Gun captured by the British.
No. 403. 144mm.   40.00
Hand Grenade with removable pin.
83mm.   30.00
Cannon Shell, inscribed: *Jack*
Johnson. No. 339. 90mm.   12.50
Bell Tent with open flaps. No. 239.
65mm.   22.50
Killin War Memorial, with extended
base and railings. 160mm.   185.00

Alcohol
Champagne Bottle. 100mm.   10.00

Sport/Pastimes
Golf Ball on tee Pepper Pot. 52mm.   12.50

Footwear
Sabot with hanging hole.
80mm long.   7.00

Miscellaneous
Ashtray on three tiny feet. No. 386.
86mm long.   4.00
Horses Hoof vase. 45mm.   6.50
Stamp Box and lid. No. 300.
50mm across.   6.50

Heraldic China

Trademark used by Sampson Hancock (and
Sons), Bridge Works, Stoke. (Usual trademark Corona).
For details of this firm and china manufacturer see The Corona China.
As very few models have been found with
this mark and all of them would have
been made before 1910 it is probable that
the mark was used before the more familiar
Corona trademark. Most of the pieces
found with the 'Herald' mark are 'smalls'.
One small vase has been found with a
monochrome (brown) transfer print of
Ellen Terry, this piece is also inscribed:
'Jubilee Souvenir 1856-1906'. Most models
and 'smalls' carry seaside crests.

Heraldic Models
Ancient Artefacts
Exeter Vase. No. 129. 70mm.   5.50
Glastonbury Bowl. 40mm.   5.50
Shakespeare's Jug. 55mm.   6.50

Animals
Bulldog in Kennel. 66mm.   17.00

Birds (including Eggs)
Baby Bird cream jug. 70mm.   8.50

Home/Nostalgic
Oil Lamp. 34mm.   8.00

Alcohol
Barrel on legs.   6.00
Tankard. 70mm.   5.00

Sports/Pastimes
Queen, chess piece. 90mm.   40.00
King, chess piece. 108mm.   40.00

Footwear
Ladies 18th Century Shoe.
105mm long.   8.50

Heraldic China

Trademark used by an unknown retailer of wares produced by Wiltshaw and Robinson (usual trademark Carlton) and Willow Art.

Only two items found.

Animals
Sitting Bulldog. 50mm.   25.00

Miscellaneous
Jug. 42mm. (Whitehead crest).   4.00

E. Hughes and Co.

Iceni Crest China

ENGLAND

ENGLAND

ENGLAND

Trademark used by E. Hughes & Co., Opal Works, Fenton. (Usual trademarks Fenton & Royal).
For details of this china and manufacturer see Fenton China and Royal China.
This mark has only been found on domestic ware and the two pieces listed below. The mark was only used for a short time during the Great War of which a commemorative has been recorded, this is a design with six Flags of the Allies and inscribed: 'In Freedoms Cause'.

Hughes China Models
Seaside Souvenirs
Oyster Shell dish. 130mm long. 4.00

Miniature Domestic
Cheese Dish and cover. 70mm long. 6.50

Domestic
Egg Cup. 62mm. 6.50

Other Domestic ware found too. 2.50-10.00

Trademark used for wholesalers by J.A. Robinson & Sons, subsequently Cauldon Ltd. (Usual trademark Arcadian).
For details of this china and manufacturer see Arcadian China.
This mark appears to have been used from around 1920 to 1925. Crests are found from all over England. Coloured transfer views, Poppies and 'Lucky Black Cats' transfers are found on 'smalls' with this mark. Stock numbers where used are the same as Arcadian numbers.

Iceni Models
Ancient Artefacts
Cadogan Tea Pot. 19.50
Goodwin Sands Carafe. 82mm. 5.50
Hastings Kettle. No. 166. 60mm. 5.50

Buildings - White
Cottage. 62mm long. 14.50

Monuments (including Crosses)
Caister on Sea Lifeboat Memorial.
150mm. 29.50

Seaside Souvenirs

Lighthouse. Sometimes named:	
Spurn Lighthouse.	18.00

Countryside

Beehive on stilts. 80mm.	15.00

Animals

Cat, sitting and smiling grotesque,	
(rather similar to Cheshire Cat).	
75mm.	12.50
Cat, Cheshire Inscribed: T*he Smile*	
that won't come off. 95mm.	14.00
Black Cats,3 on sledge.	
118mm long.	210.00
Fish, curled. 100mm long.	12.00
Frog, open mouthed. 58mm.	22.00
Sussex Pig, Model of, sitting	
inscribed: *You can push or you can*	
shuv but I'm hanged if I'll be druv.	
No. 148. 88mm long.	22.00
Sussex Pig. Model of, standing.	
Inscribed as above. No. 148.	
88mm long.	19.50
Tortoise. 68mm long.	14.00

Birds (including Eggs)

Chick, breaking out of egg.	
63mm long.	11.00
Hen, red comb. 80mm.	14.50
Owl. 67mm.	14.50
Pelican. 76mm.	40.00
Turkey, fantail on rectangular	
base. 70mm.	30.00

Great War

Monoplane, movable prop.	
149mm long.	75.00
Tank.	
2 sizes: 100mm long.	30.00
115mm long.	40.00
Trench Mortar. 47mm.	30.00
German Incendiary Bomb. 80mm.	30.00
Bell Tent. 70mm.	16.00
Clip of bullets, Model of. 87mm.	22.50
Colonial Hat, Model of. 88mm.	25.00

Home/Nostalgic

Chair, highbacked. 90mm.	8.50
Coal Bucket. 55mm.	6.00

Comic/Novelty

Policeman, left hand raised.	
146mm.	45.00

Alcohol

Soda Syphon. 100mm.	10.00

Sport/Pastimes

Football. 46mm.	9.50
Knight chess piece. 64mm.	17.50

Musical Instruments

Tambourine. 58mm Diameter.	10.00

Footwear

Ankle Boot. 74mm long.	6.00

Domestic

Candlestick, square. 35mm.	6.00

Imperial

Trademark used by Wedgwood and Co (Ltd), Unicorn and Pinnox Works, Tunstall, on cheaply produced souvenir wares.

This firm, which is often confused with the famous Josiah Wedgwood and Sons Ltd. manufactured much cheaper earthenwares. The firm specialised in table and domestic ware but obviously turned their hand to crested and view wares when these lines became good sellers. They were already making badged ware, so producing crests would be no problem. The firm began using an 'Imperial' mark in 1909 but used a much more elaborate mark than the one above on tableware. Unlike other manufacturers they did not make models to commemorate the Great War, and it seems likely that the firm was not geared

to making these models. There is no evidence that crested ware was produced after the war, and most pieces found with this mark are 'smalls', generally rather heavy and cheaply made. Colour transfer view ware is reasonably well produced, but found on the same heavy pottery 'smalls' and domestic ware.

It is interesting to note that during his most successful period, 1920 to 1930, Harold Taylor Robinson managed to gain some financial control over this firm (see Arcadian China).

Imperial Models
Ancient Artefacts

Chester Roman Vase. 55mm.	5.50
Lincoln Jack, not named. 54mm.	5.50

Traditional/National

Scotsman bust in tartan plaid and tam o'shanter.	30.00

Animals

Cat, long-necked. 115mm.	10.00
Cat, Cheshire *Always Smiling*. 90mm.	12.00
Dog, sitting. 70mm.	12.00
Elephant, walking. 52mm.	20.00
Pig, standing, fat. 93mm long.	22.50
Toad, very flat. 76mm long.	22.00

Birds (including Eggs)

Pelican jug.	8.50

Home/Nostalgic

Coal Scuttle. 35mm.	8.00
Suitcase. 79mm long.	7.00

Sport

Football. 65mm.	9.50

Musical Instruments

Tambourine. 68mm diameter.	12.00

Hats

Top Hat. 40mm.	7.50

Footwear

Dutch Sabot. 83mm long.	6.00

Domestic

Napkin ring. 40mm.	8.00
Oil Lamp. 90mm long.	8.00

Miniature Domestic

Teapot and Lid, bulbous. 68mm.	9.00

Imperial

Jmperial

Trademark used by a Foreign manufacturer, probably Kutzscher & Co, Schwarzenberg (usual trademark Impero), or C. Schmidt & Co., Carlsbad, Bohemia, (usual trademark Alexandra).
One bowl has been found, which is cream-coloured, with gold flowers, and the crest of Rothesay surrounded by a purple design.
8.00

Impero

Jmpero

JMPERO

IMPERO

Trademark used by the German manufacturer Kutzscher & Co, Schwarzenberg, Saxony on crested china for export to Britain.
This mark is mostly found on buildings and monuments and traditional souvenirs usually carrying the crest of the town for which they were designed which is very much what one would expect from a German manufacturer. Models would be made from photographs, postcards or local drawings. The two elephants on the sledge are often found unmarked and is a most attractive comic model.
Impero models are made from the usual white 'hard china' so much scorned by English manufacturers, but the models are very nicely detailed, and for the most part desirable.

Impero Models
Ancient Artefacts
Chester Roman Vase. 65mm.   5.50
Puzzle Jug with inscription. 68mm.   8.50

Buildings - White
Boston Stump Church. 125mm.   25.00
Grimsby, The Tower. 170mm.   30.00
Lincoln Cathedral, west front.
   No. 824. 120mm.   28.00
Lincoln Stonebow. 85mm.   30.00
Clock Tower, Skegness. 124mm.   12.50
York, *Bootham Bar.* 135mm.   28.00

Monuments (including Crosses)
Captain Cook's Monument, Whitby
135mm. 45.00
Captain Scott, figure on square base.
2 sizes: 135mm. 30.50
150mm. 30.50
Hall Cross, Doncaster. 158mm. 27.50
Hull Fisherman's Memorial with
inscription. 125mm. 17.50
Hull Soldiers' War Memorial, with
inscription: *Erected to the memory
of the men of Hull who fell in the late
South African War.* 120mm. 24.50
The Monument, Laceby, with
inscriptions 32.00

Traditional/National Souvenirs
Devil looking over Lincoln. 95mm. 17.50
The Lincoln Imp. 112mm. 9.50
The Fiddler, York. 120mm (rare). 40.00

Seaside Souvenirs
Fisherman. 112mm. 20.00
Lifeboatman, standing. 110mm. 20.00
Mermaid holding large fish. 84mm. 20.00
Spurn Lighthouse. 147mm. 22.00
The Lighthouse, Flamborough. 125mm. 22.00
Withernsea Lighthouse. 135mm. 22.00

Animals
Hen and Cock on circular saucepan
and lid. Base 83mm high
70mm long. 20.00
Two Elephants on Sledge. Comic.
70mm. 75.00
A Native of Shetland, Shetland Pony.
80mm. 25.00

Birds (including Eggs)
Swan posy bowl. 74mm. 4.50

Ionic Heraldic

Trademark used for the Glasgow wholesaler
CR CR & Co. by an unknown manufacturer, but probably Taylor & Kent.
(Usual trademark Florentine).
The two other marks with the initials C.R.
and Co G. were thought to have been
used by Taylor and Kent (Florentine
China) for a Glasgow wholesaler. See
Atlas Heraldic China and Caledonia
China. The 'smalls' and two models
found with the 'Ionic' trademark are not
recognisably made by Taylor and Kent,
but it is probable that they made them. All
items carry Scottish crests.

Ionic Models
Ancient Artefacts
Whiskey Cup. 60mm diameter. 5.50

Animals
Pig, fat. 70mm long. 20.00

Home/Nostalgic
Bucket with rope handle. 75mm. 6.50
Coal Bucket. 65mm long. 6.00

Domestic
Ball Vase. 45mm. 4.00
Beaker. 80mm. 4.00

Ivelcon - St. Ivel China

Ivora Ware

Trademark used by Alpin and Barrett, Yeovil, by an unknown manufacturer. A two-handled cup has been found with this mark, evidently to be used with a proprietory brand of stock cube.

Value 12.00

Trademark used by Edinburgh wholesalers and retailers William Richie and Sons Ltd., on a range of domestic ware. Manufactured by Birks, Rawlins & Co. (usual trademark Savoy).

For details of this china and manufacturer see Porcelle.

Many British manufacturers during the early twentieth century described their wares as 'Ivory'. Ivory ware, Ivory porcelain and Ivory china are terms found in many advertisements in the *Pottery Gazette* at that time.

Ivora Models
Ancient Artefacts
Puzzle Jug. 68mm.   7.00
Three-handled loving cup. 38mm.   6.00

Historical/Folklore
Miner's Lamp. 70mm.   22.00

Ivy China

Home/Nostalgic
Coal Bucket. 70mm.   6.00
Milk Churn open top. 75mm.   7.00
Policeman's Lamp. 67mm.   10.00

Footwear
Boot. 65mm long.   6.00

Hats
Top Hat matchstriker. 45mm.   7.50

Miniature Domestic
Cheese Dish and cover. 50mm.   9.50
1-handled mug. 36mm.   4.00
Saucepan and lid. 46mm.   6.00

Trademark used by a wholesaler of pieces
  produced by an unknown German manufacturer, probably Wm. Kutzscher & Co.,
  Schwarzenburg, Saxony.
NB: **Badly printed marks which appear to
  be** *Ivyknot?* **are** *Wyknot?* **(See Wy not?).**

Seaside Souvenirs
Lifeboat. 133mm long.   20.00
Lifeboat Memorial, Southend-on-Sea.
  124mm.   20.00

Miniature Domestic
Cheese Dish and Cover. 50mm.   9.00

JBC

Trademark used for the Manchester whole-saler J.B. & Co. by Hewitt & Leadbeater, Willow Potteries, Longton. (Usual trademark Willow Art).

JBC Models
Historical/Folklore
Model of James' the Fifth Chair at
Stirling Castle. 100mm.   14.50

Traditional/National Souvenirs
Welsh hat, blue band.   8.00
   Can be found with the longest
   place name round brim. No. 75.
   57mm.   12.50

Animals
Elephant, standing, trunk curved
   down. 55mm. 73mm long.   20.00
Pig, fat and standing. Tail forms a
   circle and rejoins the body.
   80mm long.   19.50
Rabbit, ears erect. No. 97.
   60mm long.   16.00

Birds
Swan posy holder. 59mm.   8.00

Seaside Souvenirs
Lighthouse on rocky base. 110mm.   10.00

Alcohol
Bottle inscribed: *One Special Scotch.*
   90mm.   9.50

Footwear
Lancashire Clog. 105mm long.   8.00

Miscellaneous
Hand holding Tulip vase. 80mm.   7.50

JBM

J.D. & Co.

Trademark used for the Manchester wholesaler JB & Co by Sampson Hancock (& Sons), Bridge Works, Stoke. (Usual trademark Corona). See JBC entry.

JBM Model
Footwear
Clog with square toe and gilded
   buckle. 80mm long.   7.00
Ladies Button Boot. No. 149. 65mm. 8.50

Trademark used by J. Dimmock & Co., Hanley. 1862-1904.
A Scent bottle & Jug & Bowl Set have been found with the above mark. The crests used are of the City Commercial College and one with a Mitre & the motto *Deus Dux Doctrinalux.*

Price range 5.00-10.00

Jerusalem & Orient Bazaar

JP

Trademark used for items produced for the bazaar in Great Yarmouth by Hewitt Bros (usual trademark Willow Art).

Trademark used by a French manufacturer for the French souvenir market.

One Vase, 70mm high, has been recorded with this mark with the crest Boulogne Sur Mer.   5.00

J.R. & Co.

JW

For further information, please see Victoria China entry.

Trademark used for an unknown retailer by J.A. Robinson Ltd. (Usual trademark Arcadian).

For details of this china and manufacturer see Arcadian China.

Unfortunately the crests on the three pieces recorded have not all been noted, but one suspects the town begins with the letter R, possibly Retford as this crest has been noted. One military badge has been recorded, this being the Devonshire Regiment.

JW Models
Great War
Tommy and his machine gun, Model of.
  130mm.   55.00
Red Cross Van. 80mm long.   40.00

Footwear
Dutch Clog. 102mm long.   7.00

JW & Co.

Kahess China

No details of mark available.

J. W. & C°

No details of manufacturer or wholesaler known. A Bronze Pot with the crest of Elstree has been sighted in very fine china, could possibly be Savoy.

Trademark used by Wiltshaw and Robinson Ltd., Carlton Works, Stoke-on-Trent. (Usual trademark Carlton).

Kahess Model
Great War
Edith Cavell Monument, unglazed
figure on glazed base. 160mm.   25.00

Kangaroo Art China

Trademark used for the retailer Valentine &
Sons, Melbourne by an English manufac-
turer, most probably Hewitt &
Leadbeater. (Usual mark Willow / Willow
Art).

Kangaroo Art Models
Animals
Kangaroo. 113mm.   100.00

Great War
Nurse, inscribed: A *Friend in Need.*
130mm.   70.00
Sailor standing. Inscribed: *Our
Brave Defender.* 127mm.   70.00

Kangaroo Brand

China manufactured by Wiltshaw &
Robinson Ltd. Under the usual Carlton
mark the following trademark can be
found:
Made in England for G.E Lucas S.F. Cal
Kangaroo Brand.
The one model found has a crest of the
Panama California Exposition. The model
was found in California and was obvious-
ly made for that market.

Kangaroo Brand Model
Animals
Bear, Polar, walking. 125mm long.   60.00

Keltic

BRITISH MAKE

KELTIC

Trademark used by Taylor and Kent (Ltd), Florence Works, Longton, (usual trademark Florentine), for Irish and Scottish retailers. Some pieces are similar to Nautilus Porcelain.

Keltic Models
Ancient Artefacts
Loving Cup. 3-handled. 40mm.   6.00
Puzzle Jug. 68mm.   7.50
Whiskey Bowl. 76mm diameter.   5.50

Historical/Folklore
Old Armchair, with verse. 90mm.   12.50
Miners Lamp. 69mm.   18.00

Seaside Souvenirs
Bathing Machine. 74mm.   18.00
The Glad Sea Waves on base. 50mm. 35.00

Animals
Camel, kneeling. 95mm long.   17.00
Pig, standing. 95mm long.   19.50

Birds
Baby Bird Cream Jug. 65mm.   8.00

Home/Nostalgic
Coal Scuttle. 65mm.   6.00
Policeman's lamp. 70mm.   18.00
Shaving Mug. 55mm.   9.50
Watering Can. 70mm.   9.00

Alcohol
Carboy in Basket. 74mm.   7.00

Sport Boxing Glove. 65mm long.   40.00

Footwear Shoe, Ladies' 18th Century.
95mm long.   8.50

Miniature Domestic
Teapot with lid. 70mm.   9.50

Kensington China

KENSINGTON
ENGLISH CHINA

ROYAL CROWN POTTERY CO
BURSLEM
KENSINGTON CHINA

Trademark used by Royal Crown Pottery Co., Burslem, a branch of J.A. Robinson Ltd. (Usual trademark Arcadian and Willow Art).

No information is available on the history of this firm and the mark was not registered. The Bevington Brothers established a firm called the Kensington Fine Art Pottery Co in 1892 but this was a very short lived partnership, that was dissolved in 1899. The Kensington Pottery Ltd. was established in 1922 in the same Kensington Works in Hanley, and later at Burslem. The name 'Royal Crown Pottery' was not registered until 1952-7 by Trentham Bone China Ltd and has no connection with the earlier name.

Many of the models with this mark are recognisably from Arcadian and Willow Art moulds, so it is most likely that this was one of the small firms bought and sold by Mr Harold Taylor Robinson between 1903 and 1920. (See Arcadian China). Many of these models carry the same stock numbers as Willow Art models and so it seems that either crested ware was produced for the firm at the Willow Pottery or that the mark was used in the same works. (Stock numbers where known will be listed below). Only town and resort crests have been found on Kensington models, 'smalls' and domestic ware.

Kensington Models

Ancient Artefacts
Carlisle Salt Pot. 50mm.	5.50

Monuments
Lifeboat memorial. 130mm.	12.50

Historical/Folklore
English Folksong Bride beside chest. No. 036. 93mm.	50.00
James V Chair, Stirling Castle. 105mm.	16.50
Mary Queen of Scots Chair, Edinburgh Castle. 80mm.	14.50

Traditional/National Souvenirs
Welsh Hat. No. 75. 57mm.	9.00

Seaside Souvenirs
Lighthouse, octagonal. 112mm.	9.50

Animals
Cat, Cheshire, inscribed: *Still smiling.* No. 159. 95mm.	12.50
Cat, haunched. 70mm.	14.50
Collie, standing. 103mm long.	25.00
Dog, sitting with shield. 80mm.	18.50
Elephant, walking. No. 113. 52mm.	20.00
Elephant Jug. 67mm.	14.00
Open mouthed Fish. 128mm long.	8.00
Pig, fat, standing. 98mm long.	30.00
Ram, curly horns. 90mm long.	28.00
Teddy Bear, sitting. 90mm.	22.50
Shetland Pony. 108mm long.	30.00

Great War
Sailor, standing. Inscribed: *Our Brave Defender.* 127mm.	70.00
Nurse, inscribed: *A friend in need.* 130mm.	70.00
Battleship, impressed: *HMS Lion.* 140mm long.	65.00
Model of New Submarine. 117mm long.	40.00
British Tank. 90mm long.	24.50
Red Cross Van. 58mm.	40.00
Field Gun, with screen. 115mm long.	35.00
Oficer's Peaked Cap, brown band. 84mm long.	22.50
Kitchen range with cooking pot, inscribed: *Keep the home fires burning.* 77mm.	18.00

Home/Nostalgic

Baby, standing, hands stretched out and up, coloured face. 110mm.	26.00
Coal scuttle. 52mm.	8.00
Grandfather Clock, inscribed: *Make use of time let not advantage slip.* Shakespeare. No. 149. 128mm.	18.50
Watering Can. 70mm.	12.00

Comic/Novelty

Billiken *The God of Luck.* 73mm.	8.00
Pixie, crouching on a rectangular base. 78mm. (Could well be the Chester Imp).	25.00

Alcohol

Barrel on stand. 58mm.	8.00

Sport/Pastimes

Golf Ball, Pepper Pot. 52mm.	15.00
Tennis Racquet, with tennis ball. 138mm long.	24.50

Musical Instruments

Bagpipes. 118mm long.	50.00
Tambourine. 70mm diameter.	12.00

Transport

Open Tourer. 115mm long.	40.00

Footwear

Clog. 70mm long.	7.00
Edwardian Shoe. Square toe, blue ribbon. 112mm long.	9.00
Ladies Riding Shoe. Square toe and blue bow. 115mm long.	8.00

Domestic

Cone Candlesnuffer. 55mm.	4.00

Miscellaneous

Hand holding Tulip. No. 74. 80mm.	6.50

Kent Bone China

For details of trademarks used by Taylor and Kent, Florence Works, Longton. (Usual trademark Florentine). See Taylor and Kent.

King China

Kingsway Art or Crest China

Trademark used for a retailer or wholesaler by Alfred B. Jones and Sons Ltd., Grafton China Works, Longton, Staffs.
For details of this china and manufacturer see Grafton China.

King China Models
Ancient Artefacts
Highland Whisky Bowl.
The Abbots Cup from the original at Fountains Abbey. No. 709.
90mm diameter.   5.50
Puzzle Jug, inscribed: *Model of Puzzle Jug original in South Kensington Museum.* Verse to rear. 65mm.   9.00

024 and 36 015 are stock numbers and paintresses marks. A whole range of these can be found.

Trademark used for W.H. Smith by Hewitt and Leadbeater and Arkinstall and Son. (Usual trademarks Willow Art and Arcadian). The standard of quality is very high.
For details of this china and manufacturer see Willow Art China and Arcadian China.
Hewitt and Leadbeater obviously supplied a large range of crested ware for this customer. Crests recorded come from all over Britain and the initials W.H.S. and S. stand for W.H. Smith and Sons whose head office at that time was in Kingsway, W.C., London. The numbers which are found in the mark are either to indicate a particular order or possibly the paintress as it would have been a valuable order and checked more carefully than usual.

The same numbers occur on several models and are normally prefixed by 0. Numbers 012, 024 and 030 are most common. (These numbers are not found on Willow Art models, where painted stock numbers also occur on models these are the same.) The range of models indicate that Hewitt and Leadbeater supplied W.H. Smith until the end of the Great War. Some Naval crests have been recorded, these being *HMS Achilles, HMS Ceres, HMS Hood,* and *HMS Valiant.* No view ware or other transfer devices have been found on models with this mark. Domestic ware and many 'smalls' have also been recorded.

Numbering System. The numerals from the mark are not recorded as they are found on many different models. Painted stock numbers are listed below.

Kingsway Models

Ancient Artefacts

Carlisle Ancient Stone Roman Altar. 123mm.	100.00
Celtic Vase. 42mm.	5.50
Colchester Cloaca Vase. 41mm.	5.00
Loving Cup, three-handled. 40mm.	6.00
Pilgrims Bottle.	5.50
Roman Vase in Lewes Castle, Model of 35mm.	5.50
Salt Maller, Model of.	5.50

Buildings - White

St. Botolph's Church, Boston. 112mm.	50.00
Westminster Abbey, west front. 115mm.	28.00

Monuments (including Crosses)

Maiwand Memorial. 98mm.	25.00

Historical/Folklore

Bunyan's Chair. 92mm.	16.00
Burn's Chair, Dumfries. 85mm.	14.50
English Folksong Bride beside chest. 93mm.	40.00
James V Chair, Stirling Castle. 100mm.	14.50
Mary Queen of Scots Chair, Edinburgh Castle, Model of. 75mm.	12.50
Man in the Moon. 50mm.	27.00

Traditional/National Souvenirs

Melton Mowbray Pie. 52mm.	20.00
Bagpipes with turquoise ribbon. 118mm long.	50.00
Burns and Highland Mary, sitting on a rock. 112mm.	35.00
Souter Johnny (impressed), some colouring. 130mm.	40.00
Welsh Lady, bust, with black hat. 110mm.	25.00
Welsh Leek. 55mm.	8.50
Dutch Boy. 80mm.	16.50
Dutch Girl. 78mm.	16.50

Seaside Souvenirs

Rowing Boat on rocks. No. 164. 110mm long.	20.00
Lifeboat, blue and yellow ropes. 116mm long.	19.50
Lighthouse. No. 027. 140mm.	14.00
Lighthouse on base, not named. 110mm.	8.00
Withernsea Lighthouse, octagonal. No. 174. 192mm.	22.50
Eddystone Lighthouse, Model of. 86mm.	8.50
Crab. 83mm long.	17.00
Scallop Shell on rocky base. 82mm.	10.50
Whelk Shell, inscribed: *Listen to the Sea.* 93mm long.	6.00
Mermaid with gilded mirror, seated on rock, combing hair. 105mm.	20.00
Yacht in full sail. 122mm.	19.50

Countryside

Acorn. 56mm.	7.50
Milk Can and lid.	8.00
Pine Cone. 87mm.	6.00

Animals

Cat, Cheshire, inscribed: *Still smiling.* 2 sizes: 80mm.	10.00
95mm.	12.50
Cat, sitting. Candlesnuffer. 57mm.	16.00
Cat sitting. 67mm.	16.00
Cat, standing, with blue bow. 70mm.	19.50
Dog, Bulldog sitting. 54mm.	19.00
Dog, black Bulldog emerging from kennel. No. 30. Inscribed: *The Black Watch.* 73mm long.	24.50
Dog, Dachshund. No. 021. 75mm long.	40.00

Dog, Scottie, wearing a Glengarry.
Some colouring.
2 sizes: 58mm.   14.50
      87mm.   18.50
Dog, Scottish Terrier, standing.
90mm long.   23.50
Donkey in Harness. 110mm long.   50.00
Elephant, sitting with trunk in air.
97mm.   40.00
Elephant, walking. 98mm.   17.00
Elephant Jug. No. 78. 70mm.   12.50
Hare. 77mm long.   12.50
Lion, walking. No. 30. 120mm long.   20.00
Monkey, holding a Coconut.
No. 429. 80mm.   22.50
Three Wise Monkeys, with usual
verse. 77mm.   15.00
Pig, sitting. Inscribed: *You may...*
75mm.   19.50
Pig, sitting on haunches, inscribed.
80mm.   20.00
Pig, standing, double chin. No. 014.
96mm.   24.50
Pig, fat, standing. 82mm long.   19.50
Rabbit, sitting. 70mm long.   9.50
Ram with curly horns.
90mm long.   40.00
Teddy Bear. 75mm.   27.50

Birds
Chick, fluffy, large feet. 70mm.   17.00
Goose. 95mm.   37.50
Owl. 115mm.   29.50
Owl, wise. 98mm.   30.00
Swan. No. 012. 65mm.   8.50

Great War
Standing soldier inscribed: *Our
brave defender.* 130mm.   70.00
Submarine. E4. 125mm long.   27.50
Red Cross Van. 87mm.   40.00
Field Gun with screen.
115mm long.   35.00
Aeroplane propeller. No. 216.
145mm long.   30.00
Officer's Peaked Cap.
70mm dia.   12.50
Bugle. 70mm.   24.50
Drum. No. 030. 60mm dia.   12.50
Kitbag. 72mm.   19.00
Cenotaph, unglazed, green wreaths,
no crests. 140mm.   35.00
Edith Cavell Statue. 115mm.
(Impressed 507).   19.00

*Edith Cavell, Nurse. Patriot and
Martyr, Memorial Statue, Norwich.*
115mm. (Found impressed 296).   19.00
Florence Nightingale Statue, Model of
160mm.   24.00

Home/Nostalgic
Anvil. 70mm long.   7.50
Basket. No. 244. 80mm long.   6.50
Bell, inscribed: *Curfew must not ring
tonight.* No. 107. 65mm.   12.50
Book. No. 76. 60mm.   12.50
Extinguisher. 65mm.   6.00
Fan, ostrich feather, fully extended.
No. 382. 135mm wide.   60.00
Flat Iron. No. 018. 65mm.   12.50
Handbell.   9.00
Pillar Box, inscribed: GVR and *If you
haven't time to post a line, here's the
pillar box.* No. 18. 80mm.   17.50
Pillar Box, impressed: G.R.
No. 203 and 024. 90mm.   16.00
Roll topped Desk. No. 030, reputedly
from Shelley range. 86mm.   18.00
Sundial, circular, with round base,
and inscription: *I Mark not the
hours.* 118mm.   10.50
Sundial, on square base. 94mm.   8.50
Sundial, circular base. No. 205 and
024. 93mm.   8.50
Thimble, large. *Just a thimble full.*
52mm.   19.50
Wheelbarrow. 108mm long.   10.00

Comic/Novelty
Baby with outstretched arms,
inscribed: *Cheerio.* No. 024.
128mm.   30.00
Billiken. 68mm.   7.50
Hammer Head match holder.
Inscribed: *My speciality is striking.*
82mm long.   24.00
Policeman, hands behind back.
96mm.   50.00
Sack of Meal with mouse, inscribed:
*May the mouse ne'er leave yer meal
wi' a tear-drop'n its e'e.* 63mm.   19.50

Alcohol
Beer Barrel. 60mm.   6.00
Foaming Tankard, inscribed: *The
more we are together the merrier we
will be.* 58mm.   8.50
Whisky Bottle, inscribed: *A Special
Scotch.* 100mm.   8.50

Sport/Pastimes

Football. 48mm.	9.50
Golf Ball. 45mm.	9.50
Club trump. 65mm.	7.00
Diamond, trump. No. 009.	
65mm.	7.00
Heart trump indicator. 70mm.	7.00
Spade, trump indicator. 70mm.	7.00

Transport

Cycle lamp, reputedly from Shelley	
range. 83mm.	50.00

Musical Instruments

Harp. 90mm.	10.00

Footwear

Clog. 70mm long.	6.00
Lancashire Clog. 78mm long.	7.50
Sabot/Clog. No. 152.	
90mm long.	7.00
Shoe with blue painted bow.	
115mm long.	12.00

Miscellaneous

Basket on 4 legs. No. 224. 70mm.	6.00
Club pintray No. 009.	
58mm long.	6.00
Diamond pintray. No. 009.	
58mm long.	6.00
Handbell. 82mm.	7.00
Hand holding Beaker. 50mm.	7.50

Kursaal China

Trademark used Hewitt Bros. Willow
Potteries, Longton probably for LLL, a
Yorkshire wholesaler, (Usual trademark
Willow Art).
The only piece recorded with this mark is a
65mm jug with the crest of Harrogate.

Kursam China

Kyle Series

No details of this mark are available, and only a 67mm jug with banded mouth has been found so far.

From 1913

Trademark used by Charles Waine (& Co.), Derby Works, Longton. (Usual trademark Venetia).
For further details see Venetia China and C.W. & Co.

Kyle Series Models
Great War
Biplane with fixed prop.
150mm long.   95.00

Transport
Tram. 50mm.   200.00

Miniature Domestic
Cheese dish and cover,
rectangular. 68mm long.   9.00

LAB

Lawrence Sheriffe Ware

"LAWRENCE
SHERIFFE"
WARE

Mark used for a Sussex and Kent wholesaler by J.A. Robinson Ltd., Stoke-on-Trent. Subsequently Cauldon Ltd. (Usual trademark Arcadian). All pieces recorded have Sussex or Kent crests.

LAB Model
Buildings - White
Cottage, brick. 49mm.   10.00

Trademark used by an unidentified manufacturer.
Lawrence Sheriffe Ware could have been produced by any of the major crest china makers, but none in fact advertised such a line. The only pieces recorded with this mark also carried the retailers mark Hands and Son, Rugby, with a crest of Rugby. This would be correct, as Lawrence Sheriffe was founder of Rugby School and a benefactor of that town.

Lawrence Sheriffe Models
Ancient Artefacts
Loving Cup, 3 handles. 37mm.   6.00

Leadbeater Art China

1920-4

This mark can also be found without the two circles.

Trademark used by Edwin Leadbeater, Drewery Place, Commerce Street, Longton. Same quality and 'feel' as Panorama China, H & L and R & M of Longton.

Mr Edwin Leadbeater was the son of the senior partner of Robinson and Leadbeater ('R & L', makers of parian ware) and worked for that firm until 1905 when he left to go into partnership with Mr Arthur Hewitt, his brother in law. Hewitt and Leadbeater at Willow Potteries was a reasonably successful firm specialising in arms ware (see Willow Art and Willow China). Edwin Leadbeater left this partnership and started up on his own at Drewery Place in November of 1919, to manufacture heraldic china and ivory porcelain. It was a small one oven pottery started on £300 capital. This business was very short lived, but there is a surprising amount of information in the *Pottery Gazette* about Drewery Place during this period, quite out of proportion to its size and importance. While he was a partner at Hewitt and Leadbeater that firm too was often mentioned in the Gazette, one can only speculate as to whether Mr Leadbeater was a friend of the Editor or just very good at selling himself as newsworthy.

In 1920 the *Pottery Gazette* reported:
' . . . he has some 80 different models in small-wares to offer, which he is decorating with crests, coat-of-arms, and various emblematic devices. These goods he is offering to all branches of the distributing trades, laying himself out specially for those retailers who can buy only in relatively small quantities. Apart from the tiny miniatures, which used to be popular selling lines at $6^1/2$d, Mr Leadbeater is bringing out models of monuments, notable buildings etc. for souvenir and commemorative purposes. These are quaintly tinted up by hand, very often quite realistically, although they are always very moderate in price. It is surprising how quickly, with enterprising zeal, some of these new models can be produced. A little time ago, Mr Leadbeater was asked by a big buyer to copy a model for a seasonal trade. Within 10 days the first sample was in the buyer's hands, and the latter was prompted to admit that it reminded him of how the German manufacturers of such wares used to handle their enquiries in the years before the war'.

In adverts for the trade at that time Mr Leadbeater announced that he specialised in arms china, miniatures, reproductions of War Memorials and historical buildings.

Edwin Leadbeater became bankrupt early in 1924, his business having run at a loss since it started. He had borrowed a great deal of money from friends and business acquaintances, and even £50 from a Bailiff to try to keep going, as he was still getting orders. Mr Leadbeater said he found he was 'selling his stuff too cheaply'.

Leadbeater Art China is often very heavy and on the whole not very well finished, but what it lacks in quality it makes up for in originality. The firm obviously got a large number of orders for War Memorials in the early years after the war and some of these were not modelled by any other manufacturers.

The firm collapsed before the vogue for 'Lucky Black Cats', 'Lucky White Heather' and other transfer devices, so these are not found marked Leadbeater. No commemoratives or view wares have been recorded either. However there is some evidence that some view ware marked 'Wagstaff and Brunt' was made by Edwin Leadbeater (see Panorama). *Numbering System*. Painted stock numbers were sometimes used and where these have been recorded they will be found in the following lists. The paintresses' mark is the number painted directly below the stock number.

Leadbeater Art Models
Parian/Unglazed

Bust of *Burns*. 175mm.	40.00
Bust of *Pope Pius XI*. 190mm.	80.00
Bust of *Scott* on column base. 172mm.	25.00

Buildings - Coloured

Burns Cottage. Inscribed: *Robert Burns, the Ayrshire poet was born in this cottage on the 25th Jan. A.D. 1759 Died 21st July 1796 aged 37¹/2 yrs*. 70mm long.	35.00
Christchurch Priory.	150.00
Gate House, Stokesay Castle. 120mm long.	160.00
Ann Hathaway's Cottage. 95mm long.	35.00
Irish Cottage. 110mm long.	60.00
Isaac Walton's Cottage, Shallowford. 114mm long.	110.00
Old Church, Bonchurch. 108mm long.	230.00
Old Market Hall, Church Stretton 1617-1839. 105mm.	155.00
The Tan House, Little Stretton. 109mm long.	80.00

Buildings - White

Ann Hathaway's Cottage, not named. 2 sizes: 58mm long.	16.00
144mm long.	20.00
Burns Cottage, with inscription. 70mm long.	22.50
Margate Clock Tower, Margate. 150mm.	20.00
Old Church, Bonchurch. 110mm long.	140.00

Monuments (including Crosses)

Limerick Monument, inscribed: *The treaty of Limerick signed AD 1696*. 114mm high, on 118mm wide base.	125.00

Margate Lifeboat Memorial. 160mm.	22.00
Plymouth Armada Memorial, with inscription: *He blew with his winds and they were scattered*. No. 107. 168mm.	35.00
Rolls Memorial, inscribed: *Charles Stewart Rolls M.A., F.R.G.S., AMI. MECH. E., Born August 27 1877 Died July 12 1910*, found with the Wirksworth crest, this being where Rolls Royce cars were test driven down a hill. 145mm.	40.00
Sir Walter Scott. Statue. 178mm.	22.00

Historical/Folklore

Bunyan's Chair 95mm.	19.00
James Vth Chair, Stirling Castle, Model of. 102mm.	12.50
Mary Queen of Scots Chair 85mm.	10.00

Traditional/National Souvenirs

Welsh Hat. No. 57. 60mm.	10.00

Seaside Souvenirs

Lifeboat. 100mm long.	17.50
Lighthouse. 110mm.	8.00

Animals

Bear. 75mm.	50.00
Cheshire Cat, inscribed: *Still smiling*. 2 sizes: 85mm.	8.50
115mm.	11.50
Dog, sitting, with bow, black eyes. No. 77. 75mm.	16.50
Dog, Pug, sitting, long-necked, coloured features. 116mm.	19.50
Dog, Staffordshire Bull Terrier sitting. 115mm.	22.00
Fish, open mouth 102mm long.	8.00
Lion, walking. 114mm long.	22.50
Pig, fat. 102mm long.	17.00

Birds (including Eggs)

Bird posy holder. 60mm long.	9.50
Duck posy holder, with yellow beak. 45mm high, 80mm long.	13.00

Great War

Red Cross Van. No. 105. 88mm long.	40.00
Cumberland and Westmorland War Memorial. 148mm.	190.00
Derby War Memorial. 150mm.	170.00

Harrogate War Memorial, an
unglazed obelisk on base with
spiral steps. 153mm.   160.00
Nottingham War Memorial.
150mm.   160.00
Nurse Cavell, Memorial. 200mm.   115.00
Crich Stand, Notts and Derby War
Memorial. 150mm.   160.00
Florence Nightingale 1820 - 1910 Statue.
175mm.   26.00
Ulster War Memorial, Thiepvel
with inscription: *They died that we
might live*. 140mm.   300.00

Home/Nostalgic
Anvil. No. 78. 58mm.   7.50
Grandfather Clock, inscribed: *Make
use of time, let not advantage slip.*
143mm.   17.50

Comic/Novelty
Jester, double faced bust, happy /
sad . 85mm.   12.50
Monk, standing. 91mm.   17.00

Sport/Pastimes
Cricket Cap. 67mm long.   60.00
Footballer with ball on plinth.
Inscribed: *Play up.* Fully coloured
figure with blue shirt, white
shorts and brown football.
158mm.   125.00

Footwear
Sabot. 80mm long.   6.00

Domestic
Tobacco Jar and Lid, lettering in red
and blue, with colour transfer of
crossed pipes on lid. 118mm.   12.00

Limoges

LIMOGES

FRANCE

FRANCE
VIGNAUD
LIMOGES

An undistinguished range of domestic ware
and small vases was made by this famous
French manufacturer mainly for the
French market with the exception of the
following. They are distinctly greyish
white with transferred coats of arms.
See also Vignaud.

Limoges Models
Seaside Souvenirs
Crab Pin Box. 60mm wide.   12.00

Home/Nostalgic
Watering Can. 75mm, 100mm long.   8.50

Comic/Novelty
Boy's Cap Money Box. 80mm long.   22.00

Transport
Open Motor Car. 90mm long.   30.00

Domestic
Match striker pot with lid (striker is
on inside of lid). 102mm long.   8.00

Lindum Co.

Lion Brand

Trademark used by an unknown English manufacturer for T. Winter, China Rooms, Lincoln.
The only piece recorded is a 68mm vase bearing The arms of Lincoln.
5.00

Trademark used by an Australian retailer probably supplied by Arkinstall and Son, Arcadian Works, Stoke on Trent (usual trademark Arcadian).
Only four small models have been recorded, these having the crests of New South Wales Victoria or West Australia.

Lion Brand Models
Ancient Artefacts
Ancient Lamp. 93mm long.   8.50
Lichfield Jug. 60mm.   5.50

Seaside Souvenirs
Whelk Shell. 39mm.   6.00

Lion China

Liverpool Rd Pottery

LIVERPOOL RD POTTERY LTD FINE BONE CHINA

Trademark used by Wiltshaw & Robinson, Ltd., Carlton Works, Stoke-on-Trent. (Usual trademark Carlton). For details of this china and manufacturer see Carlton China.

Lion Models
Monuments (including Crosses)
Rock of Ages, with inscriptions.
82mm.   12.50

Animals
Dog (Puppy) sitting on a silvered hand mirror, inscribed: *Me twice.*
105mm long.   37.50
Pug Dog with coloured features.
115mm.   25.00

Trademark used by Liverpool Rd. Pottery Ltd., Stoke.
No information is available on this firm. They were not known to register a mark and do not appear under this name in the directory of British Pottery Manufacturers published in the Twenties and Thirties. C.J. Biss & Co. (see Unmarked) worked at 82 Liverpool Rd. Stoke during the Twenties; it is just possible that this firm used the name 'Liverpool Rd. Pottery Ltd'. One transfer has been found, showing a ship and seagull.

Liverpool Models
Seaside Souvenirs
Scallop Shell menu holder.
110mm long. (This carries a map as well as a crest of Norfolk).   22.50
Scallop Shell.
55mm high. 110mm long.   7.00
Scallop Shell flower holder. 60mm.   7.50

Transport
Open Motor Car. 90mm long.   40.00

Domestic
Beer Mug. No. 199.   4.00

Miscellaneous
Dish. 110mm dia.   4.00

Lochinvar

Locke and Co

or with Nicholson and Carter in place of N & C.
Trademark used for the Scottish retailers Nicholson & Carter by Hewitt and Leadbeater, Willow Potteries, Longton. (Usual trademark Willow Art) and, Taylor and Kent Ltd, Florence Works, Longton (usual trademark Florentine), and the Nautilus Porcelain Co., Glasgow.

Lochinvar Models
Newbury Leather Bottle. 70mm.   5.50   c1898 - Nov 1902

Traditional/National Souvenirs
Welsh Hat. No. 75. 54mm.   10.00

Great War
Field Gun with screen. 115mm.   35.00
Bell Tent with open flaps. 85mm.   20.00

Alcohol
Whiskey Quaich or bowl. No. 110.
100mm long.   6.00

Comic/Novelty
Bust of Negro Minstrel in top hat.
95mm.   30.00

Nov 1902 - 1915
The above mark can also be found with the words 'Copyright Design' printed above.

Sport/Pastimes
Cricket Bag. 110mm long.   16.00

Trademark used by Locke and Co (Ltd) Shrub Hill Works, Worcester.
The firm was established in 1896, the first manager being Edward Walter Locke who had been Manager of the potting dept at Graingers, Worcester. After a high court injunction in 1902 they were

prevented by the Worcester factory from describing their wares as Worcester China or Worcester porcelain. Production eventually ceased in 1915. About 1900 the production of crested china was commenced with a new series of stock numbers started especially for it; in 1904 the *Pottery Gazette* reported they made 'a variety of arms ware in heraldic colours on ivory ground, and there are original shapes amongst them'. The porcelain is very fine and the crests well produced. Some colour transfers, commemorative and miscellaneous crests are also found, together with a series of flags and a unique 'Mirror' type decoration. Some crested shapes were decorated with hand painted landscapes, birds and animals, often signed by the artists.

Many 'smalls' and some domestic ware are found with this mark. The porcelain is very fine and the crests well produced. Some colour transfers, commemorative decorations, flags and a unique mirror type decoration have been found. The porcelain was exported and one Australian crest has been recorded. Some crested shapes were decorated with hand-painted landscapes, birds and animals often signed by the artists.

Numbering System. Stock numbers were used but unfortunately these have not been recorded. Stock numbers where known are given in the list below.

All Locke items can be found in blush ivory, as well as white.

Locke Models
Ancient Artefacts
Bath Roman Ewer, not named.
No. 46. 70mm.	12.00

Chester Roman Lamp inscribed:
Roman Lamp found at Bridge Street, Chester. 100mm long. 15.00

Chester Roman Vase, not named.
No. 78. 55mm.	12.00

Colchester Vase, not named.
No. 59. 60mm.	12.00

Hastings Kettle, not named.
2 sizes: 48mm.	12.00
No. 67. 64mm.	12.00

Irish Bronze Pot, not named. No. 99 or 66! 40mm. 12.00

Leather Jack, not named. No. 36.
72mm.	12.00

Newbury Leather Bottle, not named. No. 84. 70mm. 12.00

Reading Silchester Vase. No. 32.
52mm.	12.00

Traditional/National Souvenirs
Welsh Hat. No. 61. 56mm. 17.50

Home/Nostalgic
Thimble. 35mm. 22.50

Alcohol
Tankard, very ornate. 70mm. 14.50

Sport
Trophy. 65mm. 16.00

Hats
Top Hat, matchstriker. No. 52.
45mm.	14.50

Footwear
Dutch Sabot. No. 19.
3 sizes: 60mm long.	15.00
80mm long.	15.00
90mm long.	15.00

Miniature Domestic
Beaker. No. 51. 51mm.	12.00
Cream Jug with rope handle. No. 80. 54mm.	12.00
Cup and Saucer. 78mm dia.	14.50

Numbered Ornamental and Domestic Wares
Some of the following may well be Ancient Artefacts, not named:
No. 3. Vase. 38mm.	12.00
No. 9. Vase. 78mm.	12.00
No. 10. Bowl. 33mm.	12.00
No. 13. Vase, circular, could have a lid. 40mm.	12.00
No. 14. Vase. 53mm.	12.00
No. 16. Large Jar, wide mouthed. 65mm.	12.00
No. 17. Jar with separate lid. 70mm.	12.00
No. 18. Vase. 53mm.	12.00
No. 20. Vase. 83mm.	12.00
No. 21. Vase. 110mm.	15.00
No. 24. Jug. 30mm.	12.00
No. 25. Ewer, barrel shaped. 54mm.	12.00
No. 26. Ewer/Jug. 70mm.	12.00

No. 27. Vase. 74mm.	12.00
No. 28. Vase. 50mm.	12.00
No. 29. Vase. 62mm.	12.00
No. 31. Vase. 60mm.	12.00
No. 34. Tyg, one handle. 72mm.	12.00
No. 36. Vase. 41mm.	12.00
No. 37. Ewer. 70mm.	12.00
No. 39. Vase. 60mm.	12.00
No. 40. Diamond mouth Vase. 67mm.	12.00
No. 41. Cream Jug. 63mm.	12.00
No. 42. Cone Vase. 64mm.	12.00
No. 43. Vase. 43mm.	12.00
No. 46. Ewer. 68mm.	12.00
No. 47. Jug. 55mm and 70mm.	12.00
No. 49. Cup and Saucer. 23mm.	12.00
No. 51. Beaker. 51mm.	12.00
No. 53. Vase. 54mm.	12.00
No. 54. Vase. 70mm.	12.00
No. 55. Ewer. 78mm.	12.00
No. 55. Vase with two long handles. 80mm.	12.00
No. 58. Vase, Bagware. 53mm.	12.00
No. 60. Vase. 60mm.	12.00
No. 62. Vase. 62mm.	12.00
No. 69. Vase, 2 handles. 60mm.	12.00
No. 70. Vase, 2 handles. 70mm.	12.00
No. 74. Ewer. 59mm.	12.00
No. 77. Ewer. 75mm.	12.00
No. 79. Ewer. 62mm.	12.00
No. 80. Ewer, small twisted handle. 53mm.	12.00
No. 85. Narrow necked Vase. 90mm.	12.00
No. 87. Vase. 85mm.	12.00
No. 89. Ewer, l handle. 82mm.	12.00
No. 90. Vase. 78mm.	12.00
(This appears to be the same model as No. 9).	
No. 94. Vase, long-necked. 66mm.	12.00
No. 95. Vase, with 2 handles. 63mm.	12.00
No. 101. Vase. 2 handles. 68mm.	12.00
No. 102. Vase. 50mm.	12.00
No. 103. Oval Vase, fluted top. 67mm.	12.00
No. 112. Vase, narrow neck. 97mm.	12.00
No. 113. Two handled Vase. 62mm.	12.00
No. 116. Vase, two handles. 72mm.	12.00
No. 118. Beaker with shallow fluted top. 60mm.	12.00
No. 120. Vase. 74mm.	12.00

No. 121. Vase. 83mm.	12.00
No. 178. Crinkle-top Ball Vase. 58mm.	12.00
No. 287. Trumpet Vase, with 3 broad leaves around base. 84mm.	12.00
No. 337. Woven shopping bag with looped handle, example seen not crested. 85mm.	12.00
No. 754. Vase. 105mm.	15.00
No. 827. Beaker. 115mm.	15.00
No. 857. Base of Pepper or Salt Pot. 63mm.	12.00

Non numbered ornamental and Domestic Wares

Ball Vase, swirled, crinkle top. 67mm.	12.00
Fairy Beaker. 32mm.	12.00
Wall Pocket. 85mm.	15.00

Lynton China

M

Trademark used by an unknown retailer on one Arcadian and one Carlton piece.

Lynton Models
Animals
Black Cat on wall. Gosport crest.
70mm.   75.00

Alcohol
Toby Jug, coloured features.
73mm.   17.50

Trademark used by an unknown English manufacturer.
This very obscure and unusual mark has only been found on one Great War Commemorative.
No manufacturer was known to use the initial M in 1914, and no firm used a mark anything like the unicorn above.

The colour transfer print of five
flags and a field gun is found on a
mug with a large handle.
59mm high. Inscribed: *Allies
United 1914.*   17.50

Macintyre

H. Mackintosh

Trademark used by James Macintyre & Co. Ltd. Washington Works, Burslem. (Usual trademark Argonauta Porcelain). See Argonauta Porcelain and Caledonia China for further details. The Macintyre mark Argonauta Porcelain is exactly the same as the one above with the addition of Argonauta Porcelain printed above.

Macintyre Models
Ancient Artefacts
Loving Cup. 43mm. 8.00
The Salisbury Jug from the original found in a barrow on Salisbury Plain. Reg. No. 134142. 137mm. 20.00

Domestic
Eggcup fixed to small saucer with two depressions inscribed: *salt* and *pepper.* Saucer also holds two eggs (salt and pepper pots) one white and one speckled brown. 66mm. 12.00
Inkwell, stippled. 15.00
These often have coats of arms in intaglio.
Tea Pot and lid. 130mm. 10.50

Small vases have also been found with this mark and china was also produced for manufacturers to add silver mounts. These seem to be very early/pre 1905. 5.00-10.00

Miscellaneous
Fleur de Lys shaped vase. 42mm. 6.00

Mark of a Gairloch retailer by an unknown British manufacturer. The only piece recorded is a 65mm sugar bowl with the Gairloch arms.

Made Abroad

M & B

Mark used to comply with the Country of Origin Act, which became law in the UK around the turn of the century.

Under this act, pieces of crested china, amongst other imported items had to have their Country clearly marked. Whether this name 'Made Abroad' qualified, we do not know.

What is known is that the major competition for the UK crested china marked was from Austria and Germany and that even during WW1, the Germans were still supplying the British market with pieces misleadingly marked 'Made in Czechoslovakia' and possibly 'Made Abroad'.

A 67mm Jug has been found with the above mark, with the Taunton coat of arms.

As it has not been seen by the author we know no more except that is was made in Austria.

5.00

M.C.G.

C McDMann & Co Ltd

Trademark used by an unknown wholesaler. Probably of German manufacture.

M.C.G. Model
Footwear
Dutch Sabot. Orange lustre.
88mm long.   7.50

Retailer's mark used by Arkinstall & Son, Arcadian Works, Stoke-on-Trent. (Usual trademark Arcadian)
All items have The Forts, Boxhill crest in blue as is the retailer's mark underneath.
A number of Arcadian smalls have been found, valued at £4.00.

Ancient Artefacts
Glastonbury Bowl. 41mm.   5.50

Birds (including Eggs)
Chick hatching from egg. 69mm.   10.00

Manx Legs

Marine Art China

Trademark used by Schmidt and Co., Carlsbad (Bohemia), for a Manx wholesaler (usual trademark Gemma). Some smalls have been reported decorated with a coloured map of the Isle of Man or with the Douglas crest.

Price range 4.00-8.00

Trademark used by Hewitt & Leadbeater, Drewery Place, Commerce St., Longton, for a Brighton retailer. (Usual marks Willow and Leadbeater).

Marine Art Model
Birds (including Eggs)
Chick posy holder. 60mm long. 9.50

Marque Deposée

Maxem China

Trademark used by an unknown French manufacturer of French hard paste porcelain.
Only two models have been recorded so far and these both have the crest of Anvers Antwerpen.

Marque Deposée Models
Ancient Artefacts
Hastings Kettle. 50mm.   5.50

Footwear
Sabot with pointed toe.
100mm long.   7.00

Trademark used by Alfred B. Jones & Sons Ltd., Grafton China works, Longton, Staffs (usual trademark Grafton). The model below and all others seen have the Franco British Exhibition 1908 motif and this mark was probably only used for pieces bearing this decoration.
Vases/ewers 12.00-18.00

Maxem Model
Historical/Folklore
Charles I bottle with removable
   head lid, not named and thought
   by some collectors to be Guy Fawkes.
   No. 209. 96mm.   55.00

Maxim China

Maxim China

Trademark used by an unknown British Manufacturer.

Maxim Models
Ancient Artefacts
Loving Cup, 2 hadles. 37mm.   6.00

Seaside
Beachy Head Lighthouse, black
band. 145mm.   12.00

Great War
Drum. 64mm.   20.00

Hats
Top Hat Match Striker. 54mm.   7.00

Footwear
Sabot, pointed toe. 93mm long.   7.00

A range of 'smalls' and a trinket
box.   4.00-8.50

Trademark used by Max Emanuel & Co. Mitterteich, (Bavaria). (Usual trademark Mosanic). See also Unity China. This German firm was established around 1900 and as early as 1901 were advertising their hard paste china miniatures in the *Pottery Gazette*. (The wares were shown in Shoe Lane, Holborn and do not appear to be crested.) Max Emanuel and Co. were well known producers of pink souvenir wares and obviously turned to making crested souvenirs as soon as they would sell. The models illustrated in 1901 include comic or grotesque cats and dogs, which English manufacturers were not making at this early date. Many of the unmarked animals and buildings of German origin were probably made by this firm.

Price range 4.00-9.00

Mayfair Ware

Trademark used by Sampson Hancock (& Sons), Bridge Works, Stoke and later at the Garden Works, Hanley (usual trademark Corona).

Mayfair Models
Animals
Bulldog, standing. 125mm long.   24.50

Great War
Tank with inset wheels.
    100mm long.   24.50

Home/Nostalgic
Baby in Bootee. 75mm.   12.00

ME Bavaria

No details of mark available

Three pieces have been found with the above Bavarian trademark and English crests.

ME Bavaria Models
Footwear
Riding Boot. No. 44. 90mm.   8.00

Domestic
Butter dish and lid.   6.00
Candle holder, round with handle.
    No. 37.   6.00
Cruet Set. No. 18.   8.00
Fruit Bowl. 238mm diameter.   8.00

Meir Arms China

1912-1930

Trademark used by Barker Bros. Ltd., Meir Works, Barker Street, Longton.
Barker Bros, manufacturers of china and earthenwares, were established in 1876 and are still working today. Like most established firms they made a range of arms china during the Great War when skilled labour was unavailable. They did not advertise at this time and it probably reflected in their small production. By 1919 they were advertising 'Teddy Tail' Nursery China and had obviously turned their attention to the childrens' market.
They also bought in pieces from Hewitt and leadbeater (usual trademark Willow Art) for many of the pieces marked Meir Arms China are Willow Art.
Most models found are 'smalls' or domestic ware. The arms ware is more pot than china.

Meir Models
Ancient Artefacts
Loving Cup,3-handled.40mm.	6.00
Puzzle Jug with verse. 70mm.	7.50

Historical/Folklore
Mary Queen of Scots Chair 75mm.	12.50
Mons Meg, Edinburgh Castle, Model of. 57mm.	16.00

Seaside Souvenirs
Eddystone Lighthouse. 109mm.	9.50

Animals
Cat in Boot. 88mm long.	19.50
Cheshire Cat, inscribed: *Still Smiling.* 90mm.	12.50
Elephant. 74mm long.	20.00
Manx Cat walking, detailed fur. 95mm long.	35.00
Pig, standing. 88mm long.	19.50
Tortoise. 70mm long.	12.00

Birds
Canary on rock, yellow. 115mm.	20.00

Great War
Soldier, standing. Inscribed: *Our Brave Defender.* 128mm.	70.00
Red Cross Van. 85mm long.	40.00
Field Gun with Screen. 115mm.	35.00
British Tank, trailing wheels.	24.50
Edith Cavell Monument. 114mm.	22.00

Alcohol
Barrel. 52mm.	6.00
Bottle with cork. Inscribed: *One Special Scotch.* 90mm.	9.00

Home/Nostalgic
Sundial. 90mm.	9.00
Watering Can. 75mm.	8.00

Transport
Open Sports Tourer. 116mm long.	40.00

Hats
Welsh Hat, blue band & longest Welsh name. 55mm.	12.00

Footwear
Sabot. 92mm long.	6.00
Lancashire Clog. No. 33. 2 sizes: 70mm long.	6.00
115mm long.	6.50

Miniature Domestic
Cheese Dish and lid. 70mm long.	9.50
Coffee Pot and Lid. 68mm.	9.00
Vase, bud-shaped. 35mm.	4.00

Miscellaneous
Hand holding a Tulip. 83mm.	6.00

Melba China

Trademark used by Mayer & Sherratt, Clifton Works, Longton.

Original china made by Mayer & Sherratt, Clifton Works, Longton. Over printed mark used by Sampson Hancock (& Sons), Bridge Works, Stoke. (Usual trademark Corona).

It seems likely that Mayer and Sherratt produced china which was later decorated with crests by S. Hancock perhaps to fill an urgent order!

This Melba china mark is earlier than the Melba bone china mark which was used from about 1925.

This mark has been found overstamped 'Grosvenor Ware'. (Usual trademark also Corona).

Domestic Wares

Cream Jug. 60mm with a Chesham Crest.   5.00

Mermaid

Trademark used by wholesaler and retailer William Ritchie and Sons Ltd. 24, 26 and 28 Elder Street, Edinburgh. (Usual trademark Savoy).

For further details of this china and manufacturer see Savoy.

Mermaid Models
Ancient Artefacts
Aberdeen Bronze Pot. 65mm.   5.50
Salisbury Kettle. 110mm.   5.50

Animals
Camel, kneeling. 90mm long.   17.00

Great War
Tank, sometimes inscribed: *HMS
Donner Blitzen,* with details of
Ancre. 130mm long.   40.00

Home/Nostalgic
Water Pitcher. 75mm.   6.50

Sport/Pastimes
Cricket Bag. 110mm long.   16.50

Footwear
Ladies 18th Century Shoe.
  80mm long.   8.50

Domestic
A range of domestic ware was
  produced.   4.00-8.00
Egg Cup. 60mm.   6.00

Mikado Ware

For Mikado Ware see W. & Sons.

The Milton China

Alternative mark found on domestic ware with transfer prints.

Trademark used by Hewitt Bros., Willow Potteries, Longton, on china for a London wholesaler (G.G. & Co.).
For details of this china and manufacturer see Willow Art China.
This trademark appears to have been used after the Great War, until at least 1926. No view ware has been found with this mark which indicates its later date, Willow view ware was made before the war. One military badge has been recorded, the Royal Flying Corps. Many *Lucky Black Cat* transfer devices are found, usually with red or blue edging and rims.
Some Carlton models have also been recorded, probably from the period when Harold Taylor Robinson owned most of the crested

china industry.
Numbering System. Stock numbers where recorded are not necessarily the same as those found on Willow Art pieces. Milton China was probably offered as a separate range. Stock numbers where known are listed below. Single painted numbers found on models are paintresses' marks.

Milton Models

Ancient Artefacts

Aberdeen Bronze Pot, not named. 52mm.	5.50
Ancient Tyg, 2 handled.	5.50
Loving Cup, 3 handled. 55mm.	6.00

Monuments (including Crosses)

Bunyan Statue. 160mm.	20.00
Drake Statue, Plymouth. 160mm.	13.00
Fisherman's Memorial. 132mm.	12.50
Hull Fisherman's Memorial.	20.00

Historical/Folklore

Bunyan's Chair. 90mm.	19.00
Crown. 60mm.	25.00
Sword in decorative scabbard. No. 374. 135mm long (rare).	70.00
Model of Mons Meg, Edinburgh Castle. 130mm long.	20.00
Sir Walter Scott's Chair. 88mm.	14.50

Traditional/National Souvenirs

Bagpipes with turquoise ribbon. 115mm long.	50.00
Welsh Hat. 54mm & 62mm.	10.00
Dutch Girl, standing. 76mm.	16.50
Judge, bust of. 78mm.	24.00

Seaside Souvenirs

Bathing Machine. Can be inscribed: *A Morning Dip.* 70mm long.	16.50
Lifeboat, some colouring. 117mm long.	22.00
Lighthouse, octagonal. 114mm.	10.50
Lighthouse, round, on rocky base. 110mm.	12.00
Shell on coral base. 93mm.	9.00
Spurn Lighthouse. 130mm.	22.00

Animals

Bear, Polar, standing upright. 95mm.	50.00
Cat, sitting, looking to sinister with shield round neck. 74mm.	20.00
Cat, standing, chubby. 70mm.	22.00

Cheshire Cat, inscribed: *Still*
   Smiling. 90mm.   12.50
Dog, Scottie, wearing a glengarry.
   60mm.   14.50
Donkey with saddle. No. 904.
   120mm long.   65.00
Elephant, with trunk in the air.
   80mm long.   50.00
Elephant, (trunk down).
   75mm long.   20.00
Elephant, walking. No.113. 52mm.   20.00
Elephant Jug. 70mm. (Trunk is
   handle).   14.00
Frog, with open mouth. 60mm.   22.00
Hare, ears laid back. 75mm long.   19.00
Lion, poised to pounce, red roaring
   mouth. 83mm long.   30.00
Lion, standing. 115mm long.   24.50
Lion standing on ashtray, inscribed:
   Ash Tray and *Who burned the*
   tablecloth. 110mm long.   40.00
Lion, roaring at mouse, sitting on
   apple. Inscribed: *Much Ado About*
   Nothing. Some colouring.
   115mm long.   80.00
Pig, standing. 95mm long.   24.50
Pig, sitting, inscribed: *You may push*
   and... 72mm.   30.00
Rabbit, ears erect. 83mm long.   9.00
Pony, standing. Inscribed: *A Native*
   of Shetland.   40.00
Rabbit, sitting with ears flat on back.
   54mm long.   9.50
Ram, with curly horns. 90mm long.   65.00

Birds (including Eggs)
Chick, standing, with large feet,
   very fluffy. No. 325. 65mm.   20.00
Swan. 69mm.   9.50

Great War
Nurse, inscribed: *A friend in need.*
   130mm.   70.00
Soldier, with rifle inscribed *Our*
   Brave Defender. 132mm.   90.00
Bulldog in Kennel. Inscribed: *The*
   Black Watch. 75mm.   45.00
Aeroplane Propeller. Rarely factory
   marked. 150mm long.   35.00
Airship (Observation Balloon) not
   named. 80mm long.   90.00
Submarine, impressed: *E4.* 116mm
   long.   25.00
British Tank, Model of.
   98mm long.   22.50

British Tank, with steering wheels.
   120mm long.   30.00
Red Cross Van. 90mm long.   40.00
Field Gun with sightscreen. 116mm
   long.   30.00
Incendiary Bomb, rope handle. 82mm.   15.00
Bandsman's Drum with cording.
   60mm.   12.50
Bugle. 70mm.   24.50
Kit Bag with verse: *Pack up your*
   troubles. 74mm.   24.50
Peaked Cap, officers. No. 100.
   80mm long.   20.00
Telescope. 70mm.   16.00
Kitchen Range, pot on fire.
   Inscribed: *Keep the home fires*
   burning. Some colouring. No. 6.
   80mm long.   20.00

Home/Nostalgic
Anvil. 60mm.   7.50
Book. 60mm.   12.00
Coal Scuttle. 65mm.   6.50
Grandfather Clock *Make use of time...*
   125mm.   19.00
Pillar Box. 70mm.   19.00
Shaving Mug. 55mm.   9.50
Watering Can. No. 126. 74mm.   9.50
Wheelbarrow. 105mm long.   19.50

Comic/Novelty
Bust of Negro Minstrel. 96mm.   30.00

Cartoon/Comedy Characters
Baby, saluting, inscribed: *One of the*
   b'hoys. Some colouring. 160mm.   55.00
   The B'hoys were an Alsager,
   Cheshire gentlemans club to
   which many pottery owners
   belonged.
Baby, sailor, on circular base
   inscribed: *SHIP AHOY.* Some
   colour. 150mm.   82.50
Dr. Beetle, impressed: Charlie
   Tolkard's character in *Daily Mail.*
   142mm.   125.00

Alcohol
Barrel on its stilts. 53mm long.   6.50

Sport/Pastimes
Racehorse. 102mm.   75.00

Musical Instruments
Guitar. 163mm long.   19.50
Tambourine. 70mm diameter.   12.00

Transport
A truck of coal from... Wagon of black
coal. 90mm long.   40.00

Footwear
Ladies' 18th century shoe.
90mm long.   8.50
Lancashire Clog. 90mm long.   7.00
Slipper wall pocket, blue bow.
No. 259. 150mm long.   12.50

Miniature Domestic
Coffee Pot and lid.   9.50
Jug, bagware, no colour. No. 161
or 191. 55mm.   4.50
Mug, one handled. 38mm.   4.50
Tea Pot with lid. 53mm.   9.50

Domestic
Hair Pins oval fluted box and lid.
105mm long.   7.00

Moore Bros

Mark used from 1891.

Mark used from 1891-905.

Trademark used by Moore (Bros).), St Mary's
Works, Longton.

A range of 'smalls' with a Christmas
crest and a sprig of holly have been
recorded these are also inscribed:
CARPE DIEM (Seize the day).   20.00

The Moore England mark can be found on
very Victorian / ornate looking smalls, one
being a 94mm crinkle ball vase with NR
monogram in blue.

The Moore Bros mark can also be found on
similar small vases, green trim and green
lettering, "THE GIFT is small but GOOD-
WILL is ALL" with a colour transfer of a
snow scene of a series of houses and trees
around the rim and a frontal view of 2
Victorian girls in pinafores and bonnets
carrying a Christmas Pudding between
them.

Mosanic

MOSANIC
MADE
IN
BAVARIA

Impressed mark.

Trademark used by the German firm, Max Emanuel & Co., The Mosanic Pottery, Mitterteich, Bavaria. They exported a range of brown/stone unglazed buildings to Britain.

Max Emanuel & Co. produced souvenir china for the British market. The buildings marked Mosanic are unusual in that they are usually a drab brown colour and are unglazed. The models although very attractive and detailed are rather heavy. They were made before the war and several models have been found with the mark defaced, one can only speculate whether this was done by unhappy owners or disgruntled retailers who still held German stock at the beginning of the war. These models are usually found without crests, but some crested examples exist.

One could properly argue that this range, being a type of brown stoneware and uncrested has no place in this book, but Mosanic pieces are eagerly collected by heraldic china buffs and so have been included.

Numbering System. Stock numbers are impressed above the mark, registration numbers at the side. Model numbers are four figure and begin with 0. The Registration numbers are six figure and begin with 5 or 6. Where these have been recorded they are listed below.

All models unglazed and brown/stone coloured. With the single exception of Auckland Industrial Exhibition.

Mosanic Models
Buildings

Abbots of Buckfast Town House, inscribed: Ye *olde town house of ye* Abbots of Buckfast ye close Exeter No. 0372. Rd. No. 567827. 100mm long.	40.00
Aberdeen, Old Machor Cathedral. No. 1313. Rd. No. 55628(?). 75mm long.	40.00
Aberystwyth, The College. No. 0350. Rd. No. 561630. 110mm long.	50.00
Auckland Industrial Agricultural Exhibition 1913-14. 170mm long, 75mm high. White, unglazed.	80.00
Bank of Ireland. No. 0365. Rd. No. 587364. 129mm long.	45.00
Birmingham Town Hall. 72mm long.	50.00
Town Hall, Bradford. No. 554743.	50.00
Bridlington Priory Church. No. 7533. 65mm.	40.00
Burns Cottage. 113mm long.	35.00
Canterbury Cathedral. No. 0326. Rd. No. 558188. 112mm long.	35.00
Carlisle Cathedral. No.0361 Rd. No. 576552. 97mm long.	45.00
Chester Cathedral. No. 0340 Rd. No. 559941. 100mm long. Two varieties with east and west transepts transposed.	40.00
Christchurch Priory. Rd. No. 562002 2 sizes: No. 0345I. 98mm long.	40.00
No. 0345II. 133mm long.	40.00
Crosthwaite Church, Keswick No. 0382. Rd. No. 579266. 127mm long.	50.00
Crystal Palace. No. 0386 Rd. No. 58157(?). 170mm long.	50.00
Dartmouth, The Old Butterwalk No. 0375. Rd. No. 576629. 105mm long.	40.00
Douglas, Tower of Refuge. 75mm long.	40.00
Durham Cathedral. No. 0353. No. 570731.	40.00
Edinburgh Castle. No. 0337. Rd. No. 559939. 113mm long.	45.00

Exeter Cathedral. No. 0348. Rd. No. 564035. 150mm long.	40.00
Exeter Guildhall, inscribed: *Ye olde Guild Hall of ye Ancient and Loyal Cittie of Exeter.* 65mm.	40.00
Exeter, St Mary's Steps & Stepcote Hill. No. 0304. Rd. No. 598554. 93mm long.	45.00
Fairmaids House, Perth. No. 0318. Rd. No. 558196. 72mm.	40.00
Gloucester Cathedral. No. 0347 Rd. No. 579265. 120mm long.	40.00
Guy's Cliff, The Mill. No. 0309 Rd. No. 554739. 93mm long.	45.00
Halifax, Parish Church. No. 0323 Rd. No. 558194. 90mm long.	40.00
Harrogate, Royal Pump Room, Old Sulphur Well. No. 1301. Rd. No. 554744. 60mm.	40.00
Hathaways Cottage, Stratford No. 0378. Rd. No. 576880. 120mm long.	30.00
Hereford Cathedral. No. 0325. No. 558195. 92mm long.	40.00
Hexham, The Abbey. No. 0371. Rd. No. 581571. 109mm long.	40.00
Hawarden Castle. No. 0335 Rd. No. 559936. 110mm long.	40.00
Hawarden Church. No. 0333 Rd. No. 559934. 85mm long.	40.00
Hawarden, Gladstone Memorial Public Library. Rd. No. 0330. No. 559937. 115mm long.	45.00
Hawthorns Hotel, Centenary Fetes, Bournemouth 1910.	50.00
Houses of Parliament. No. 0398 Rd. No. 599955. 70mm.	40.00
Iffley Church, Oxford. No. 0360. Rd. No. 587402. 113mm long.	40.00
Kirk Braddon Church. Rd. No. 557800. 80mm long.	45.00
Lancaster Castle. No. 0363. No. 578553. 130mm long.	40.00
Lichfield Cathedral. No. 0352 Rd. No. 580372.	40.00
Lincoln Castle. No. 0315. Rd. No. 556282. 110mm long.	40.00
Londonderry Cathedral. No. 0391. No. 587036.	40.00
Lowther Castle. No. 0317. Rd. No. 566283. 105mm long.	50.00

Madame Tussauds. No. 0388. No. 582363.	65.00
Malvern Priory. No. 0322. Rd. No. 558186. 95mm long.	40.00
Manchester Cathedral. No. 0356. Rd. No. 100mm long.	40.00
Marble Arch (white). No. 0422 90mm.	20.00
Molls Coffee House, Exeter. No. 6936. 70mm long.	45.00
Newark Castle. No. 0307 Rd. No. 554738. 108mm long.	40.00
Medieval Bridge, Newcastle on Tyne. No. 0392 No. 591208.	45.00
Newcastle Cathedral. No. 0343 Rd. No. 560727. 95mm long.	50.00
Newcastle-on-Tyne, Black Gate. No. 0389. No. 585808. 80mm long.	45.00
Newcastle-on-Tyne, The Castle. No. 0307, 0419 or 0390. Rd. No. 554738 or 585809. (it is possible that there is more than one model). 95mm.	50.00
Nottingham Castle. No. 7556. 42mm.	45.00
Plas Newydd, Llangollen, No. 0319. No. 521568. 86mm long.	45.00
Ripon Cathedral. No. 0385 Rd. No. 580773. 109mm long.	40.00
Robinson Brewers Ltd. Ho'ton (Ales & Stout). No. 0379. 112mm long.	40.00
Rowton Tower, inscribed: *King Charles stood on this tower Sep 2nd 1645 and saw his army defeated on Rowton Moor.* No. 0327. No. 558197. 85mm.	45.00
St Andrews's Home, Folkestone. No. 0331. No. 559935. 54mm.	40.00
St Johns Church, Perth. No. 0357 Rd. No. 568187. 85mm.	40.00
St Mary's Church, Scarborough. No. 0303. 97mm long.	40.00
St. Mary's Church, Taunton. No. 0403. No. 604413.	40.00
St Patrick's Cathedral. No. 587037. 103mm.	45.00
St Paul's Cathedral, not named. Two numbers recorded, No. 0387 and No. 7332. Rd. No. 564098 & 554737. 88mm long and 148mm long.	30.00
St Tudno's Church, Llandudno. No. 0303. Rd. No. 564142. 84mm.	40.00

Salisbury Cathedral. No. 0351. Rd.
No. 567854. 105mm long.   40.00
Scarborough, The Castle. No. 0398.
78mm.   40.00
*Shakespeares House, Stratford-on-
Avon.* No. 0380. Rd. No. 576829.
110mm long.   25.00
Tintern Abbey. No. 0328.
No. 558187.   40.00
Upleatham Church, red roof.
No. 0381 Rd. No. 582362.
97mm long.   50.00
Wells Cathedral. No. 583280.
105mm long.   45.00
Westminster Abbey. No. 0341.
Rd. No. 560726. 110mm long.   40.00
Whitby Abbey No. 0370. Rd. No.
578552. 105mm long.   40.00
Winchester Cathedral. No. 0430 Rd.
No. 632519. 144mm long.   40.00
Worcester Cathedral. No. 0334.
No. 564564.   40.00
York Minster Rd. No. 556287.
2 sizes: No. 0312. 82mm long.   35.00
No. 0312II. 138mm long.   40.00

Monuments (including Crosses)
The Cross, Banbury. No. 0316. No.
536284 and No. 556281.
110mm.   35.00
John Ruskin memorial. No. 0396.
128mm.   40.00

Historical/Folklore
Christchurch, Rogers Tomb, Trinket
box and lid. Inscribed: WE WERE
NOT SLAYNE BUT RAYSD,
RAYSD NOT TO LIFE, BUT TO
BVT BURIED TWICE BY MEN
OF STRIFE WHAT REST COULD
LIVING HAVE WHEN DEAD
HAD NONE AGREE AMONGST
YOU HEERE WE TEN ARE ONE.
HEN: ROGERS DIED APRILL
17.1641: IR No. 0429. No. 632133.
113mm long.   40.00
*Old Norman Font, St Mary's Church
Steps, Exeter.* No. 0376. Rd. No.
579668.   30.00
Scott Memorial, Edinburgh.
No. 0332. No. 559938.   30.00
Westminster Abbey Coronation Chair.
116mm.   17.00

Seaside Souvenirs
Corbierre Lighthouse, Jersey, Model of.
No. 0419. Rd. No. 558636. 84mm.   20.00
Flamborohead Lighthouse. 67mm.   30.00

Moschendorf

**MOSCHENDORF
BAVARIA**

Trademark used by the German firm Hof-Moschendorf (Bayern).

This mark has only been found on a crested tea plate. 150mm wide.   5.00

Mother Shipton China

Trademark used for the retailer J.W. Simpson, Dropping Well, Knaresborough by Wiltshaw and Robinson Ltd. Carlton Works, Stoke-on-Trent. (Usual trademark Carlton).

For details of this china and manufacturer see Carlton China.

All models found with this mark have either a crest of Knaresboro' or Mother Shipton, accompanied by the inscription: *Near to the Knaresboro Dropping Well. I drew breath as records tell.* Models can be found in lustre. Some 'smalls' and models are found with a hand coloured transfer print of Mother Shipton surrounded by a ship, aeroplane, train, telephone or radio wires, inscribed: *Prophecies of Mother Shipton.*

Such items usually have the following verse on the reverse: *Around the world thoughts shall fly, in the twinkling of an eye. In the air shall men be seen, carriages without horses shall go, iron in the water shall float, as easy as a wooden boat.* No wonder Mother Shipton was so popular as a folklore figure in 1920.

Stock Numbers where found seem to be those found on Carlton models.

Mother Shipton Models
Ancient Artefacts
Loving Cup 3-handled. 42mm.   6.50

Historical/Folklore
Knaresborough Dropping Well,
  with colouring and inscription.
  103mm. (White £19.00).   35.00

Model of Mother Shipton's Kail Pot
A cauldron over a fire supported
on a tripod. 120mm.   35.00
Mother Shipton, with some
colouring.
3 sizes: 92mm.   30.00
       110mm.   40.00
       190mm.   55.00
Mother Shipton with some
colouring, standing on lustre oval
base. 90mm.   30.00
Mother Shipton, some colouring,
standing on ashtray base, with
inscription.   30.00

Countryside
Tree trunk hatpin holder. 115mm.   16.50

Animals
Cat, sitting wearing black top hat
and bow tie. 85mm.   30.00
Cat, blue collar, on cushion. 82mm.   22.00
Bulldog, French. 55mm.   20.50
Stag, with antlers, on oval base,
can be found facing left or right.
217mm.   110.00

Great War
Munitions Worker, inscribed: *Doing
her bit. Shells and more shells.* Some
colouring. 140mm.   190.00
HMS Tiger. Battleship. 170mm long.   110.00
French 75mm Field Gun.
125mm long.   30.00
Edith Cavell, statue, inscribed:
*Brussels dawn October 12th 1915.
Sacrifice, Humanity.* 163mm.   23.00

Home/Nostalgic
Frying Pan. 110mm long.   17.00
Grandfather Clock inscribed: *Gude
Morn.* 105mm.   17.00
Suitcase. 36mm. With inscription:
*Near to the Knaresboro' Dropping
Well*   10.50
Warming Pan. No. 392. 127mm long.   13.00
Water Pump, with trough. 100mm.   16.00

Comic/Novelty
I'm forever blowing bubbles. Pears
advert Blue Boy blowing bubbles.
Clothes blue, bubble and bowl
lustre. ll0mm.   75.00

Alcohol
Toby Jug, with inscription. 70mm.   7.50

Musical Instruments
Upright Piano open keyboard.
64mm.   22.50
Banjo. 130mm.   20.00

Modern Equipment
Radio Operator. 85mm.   140.00

Footwear
Boot, with prophesies verse. 72mm.   8.50
Lancashire Clog. 90mm.   7.00

Myott

N

Trademark used by Myott Son & Co. of Hanley, Stoke-on-Trent.

One piece of crested ware has been recorded from this manufacturer.

Domestic
Teaplate 130mm dia. decorated with
Flags of the Allies, a field gun
and inscribed: *Allies United 1914*   12.00

Trademark printed in blue, used by a foreign manufacturer.

Only one piece has been found to date, this being an 85mm oval pin tray with blue rim and coloured ladybird valued at £20.00.

Nautilus Porcelain

1896-1913

Trademarks used by the Nautilus Porcelain Co., Possil Pottery, Glasgow.

1903-1913
The above two marks can be found with the word BRITISH printed above.

1907-1913

This firm, established in 1896, and for sometime restyled the Possil Pottery Co., was disbanded in 1914. Based in Glasgow, the Nautilus Porcelain Co. made many Scottish crested pieces, but English crests can be found, the firm having showrooms in 47, Holborn Viaduct, London. The company specialised in producing ornamental porcelain, tea sets, dessert services, trinket sets and figures, so naturally they quickly turned to arms and view ware. The Nautilus Porcelain Co. were making a special feature of these as early as 1903, and by 1907 were producing large quantities. Crests were applied to a range of domestic porcelain ware as well as a 'large assortment of small fancy china pieces'.

Nautilus is fine china and some pieces of 'egg shell' lightness can be found. The china certainly has a different feel to that produced in Staffordshire. The crests and the very small quantity of view ware that has survived are very well produced. 'Smalls' with the early mark often have a black transfer print of a tudor rose, thistle or tartan shield on the reverse, and these can be found hand painted.

Obviously the range of models is small as the firm went out of business at the beginning of the Great War, but there are many 'smalls' and much domestic ware to be found, and these are well worth looking for as they are of such good quality.

Numbering System. No stock numbers are printed on the china. The painted numbers on the base are paintresses' works numbers, 10 and 14 being most often found.

Nautilus Models
Ancient Artefacts

Aberdeen Bronze Pot. 65mm.	7.50
Hastings Kettle. 52mm.	7.50
Irish Bronze Pot. 50mm.	7.50
Loving Cup, three handled.	
4 sizes: 37mm.	7.50
39mm.	7.50
40mm.	7.50
50mm.	7.50
Puzzle Jug. 70mm.	10.50
Rayleigh Ancient cooking pot.	
35mm.	7.50

Monuments (including Crosses)

Iona Cross. 162mm.	17.00

Traditional/National Souvenirs

Irish Wooden Noggin. 57mm.	10.00
Highland Whisky Bowl. Can have 2 or 3 handles. 60mm dia.	10.50
Thistle Jug. 64mm.	8.50

Seaside

Canoe. No. 12. 125mm long.	12.00
Conch Shell on three coral legs. 155mm long	18.00

Countryside

Milk Churn. 76mm.	8.50
Treetrunk shaped vase. 105mm.	12.00

Animals

Pig, fat and standing. 70mm long.	25.00
Pig, tiny, standing and fat. 67mm long.	24.00

Great War

Shell case. 57mm.	10.00

Home/Nostalgic

Coal Bucket. 58mm.	8.50
Coal scuttle, cylindrical on bow feet. 70mm long.	10.50
Dust Pan. 50mm long.	15.00
Garden Urn. 63mm.	7.50
Miner's Lamp. 63mm.	22.00
Shaving Mug. 53mm.	12.00
Watering Can, flat top. 50mm.	12.00

Alcohol

Carboy. 70mm.	9.00

Musical Instruments

Tambourine. 70mm dia.	11.00

Modern Equipment

Policeman's Lamp. 65mm.	15.00

Footwear

Dutch Sabot. 90mm long.	10.50
Old Boot. 63mm long.	10.50
Oriental Slipper. 92mm long.	10.50

Hats

Balmoral Bonnet, not named.	
75mm dia.	26.00
Top Hat, match striker. 46mm.	11.00

Sport/Pastimes

Curling Stone. 55mm.	20.00

Miniature Domestic

Beaker. 39mm.	7.50
Candlestick. 52mm.	7.00
Cheese Dish and cover.	
70mm long.	13.00
Cup. 39mm.	4.50
Diamond mouth Vase. 80mm.	7.50
Jelly mould. 96m long.	0.00
Jug, barrel shaped. 52mm.	7.50
Jug, shaped. 45mm.	7.50
Milk Jug, tall and ornate.	
95mm.	10.00
Mug, one handle. 40mm.	7.50
Tea pot with lid.	
2 sizes: 48mm.	10.00
55mm.	11.00
Vase, long neck. 140mm.	7.50

Domestic

Bamboo Spill Holder. 103mm.	8.00
Cup and Saucer.	5.00
Hatpin Holder. 105mm.	19.00
Match Holders:	
Straight-sided. 57mm.	8.00
Ridged. 50mm.	8.00
Pin Tray, leaf-shaped with twig handle. 120mm long.	10.50
Teaplate.	5.00
Vase, two-handled. 74mm.	7.50
Vase, long neck, fluted top,2 small handles. 125mm.	7.50
Vase, two-handled. 170mm long, 100mm high.	7.50

Nelson China

Ness China

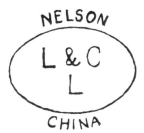

"NESS CHINA"

Trademark used for a Liverpool retailer by an unknown English manufacturer but probably a branch of J.A. Robinson & Sons. (Usual trademark Arcadian).

Nelson Models
Seaside Souvenirs
Bathing Machine. 65mm.   16.00

Great War
Model of a pair of Field Glasses.
60mm long.   25.00

Trademark used for an Inverness firm by Schmidt and Co., Carlsbad (Bohemia). (Usual trademark Gemma).

Ness Models
Ancient Artefacts
Puzzle Tankard. 70mm.   8.00

Seaside
Lifeboat with lifebelt on side. No.
536 or No. 636. 130mm long.   19.50

Great War
French Infantry Helmet. 60mm long.   40.00

New Chelsea

New Milton

Trademark used by the New Chelsea Porcelain Co. Longton. For further details of this china and manufacturer see Chelson China.

A 54mm vase decorated with a bird transfer has been found with this trademark. 17.50

No details of trademark available. Only one model has been recorded with this mark so far. Probably the mark of a retailer in New Milton, Hampshire on a piece produced by Arcadian or Willow.

New Milton Model
Great War
Monoplane, with moveable propeller. 145mm. 75.00

Niagara Art China

Norfolk Crest China

NIAGARA
ART
CHINA

Trademark used by Hewitt and Leadbeater, Willow Potteries, Longton, subsequently Hewitt Bros. (Usual trademark Willow Art).

Niagara Art Models
Traditional/National Souvenirs
Dutch Girl. 75mm.   16.50

Great War
Tommy's Steel Helmet. 76mm long.   40.00

Footwear
Lace-up Riding Shoe. 115mm long.   12.00

Mark has also been found with CHEST rather than crest, obviously a misprint.

Trademark used for W.H. Smith & Sons by Hewitt & Leadbeater, Willow Potteries, Longton - subsequently Hewitt Bros. (Usual trademark Willow Art).
For details of this china and manufacturer see Willow Art China.
This is the second mark used by Hewitt and Leadbeater for W.H. Smith and Sons, the other being Kingsway Art China. This appears to be a later mark, used from the end of the Great War to the mid-twenties. Mugs, cups and plates have been recorded with the Norfolk mark, usually decorated with colour transfer prints of H.M.S. Iron Duke, an aeroplane, the Flags of the Allies and a peace inscription. Black Cat transfers are also found indicating the later date and some models could have come from Arcadian moulds once the firms had combined. Identical decorations were also used on pieces marked CHELSON China.

Stock numbers where found would be the same as Willow Art models.

Norfolk Models
Parian/Unglazed
Bust of Burns on circular plinth.
    170mm.   40.00

Buildings - White
Ann Hathaway's Cottage. 55mm long. 14.00
Shakespeare's House. 59mm long.   12.00

Monuments (including Crosses)

Plymouth Armada Memorial. 170mm.	20.00
Queen Victoria's Statue, Wakefield.	
165mm.	40.00
Sir Robert Peel statue. 168mm.	35.00

Historical/Folklore

Burns Chair. 87mm.	12.00
James V Chair. 101mm.	12.50
King Alfred statue on stepped base.	
160mm.	40.00
St. Winefride unglazed figurine on	
square base. 190mm.	50.00

Traditional/National Souvenirs

Thistle Vase. 58mm.	6.00
Welsh Hat, with blue or white band.	
No. 75. 57mm.	12.00

Seaside Souvenirs

Lifeboat. 95mm long.	22.50
Lighthouse, not named. No. 135.	
105mm.	8.00

Animals

Cat, on cushion, playing fiddle	
holding bow. 110mm. inscribed:	
Cat and Fiddle, Buxton.	50.00
Cat, standing, chubby, looking left,	
tail up. 76mm.	22.00
Dog, Bull Terrier, standing.	
60mm.	16.50
Dog, sitting, bow at neck. Brown	
eyes. No. 22. 76mm.	22.50
Dog, sitting, head to one side.	
No. 23. 70mm.	22.00
Dog, wearing medallion.	22.00
Elephant, walking. 52mm.	20.00
Elephant, walking, trunk over head.	
No. 113. 53mm.	20.00
Pig, standing. 85mm long.	20.00
Pony inscribed 'A Native of	
Shetland'.105mm long.	40.00

Birds (including Eggs)

Bird posy holder. 75mm.	12.00
Duck posy holder, yellow beak.	
80mm long.	14.50
Hen egg cup. 76mm long.	10.50
Swan, open back. 63mm.	6.50

Great War

Battleship, impressed: HMS Lion.	
140mm long.	40.00
British Tank. 102mm long.	22.50

Cenotaph. 154mm.	20.00
Tank with trailing wheels.	
123mm long.	22.50
Red Cross Van. No. 712.	
88mm long.	40.00
Field Gun with screen. 155mm long.	35.00
Officer's peaked Cap. 80mm dia.	20.00
Kitbag with verse. 74mm.	19.50
Blackwatch Memorial Scottish soldier	
on square base. Inscribed: *Am*	
freiceadan dubh and *To the memory*	
of officers, non commissioned officers	
& men of Blackwatch who fell in	
South African War 1899-1902.	
168mm.	75.00
Nurse Cavell, War Memorial statue.	
Large, impressive model.	
194mm.	95.00
Matlock Bath War Memorial.	
182mm.	40.00
Florence Nightingale statue.	
2 sizes: 160mm.	22.00
175mm.	25.00

Home/Nostalgic

Grandfather clock, inscribed: *Make*	
use of time let not advantage slip.	
Shakespeare. 128mm.	19.50

Comic/Novelty

Jester, double faced bust. Some	
colouring.	
2 sizes: 65mm.	14.50
80mm.	16.00
Monk, jovial and plump. No glass.	
90mm.	16.50
Monk, jovial and holding glass.	
70mm.	14.50

Sport

Cricket Cap. 67mm long.	60.00

Footwear

Edwardian Shoe, blue bow.	
110mm long.	10.00
Lancashire Clog. 88mm long.	7.50

Domestic

Hatpins holder. 124mm.	16.50

Noritaké

Noritaké

Made in Japan.

A selection of coloured vases were made, many with a transfer print of St Annes with a crest in foreground and some with crests of London or Blackpool. There is very little Japanese souvenir ware around and certainly the British Potteries did not see the Japanese as much of a threat as they did the Germans.   10.00

Dish, shaped. 140mm dia.   10.00

Nornesford China

Trademark registered in 1920 and used by R.H. and S.L. Plant (Ltd), Tuscan Works, Longton. (Usual trademark Tuscan).

Nornesford Models
Seaside Souvenirs
Lighthouse.   7.50

Animals
Bulldog in kennel. 65mm.   16.50
Cheshire Cat, with brown bead
   right eye. 90mm.   21.00
Fish with open mouth and bead
   eyes. 120mm long.   9.50

Birds (including Eggs)
Chick hatching from egg.
   70mm long.   12.50

Home/Nostalgic
Anvil on base. 60mm.   7.50
Bellows. 105mm.   14.50
Loaf of Bread. 55mm.   20.00
Pillar Box. No. 181. 73mm.   16.00
Shaving Mug. 53mm.   9.50
Wee Willie Winkie Candle Snuffer.
   90mm.   22.00

Hats
Top Hat. No. 173. 45mm.   6.50

Domestic
Hatpin holder, bamboo. 100mm.   16.00

One and All

ONE AND ALL

BRITISH

Trademark used by J.A. Robinson & Sons, Stoke-on-Trent. (Usual trademark Arcadian). Most china found with this mark are 'smalls' with 'Lucky Black Cat' transfers, and were produced by J.A. Robinson Ltd. This mark is very like a mark used by Cauldon for Pearsons of Blackpool. (See Palatine China).

These models often have Cornish crests.

One and All Models
Ancient Artefacts
Salisbury Jack, not named. 50mm.   4.00

Buildings - White
Anne Hathaway's Cottage.
105mm long.   16.00

Seaside Souvenirs
Sea-Shell Pin Tray, 3 tiny feet.
75mm long.   8.00

Animals
Black Cat on jug. No. 1. 65mm.   65.00
Black Cat on telephone. No. 4. 68mm.   115.00
Black Cat on swing. No. 11. 67mm.   75.00
Black Cat with double bass. No. 20.
76mm.   210.00
Black Cat playing piano. No. 24.
50mm.   210.00
Bulldog, sitting. 50mm.   40.00
Crocodile. 127mm long.   80.00
Dog, Collie lying down.
78mm long.   30.00

Teddy Bear. No. 27. 65mm.   22.50
Squirrel, eating nut. 60mm.   30.00
Tortoise. 60mm long.   12.00

Birds (including Eggs)
Cockerel on circular base. Some
   colouring. 90mm.   24.50
Goose. 95mm.   38.00
Stork on circular base. 80mm.   35.00

Home/Nostalgic
Cauldron with handle. 82mm.   6.00
Fire Bucket. 53mm.   5.00
Grandmother Clock. 110mm.   16.50
Jardiniere on fixed stand. 95mm.   6.00
Ring Stand. 52mm.   9.50

Comic/Novelty
Black Boy and Girl on log, coloured.
   75mm long.   120.00
Jester, sitting on heart shaped
   ashtray. 65mm.   75.00

Transport
Petrol Can, impressed: *Motor Spirit.*
55mm.   22.00

Footwear
Ladies Ankle Boot. 72mm long.   6.00

Miscellaneous
Domed Jam Pot and cover. 80mm.   7.00

Oxford Art China

P

Trademark used by Hutschenreuther, Probstzella, Thuringia (not the more famous Bavarian firm of the same name). Trademark can be found without the crown.
This mark is found on 'smalls', ancient arte-facts and domestic ware with crests and coloured transfers from all over Great Britain. The ware is the continental hard china, and the models recorded indicate that the mark was used before the Great War.

Trademark used for an Oxfordshire retailer by Hewitt & Leadbeater, Willow Potteries, Longton. (Usual trademark Willow Art).
For details of this china and manufacturer see Willow Art China.
One model found with this mark has a Barrow-in-Furness crest which seems to indicate that the W. & Co. in the mark had a chain of gift shops, the original shop being in Oxford.

Oxford Art Model
Historical/Folklore
James the V chair at Stirling Castle.
  102mm.   16.00
Sir Walter Scott's Chair, Abbotsford.
  80mm.   14.50

Home/ Nostalgic
Grandfather Clock inscribed: *Make use of time...* 124mm.   18.50

Footwear
Lancashire Clog.   6.00

P Models
Ancient Artefacts
Aberdeen Bronze Pot. 68mm.   5.00
Ancient Tyg, 2 handled.   5.00
Loving Cup, 3 handled & 2
  handled. 38mm.   6.00
Puzzle Jug. 67mm.   6.50

Home/Nostalgic
Cauldron. 40mm.   6.00
Shaving Mug. 55mm.   8.50
Suitcase. 90mm.   6.00

Miniature Domestic
Cheese Dish and cover, 2 pieces.
  55mm.   8.50
Tea Pot with lid. 65mm.   8.50
Tea Urn with lid, tapered.
  65mm.   8.50

Domestic
Candlestick and snuffer. 85mm
  dia.   6.50
Oviform Pepper Castor. 70mm.   5.50

Palantine China

Palmer

MANUFACTURED FOR
'PEARSONS'
BLACKPOOL

Trademark used for Pearsons, of Blackpool by J.A. Robinson Ltd. (Usual trademark Arcadian).

For details of this china and manufacturer see Arcadian China.

This mark was probably used for a 'Palatine Bazaar' in Blackpool, as only Blackpool crests have been recorded. This mark is very similar to one used in the mid-Twenties, on Willow Art moulds indicating that both marks were used by the Cauldon group. (See One and All). The models below seem to be earlier than the 'One and All' models, indicating that the mark was re-used later.

Palatine Models
Animals
Dog, sitting with a tear on cheek.
80mm.   30.00

Great War
Armoured Car, Model of.
120mm long.   55.00
Red Cross Van, inscribed: *EH139.*
88mm long.   40 00
Tank, Model of. 115mm.   26.00

Trademark used by Hewitt and Leadbeater, Willow Potteries, Longton. (Usual trademark Willow Art.) This piece was obviously ordered by their Buckingham agent and it bears the arms of the town.

The inclusion of this mark is for information purposes, as generally, retailers marks have not been included in this book. Crested china authority and researcher Lionel Hemsley considers that this entry should be deleted or several dozen others included. He is correct, but this and several similar are included as examples.

Palmer Model
Comic/Novelty
Billiken sitting. 78mm.   8.50

P.A.L.T.

Panorama

Trademark used by an unknown German firm on domestic wares, after the Great War.

This mark has been found on domestic ware with crests from all over Great Britain. The use of 'Czecho-Slovakia' as the country of origin proves that the mark was used after 1920.

Domestic ware only.   from £4.00

Candle stick, square base, 4 small
feet. 135mm.   4.00

Trademark used by Wagstaff and Brunt on china manufactured by Edwin Leadbeater, Commerce Street, Longton, who also made Leadbeater Art China and H&L.

For details of this china and manufacturer see Leadbeater Art China.

Wagstaff and Brunt were registered as pottery manufacturers from 1880 to 1927 but most of the wares stamped with their name appears to have been made by other manufacturers. They specialised in commemorative china, and it could well be that they were dealers rather than manufacturers. The miniatures marked 'Panorama' were definitely made by Edwin Leadbeater, who could possibly have taken this contract with him from Hewitt and Leadbeater. I suspect the trademark Panorama was chosen because the range was intended to be only view ware. Many pieces marked Panorama carry coloured transfer views rather than a crest, but crests do occur those from Sussex and the Isle and Manor of Portland being common. Apart from the usual views of castles and sea fronts there are some transfers of War Memorials to be found, including The Cenotaph, Stoke under Ham and Hemyock War Memorials. Stock numbers where they are used coincide with Leadbeater Art stock numbers.

Panorama Models
Many of these wares are found with a transfer print view rather than a crest.   Add 8.00

Unglazed/Parian
Burns and Highland Mary. 125mm.   30.00
Bust of Dickens, on circular glazed
   base. 170mm.   35.00
Sister Dora statue of nurse on base.
   170mm.   70.00

Ancient Artefacts
Model of Bowl found in lake village
   Glastonbury. 65mm dia.   5.00

Monuments
Drakes' Statue. 153mm.   17.50
Sir Robert Peel statue on large
   plinth. 165mm.   55.00

Historical/Folklore
Bunyans Chair, Model of. 95mm.   19.50
Model of Mons Meg Edinburgh Castle.
   130mm long.   17.00
Sir Walter Scott's Chair at Abbotsford.
   No. 85. 80mm.   10.00

Traditional/National Souvenirs
Welsh Hat. No. 57. 60mm.   10.00

Seaside Souvenirs
Lifeboat. 95mm long.   17.00
Lighthouse. 110mm.   8.50
Lighthouse Pepper Castor. ll0mm.   8.50

Animals
Cat sitting, left ear raised, one green
   eye. 105mm.   16.50
Labrador sitting, red eyes. 74mm.   16.50
Dog, Pug, sitting, black eyes. 67mm.   17.50
Dog, Staffordshire Bull Terrier,
   sitting. 115mm.   22.00

Birds (including Eggs)
Chick. 33mm.   9.00
Crested Tit Posy Holder.
   80mm long.   9.50
Duck, open wings.
   80mm long.   13.50

Great War
Red Cross Van. No. 103.
   88mm long.   40.00

Home/Nostalgic
Anvil. No. 78. 58mm.   7.50

Comic/Novelty
Kewpie doll. 95mm.   24.00
Monk. 95mm.   17.00

Alcohol
Toby Jug. 74mm.   12.50

Sport
Cricket Cap. 67mm long.   50.00
Footballer, coloured holding brown
   ball on white and green plinth.
   Inscribed: *Play Up* 166mm.   125.00

Modern Equipment
Horn Gramophone. 81mm.   25.00

Paragon China

PARAGON
CHINA
ENGLAND

Trademarks used by Star China Co., Atlas
Works (and other addresses), Longton.
Subsequently Paragon China (Co) Ltd.

The star mark was used on
domestic wares with the Great
War commemorative, Four Flags
of the Allies with inscription: *For
right and freedom.*   from 10.00

The crown mark (not shown here)
is found on smalls with ordinary
crests.   4.00

Park, For the People, China

PARK,
FOR THE PEOPLE
CHINA

Mark used by unknown English manufacturer for a charity, (possibly) in
Newtown, Mid-Wales.

This mark has been found on
several 'smalls' all with a
Newtown crest, apart from one
with the crest of Machynlleth
about 30 miles from Newtown.
Could they have been sold at a
charity or fund raising bazaar?   5.00

Patriotic China

PATRIOTIC
× BR &C ×

CHINA
STOKE ON TRENT

Trademark used during the Great War by
Birks, Rawlins and Co (Ltd), Vine Pottery,
Stoke. (Usual trademark Savoy).
For details of this china and manufacturer
see Savoy China.
The items with this mark so far recorded
carry military crests and were obviously
made to commemorate the Great War.
Colour transfer prints of a soldier holding
a rifle with the Union Jack and Royal
Standard flags and ribbon inscribed "A
soldier of the the King" are found on various models with the names of particular
regiments on the front and Shakespeare's
verse "This Britain never did, nor never
shall..." on the reverse. The following
have been recorded:
Gordon Highlanders
East Lancashire Regt.
Seaford Camp 13th Batt Manchester
11th Welsh
These pieces are obviously of great interest
to the Great War collector and one would
assume that there must be further badges
to record possibly all the similar Savoy
transfers.

Patriotic Models
Range of wares all with
military crests and Great
War inscriptions.   £12.50 upwards

Parian/Unglazed
Bust of Admiral Sir David Beatty.
Union Jack and laurel wreath.
Inscribed: To Victory. Verse at rear
Be Briton still to Briton true. 150mm. 75.00

Animals
Bulldog standing. Identical Union
Jack and Laurel Wreath.
Inscribed: *To Victory* and verse as
on the bust. 135mm long.   65.00
Lion, walking with Burns verse: *Be
Briton still to Briton true.*
135mm long.   35.00
Can be found draped in Union
Jack *To Victory.*   55.00

Miniature Domestic
Beaker. 80mm.   7.00
Tea Pot with lid. 65mm.   13.50

Pearl Arms China

The middle initial is 'C' and not a 'G' as formerly thought.

Trademark used for a wholesaler by Hewitt Bros, Willow Potteries Ltd. Longton. (Usual trademark Willow Art). For details of this china and manufacturer see Willow Art China. The initials A.C.R. & Co. Ltd. were used by the firm of A.C. Richardson and Co., Gordon Pottery, Tunstall, Staffs, established in 1915. This firm manufactured Crown Ducal ware and did not advertise crested miniatures. The models with the Pearl Arms mark are undoubtedly from the same moulds as those marked Willow Art. Whether this range was made for another manufacturer or retailer or was an alternative trademark used by Hewitt Bros must remain a mystery. The use of the initials A.G.R. and A.C.R. for both were used, is a mystery and the diversity of crests seems to indicate that a range was made for another manufacturer. No transfer devices or views have been recorded on china with this mark and only two military badges, *Royal Artillery* and *Royal Engineers*. Domestic ware and 'smalls' are often found. Stock numbers where they occur coincide with those found on Willow Art models.

Pearl Arms Models
Ancient Artefacts
Carlisle Salt Pot, not named.
46mm.   4.00

Nottingham Urn, not named.
No. 172. 45mm.   3 00
Portland Vase. 62mm.   5.50
Puzzle Tea Pot. 56mm.   20.00
York Ewer. 58mm.   5.50

Monuments (including Crosses)
Hull Fisherman's Memorial. 132mm.   20.00

Historical/Folklore
Burns Chair. No. 49. 88mm.   14.00
James V Chair, Stirling Castle.
100mm.   16.50
Man in the Moon. 55mm.   30.00
Mary, Queen of Scots Chair, Edinburgh Castle, Model of. 75mm.   10.50
Royal Crown. 55mm.   30.00
Sword, ornate, in scabbard.
135mm long.   70.00

Traditional/National Souvenirs
Blackpool Big Wheel. 100mm.   22.00
Welsh Hat with longest Welsh place name around brim. No. 75.
55mm.   12.50
Thistle Vase *A wee Deoch an Doris.*
65mm.   7.00

Seaside Souvenirs
Rowing Boat on rocks.
110mm long.   16.00
Lighthouse. No. 135. 105mm.   7.00
Mermaid seated on rock combing hair. 105mm.   30.00

Animals
Cat, angry, tail in the air. Bow not coloured. 80mm long.   22.00
Cat, Cheshire. *Still Smiling.* 80mm.   10.00
Cat, sitting. 70mm.   22.00
Cat sitting in boot, blue bow.
88mm long.   16.50
Cat, standing, blue bow.
80mm.   14.00
Cat, standing, chubby. 70mm.   22.00
Bulldog, black, emerging from kennel, inscribed: *The Black Watch.* 70mm long.   30.00
Dog, Collie, standing. 85mm.   30.00
Dog, Scottie with tam-o'-shanter.
95mm.   16.50
Elephant, walking. 52mm.   20.00
Elephant, trunk thrown back up.
No. 336. 102mm long.   50.00
Elephant, cream jug. 72mm.   14.50

Fish. 128mm long.	7.00
Hampshire Hog with inscription.	
100mm long.	40.00
Lion crouching. 82mm long.	30.00
Mouse. 62mm.	25.00
Pig standing. 95mm long.	19.50
Pig, sitting, inscribed: *You may push*	
me etc. 73mm.	20.00
Rabbit, right ear erect.	
66mm long.	12.50
Teddy Bear, sitting. 73mm.	24.00

Birds (including Eggs)

Canary on rock. 98mm.	19.00
Swan, with head on breast. 58mm.	9.50

Great War

Sailor, inscribed: *Our brave defender.*	
130mm.	70.00
Monoplane, with movable prop.	
150mm long.	80.00
Monoplane, with fixed prop.	
146mm long.	75.00
Monoplane, moveable prop.,	
coloured roundels and tail	
markings. 150mm long.	140.00
Battleship, 4 funnels.	
127mm long.	30.00
Battleship, 3 funnels. Impressed	
HMS Lion. No. 213. 140mm long.	40.00
British Tank, Model of, with trailing	
wheels. 130mm long.	22.50
British Tank, Model of.	
92mm long.	22.50
Bugle. No. 370. 70mm.	24.50
Kit Bag with verse: *Pack up your*	
troubles in your old kit bag.	
74mm.	24.50
Officer's Peaked Cap.	
70mm dia.	20.00
Pickelhaube. (German spiked	
helmet).50mm.	30.00
Fireplace inscribed: *Keep the home*	
fires burning. Some colouring.	
100mm long.	20.00

Home/Nostalgic

Anvil. 60mm.	7.50
Basket, oblong with handle.	
76mm long.	6.50
Book, leather bound. 60mm.	12.00
Bucket. 65mm.	6.50
Coal scuttle, helmet shaped. No. 101.	
53mm.	8.00

Grandfather Clock, inscribed: *Make*	
use of time let not advantage slip.	
Shakespeare. 128mm.	10.50
Pillar Box, outpressed: *G.R.*	
90mm.	22.00
Shaving Mug. 55mm.	9.50
Sundial, circular on square base,	
with inscription: *I mark not the*	
hours. 98mm.	10.50
Watering Can. 72mm.	9.50

Comic/Novelty

Billiken, the God of Luck, often found	
unnamed. 73mm.	7.50
Billiken, the God of Luck, sitting on	
high-backed chair. 100mm.	9.50

Alcohol

Barrel, on its side. 55mm long.	5.00
Thistle Vase, inscribed *A wee Deoch*	
and Doris. 64mm.	6.00
Whiskey Bottle with cork, inscribed:	
One special scotch. 88mm.	9.50

Transport

Open Tourer,4 seater. 114mm long.	40.00

Hats

Policeman's Helmet.	17.50

Footwear

Lancashire Clog. 88mm long.	6.50
Sabot. 73mm long.	6.00

Miniature Domestic

Cheese Dish and cover. 45mm.	9.50
Cup and Saucer. 35mm.	5.50
Coffee Pot with lid. 69mm.	9.50

Domestic

Octagonal *Salt* pot. 95mm.	5.00

Miscellaneous

Hand holding a tulip. 80mm.	7.00

Phoenix China

Podmore China

1921-c1927 on crested china

Trademark used by Thomas Forester & Sons (Ltd.), Phoenix Works, Longton.

A range of crested domestic ware was produced.

Phoenix China Models
Miniature Domestic
Wash Bowl. 50mm.   4.50
Wash Jug. 80mm.   4.50

Domestic
Teaplate. 180mm dia.   4.00

Trademark used by Podmore China Co., Elm Street, Hanley.
A Mr A.J. Podmore of the Tunstall Art Pottery Co. in 1920 announced that in consequence of the expiration of his lease the blocks, moulds and cases and other implements connected with his range of useful and ornamental pottery were for disposal. In 1921 The Podmore China Co. was established in Hanley and one can only assume that Mr A.J. Podmore had found new premises. (This indication of the sale of moulds in Staffordshire helps to explain why so many firms produced similar if not identical models during this period.) The Podmore China Co. continued until 1941 when it became Sylvan Pottery Ltd.
Podmore China Co. produced crested china miniatures from 1921 to at least the middle if not late twenties. No early historical shapes have been recorded and the whole range of models seems to be from the twenties and not earlier. The range includes some coloured models including two delightful children at the seaside which would have sold well in the mid-twenties. The models are rather on the large and heavy side but well finished and

painted. Some 'Lucky White Heather' transfers have been found on models and 'smalls' but no other transfer devices, views or commemoratives have been recorded.

(No stock numbers are found on Podmore China, the small dots and dashes in colour found on the base are paintresses' marks.)

Podmore Models
Unglazed/Parian

Bust of *Bunyan*, square unglazed base. 135mm.	22.00
Bust of Burns, on square unglazed base with crest. 150mm.	24.00
HRH, Prince of Wales, in uniform, standing on square base. Parian or glazed on glazed base. 155mm.	100.00

Ancient Artefacts

Puzzle Jug. 74mm.	10.00

Buildings - Coloured

Bell Hotel, Abel Fletcher's house in John Halifax Gentleman.	
2 sizes: 67mm.	35.00
85mm.	40.00

Buildings - White

Bell Hotel, Abel Fletcher's house in John Halifax Gentleman. 67mm.	26.00
Big Ben.	
2 sizes: 101mm.	17.50
119mm.	17.50
Blackpool Tower. 130mm.	9.50
Bunyan's Cottage. 90mm long.	24.00
Clifton Suspension Bridge. 190mm long.	75.00
God's Providence House, Chester. AD1652.	
2 sizes: 70mm.	22.00
90mm.	22.00
Hastings Clock Tower. 167mm.	12.50
Leicester Clock Tower. 184mm.	25.00
Lincoln Cathedral, West front. 106mm.	30.00
Margate Clock Tower 143mm.	15.00
Matlock Bath, The Tower. 120mm.	125.00
Ross on Wye Town Hall. 106mm.	50.00
Rowton Tower (*King Charles Tower, Chester*). 80mm.	20.00
St. Albans, Clock Tower. 125mm.	50.00
St. Pauls Cathedral. 105mm.	22.50
Westminster Abbey. 127mm.	20.00

Monuments (including Crosses)

Banbury, The Cross. 158mm.	25.00
Black Watch Memorial. 130mm.	75.00
Bunyan's Statue, Model of.	
2 sizes: 173mm.	20.00
206mm.	22.00
Nelsons Column 140mm.	40.00
St Albans Clock Tower. 160mm.	37.50

Historical/Folklore

Armour, breast plate. 75mm.	35.00
Bunyan's Chair. 99mm.	16.00
Burns Chair, Model of. 93mm.	12.50
Mary Queen of Scots Chair in Edinburgh Castle, Model of. 80mm.	7.50
Mother Shipton, standing figure. 75mm.	8.00
Mother Shipton, figure with black cat arching its back at her feet. Coloured features. Can be found inscribed: *Near to the Knaresborough Dropping Well I first drew breath as records tell.* 118mm.	16.00
Mother Shipton's Well. 84mm.	20.00
Tewkesbury Cross Stocks and Whipping Post. 105mm (rare).	70.00

Traditional/National Souvenirs

Blackpool Big Wheel.95mm.	20.00
Chester Imp, recumbent. 100mm long.	30.00
Lincoln Imp sitting on pedestal. 105mm.	7.50
Dutch Girl on ashtray base. Fully coloured. 100mm.	22.00

Seaside Souvenirs

Lifeboat with deep blue cord. 115mm long.	22.00
Lifeboat collection box. 170mm long.	60.00
Yacht. 111mm.	15.00
Lifeboatman on plinth. 142mm.	17.00
Beachy Head Lighthouse, with black band.	
2 sizes: 120mm.	12.00
140mm.	12.00
Needles Rocks and Lighthouse, Isle of Wight. 125mm long.	45.00
North Foreland Lighthouse, Broadstairs. 128mm.	25.00

Oyster Shell on coral base.
  80mm. — 7.00
Scallop shell on coral base, hatpin
  holder. 77mm. — 8.00
Whelk Shell, inscribed: *Listen to the
  sea*. 100mm long. — 7.00
Fish Basket. 70mm long. — 10.00
Child, sitting with knees under chin,
  wearing bathing suit. Impressed:
  Splash me. Some colouring.
  140mm (rare). — 85.00
Child, with blonde hair, standing on
  rock draped in towel. 115mm. and
  140mm. White. — 40.00
  With some colouring. — 70.00

Animals

Cat, standing with arched back and
  tail up. Coloured eyes and
  mouth. 110mm. — 14.50
Cat, with human face and wearing a
  black cap. Inscribed: *Puss Puss*.
  105mm. — 65.00
Cat, grotesque with long neck,
  named in orange *Luck*. 136mm. — 8.50
Cat with long neck and funny face.
  125mm. — 10.00
Cat, Cheshire, sitting with long neck.
  117mm. — 17.00
Cat on round pouffe. Inscribed:
  Luck in orange. 80mm. — 16.50
Bulldog, Staffordshire, sitting.
  65mm. — 20.00
Dog, Scottie, looking out of kennel.
  77mm. — 12.50
  Inscribed: *Black Watch*. — 12.50
Dog, black with green bow.
  70mm. — 17.00
Dog, possibly St. Bernard, sad,
  sitting (Lustre). 48mm. — 22.50
Dog, Scottie, wearing a tam-
  o'shanter, orange pom-pom.
  75mm. — 12.50
Dog, with letter, sitting next to a
  bright red pillar box on ashtray.
  Inscribed: *Sorry I've missed the
  post*. 90mm. — 65.00
Dog, terrier, standing.
  80mm long. — 14.50
Elephant, trunk to the right.
  60mm long. — 22.00
Pig, standing. 80mm long. — 0.00
Pig, standing. 100mm long. — 17.00
Shetland Pony. 100mm long. — 22.00

Birds (including Eggs)

Cock, standing, red comb.
  65mm. — 16.00
Cock with red comb, on green base.
  45mm. — 14.00
Hen on green base. 70mm long. — 13.00
Hen, with red comb. 66mm. — 13.50
Kingfisher, coloured, on pearl lustre
  trinket tray. 82mm long. — 30.00
Penguin. 88mm. — 13.50

Great War

Monoplane with revolving prop. — 75.00
Grandfather Clock, same mould as
  usual Grandfather clock but
  clockface at 3.25, inscribed: *World
  War 1914-1919, Peace signed 3.25pm
  June 28th 1919*. 137mm. — 70.00
Fireplace with kettle, teapot &
  coloured fire. Inscribed: *Keep the
  home fires burning 'till the boys
  come home*. 90mm. — 30.00
Cenotaph, inscribed: *The Glorious
  Dead. MCMXIV-MCMXIX*. Green
  wreaths.
  4 sizes: 84mm. — 6.50
         130mm. — 7.50
         165mm. — 8.50
         185mm. — 12.00
Edith Cavell Memorial, London.
  Inscribed: *Edith Cavell Brussels
  dawn October 12th 1915. Humanity
  Sacrifice*.
  2 sizes: 142mm. — 19.50
         170mm. — 22.00
Edith Cavell Statue, Norwich.
  165mm. — 22.00
Leek War Memorial. *Model of War
  Memorial Leek, presented by Sir
  Arthur & Lady Nicholson*. 158mm. — 140.00
Matlock Bath War Memorial. Often
  found unnamed.
  2 sizes: 160mm. — 50.00
         190mm. — 50.00
Ad Astra, R.A.F. Memorial. *Unveiled
  by HRH Prince of Wales July 16th
  1923*. 152mm. — 85.00
Rushden War Memorial. *Their names
  liveth for ever, To keep in mind those
  from this town who gave their lives
  in the Great War. 1914-1918*.
  155mm. — 85.00
Blackpool War Memorial, inscribed:
  *1914 in memory of our glorious dead
  1918*. 145mm. — 155.00

Home/Nostalgic

Baby's Bootee. 52mm.	12.50
Baby's Cradle. 65mm long.	9.50
Basket. 72mm long.	5.00
Grandfather Clock, with	
inscription: *Make use of time*	
120mm.	16.50
140mm.	17.50
Fireplace with clock on mantelpiece,	
inscribed: *Home sweet home. East*	
or west home is best. Some	
colouring. 98mm.	26.00
Thimble. 47mm.	16.00
Water Pump. 75mm.	12.00

Comic/Novelty

Billiken, sitting on high backed chair,	
inscribed: *The God of things as they*	
ought to be.	
102mm.	7.50
Inscribed	8.50
The Bridegroom, God Help Him.	
145mm.	55.00
Child, some colouring, standing on	
ashtray base. 95mm.	30.00
Fully coloured	35.00
Sack of Coal, some colouring.	
2 sizes: 60mm.	17.50
95mm.	17.50
Can be found inscribed: *If you*	
can't afford a truck - buy	
a sack.	26.00
Schoolboy, comic coloured face.	
100mm.	50.00

Cartoon/Comedy Characters

Mr Pussy Foot. All water!! we don't	
think. Standing by a pump, some	
colouring. 96mm.	50.00
Wilfred Wilfred, coloured.	55.00

Alcohol

Beer Barrel on stand, fixed.	
60mm.	6.50
Toby Jug with verse on base,	
red nose. 88mm.	14.50

Sport

Golf Ball, inscribed: *The ancient game*	
of golf was first played in 1448.	
40mm.	12.00
The Sprinter, gangly athlete with	
comic face, kneeling, on oval	
base, some colouring. 98mm.	65.00

Musical Instruments

Double Bass. 140mm long.	35.00

Transport

Charabanc *Over the Hills &*	
Far Away, XL 100. 125mm long.	40.00

Modern Equipment

Horn Gramophone. 93mm.	30.00

Footwear

Lancashire Clog. 73mm long.	6.00

Miniature Domestic

Cheese Dish,1 piece. 50mm.	7.50
Cheese Dish and cover.	
71mm long.	7.50

Domestic

Hatpins holder. 134mm.	12.00

Miscellaneous

Hand holding a tulip. 95mm.	7.00
Horseshoe Pintray. 80mm long.	5.00
Vase, ornate with buttercups in	
relief. 110mm.	7.00

Poppyland

Porcelle

POPPYLAND
CHINA
ENGLISH
B.A.WATTS
SHERINGHAM

Trademark used by Taylor and Kent Ltd. Florence Works, Longton. (Usual trademark Florentine.)

The only piece recorded is a 60mm 2 handled vase decorated with red poppies for the Norfolk Broads market.   20.00

From c19101924

Trademark used by William Ritchie & Son Ltd., 24, 26, 28 Elder Street, Edinburgh. The majority of these models are from Savoy moulds and this firm was a retailer of heraldic china, obtaining supplies from Birks, Rawlins and Co. (Usual trademark Savoy) and Arkinstall & Son Ltd, Arcadian Works, Stoke-on-Trent (usual trademark Arcadian). William Ritchie was an Edinburgh wholesale stationer who also issued heraldic postcards.

This mark was registered in 1910 and published in the *Pottery Gazette* in October of that year. William Ritchie and Son Ltd were described as Porcelain and Earthenware manufacturers. No information or record of this firm can be found in standard works on the pottery industry or in the *Pottery Gazette* and therefore for the moment we have little other information. The firm does not, in fact, appear to have been a manufacturer at all and stopped dealing in crested china before the mid 1920's, as no coloured models or 'lucky' transfers have been found. Most crests recorded are from Scotland, Ireland and the North of England and obviously the firm concentrated its sales efforts in these areas.

No commemorative transfer items, view ware or any other form of decoration on miniatures or domestic ware has been recorded. A great deal of crested domestic ware has been recorded including teapot stands, plates, butter dishes and trays of various kinds. These sometimes are found with a buff instead of a white body. Porcelle china is more cream or ivory than white, and is fairly fine. The crests are rather well produced.

Numbering System. Stock numbers are sometimes found painted on the base of models and these are listed where known.

Porcelle Models

Unglazed/Parian

Bust of Robbie Burns on glazed plinth. *Burns* outpressed.

2 sizes: 115mm.	30.00
135mm.	35.00

Bust of Sir John Jellicoe, impressed: *WC. Lawton sculp. copyright. 23rd Sept 1914.* 170mm. 55.00

Ancient Artefacts

Altar Candlestick. 144mm.	7.00
Newbury Leather Bottle. 65mm.	5.00
Puzzle Jug. 70mm.	7.50
Whiskey Quaich. 30mm.	6.00

Buildings - White

Burns Cottage, Model of.

2 sizes: 70mm long.	17.00
108mm long.	25.00
Cottage. 75mm long.	10.50
An Irish Cottage. 110mm long.	18.00

Windmill, with revolving sails. 108mm. 40.00

Historical/Folklore

Mary Queen of Scots Chair, Edinburgh Castle, Model of. 70mm. 12.50

Execution Block. 100mm long. 18.00

Traditional/National Souvenirs

Irish Harp with moulded shamrocks. 105mm.	12.50
Bagpipes. 115mm long.	50.00
Thistle vase. 48mm.	6.00
Welsh Hat. 63mm.	8.50

Seaside Souvenirs

Bathing Machine, inscribed: *Morning dip.* 87mm. 16.00

Rowing Boat, no seats.

132mm long.	14.50
Yacht in full sail. 125mm.	15.00

Lighthouse on rocky base. 104mm. 9.00

Fisherman, with Tub, inscribed: *Waiting for the smacks.* 67mm. 65.00

Shell ashtray. 81mm long.	6.00
Scallop Shell. 70mm long.	6.00

Whelk Shell. No. 451. 100mm long. 6.50

Countryside

Acorn. No. 119. 56mm.	8.50

Milk Churn with fixed top. 60mm. 8.00

Animals

Cat, sitting, long neck and tail joined to shoulders. 105mm. 16.00

Cat, sitting. 57mm. No. 992 or 560. 16.50

Cat, sitting, detailed fur, looking to sinister. No. 254. 90mm. 65.00

Cat, squatting, wide grin. 105mm. 40.00

Dog, puppy begging. 68mm. 16.50

Labrador Puppy sitting, all legs forward. 80mm. 18.00

Dog, sitting with short turned down ears. No. 584. 67mm. 16.00

Dog, Terrier, looking out of kennel, inscribed: *Black Watch,* dog black. 55mm. 30.00

Donkey. 90mm. 120mm long.	65.00
Elephant with Howdah. 70mm.	30.00
Elephant, raised trunk. 103mm long.	22.00
Fish, open mouth. 112mm long.	10.00

Hare, sitting, one ear raised. 110mm. 45.00

Hare, sitting up. Pepper Pot. 106mm. 30.00

Lion, walking. No. 288. *Be Briton....* 135mm long. 30.00

Pig, alert ears. No. 199. 65mm long.	22.50
Pig, kneeling. 65mm long.	19.50
Pig, lying down. 80mm long.	17.00
Pig, standing. 70mm long.	19.00
Piglet, standing. 83mm long.	19.00

Rabbit, crouching with flat ears. No. 548. 30mm. 12.00

Rabbit, sitting. 80mm.	19.00
Seal. 50mm.	16.00

Animal jug, tail is handle. 70mm. 8.50

Birds (including Eggs)

Duck, swimming. 70mm long.	13.00
Hen, sitting, red comb. 93mm long.	9.50
Cockerel Pepper Pot, egg shaped.	
85mm.	10.00
Grotesque Bird. 100mm.	12.00
Owlet, plump. No. 549. 62mm.	18.50
Penguin. 75mm	20.00
Swan. 55mm long.	9.50
Cruet in form of pair of eggs	
in egg cups.	
70mm.	19.00
Pepper Pot, Egg in wooden	
egg cup.	
68mm.	pair 16.00

Great War

British Soldier, standing to attention,	
rifle touching hat. 135mm.	70.00
Sailor, standing with hands on hips.	
130mm	85.00
Bust of Sailor. Inscribed: *HMS*	
Queen Elizabeth. 90mm.	45.50
Monoplane with moveable	
propeller and pointed wings.	
No. 527.	
130mm long.	70.00
Zeppelin with revolving propeller.	
No. 567. 175mm long.	195.00
British Airship on stand. 130mm long.	40.00
Battleship, inscribed: *HMS Lion,*	
with 3 funnels, 168mm long.	110.00
Battleship, inscribed *HMS King*	
George V, with 2 funnels.	
168mm long.	110.00
Battleship, *HMS Queen Elizabeth.*	
165mm long.	90.00
Battleship, Queen Elizabeth.	
120mm long.	25.00
Torpedo Boat Destroyer, Model of.	
2 sizes:110mm long.	30.00
(Arcadian mould)	
140mm long.	170.00
(Savoy mould)	
Submarine, inscribed: *E1.*	
150mm long.	70.00
Submarine, inscribed: *E4.* 95mm.	29.50
Armoured Car with 2 guns.	
127mm long.	125.00
British Motor Searchlight, Model of	
90mm long.	175.00
This model is prone to firing	
flaws or sinking in the middle	
which would reduce its value.	
Red Cross Van. 110mm long.	40.00

Tank with 2 inset steering wheels,	
inscribed: *HMS Donner Blitzen*	
and *Model of British tank first used*	
by British troops at the Battle of	
Ancre Sept. 1916.	
2 sizes: 130mm long.	50.00
160mm long.	55.00
Tank, no wheels. 126mm wide.	45.00
Field Gun. Fishtail, 140mm long.	140.00
Howitzer.	
2 sizes: 140mm.	35.00
168mm long.	40.00
Machine gun, Model of, on tripod (2	
pieces). 80mm.	165.00
British Trench Mortar Gun.	
98mm long.	90.00
Land Mine. Similar to curling stone	
but with rectangular firing	
mechanism. No. 429. 52mm.	75.00
Mills Hand Grenade. 80mm.	30.00
Shell incribed: *Iron rations for Fritz.*	
78mm.	12.50
Balmoral Bonnet, model of, 70mm dia.	25.00
Glengarry.	
2 sizes: 70mm.	25.00
100mm long. (Ornate).	35.00
Larger model has coloured	
heather in band.	
Anzacs Cap, Model of, with maple	
leaf, impressed: *CANADA.*	
90mm long.	35.00
Colonial Soldiers Hat.	
90mm long.	25.00
Peaked Cap. No. 516.	
70mm long.	17.50
Pith Helmet or Solar Topee.	
80mm.	30.00
French Trench Helmet.	
84mm long.	50.00
RFC Cap. 80mm long.	85.00
Sailors Cap, *HMS Iron Duke.*	
70mm dia.	70.00
Tommy's Steel Helmet.	
82mm long.	40.00
Bell Tent, open flap. 64mm.	16.50
Fireplace, inscribed: *Keep the home*	
fires burning. 70mm.	19.50
Nurse Cavell, standing on plinth,	
holding bandage. 167mm.	125.00

Home/Nostalgic

Baby's Cradle. 55mm.	15.00
Grandfather Clock. 132mm.	14.50
Grandfather Clock *Nae man can*	
Tether Time nor Tide. 145mm.	18.00

Holdall. 95mm long.	17.00
Flat Iron and Trivet. 70mm long.	23.50
Jelly Mould. 55mm.	13.00
Lady in bonnet and muff,	
candlesnuffer. 80mm.	22.00
Pillar Box. 60mm.	16.00
Policeman's Lamp. 67mm.	16.00
Stool, 3-legged. 36mm.	9.00
Sundial on square base. 84mm.	5.50
Thimble. 57mm.	19.50
Watering Can, miniature.	
2 sizes: 50mm.	10.50
67mm.	10.50
Wheelbarrow. 114mm long.	10.50
Wooden Tub. 39mm.	6.00

Dutch Sabot. 75mm long.	6.00
Ladies 18th century Shoe.	7.50
Lancashire Clog. 85mm long.	6.00
Oriental Shoe with turned up toe.	
2 sizes: 88mm long.	11.00
107mm long.	11.50

Miniature Domestic

Cup and Saucer. 40mm.	5.00
Mug. 47mm.	4.00
Teapot with lid, melon shaped. 56mm.	12.00
Thistle Shaped Jug. 65mm.	5.00

Comic/Novelty

Felix the Cat on oval base. Black.	125.00
Hindu God on circular base wearing	
beads. No. 35. 88mm.	12.00
Policeman, hands behind back.	
No. 327. 113mm.	5.00

Cartoon/Comedy Characters

Winkie the Gladeye Bird. 65mm.	30.00
Winkie the Gladeye Bird cruet set,	
salt, pepper and mustard.	
68mm.	each 20.00
Can be found coloured.	each 30.00

Alcohol

Beer Bottle. 92mm.	7.50
Toby Jug. 60mm.	12.50

Sport/Pastimes

Curling Stone. 52mm.	24.50
Golf Club Head. 65mm.	25.00
Golf Ball on Tee. 60mm.	16.00

Musical Instruments

Banjo. 137mm long.	19.50
Double Bass. No. 306. 137mm long.	75.00

Transport

Open Motor Car.	40.00

Modern Equipment

Square Gramophone. 55mm.	35.00

Hats

Top Hat matchstiker. 45mm.	6.50

Footwear

Ankle Boot. 72mm long.	6.00
Boot. 58mm long.	6.00

Premier

Trademark used by a wholesaler on china manufactured by Taylor & Kent (Ltd), Florence Works, Longton. (Usual trademark Florentine).
For details of this china and manufacturer see Florentine China.
This china was made by the great mass producers of crested ware, Taylor & Kent. H. & M. Co. were probably a London firm of wholesalers, as crests are found from all over Britain but mostly from the South of England. A colour transfer has been found on china with this mark and one military crest has been recorded. 'Royal Military College, Camberley' (This must be the most common military crest - presumably everyone bought a souvenir of their stay there!) Domestic ware, including Bagware and 'smalls' are often found.

Premier Models
Ancient Artefacts
Fountains Abbey Cup. 48mm.	5.50
Leather Jack. 47mm.	5.50

Monuments (including Crosses)
Iona Cross. 108mm.	12.50

Traditional/National Souvenirs
Welsh Hat. 57mm.	8.00

Seaside Souvenirs
Lighthouse, open base. 105mm.	9.00
Whelk Shell. 94mm long.	7.00

Animals
Cheshire Cat *always smiling.* 87mm.	12.50
Manx Cat. 61mm.	30.00
Elephant, kneeling. 88mm long.	22.00
Fish. 120mm long.	9.00
Frog Jug. 50mm.	8.50
Pig, standing, inscribed: *The pig that won't go.* 95mm long.	20.00
Toad. 72mm long.	30.00

Birds (including Eggs)
Baby Bird Jug. 65mm.	8.50

Home/Nostalgic
Bellows. 107mm long.	16.50
Coal Bucket. 64mm.	7.00
Coal Scuttle, helmet shaped. 65mm.	8.00
Oriental Lamp. (Aladdin's Lamp). 100mm long.	10.00
Policeman's Lamp. 70mm.	16.00
Portmanteau. 77mm.	8.00
Shaving Mug. 60mm.	9.50
Watering Can. 68mm.	9.50

Musical Instruments
Tambourine. 70mm dia.	12.50

Footwear
Shoe, Ladies,18th Century. 95mm long.	8.50

Miniature Domestic
Coffee Pot with lid. 55mm.	9.50

Miscellaneous
Sack, tied with blue ribbon. 48mm.	8.00
Vase, dark red, black trim and handles. 85mm.	4.00

Princess China

Queen China

Trademark used for a Blackpool retailer probably by Wilhelm Kutzscher & Co., Schwarzenberg Porzellanfabrik, Schwarzenberg, Saxony. (This firm used several trademarks and produced a large number of German models just labelled; Germany, Saxony or foreign).

Princess Models
Buildings - White
Blackpool Tower, with buildings.
155mm.   16.00
Blackpool Tower, no buildings,
pierced 3 sides. 145mm.   16.00

Traditional/National Souvenirs
Blackpool, Big Wheel. 89mm.   18.50

Birds (including Eggs)
Bird standing on rock. 80mm.   12.00

Seaside Souvenirs
Lighthouse with pierced windows.
125mm.   8.50

Unknown German manufacturer's mark, possibly the product of a German prison where the inmates specialised in exporting souvenir ware to the English market to avoid competition with their own German potteries at home. The mark is very like those used by several German potters, especially HofMoschendorf (Bayern). Two models known:

Queen China Models
Home/Nostalgic
Watering Can. 44mm.   8.00

Domestic Wares
Napkin ring with a crest of Ripon.
50mm dia.   7.00
Small square dish, crest of Swanage.   4.00

Queen China

Queens China or Ware

Trademark used by an unknown manufacturer, possibly Taylor & Kent (Ltd),
Longton, as the only pieces recorded are
similar to Florentine.

Queen China Models
Birds
Baby Bird Cream Jug. 68mm.   8.50

Trademark used by Birks, Rawlins & Co
(Ltd), Vine Pottery, Stoke. (Usual
trademark Savoy). Pieces marked Queens
are usually seconds and have firing flaws,
only pristine wares carrying the Savoy
mark. Prices are the same as Savoy
however unless flaws are particularly
noticeable.
For further details of this china and
manufacturer see Savoy China.
Birks, Rawlins & Co. manufactured china
and earthenware and advertised Queens
China as a line of tableware. This mark is
found on much heavier models generally
than those marked Savoy so one can only
assume that this was a cheaper range. (The
lack of the usual initials B.R. & Co. seems
also to indicate that the firms were not
very proud of this range.) The mark
appears to have been used during the

same period as Savoy. Some of the models below have not been recorded in the Savoy range.
Pieces found named or with inscriptions when sold as Savoy were usually sold without them as Porcelle. Prices quoted in this section are therefore for items without inscriptions.
'Smalls' have been found with the same Great War commemorative inscriptions and crests as recorded on Savoy models, and the badge of the Royal Army Medical Corps. No other transfer devices or views have been found.
Stock numbers were used and do not coincide with Savoy stock numbers. (Birks & Rawlins use of stock numbers is often unreliable - see Savoy China for details.) Stock numbers are given where known in the following lists.

Queens Models
Ancient Artefacts

Chester Roman Vase. 60mm.	5.50
Glastonbury Bowl. 40mm.	5.50
Phoenician Vase. 85mm.	5.50
Puzzle Jug. 68mm.	7.50
Reading Silchester Vase, unnamed.	
No. 49. 55mm.	5.00
Shakespeare's Jug. 63mm.	6.00

Buildings - White

Burns Cottage. 70mm long.	17.50

Historical/Folklore

Burns Chair. 76mm.	11.50
Execution Block. 98mm long.	17.50
Mons Meg Cannon. 132mm long.	22.00
Rufus Stone. 100mm.	9.00

Traditional/National Souvenirs

Cornish Pasty. 104mm long.	12.50
Welsh Hat. 50mm.	10.50

Seaside Souvenirs

Bathing Machine. No. 425 and	
No. 428. 60mm.	16.50
Fisherman leaning into barrel of fish.	
67mm.	30.00
Lighthouse on rocky base.	
134mm.	12.50
Rowing Boat. 127mm long.	14.50
Oyster Shell dish. 80mm long.	6.50
Shell on base. 80mm long.	6.00
Sea Urchin Vase. 45mm.	5.50

Countryside

Beehive. 70mm.	16.50

Animals

Bear dancing, with muzzle.	
102mm.	80.00
Camel Jug, sitting with hexagonal	
opening on back. 80mm.	40.00
Cat, sitting, long necked, looped tail.	
No. 217. 106mm.	25.00
Cat, detailed fur. 80mm.	20.00
Cat, Manx. 80mm.	30.00
Bulldog, standing. 138mm long.	30.00
Dog, angry and barking.	
100mm long.	30.00
Dog, looking out of kennel. No. 259.	
55mm.	25.00
Elephant with Howdah. No. 228.	
76mm long.	30.00
Fish. 102mm long.	8.00
Puffer Fish vase. 90mmm.	12.00
Frog, realistic, giant-size.	
73mm long.	65.00
Grotesque Animal Jug. No. 555. 72mm.	9.50
Grotesque Animal. 100mm.	10.00
Hare. 74mm.	40.00
Lion, walking. No. 889. 137mm long.	22.00
Lion, sitting on base. (This was	
Originally designed by Alfred	
Stevens for the British Museum).	
105mm.	35.00
Pig, lying down. 80mm long.	20.00
Pig, sitting, large. No. 549.	
100mm long.	24.50
Pig, standing. 65mm long.	19.50
Seal. No. 541. 55mm long.	16.00

Birds (including Eggs)

Baby Bird jug. 70mm.	8.50
Bird on tree trunk. 82mm.	23.00
Duck, swimming. 40mm high,	
66mm long.	13.00
Duck's head feeding bottle.	
130mm long.	17.00
Penguin. No. 459. 83mm.	20.00
Swan, detailed. 74mm long.	9.00

Great War

Highland Infantryman, standing.	
160mm.	190.00
Zeppelin with double bladed	
revolving propeller, without	
inscription. 175mm long.	160.00
Submarine. E1, without inscription.	
149mm long.	35.00

Tank. 152mm long.	45.00
Tank. No. 651. 132mm long.	40.00
Red Cross Van. 108mm long.	40.00
Ambulance, with Rolls Royce front.	
115mm long.	75.00
Armoured Car. 125mm long.	125.00
British Motor Searchlight. No. 665.	
100mm long.	145.00
This model is prone to firing	
flaws or sinking in the middle	
which would reduce its value.	
Field Gun, with fish tail.	
140mm long. (scarce).	125.00
Field Gun, with screen.	29.50
Machine Gun on tripod, two-piece.	
80mm.	145.00
British Trench Mortar Gun.	
110mm long.	80.00
Howitzer. 145mm long.	35.00
Hand Grenade. 88mm.	30.00
Shell. 70mm. No. 556.	9.50
Can also be salt pot.	
Shell Pepper Pot. No. 662. 80mm.	9.00
Balmoral Bonnet. 70mm long.	27.00
R.F.C. Cap. 72mm long.	65.00
Colonial Hat. 92mm long.	25.00
French Trench Helmet. No. 569.	
72mm long.	50.00
Glengarry. No. 610. 70mm long.	22.00
Officer's Peaked Cap.	
72mm long.	17.00
New Zealand Hat. No. 612.	
83mm long.	30.00
Sailors Cap. No. 533. 70mm.	60.00
Bandsman's Drum. 55mm dia.	12.50
Fireplace. No. 629. 95mm.	20.00

Home/Nostalgic

Baby Boy, sitting, grinning. 73mm.	14.00
Dog Kennel. 55mm.	12.50
Grandfather Clock, narrow design.	
149mm.	22.00
Pillar Box. 60mm.	14.00
Pillar Box 'ER'. 110mm.	25.00
Suitcase, closed. 96mm long.	13.00
Watering Can. 80mm.	10.50

Comic/Novelty

Hindu God. No. 550. 90mm.	12.50
Humpty Dumpty salt and pepper	
pots. 80mm.	pair 60.00
Man's Head Teapot, spout coming	
out of mouth. 60mm.	18.00
Policeman holding truncheon.	
105mm.	50.00

Cartoon/Comedy Characters

Bonzo, not named. 118mm.	55.00
Toby Jug, large hat. 75mm.	12.50

Sport/Pastimes

Cricket Bat. 120mm.	75.00
Golf Caddie with bag of clubs on	
heart shaped pin tray/ashtray.	
80mm.	50.00
Golf Club Head. 80mm.	25.00
Curling Stone, not named. 53mm.	20.00

Musical Instruments

Banjo. 136mm long.	19.50
Piano, upright, open keyboard.	
94mm long.	22.50

Footwear

Clog. 75mm long.	6.00
Lancashire Clog. No. 485.	
95mm.	7.00

Miniature Domestic

Cheese Dish and Lid, on of two	
pieces. 55mm long.	9.00

Domestic

Cone Candlesnuffer. 62mm.	6.00
Match holder, circular, rope base	
for striking matches. 55mm.	10.00

Queens Crest China

Trademark used for S.P. & Co Ltd. of 57 King St, Manchester, by Arkinstall & Son Ltd. Arcadian Works, Stoke-on-Trent, (usual trademark Arcadian), and Wiltshaw and Robinson, Carlton Works, Stoke-on-Trent, (usual trademark Carlton).
For details of this china and manufacturer see Arcadian China and Carlton China. As models with this mark have been found with crests from all over Great Britain, and also of Paris, one must assume that S.P. & Co. Ltd. of Manchester was a wholesaler. (Possibly some wares printed with this mark would also have been used by Arkinstall to supply other retailers if they had production problems.)
Arkinstall produced a range for this firm that was much finer and more carefully finished than their own Arcadian range. Most items found with this mark are 'smalls', some of which may well be un-named ancient artefacts. The models recorded indicate that the mark was used before the Great War, several pieces have been found with the crest 'La Ville-de-

Paris' and the addition to the mark of 'Importe D'Angleterre'. However, one small has been found with a transfer of RMS *Hebrides*, similar to those used by the Carlton factory.
Numbering System. Stock numbers found on Queens Crest models do not coincide with Arcadian numbers. Queens Crest was obviously offered as a completely separate range. Stock numbers where known are given in the following lists.

Queens Crest Models
Parian/Unglazed
Bust Albert, King of the Belgians.
153mm.   70.00

Ancient Artefacts
Colchester Vase. No. 504. 50mm.   5.50
Dorchester Jug, inscribed: *Model of
old jug found in North Square,
Dorchester.* No. 1774. 52mm.   5.50
Fountains Abbey Cup. No. 23821.
50mm.   5.50
Glastonbury Bowl, inscribed: *Bowl
from the Ancient British Lake Village
near Glastonbury.* No. 1724. 40mm.   5.50
Hastings Kettle, inscribed *Model of
Ancient Kettle Dredged up near
Hastings in Hastings Museum.* 60mm. 5.50
Irish Bronze Pot. No. 1834. 45mm.   5.50
Jersey Milk Can and lid. No. 3424.
60mm.   6.00
Lincoln Jack from original in museum.
No. 1564. 65mm.   5.50
Loving Cup, 3-handled. 40mm.   6.00
Newbury Bottle, inscribed: *Leather
bottle found at Newbury 1644 on
Battlefield now in museum.*
No. 2294. 65mm.   5.50
Silchester Vase, inscribed *Model of
vase from Silchester in Reading
Museum.*   5.50

Animals
Bear and Ragged Staff. 90mm.   50.00
Manx Cat, sitting. 63mm long.   30.00
Elephant, Indian. 77mm long.   20.00
Elephant with howdah. No. 228.   30.00
Lion, sitting (British Museum).
2 sizes: 45mm.   30.00
105mm.   35.00
Pig, standing, inscribed: *Wunt be
druv.* 84mm long.   20.00
Tortoise. 72mm long.   14.00

Miniature Domestic
Bag Vase. 45mm.   4.00

Numbered Ornamental Wares
Some of these could be unnamed
    ancient artefacts.
    Value £4.00 each.
No. 594. Fluted jug. 54mm.   4.00
    No. 1724. Small pot on three feet.
    This is also the number of a
    Glastonbury bowl - see above.
    43mm.   4.00
No. 1824. Ewer. 60mm.   4.00
No. 3164. Pot. 50mm.   4.00
No. 3594. Vase. 50mm.   4.00
No. 3884. Vase. 54mm.   4.00
No. 7061. Vase. 65mm.   4.00
No. 14715. Vase, with narrow neck.
    100mm.   4.00
No. 32012 Narrow neck vase. 60mm.   4.00

Queeny China

No details of mark available.

Mark used by an unknown manufacturer for
an agent in Hastings.

**Queeny China Model
Buildings - White**
Cottage. 70mm long. Bears the arms
    of Hastings.   12.00

Raleigh China

Miniature Domestic

Cheese Dish and cover, one piece.	9.50
45mm.	9.50
Cheese Dish and cover, two piece.	
55mm.	9.00

Domestic

Candlestick. 105mm.	8.00

"RALEIGH CHINA"

Trademark used for a retailer by Sampson
Hancock (and Sons), Bridge Works, Stoke
and later at the Garden Works, Hanley
(renamed Corona Pottery). (Usual
trademark Corona).

Raleigh China Models
Historical/Folklore

Ark. 92mm long.	7.00

Traditional/National Souvenirs

Welsh Hat. No. 198. 45mm.	8.00

Seaside Souvenirs

Bathing Machine. 70mm.	16.00

Great War

Submarine, inscribed: E4.	29.50
Tank, with inset wheels.	
2 sizes: 103mm.	25.00
160mm long.	30.50
Red Cross Van. 100mm long.	40.00
Field Gun. 125mm long.	35.00
Bell Tent, open flap. 80mm.	22.00

Modern Equipment

Gas Stove. 70mm.	13.00

Musical Instruments

Upright Piano. 60mm.	22.00

Footwear

Lancashire Clog. 102mm long.	7.50

Ramshorn

R&M

Trademark used by Hewitt and Leadbeater (usual trademark Willow Art), or possibly the retailer's mark.

For details of this china see Willow Art China.

Ramshorn Model
Animals
Elephant, walking. No. 113. 75mm long. 20.00

Trademark used by Roper & Meredith, Garfield Pottery, Longton. The china is similar to Leadbeater Art.

Roper & Meredith was established in 1913 and manufactured earthenwares until 1924, when the firm went out of business. This firm, like most other manufacturers, would have turned to crested models during the Great War, when skilled labour needed to make tableware was in short supply. The firm did not advertise as makers of crested china and it would be correct to assume that this was a small side line. The models recorded are however very interesting and not just copies of other manufacturers wares. R & M also made a range of unglazed busts of poets, composers and other historic personalities.

R & M Models
Animals
Bulldog, Staffordshire, long neck, green eyes, red mouth.
113mm high. 25.00

Birds (including Eggs)
Bird, with open wings.
75mm long. 12.50
Chicken, standing, separate feet.
80mm. 12.50

Great War
March War Memorial. Unglazed.
174mm. 175.00
St. Ives War Memorial Cross.
135mm. 175.00

Comic/Novelty
Truck of Coal, inscribed: *Black
Diamonds*. Black coal. 79mm long.   40.00

Sport/Pastimes
Cricket Cap. 67mm dia.   50.00
Rugby Player, holding rugby ball,
on oval ashtray. Inscribed: *Play
up*. Fully coloured. 126mm.   125.00

Domestic
Candlestick. 128mm.   9.00

Raphael China

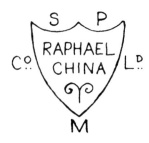

Trademark used for S.P. & Co. Ltd. of 57 King
St, Manchester, by Arkinstall & Son Ltd.
Arcadian Works, Stoke-on-Trent. (Usual
trademark Arcadian).

A range of vases were produced with
Raphael Tuck cartoons and verses. The
name RAPHAEL CHINA appearing with
Raphael Tuck cartoons seems more than a
coincidence.
The only other items known are smalls with
either printed decorations or the crests of
Russia, Canada, Sweden, Switzerland or
Austria. (Spelt that way so not for export).

Raphael Models
Ancient Artefacts
Canterbury Ewer, inscribed: *Model
of Roman Ewer found near
Canterbury and now in Canterbury
Museum*. No. 94. 62mm.   5.50
Kendal Jug. 76mm.   5.50

Alcohol
Highland Whisky Bowl, Model of.
No. 4158. 90mm dia.   6.50

Domestic
Lip Salve Pot, inscribed *Deeds are
Fruits words are but leaves*. 35mm.   18.00

Miscellaneous
Vases decorated with Raphael Tuck
cartoons.   each 20.00

Real English China

Can be found without the box surround. Trademark used by Hewitt & Leadbeater (usual trademark Willow Art).

Real English China Models
Buildings - White
Cottage not named. 60mm.   10.00

Animals
Collie Dog, sitting with shield. 76mm. 16.00

Home/Nostalgic
Anvil. 60mm.   7.00
Watering Can. 77mm.   8.00

Regency Ware

Mark can sometimes be found without the 'S' after the initials 'J.B.'

Trademark used for a retailer by Sampson Hancock (& Sons), Bridge Works, Stoke. (Usual trademark Corona).
For details of this china and manufacturer see The Corona China.
The above Regency garter mark is identical to the Grosvenor mark used by Sampson Hancock with the addition of the initials. Some of the models listed below were made by Hancocks for other wholesalers including CEB.L. (see Alexandra China) so it seems probable that Hancocks used this mark for another wholesaler during the Great War.

Regency Models
Buildings - White
Model of Clifton Suspension Bridge.
   120mm long.   75.00

Seaside Souvenirs
Bathing Machine. 75mm.   14.50
Houseboat. 87mm long.   8.00
Lighthouse on Rocky Base.
   125mm.   8.50

Animals
Cat, sitting with ruff of fur round
   neck. 100mm.   29.50
Cat, standing. 60mm.   16.00
Cat, Manx standing. 60mm.   30.00
Pig, standing. 85mm long.   20.00

Great War

Airship. 153mm long.	35.00
Flash Lamp. 85mm.	11.00
Ghurka Knife. 140mm long.	22.00
Bell Tent. No. 209. 84mm.	16.50
Military Drum. 50mm.	12.50

Home/Nostalgic

Cigarette Case. 70mm.	13.00
Tobacco Pouch. 72mm long.	9.50

Musical Instruments

Banjo. 140mm long.	17.00

Modern Equipment

Gas Cooker. 68mm.	13.00
Gramophone, square cabinet, no horn. 85mm.	25.00

Sport/Pastimes

Pawn, chess piece. 90mm.	25.00

Footwear

Lancashire Clog. 86mm long.	7.00

Miniature Domestic

Jardinière on fixed stand. No. 214 80mm.	8.00
Tea Pot with lid. 72mm.	10.50

Regent China

REGENT
CHINA

Trademark used by Wilhelm Kutzscher & Co., Schwarzenberg (usual trademark Saxony).

Regent China Model
Seaside Souvenirs

Lighthouse, with windows. 123mm.	9.00

Animals

Cat on drum. 90mm.	16.00

Regis

REGIS

Trademark used by Hewitt Bros, Willow Potteries, Longton. (Usual trademark Willow Art).
For details of this china and manufacturer see Willow Art China.
Models found with this mark have crests from all over Great Britain, but many pieces have crests from Jersey, Ireland and Scotland. It seems very probable that the mark was offered to retailers in these areas as an alternative to Willow Art. Many 'Weymouth' crests have also been recorded and why this seaside resort and port should have been sold 'Regis' is a mystery (Did the Willow traveller stay in Weymouth on his way to Jersey and manage to get an order from a local retailer? It is possible the name 'Regis' derived from Weymouth and Melcombe Regis.) The mark seems to have been used for some time; from before the Great War until the early Twenties. No view ware, commemoratives or transfer devices have been recorded with this mark.
Numbering system. Where stock numbers are found they are the same as Willow Art models. Stock numbers where known are listed below.

Regis Models
Parian/Unglazed
Bust of Lord Beatty. 165mm.   55.00
Bust of *Burns.* 157mm.   40.00
Bust of *Scott.* 140mm.   30.00

Buildings - White
Weymouth Jubilee Clock Tower.
126mm.   20.00

Monuments (including Crosses)
Burns Statue. 166mm.   35.00
Highland Mary statue. 155mm.   35.00

Historical/Folklore
Mary Bull holding black cat in basket. Standing figure. (Mary Bull was a witch!) 105mm.   50.00
Mary Queen of Scots Chair, Edinburgh Castle, Model of. No. 163. 75mm.   10.50
Mons Meg Cannon. 138mm long.   20.00

Traditional/National Souvenirs
Bagpipes. 120mm long.   50.00
Souter Johnny sitting on chair on square base. 133mm.   30.00
Welsh Hat. 58mm.   8.00
Dutch Girl. 78mm.   16.50
Dutch Boy. 78mm.   16.50

Seaside Souvenirs
Lifeboat, coloured ropes.
118mm long.   16.50
Lifeboatman. 113mm.   16.00
Lighthouse, not named. 100mm.   8.00
Corbiere Lighthouse, with coloured rock base. 100mm.   26.00

Animals
Bear. 75mm.   50.00
Cat, sitting, candlesnuffer. 56mm.   22.00
Cat with bow, standing. 85mm.   22.50
Cat, chubby & standing. 70mm.   22.00
Cow with gilded horns, sitting looking left. 140mm long.   60.00
Dog, Collie, standing. 85mm.   30.00
Dog, Labrador, standing.
90mm long.   24.50
Dog, Scottie, wearing a glengarry, some colouring on hat. 85mm.   17.50
Elephant with hunter and two Indian riders on back. 90mm.   40.00
Pig, standing, fat, ears pointing forward. 80mm long.   20.00
Rabbit, erect ears. 60mm long.   9.00
Shetland Pony. A *Native of Shetland.* 113mm long.   40.00

Birds (including Eggs)
Swan Posy Holder. 65mm long.   7.00

Great War

Sailor, standing. *Our Brave Defender.*	
130mm.	70.00
Airship, *Beta.* 80mm long.	90.00
Battleship. *HMS Lion.*	
140mm long.	40.00
British Tank. 92mm long.	22.00
British Tank with trailing wheels.	
127mm long.	22.50
Red Cross Van. No. 812. 84mm long.	40.00
Cannon Shell salt pot. 83mm.	9.00
Kit Bag with verse: *Pack up your*	
troubles in your old kit bag.	
74mm.	24.50
Forage Cap. 83mm long.	20.00
Officers Peaked Cap. 75mm long.	20.00
Cenotaph. 145mm.	10.50
Black Watch Memorial. 182mm.	75.00
Florence Nightingale Statue,	
inscribed: *Florence Nightingale*	
1820-1910. 160mm.	22.00
Weymouth War Memorial. 152mm.	100.00

Home/Nostalgic

Anvil. 76mm.	7.50
Bucket, rope handle. 65mm.	6.00
Coal Scuttle. 55mm.	7.00
Grandfather Clock, inscribed: *'Make*	
use of time let not advantage slip'.	
145mm.	16.50
Pillar Box. 90mm.	17.50
Shaving Mug. 55mm.	9.50
Sundial. 95mm.	9.00

Comic/Novelty

Billiken. 73mm.	8.50
Billiken, the God of Luck, sitting on	
high backed chair. 100mm.	12.50

Cartoon/Comedy Characters

Baby, standing to attention, some	
colouring. Inscribed: *One of the*	
B'hoys. 160mm.	40.00
Baby, standing with arms outstretched.	
Some colouring to face. 110mm.	30.00
Mr. Pussyfoot. 98mm.	45.00

Alcohol

Toby Jug. 83mm.	16.50

Miniature Domestic

Cheese dish & lid. 70mm long.	9.00

Miscellaneous

Hand holding tulip. 80mm.	7.00

Registry Ware

Trademark used by an unknown manufacturer.

This mark has been found with Scarborough crests on the curved sided lip salve pot and the small vases listed below.

Vase inscribed: *Ca' Canny but ca'*	
awa. 45mm.	10.00
Vase.	4.00
Lip Salve Pot, curved.	6.00

C.L. Reis Co.

Pig, standing, inscribed: *Want be
 druv.* 70mm long.   20.00
Terrapin, 90mm long.   22.00

Birds (including Eggs)
Penguin. 95mm.   30.00

Footwear
Oriental Shoe. 105mm long.   7.00

Miscellaneous
Basket. No. 240.   6.00
Vase inscribed: *Shamrocks from the
 Dear Emerald Isle.* (Carlton
 mould).   6.50

C.L. Reis is probably a retailer, trademark
being used on porcelain mainly with Irish
crests although Glasgow has also been
found. (It seems likely that the china was
manufactured by Alfred B. Jones & Sons
Ltd. - usual trademark Grafton). The
porcelain is much greyer than Grafton
although typical Grafton shapes.

C.L. Reis Models
Ancient Artefacts
Butter Pot, not named. 40mm.   5.50

Seaside Souvenirs
Whelk Shell. 82mm long.   7.00

Animals
Pig, sitting, inscribed: *Wun't be
 druv.* 60mm high. 93mm long.
No. 341.   30.00

Reliance Art China

Rex China

REX
CHINA

Trademark used by Hewitt & Leadbeater Ltd., Willow Potteries, Longton (usual trademark Willow Art).

For details of this manufacturer and china see Willow Art.

Reliance Art Models
Animals
Rabbit. 60mm long.   12.00

Miniature Domestic
Miniature Cheese Dish & Cover.   9.00

The above trademark was used by Moschendorf, Hof, Bavaria but the pieces listed below were produced by an unknown British manufacturer, possibly Florentine or Savoy.

Rex Models
Ancient Artefacts
Highland Cuach. 60mm long.   6.00
Puzzle Jug. 73mm.   7.00
Southwold Vase. 85mm.   5.00

Traditional/National Souvenirs
Tam-o'shanter. 72mm dia.   25.00

Animals
Pig, ears pointing forward.
    68mm long.   22.00

Countryside
Pail, loop handle. 75mm.   6.00
Milk Churn and lid. 75mm.   7.00

Miniature Domestic
Cheese Dish, with gilded rope
    handle. 70mm.   9.50

RH & SL Plant

Rialto China

For all details of this china and manufacturer, see Tuscan China.

1920-6

Trademark used by British Art Pottery Co. (Fenton) Ltd. Rialto Works, High Street, Fenton. Resembles Carlton China.
This small firm was established in 1920 and manufactured china.
Although the 'Rialto' mark was registered and the firm appeared in the list of manufacturers, they did not advertise and one can only guess from the name of the firm that they produced novelty wares. The firm went into voluntary liquidation in May 1926, so could have only produced crested china between 1920 and 1926.
Some domestic ware has been found with the mark and one coloured transfer view of 'Plas Newydd' has been recorded.

Rialto Models
Ancient Artefacts
Salisbury Kettle. 88mm.   5.50

Seaside Souvenirs
Beachy Head Lighthouse.
   105mm.   9.00
   Unnamed.   7.50
Dolphin supporting sea shell.
   85mm.   20.00

Countryside
Milk Churn. 78mm.   8.00

Animals
Bulldog in kennel, inscribed: *The*
Black Watch. 79mm.   22.00
Bulldog can be found coloured
black.   30.00
Cat, comical, sitting with red bow,
head on one side, winking. 130mm. 30.00

Great War
Battleship with inscription: *Great*
War 1914-1918. The German Fleet
surrendered 74 warships Nov 21st
1918. 153mm long.   35.00
Pair of Fieldglasses. 70mm.   30.00

Home/Nostalgic
Watchman's Lamp.   8.00
Ornate carved wooden Chair.
110mm.   12.50

Ribblesdale China

"RIBBLESDALE" CHINA
ENGLISH MANUFACTURE
GIBSON & HOWORTH
13 FISHERGATE
PRESTON

Trademark used by an unknown English
manufacturer for the Lancashire market.
Only a few pieces have been recorded so far.

Shoes
Pointed Sabot. 100mm long.   7.00

Miniature Domestic
Fairy Cup & saucer. 41mm.   6.00
One-handled mug. 39mm.   5.00
Two-handled vase. 65mm.   5.00
Jug. 73mm.   5.00

Eugene Rimmel

Rita China Series

```
"RITA"
CHINA SERIES
L & L
W. S. MARE
```

Trademark used by Wiltshaw and Robinson Ltd., Carlton Works, Stoke-on-Trent.

The only piece recorded is a small, 78mm., scent bottle known with a Brighton crest and metal screw top. Rimmel was a perfumier of great repute in the mid 19th century.   22.50

Trademark used for the retailer L & L of Weston-Super-Mare   by   unknown manufacturers. All recorded crests are from Somerset.

The models recorded are not recognisably made by any well known manufacturer. Hewitt and Leadbeater (see Willow Art), Taylor & Kent (see Florentine China) and Wileman & Co. (see Shelley China) made some similar models. It is possible that several manufacturers used the same retailer's mark. A cream jug has been found bearing a Sutherland Art mark in addition to the RITA mark above.

Rita Models
Unglazed/Parian
Robert Blake Statue, unglazed. 170mm. 90.00
Bunyan Statue. 125mm.   29.50
Burns, bust, on circular unglazed
  base. 176mm.   30.00
Rt. Hon. D. Lloyd George, on square
  unglazed base. 192mm.   45.00
Scott, bust, on circular unglazed
  base. 176mm.   30.00

Ancient Artefacts
Loving cup, 2 handled.   6.00

Buildings - White
Clock Tower, Triangle, Clevedon.
  135mm.   80.00
Ann Hathaway's Cottage. 55mm long.   16.00
The Folly, Pontypool. 80mm.   125.00
Glastonbury Tor. 83mm.   45.00
Llangynwyd Church. 107mm long.   110.00

Monuments (including Crosses)

Drake Statue. 160mm.	25.00
Great Rock of Ages, Burrington Coombe, Near Cheddar, Somerset, with verses of hymn. 125mm.	22.00
King Alfred Statue. 160mm.	50.50

Historical/Folklore

Burns Chair, Model of. 88mm.	12.50
James V Chair Stirling Castle.	14.50
Leominster Ducking Stool (2 piece). 123mm long.	75.00
Mary Queen of Scots Chair, Edinburgh Castle, Model of. 85mm.	14.50

Animals

Dog, sitting with bow. 75mm.	17.00
Dog, Staffordshire Bull Terrier. 115mm.	20.50
Cat, long neck, features coloured. 110mm.	12.50
Fish. 115mm long.	9.00

Birds (including Eggs)

Bird posy holder, tiny. 57mm long.	8.50
Duck posy holder, yellow beak. 74mm long.	12.00

Great War

Florence Nightingale Statue. 1820-1910. 180mm.	30.00

Home/Nostalgic

Grandfather Clock, inscribed: *Make use of time, let not advantage slip. Shakespeare.* 145mm.	16.50

Comic/Novelty

Clown, bust.	19.50
Jester, double faced bust, inscribed: *Awake Asleep.*	30.00
Monk, jovial & plump. No glass. No. 95. 90mm.	20.00

Alcohol

Toby Jug. 95mm.	12.50

Sport/Pastimes

Castle chess piece. 48mm.	8.50

Modern Equipment

Horn Gramophone. 90mm.	30.00

Hats

Cricket Cap. 65mm long.	50.00
Straw Boater. 85mm long.	14.50

Footwear

Dutch Sabot. 85mm long.	7.00
Lancashire Clog. 87mm long.	8.50

Domestic

Egg Cup.	
2 sizes: 55mm.	7.00
68mm.	8.50

Miniature Domestic

Tea Pot with lid, ball-shaped. 78mm.	10.50

Robertson Art China

Robinson & Leadbeater

Mark used by an unknown British manu-facturer, probably Wiltshaw and Robinson Ltd (usual trademark Carlton).

One small Bagware Jug, 80mm high has been recorded.

5.00

Impressed mark, also found printed.

used before 1906.

Lead was found to be unhealthy so a leadless glaze was introduced, mainly for tableware.

Trademarks used by Robinson & Leadbeater, Wolfe Street, Stoke-on-Trent and subsequently a branch of J.A. Robinson Ltd.

Robinson & Leadbeater was established in 1850 and specialised in the production of Parian statuary imitation antique ivory and Ecclesiastical statuary. R & L busts are exceedingly popular with Parian collectors, the firm having made a large and well produced range, including busts of heroes (of the South African War), Royalty, Celebrities and literary figures. These busts were obviously made before the craze for crested china and cannot be considered to be 'crested china' and are therefore not listed here. The firm became insolvent in 1904, no explanation was given, but possibly one of the partners died. Robinson & Leadbeater was taken over by Harold Taylor Robinson (see Arcadian China) in 1906, and was formed into a Limited Company, Robinson & Leadbeater Ltd in 1908. In 1910 the firm became a branch of J.A. Robinson Ltd.

It is probable that the small amount of crested china found marked R & L was produced after 1904. Some R & L moulds including busts are found over-stamped 'Arcadian'. The mark was not used after 1924.

Several transfer prints have been found, including a colour transfer of a battleship on a shallow bagware bowl, a Nelson commemorative and a Hereford Red Coat man. (No numbering system appears to have been used.)

R & L Models
Parian Busts

A large range of parian and small busts were produced but as none of these carry coats of arms they should not really be listed in this book but I do so for the convenience of collectors.

The following busts are all white unglazed parian and are between 150mm - 200mm in height, with a few exceptions, and are mounted on square bases unless otherwise stated.

Alexandra, Princess (dated 1897, jewelled orders on dress). 223mm.
Alexandra, Queen (dated 1901, maple leaf motif on dress. 235mm, socle base). 235mm.
Apollo. 198mm.
Bach. 190mm.
Baden-Powell (by Lawton 16 Jan 1900). 215mm.
Balfour A.J. 200mm.
Beethoven. 188mm.
Bismarck. 188mm.
Booth, Gen. 198mm.
Bright. 165mm.161mm.
Browning. 198mm.
Buller, Gen (by Lawton 30 Oct 1899). 203mm.
Burns. 155mm.
Byron (with embroidered smock). 198mm.
Byron (with open neck shirt, waistcoat & drape). 180mm.
Carlyle. 192mm.
Chamberlain, Joseph. 200mm.
Child (with narrow hair band & curly locks). 198mm.
Chopin. 198mm.
Christ (without thorns). 195mm.
Clarence, HRH Duke of. 198mm.
Clark, Rev F E (by Lawton 20 Apr 1903). 198mm.
Clytie 195mm.
Collins. (Gen Michael, in uniform). 195mm.
Cooper, Rev J J (by Lawton 9 Jul 1900). 198mm.
Cromwell. 195mm.
Dante. 203mm.
Darwin. 192mm.
Derby, Rt. Hon. Earl. 358mm.
Diana. 198mm.
Dickens. 191mm.
Disraeli. 198mm.
Edward VII (younger head. This same model originally produced as Prince or Wales dated 1897). 194mm.

Edward VII (older head. By Lawton 9 Nov 1901). 198mm.
Emerson. 198mm.
French, Gen (by Lawton 2 Mar 1900). 205mm.
Garfield, President. 192mm.
Garrett, Rev C (by Lawton 24 Oct 1905). 177mm.
Gladstone (older head). 200mm.
Gladstone (younger head. Similar to above Bust but face is less lined, Head has more hair on back and sides. Bow tied differently). 198mm.
Goethe. 190mm.
Gordon, Gen. 200mm.
Gounod. 190mm.
Grace, W G. 202mm.
Grant, U.S. 228mm.
Hahnemann.
Halle, Sir Charles. 205mm.
Handel. 192mm.
Hathaway, Anne. 158mm.
Haydn. 188mm.
Hermes. 190mm.
Holmes, O W. 203mm.
Holyoake.185mm.
Huxley, T H. 200mm.
Irving, Sir Henry. 193mm.
Johnson, Dr. (by Lawton 8 Mar 1905). 182mm.
Kipling. 203mm.
Kitchener, Lord (younger head). 188mm.
Kitchener, Lord (older head. By Lawton 9 Feb 1900). 203mm.
Laidlaw, A ("L. pool 1895"). 375mm.
Lawson, Sir W (by Lawton 27 Aug 1903). 189mm.
Leo XIII, Pope. 220mm.
Lincoln, Abraham. 190mm.
Longfellow. 198mm.
MacDonald, Gen (by Lawton 6 Mar 1900). 198mm.
McKinley, President. 195mm.
Manning, Cardinal (younger version with cross). 188mm.
Manning, Cardinal (older version without cross). 200mm.
Mary, Queen of Scots. 203mm.
Maxwell, William. 278mm, socle base. 275mm.
May, Princess. 215mm.
Mendelssohn. 190mm.
Mercury. 205mm.
Milton. 188mm.
Mitchell, J T W. 238mm, socle base.
Moore, Tom. 198mm.
Mozart. 192mm.
Napoleon. 198mm.
Neale, E V. 195mm.

Nelson. 188mm.
Newman, Cardinal. 195mm.
Paderewski. 204mm.
Parker, Joseph, D D. 200mm.
Parnell, Charlers Stewart. 190mm.
Patti, Adelina. 226mm.
Pio Nono (Pope Pius IX). 316mm.
Pitman, Sir Isaac (270mm on separate square base. By Brock "London 1887").
Rhodes, Cecil. 203mm.
Roberts, Lord (by Lawton Jan 1900). 200mm.
Rosebery, Lord. 198mm.
Rubinstein. 200mm.
Ruskin. 205mm.
Salisbury, Lord. 198mm.
Sarasate. 200mm.
Schiller. 185mm.
Schumann. 194mm.
Scott, Sir Walter. 195mm.
Shakespeare. 158mm & 195mm.
Shakespeare (On cushion. Tomb figure. Coloured 140mm. Dated 14 Sept 1900). 140mm.
Shakespeare (Tomb Figure). 205mm.
Shelley. 202mm.
Spurgeon. 188mm.
Stanley. 190mm.
Sullivan, Sir Arthur. 198mm.
Sumner, Charles. 330mm, socle base.
Tennyson. 192mm.
Thackeray. 175mm.
Unknown Gentleman. 360mm.
Venus de Medici. 195mm.
Venus de Milo. 198mm.
Venus Genetrix. 210mm.
Victoria, Queen (without crown 'Jubilee 1887'. 195mm.)
Victoria, Queen (with crown 'Jubilee 1887'. 203mm.
Victoria, Queen (with crown '60th Year of Reign' older face than above busts). 230mm.
Victoria, Queen (without crown). 155mm.
Virgin Mary. 190mm.
Wagner (with hat). 200mm.
Wagner (without hat). 188mm.
Wales, Prince of (see Edward VII).
Wales, Princess of (later Queen Mary, by Lawton 3 Mar 1902). 195mm.
Washington. 255mm.
Wellington, Duke of. 195mm.
Wesley, John. 192mm.
White, Gen (by Lawton 24 Feb 1900). 203mm.
Wilson, Prof John. 318mm.
York, Duke of (Later George V). 210mm.

Ancient Artefacts
Chester Roman Vase. No. 170.
  2 sizes:
  63mm and 76mm.   5.50
  Greek Vase 200 years B.C. No. 173. 65mm. 5.50
  Loving Cup, 2 handled. 45mm.   6.00
  Loving Cup, 3 handled. 39mm.   6.00
  Oxford Jug. 83mm.   5.50
  Peterborough Tripod. 37mm.   6.00
  Scarborough Jug inscribed Jug about
    600 years old found in acient moat
    Scarboro (sic). No. 180. 42mm.   5.50

Buildings - Coloured
Mason Croft, the house of Miss Marie
  Corelli.
  2 sizes: 75mm long.   85.00
          90mm long.   95.00
Shakespeares Cottage.
  40mm long.   30.00

Seaside Souvenirs
Scallop Shell on two small feet.
  2 sizes: 73mm dia.   6.00
          110mm dia.   8.00
Scallop Shell on 3 tiny feet.
  120mm long.   8.00

Birds (including Eggs)
Egg flower holder. 80mm long.   10.00
Swan posy holder with yellow beak
and feet. 70mm.   12.00

Home/Nostalgic
Bellows. 105mm long.   12.50
Thimble salt pot. 37mm.   12.50

Miniature Domestic
Cheese Dish and cover.
  80mm long.   9.50
Tea pot with lid, thistle knob on lid.
  100mm.   13.00
Bagware Tea pot. No. 158. 98mm.   12.50

Domestic
Match holder, circular, unglazed.
  No. 143. 76mm dia.   7.00

Pin Tray, crinkle edged.
  75mm diamter.   6.00

Trinket box and lid, oval, with floral
  decoration in relief. 115mm.   12.50

Rococco

Trademark used by C. Schmidt and Co.
Carlsbad (Bohemia). The only shapes seen
are very white, hard-past porcelain, decorated with ornate gold and green pattern
with pink roses.

Rococco Model
Puff Box and lid, round, 68mm dia.   8.50
Trinket Box and lid rectangular.
  88mm long.   8.50

Roman Bath China

Trademark used for a retailer by Hewitt & Leadbeater, Willow Potteries Ltd. Longton. (Usual trademark Willow Art).

One small found with this mark and
Chester crest.   4.00

Rosina Queens China

The above mark can also be found with the word Ltd after G.W. & S.

Trademark can also be found with 'China' rather than Bone China and Made in England on one line.

Trademark used by George Warrilow & Sons (Ltd), Queens Pottery, Longton. George Warrilow was established in 1887. They specialised in the production of Tea-sets, badged ware and Queens White Ware. Most firms making badged ware were capable of producing crested china, but this firm seems to have produced just a small quantity of crested domestic ware.

Domestic

Domestic items	from 4.00
Jam Pot on small dish with lid.	
Some colour. 75mm.	9.50

Rowena China

Trademark used by R.H. & S.L. Plant (Ltd), Tuscan Works, Longton. (Usual trademark Tuscan).
For history see Tuscan China.
This factory is noted for its range of unglazed pastel coloured cartoon charactrers which are scarce and much sought after.

Rowena Models
Ancient Artefacts

Gastrica Cyprian Bottle. 71mm.	6.00

Animals

Fish posy vase. 130mm long.	10.00
Giant open-mouthed fish.	
130mm long.	12.50
Dog kennel.	8.00

Home/Nostalgic

Anvil on block. 57mm.	8.50
Grandfather clock, inscribed *Time for tea 5 O'Clock*. 130mm.	20.00

Comic/Novelty

Lemon, open top. 75mm long.	12.50
Loaf of Bread. 65mm.	20.00
Two seater Car ashtray, inscribed: *Petrol consumption nil.* 135mm long.	200.00
The car ashtray is identical to the Tuscan example called 'Dennis Two Seater'	
Tomato, green leaves. 57mm dia.	19.00

Cartoon/Comedy Characters

These fine coloured models form a series from *The Daily Sketch* Cartoon. Some white, glazed, examples have been seen.

Don, little boy in short trousers and blue cardigan. 130mm.	100.00
Dr. Dromedary, camel, in black top hat and suit. 130mm.	100.00
Lord Lion, lion in pale blue jacket with coloured head and feet. 139mm.	100.00
Glazed version, inscribed: *Souvenir of Wembley 1924*.	125.00
Oo Jah, *Flip Flap*, Elephant, in pink striped pyjamas. 130mm.	100.00
Pa Piggins, Pig, in Edwardian Sporting clothes, some colour. 139mm.	100.00
Glazed version, inscribed: *Souvenir of Wembley 1924*.	125.00
Snooker, or the kitten cat, yellow with crown on head. 130mm.	100.00

Royal Albert Crown China

Garter Mark used 1905-7

Mark used 1905-07

Mark used 1927+

Trademark used by Thomas C. Wild, Crown China Works, High St, Longton.
This mark used by Thomas C. Wild, the well established china manufacturers, is found on domestic ware and 'smalls' made between 1905 and 1907. This firm obviously did not need to turn to model making during the Great War but survived by selling the table wares and fine china they specialised in.
The china is very white and thicker than that of other factories.

A small range of domestic ware and 'smalls' has been found with this mark, mostly with Isle of Wight crests. One vase bears a cartoon featuring children and insects.   18.00

Royal Albert Crown Models
Home/Nostalgic
Cradle, 78mm long, 60mm high.   16.00

Royal Arms China

Trademark used for a Birmingham retailer by an unknown manufacturer.

Royal Arms Models

Ancient Artefacts
Three-handled loving cup. 38mm.   6.00

Buildings - White
Thatched cottage. 48mm.   12.50

Animals
Toad. 73mm long.   22.50

Royal China

Mark used 1912-41

Trademark used by E. Hughes and Co., Opal Works, Fenton. (Also used marks, Fenton & E. Hughes & Co.).

For details of this china and manufacturer see Fenton China and E. Hughes & Co. China.

This mark has only been found on smalls. The mark is usually found on badged hotel ware and domestic china.

Royal Models
Miniature Domestic
Cheese Dish and cover. 50mm.	9.50
Cup & Saucer. 35mm.	5.00

Royal China Works, Worcester

1889-1902

Trademark used by Grainger, Worcester, when taken over by the Worcester Porcelain Co. Ltd.

The very famous firm of George Grainger at Worcester was taken over by the Worcester Royal Porcelain Co. Ltd. in 1889. This mark was only used after the takeover and not after 1902, so china with this mark can be accurately dated. A small number of 'smalls' have been found and the models listed below. The china, as one would expect, is very fine and the crest, normally of Worcester, well produced.

Royal China Works Models
Miniature Domestic
Two handled Loving Cup. 45mm.	30.00
Mug, with one handle. 40mm.	30.00
Vase, swirl pattern. 65mm.	25.00

Domestic
Orchid Wall pocket. 135mm.	40.00

Royal Coburg

Royal Coleston

No details of this mark available.

Trademark used by an unknown manufacturer.

This mark was not registered and there are no initials or country of origin given to help with identification. Most pieces found are 'smalls' and carry crests of the South of England. It is possible that the china, which is a hard paste porcelain, was manufactured in Germany, but unlikely. It is of poor quality and tends to be crazed in appearance. The Royal Family's connection with Coburg would have made this a respectable name before the Great War and this mark was probably used before 1914.

Royal Coburg Models
Home/Nostalgic
Chair with 2 gold tassels.   10.00

Footwear
Ladies open shoe. 115mm long.   7.50

Miniature Domestic
Cheese Dish and cover. 50mm.   7.50

One small jug with blue trim and Flags decoration and *Freedom and Justice* inscription has been recorded. No other information is available.
                                   20.00

Royal Crown Pottery Company

Royal Doulton

Mark used from 1902

For details of the Royal Crown Pottery Company, Burslem see Kensington China.

Trademark used by Doulton & Co. (Ltd), Nile St, Burslem.

This well-known firm produced a very small range of crested ware. Most of it seems to have been for export, crests recorded including New Zealand, Seal of Wellington, Tasmania, Western Australia and Jamaica. Most pieces of Doulton with crests are small vases, jugs or domestic ware. The RN Training School badge has been recorded and Taunton Theological College. As one would expect the china is well produced.

Royal Doulton Models
Range of smalls with foreign and
English crests.   25.00 each

Ancient Artefacts
Loving Cup, 3 handled. 49mm.   30.00

Royal Grafton

Mark used from 1957.

Trademark used by Alfred B. Jones and Sons Ltd., Grafton China Works, Longton, Staffs. (Usual trademark Grafton). The above mark is usually found on fairly modern pieces with the crest of St. Helena.

Domestic
Ashtray. 118mm dia.   8.00

Royal Ivory Porcelain

1905-1924

Trademark used by Robinson & Leadbeater Ltd and for the London wholesalers E.B. & Co. (Usual trademark R. &L.).

For details of this china and manufacturer see R. & L.

Royal Ivory Porcelain was the printed mark used on small crested wares by Robinson & Leadbeater Ltd., Wolfe Street, Stoke-on-Trent, which subsequently became a branch of J.A. Robinson Ltd. The same mark occurs with the initials E.B. & Co., these same initials appearing with another mark used by a London wholesaler (see The Dainty Ware).

E.B. & Co. china with the Royal Ivory mark is much finer than the Dainty Ware range, and probably was more expensive. Most items which are recorded are found with boths sets of initials, indicating that E.B. & Co. sold the whole R. & L. range.

Most pieces with this mark are 'smalls' or domestic ware, including pill boxes. Some transfer view ware has been recorded, but no commemoratives appear to have been made. Royal Ivory was exported and some foreign crests have been found. Crests of the Allies are found on 'smalls' with the E.B. & Co. initials.

Royal Ivory Models
Ancient Artefacts

Alderney Milk can and lid. 52mm.	7.00
Chester Roman Vase. 63mm.	5.50
Kendal Jug. 70mm.	6.00
Loving Cup, 2 & 3 handled. 45mm.	6.00

Buildings - White

Cottage on rectangular base. 57mm.	12.50

Animals

Bill Sykes Dog, model of Bulldog.

95mm long.	25.00

Birds (including Eggs)

Swan posy holder. Some colouring.

70mm.	6.00

Home/Nostalgic

Bellows. 115mm long.	16.00
Child in Nightdress candlesnuffer.	
100mm.	22.00
Egg, broken top, on stand. 68mm.	12.00

Comic/Novelty

Bust of double faced jester *Ye Jester Awake/Ye Jester Asleep.* 70mm.   20.00

Alcohol

Highland Whisky Bowl, Model of.	6.50

Hats

Bishop's Mitre.	15.00

Footwear

Slipper wall pocket. 100mm long.	7.50

Miniature Domestic

Cheese Dish and cover.	
74mm long.	9.50
Tea Pot with lid. 55mm.	9.50
Shaped dish and cover, ornate.	
100mm long.	10.00

Royal Scenic China

Royal Stafford China

Trademark used by a Czechoslovakian manufacturer.

There are no details of crested china models recorded to date.

Mark used 1929-1940

Mark used from 1912. Can have made in England in place of England.

Mark used from 1929-40

Mark used after 1952

The above mark has been found on a 68mm cup and saucer with a Perth crest, and would have been used specifically for Watson's of Perth who were local retailers.

Trademark used by Thomas Poole, Cobden Works, Longton. Products identical to Willow Art.
This firm obviously turned to crested china production for a short time during the Great War as many firms did. This firm, unusually continued to produce crested tableware after World War Two. Most items recorded are domestic, including the inevitable ashtrays, but typical crested china shapes date from 1912.

Royal Stafford Models
Animals
Elephant, walking. 52mm.   20.00
Elephant cream jug. 65mm.   17.50

Great War
Submarine, inscribed: *E4*. 115mm long. 25.50
Red Cross Van. 88mm long.   30.00
Kitchen Range, inscribed: *Keep the home fires burning*. 78mm.   18.50
Bell Tent, open flap. 70mm.   22.00
Bugle. 72mm.   22.50
'Florence Nightingale 1820-1910' statue. 170mm.   24.50

Sport/Pastimes
Spade, playing card suit. 68mm.   7.00

Domestic
Cup and saucer. 68mm.   4.00
Egg Cup, goblet shaped. 45mm.   6.00
Tea Plate. 105mm. 105mm dia.   4.00

Royal Vale China

Mark used from 1908

Mark used 1928-37

The above mark has also been recorded, apparently for a retailer, J.W. Alder of Coolangatta, N.S.W., Australia.

Trademark used by H.J. Colcough, Vale Works, Goddard Street, Longton for goods supplied by Taylor and Kent (Ltd), Florence Works, Longton (usual trademark Florentine).
View ware can be found on the domestic and table ware which this firm made. (In 1907 the firm advertised 'Best English China at Foreign prices. Seaside and present ware or Bazaar Goods in Views, plain or coloured or gilt'). However the range of crested china was bought in from Taylor & Kent.

Royal Vale Models
Ancient Artefacts
Hastings Kettle, not named. 55mm.   5.00

Seaside Souvenirs
Lighthouse. 105mm.   9.00
Lighthouse on circular base. 115mm.   12.50

Animals
Pig, fat, lying forward, pricked ears.
  100mm long.   50.00
Pig, fat, sitting. 63mm.   22.50

Great War
Water Bottle. 70mm.   22.00
Cenotaph. 146mm.   14.50

Footwear
Ladies 18th Century Shoe.
  95mm long.   8.50

Domestic
Beaker. 97mm.   4.00
Tall Jug. 110mm.   8.00
Octagonal Vase. 74mm.   4.00
Sugar Bowl, fluted. 100mm dia.
  65mm high.   4.50
Tea Plate. 163mm dia.   4.00

Royal Worcester

Trademark used by Worcester Royal Porcelain Company Ltd. (Royal Worcester). The majority of small items carrying the famous Worcester mark were made at the turn of the century and are of high quality porcelain. Items of domestic ware and pierced vases and dishes can be found with well produced crests, usually of Worcester. It seems that well established firms only made crested ware when it was considered tasteful and new, in other words a 'middle class' souvenir. Some pieces have been found with a cream instead of a white body. One 39mm. mug has been recorded with a transfer print of the Manx legs and a black bird (thought to be the Manx Shearwater). A lip salve pot has been found decorated with the triple entente flags over a battleship.

Royal Worcester Models
Ancient Artefacts
Chester Roman Vase. 60mm.   25.00
Loving Cup. 2 & 3 handled. 40mm.   25.00

Miniature Domestic
Mug, one handled. 45mm.   20.00
Jug, with high looped handles and
  acanthus leaves under spout.
  55mm.   20.00

Domestic
Lip Salve Pot and lid. 26mm.   25.00
Jam dish half barrel shape. 50mm.   20.00
Barrel Jug, strap handle. No. 232.
  67mm.   20.00

Ryecroft China Series   S

Trademark used by Robinson & Leadbeater, Wolfe Street, Stoke-on-Trent for an unknown retailer.

Ryecroft China Series
Unglazed/Parian
Bust of *Burns* on circular base.
176mm.   35.00

Buildings - White
Roche Abbey, ruins, unglazed.
  inscribed: *Pinners Schools Outing*
  Rotherham 1921 and Roche Abbey,
  founded 30 July 1147, deed of
  surrender to Henry the VIII
  23 June 1550. 85mm.   80.00
Town Hall, Stockton-on-Tees,
  glazed. 94mm.   75.00

Monuments (including Crosses)
Woodhouse Eaves Cross.   45.00

Seaside Souvenirs
Lifeboat. 101mm long.   21.50

Birds (including Eggs)
Duck posy bowl, yellow beak.
  50mm.   12.50

Comic/Novelty
Jester, two-faced. 90mm.   20.00

Sport
Cricket Cap. 65mm long.   50.00

Trademark used by P. Donath, Tiefenfurt. (Silesia).

Very little crested china of this manufacture has been found and all known pieces are domestic items of only nominal value. One of the firms main areas of specialization was pink souvenir domestic ware and white souvenir ware bearing transfer printed views. The company was nationalised after the last war, and is now in Poland.

Animals
Full size Fish Tray. 350mm long.
  (Bognor crest).   17.00

Home/Nostalgic
Coal Scuttle, box-shaped. 57mm.   8.00

St. George China

The above mark can be found with SCWARZENBERG replacing ST GEORGE CHINA or with 'ST GEORGE CHINA' simply omitted.

AUSTRIA

Trademark used by Wilhelm Kutzscher & Co., Schwarzenberger Porzellanfabric, Schwarzenberg, Saxony. (Now in Germany). (Usual trademark Saxony) This manufacturer made many unmarked pieces for the English market. This mark is found on some typically German comic animal models. The elephants on the slide are often found unmarked, and it is possible that this manufacturer usually left his models unmarked. One small jug and an Irish Bronze Pot have been recorded with a black transfer view of 'The Old Curiosity Shop' on one side and 'Charles Dickens' on the other. (German manufacturers specialised in transfer view production and exported a great deal to Great Britain before the Great War.)

St. George Models
Ancient Artefacts
Irish Bronze Pot.   4.00
Loving Cup, 3-handled.53mm.   5.00
Puzzle Jug, with verse. 60mm.   6.00
Puzzle Tankard. 50mm.   7.00

Seaside Souvenirs
Lighthouse. 121mm.   10.00

Animals
Two Puppies and a Kitten in a
    basket. 62mm.   27.50
Cat, with drumstick, sitting on a
    drum. 90mm.   27.50
Dog, coal hod with handle. 80mm.   18.50
Dog, King Charles Spaniel with blue
    bow, on cushion with tassled
    corners. 80mm long.
Elephants, two on a sledge on slope.
    70mm.   65.00
Grotesque Animal with winged
    legs, sitting. 80mm.   12.00

Birds (including Eggs)
Hen and Cock on circular base, one
    pecking and one standing. 80mm.   16.00

Home/Nostalgic
Basketweave Basket. 90mm.   5.00
Jardiniere on stand, fixed. 95mm.   5.00
Pail with wire handle. 45mm.   5.00

Musical Instruments
Drum Set with cymbols, green base.
    65mm.   20.00

Sport/Pastimes
Tennis Racquet with ball.
    140mm long.   22.50

Footwear
Ladies heeled shoe. 84mm.   7.50
Ladies heeled shoe with eyelets.
    85mm long.   12.50

Miniature Domestic
Teapot & Lid. 90mm.   8.00

Domestic
Hatpin Holder. 110mm.   22.50

St. Pauls

Sandifords Ceramic China

Trademark used for export to Canada by Hewitt & Leadbeater, Willow Pottery, Longton. (Usual trademark Willow Art).

St. Pauls Models
Traditional/National Souvenirs
Welsh Hat. No. 75. 54mm.   9.50

Historical/Folklore
Skull, inscribed: *Alas Poor Yorick*.
  65mm. (This has a crest of
  Alberta).   12.00

Home/Nostalgic
Closed Book. 58mm.   12.00

Trademark used by the manufacturers of Ceramic China (usual trademark Ceramic China), for the retailer Sandifords.

Only a pin tray and two 'smalls' recorded all with the Chorley
crest.   each 6.00

San Juan

Savoy China

Mark used by an unknown manufacturer. One model has been found with this mark; it carried a Madrid Crest. It would have been made by any English firm that exported to tourist areas. The initials S.M. & Co. were not used by any manufacturer working during the 'crested china' period and so are probably the initials of the retailer.

San Juan Model
Ancient Artefacts
Portland Vase. 51mm.   6.00

1910-1933

Trademark used by Birks, Rawlins and Co (Ltd), Vine Pottery, Stoke. Merged in 1932 with Wiltshaw & Robinson Ltd. (Makers of Carlton).

Mark found on a Carlton mould fisherman and on a black cat on pouffé - obviously after firms merged.

The firm Birks, Rawlins and co., China Manufacturers, was founded in 1900. It had previously been known as L.A. Birks and Co. (founded 1896). Who Mr Rawlins was will probably remain a secret but Mr L.A. Birks managed the pottery and was responsible for the designs. The firm's early products were 'breakfast and teas' in the usual number of printed patterns and other decorative domestic ware including pierced white pieces.

Birks, Rawlins and Co. began producing what were described as china miniatures for the seasonal souvenir trade around 1910 using the trade-name Savoy China. The production of this work was stepped up in 1919 to take advantage of the gap left in the market by the banning of German goods. It was reported in the *Pottery Gazette* in 1919 and 20 that the firm were producing miniature architectural models and could execute copies of any well known building to order. Aberystwyth University, St. Paul's, Westminster Abbey, Truro Cathedral, King Charles Tower, Hastings Clock Tower and Portsmouth Town Hall were all said to be in production. (Only some of these have been found so far.) Even more perplexing to the collector is a list printed in 1920 of 'Small figures which aim at filling a need that was created when German supplies to this country ceased. 'Birks Grotesques' included 'Old Bill' in camouflage or in khaki, 'Sunny Jim', 'Weary Willy', 'Artful Eliza', 'Saucy Sue', 'Peter Pan', 'Conchy', 'Blighty' and 'C3' all well known cartoon and comic strip characters of the time. None of these have been reported with or without crests or marked Savoy and one wonders if they were ever produced in any numbers.

Many coloured novelties were made in the 1920s including figures, birds, floating bowl decorations (butterflies and other insects) and plump pixies sitting on toadstools. These were not crested so have not been listed here.

In 1925, Birks, Rawlins and Co. exhibited at the British Empire Exhibition, showing Parian China and novelties. Presumably the return of cheap continental souvenir ware and the effect on trade of the Depression were too much for the firm, for by 1931 the company was put into the

hands of the Receiver FW. Carder ceased to act as Receiver. On 7th March 1932 and it was announced that Birks, Rawlins and Co. had merged with Wiltshaw and Robinson Ltd (makers of Carlton China). Wiltshaw and Robinson continued to use the Savoy trademark for a short time and some Carlton moulds can be found with the Savoy mark.

The Savoy range, although described as 'china' and even 'porcelain miniatures', cannot really be considered delicate and has a slightly 'gritty' texture. It is obvious that Birks, Rawlins and Co. lowered their standards to produce cheap items for the lower end of the souvenir market, but they did produce some very unusual and original models. Very few Savoy models are found with transfer prints of any kind and these are mostly larger pieces. Some of the early colour transfers of castles are quite subtly coloured and very fine. 'Lucky Black Cat' transfers are occasionally encountered but no 'Lucky White Heather' devices have as yet been recorded.

Birks, Rawlins and Co. produced a few military badges, these being:

Argyll & Sutherland Highlanders
Army Medical Corps
Army Service Corps
Black Watch
Cameronians, Scottish Rifles
Gordon Highlanders
Highland Light Infantry
Queen's Own Cameron Highlanders
Royal Army Medical Corps
Royal Engineers
Royal Field Artillery
Royal Military College, Camberley
Royal Scots Greys
Seaforth Highlanders
Worcestershire Regiment
H.M.S. Lion
H.M.S. War Spite

They did however print the most interesting range of Great War commemorative inscriptions sometimes found on military models but more often on 'smalls'. These celebrate, if that word can possibly be used to describe such carnage, battles and events in the war and carry matching crests. The following are known:

Albert 'British advance commenced July 1st 1916. Battle of the Somme.'

Amiens 'Germans defeated at Moreuil and Ovise near Amiens August 27-29,1914.
Amiens taken by the Germans September 1 1914.'
Antwerpen 'Antwerp invaded Oct. 1st 1914. Bombarded Oct. 4th 1914, evacuated Oct. 7th 1914. Captured Oct. 13th 1914.'
Armeties 'Desperate Battles between British and Germans, Nov. 1914, June 1915.'
Arras 'Great Battle between French and Germans. French gain trenches June 1915.' Or '13,000 German prisoners, 160 guns captured 1917.'
Australia 'Herbertshore German Pacific Island captured by Australian Navy September 11th 1914. The German cruiser Emden attacked and burnt by H.M.S. Sydney Nov. 8th 1914.'
Advance Australia 'The Australians have made an undying name in storming the Turkish trenches April May 1915.' This inscription is in addition to the previous inscription.
La Bassee No inscription.
Beaumont-Hamel 'British victory German fortress of Beaumont-Hamel, Beaucourt and St. Pierre Divion, captured Nov. 13-141916.'
Belgium 'Belgium invaded by Germany August 4th 1914. Capital occupied August 20th 1914.'
Boulogne 'Hospital base for British wounded soldiers . '
B.E. Africa 'South Togoland seized by Great Britain August 7th 1914.
British East Africa 'South Togoland seized by Britain August 7th 1914.'
Brugge/Bruges 'Bruges occupied by the Germans Oct. 16 1914.'
Brussels 'Occupied by the Germans August 20th 1914.'
Bucharest 'Rumania declares war on Austria-Hungary August 27th 1916.'
Calais 'German life and death advance.'
Canada 'The Canadians at Ypres braved the Fiendish Foe April 22nd, 1915.'
Combles 'Great German fortress captured by the British Sep. 26. 1916. Greatest British success of the war.'
Compiègne 'Battle of Compiegne Sept. 1st. 1914.'
'Cruiser New Zealand took part in Dreadnought battle in North Sea resulting in defeat of German fleet. Jan 24th 1915'

Dinant 'Sacked and burnt by the Germans August 23rd 1914.'
Dornock 'Perseverance overcomes.'
Doullens No details of inscription available.
Dunkerque 'Dunkerque bombarded by long range German guns.'
Egypt 'Defended by British troops with Australian and Indian contingents.'
England 'Declared war on Germany August 4th 1914.' British Naval Victory in the North Sea German cruiser Blucher sunk January 24th 1915.
Falkland Islands 'British naval victory Dec 8th 1914 German Cruisers Scharnhorst, Gneisenau, Leipzig and Nurnberg destroyed.'
French Republic 'French Territory invaded by German troops August 2nd 1914. Battle of the Marne Sept. 8th to Sept. 12th.'
Gand 'Ghent. Occupied by the Germans October 13th 1914.'
Greece 'Allies land at Salonika October 5th 1915.'
Hartlepool 'Bombardment of Hartlepool by the German fleet December 16th 1914.'
Italia 'Italy declared war on Austria.'
Japan 'Declared war on Germany Aug. 23rd 1914. The fortress Kido-Chau stormed and taken by the Japanese Nov. 7th 1914.'
Liege Invested and bombarded by the Germans August 9th 1914.
Lille 'Lille captured by the Germans Sept. 1914.'
Loos No details of inscription available.
Louvain 'Louvain burned and destroyed by the Germans, August 25th 1914.'
Luxemburg 'Luxemburg invaded by Germans August 1914.'
Malines 'Town and cathedral bombarded by Germans August 27th 1914.'
Messines Battle of Messines. Great British victory 7342 German prisoners. June 7th 1917 also 47 guns captured.'
Monastir 'Recaptured by the Bulgars from the Serbians Nov 19th 1916.'
Mons 'Battle of Mons, Historic Retreat begun August 23rd 1914.'
Namur 'Namur Forts destroyed by the huge German guns captured August 23rd 1914.'
Neuve Chapelle 'Brilliant British Victory over Germans at Neuve Chapelle March 10th 1915.'
Neiuport 'Bombarded January 1915.'
Ostend 'Occupied by the Germans October 16th 1914. British ships begin to take part in coast battle October 18th 1914.'

Paris 'German rush on Paris; reached 20 miles from Paris Sept 3rd 1914.'

Persia 'Persia; British defeat Turks at Kut-el-Amara Sept 28th 1915.'

Ville de Rheims 'Rheims bombarded by Germans Sept 21st 1914; Cathedral destroyed Sept 19th 1914.'

Russia 'Przemysl captured by the Russians 119,600 prisoners of war March 22nd 1915.'

Russia 'War declared upon Russia by Germany Aug. 1st 1914.'

Servia 'Austrians defeated by Serbians at Kolubra Dec 3-6 1914.'

Sheringham 'German air raid on Sheringham Jan. 19th 1915.'

Soissons 'Battle of Soissons.' 'Soissons recaptured from the Germans August 2nd 1918. Soissons cathedral captured by the Germans January 10th 1915. Soissons cathedral bombarded by the Germans January 10th 1918.'

Union of South Africa Revolt of Rebel Oct 8th 1914 De Wet captured.

Union of South Africa Conquest of German South West Africa by General Botha June 8th 1915.

United States of America 'America declared war on Germany, Good Friday April 6 1917.'

Verdun 'German defeat before Fort Douaumont February 26th 1916.'

The Worcestershire Regiment. 'The Worcesters at Ypres charged twenty times their number and turned the fortunes of the fray, Oct 1914.'

Ypres 'German rush stemmed by the Valour of the British troops October 27th 1914. 2nd battle of Ypres. The Canadians gallantry saved the situation April 24th 1915.'

Some superb patriotic transfers were made including Black Watch (depicting a private), Gordon Highlanders, soldier of the King, 13th Manchester, Seaford Camp, Grenadier Guards (private), Territorial Soldier (private), and the 11th Welsh.

Commemoratives can also be found of the Scottish Exhibition, Glasgow 1911 and the Wembley British Empire Exhibition 1924/5.

Numbering System. Savoy models tend to be over endowed with printed and painted numbers on their bases. Many models have a very clear printed number which was obviously a stock number. Unfortunately for the collector the same low numbers often appear on different models. There are possibly one or two reasons for this, one theory being that as models were deleted from the range new models were given their numbers. Another theory for which there is some evidence is that the numbers were badly printed and often only the first or last one or two are in evidence. Sometimes where this has happened a larger stock number is painted in black beside the printed number. Other coloured painted numbers found near the mark seem to be paintresses' marks, these often appearing directly under the painted stock number also in black.

Where stock numbers have been found consistently (printed or painted on models) they have been recorded in the following lists.

Savoy Models
Parian/Unglazed

Bust of Edward VII as the Prince of Wales with inscription. 135mm.	65.00
Bust of *Albert King of the Belgians,* round glazed base. 155mm.	75.00
Bust of Admiral Sir David Beatty, found with inscription: *British Naval Victory, German Cruiser Blucher sunk January 24th 1915. England declared War on Germany August 4th 1914* or Soudon Campaign 1898 Naval Victory off Heligoland Bigh August 28th 1914. Battle of Dogger Bank "Blucher" sunk Jan 24th 1915. Naval victory of Jutland - We have only had the First Round, May 31st 1916'. 150mm.	75.00
Bust of David Lloyd George with inscription on reverse. 186mm.	55.00
Bust of Lord Kitchener, found with inscription: *Lord Kitchener of Khartoum Field Marshall KG KP Secretary for War. Born 1851. drowned at sea off the Orkneys June 5th 1916.*	
2 sizes: 107mm.	40.00
120mm.	45.00

Bust of Sailor, inscribed either:
HMS Iron Duke
HMS Lion
HMS Ocean
HMS Tiger
HMS Warspite
(rare), on round glazed base.
No. 532. 135mm.   160.00
Bust of John Travers Cornwell,
inscription: *John Travers Cornwell,*
age 16. Faithful unto death. Hero
Battle of Jutland, impressed: *HMS*
Chester on cap band. No. 580.
108mm.   325.00

Ancient Artefacts
Ancient Jug. No. 87. 74mm.   5.50
Ancient Jug, Model of. Dug out of the
Foundations of Lichfield Museum.
62mm.   5.50
Barrel Mug, Model of. No. 7.
45mm.   5.50
British Urn. 50mm.   5.50
Carlisle Elizabethan Measure,
inscribed: *Model of 1 gallon*
Elizabethan standard measure in
Carlisle museum by permission of
Com. Tullie House. No. 183. 58mm.   10.00
Carlisle Cup *Late Celtic Cup found*
in Friars Gardens Carlisle now
in Carlisle Museum by permission
of Com. Tullie House. No. 178. 45mm. 7.50
Carlisle Jug, *14th Century Jug found*
in an old tank at Carlisle gaol, by
permission of Com Tullie House.
No. 179. 70mm.   6 00
Carlisle Salt Pot *14th Century Salt*
Pot found at Penrith now in Carlisle
Museum. By Permission of Com.
Tullie House. No. 182. 65mm.   5.50
Carlisle Vase, 14th Century. No. 177.
70mm.   5.50
Celtic Vase in British Museum. No. 25.
45mm.   5.50
Chester Roman Altar No. 185 122mm.   30.00
Chester Roman Vase, inscribed:
Roman Vase, original now in
Chester Museum. No. 134. 70mm.   5.50
China Tot, Model of. No. 33.   5.50
Chinese Vase in South Kensington
Museum. No. 67 or 219. 70mm.   5.50
Chinese Jade Vase, inscribed: *Model of*
Vase of Chinese Jade. No. 152. 68mm. 5.50
Colchester Vase. *Ancient Vase*
original in Colchester Museum.
No. 349. 50mm.   5.50

Colchester Roman Vase, inscribed:
Roman Vase found in Cloaca, now in
Colchester Castle. No. 196.
30mm.   5.50
De Nevers Vase in Kensington
Museum. No. 150.   5.50
Exeter Vase from original in Museum.   5.50
Globe Vase. No. 62. 42mm.   5.50
Greek Vase. No. 77. 69mm.   5.50
Hastings Kettle. No. 140. 60mm.   5.50
Horsham Jug. No. 89. 72mm.   5.50
Model of Ancient Irish Bronze Pot.
No. 18. 50mm.   5.50
Italian Vase. No. 30.   5.50
Itford Urn. No. 195. 44mm.   6.00
Launceston Bottle. No. 193.
65mm.   5.50
Lewes Vase, inscribed: *Model of*
Roman Vase in Lewes Castle.
No. 197. 35mm.   5.50
Loving Cup. *Model of Loving Cup,*
original by Henry of Navarre, King
of France. No. 49. 42mm.   7.50
Maltese Fire Grate. No. 39 and
No. 721. 45mm.   9.00
Newbury Leather Bottle. *Model of*
Leather Bottle found at Newbury
1044 on battlefield now in museum.
No. 14. 63mm.   5.50
Old Beer Jug, Model of No. 84. 80mm.   5.50
Penrith Salt Pot. No. 182. 60mm.   5.50
Persian Bottle. No. 68. 85mm.   5.50
Persian Porcelain Vase, Model of now in
Kensington Museum. No. 144. 95mm.   5.50
Pilgrims Bottle Nevers ware.
No. 172. 75mm.   5.50
Pompeian Vase. No. 161. 124mm.   8.50
Pompeian Vessel. No. 264.   5.50
Portland Vase. No. 16. 51mm.   5.50
Puzzle Jug with verse. No. 378. 68mm.   13.00
Salt Maller, Model of. No. 106.
60mm.   6.00
Scarborough Jug. No. 454 or No. 10.
48mm.   5.50
Silchester Roman Urn. No. 74.
51mm.   5.50
Shakespeare's Jug, *the jug of William*
Shakespeare, with his signature.
60mm.   6.50
Shrewsbury Ewer. No. 19.
72mm.   5.50
Southwold Jar. No. 175. 90mm.   5.50
Staffordshire salt glaze tea pot, Model
of, diamond shaped, with
separate lid. No. 202.
75mm.   20.00

Tear Bottle. No. 17. 70mm.   5.50
Teapot, copy of early 18th century
   stoneware (shaped as as camel).
   100mm long. (Rare).   30.00
Tyg, two-handled. 62mm.   5.50
Tyg, one handle. No. 37. 61mm.   5.50
Uriconium Urn. *British Urn found at*
   Uriconium. No. 24. 55mm.   5.50
Winchelsea Ancient Ewer, Model of
   No. 145. 57mm.   6.00
Windsor Roman Urn. *Roman urn*
   dug up at old Windsor from original
   now in British Museum. No. 138.
   45mm.   5.50
York Roman Ewer. *Roman Ewer from*
   the original in Hospitium found at
   York. No. 20.   5.50

Buildings - Coloured
Exeter Cathedral, brown coloured.
   150mm long.   125.00
St Paul's Cathedral, brown
   unglazed. 125mm long,
   88mm high.   125.00
Tumbledown Cottage, not named,
   highly coloured and glazed.
   Impressed 1800. 105mm long.   95.00

Buildings - White
Aberystwyth, The University.
   No. 68. 146mm long.   135.00
Burns Cottage. 70mm long.   17.50
Citadel Gateway, Plymouth.
   No. 209. 114mm.   32.50
Birmingham Town Hall. 94mm
   long, 62mm high.   30.00
Clifton Suspension Bridge.
   132mm long.   75.00
Derry's Clock, Plymouth. No. 17.
   152mm.   18.00
First and Last Refreshment House in
   England. No. 301. 72mm.   18.00
Hastings Clock Tower. No. 677.
   156mm.   18.00
Log Cabin, not named, inscribed: *I*
   wouldn't leave my little wooden hut
   for you. 63mm long.   30.00
Margate Clock Tower. 160mm.   18.00
Monnow Gate, Monmouth. 112mm.   50.00
Portsmouth Town Hall.
   No. 7. 80mm.   80.00
Windmill with revolving sails. 110mm.   40.00
Tumbledown Cottage. 105mm long.   50.00

Monuments
Model of Lewes Martyr's Memorial.
   Erected in 1901 to the memory of
   the 16 Protestants burnt to death
   in front of the Star Hotel
   1555-1557. 140mm. No. 791.   80.00
Margate Surf Boat Memorial, with
   inscription. 130mm.   20.00
Rufus Stone, with usual inscriptions.
   100mm.   7.50
The Globe, Swanage. 90mm high,
   138mm wide (large, imposing
   model).   40.00

Historical/Folklore
Burns Chair, Dumfries. 85mm.   12.50
Elizabethan Girl, full figure.
   155mm.   80.00
Execution Block. No. 411.
   100mm long.   18.00
Gargoyle or Devils Head, open
   mouth, inscribed: *My word if*
   you're not off. No. 230.
   90mm long.   14.50
Mary Queen of Scots Chair, Edinburgh
   Castle. 77mm.   12.50

Traditional/National Souvenirs
A Cornish Pasty. 100mm long.   12.50
Ripon Horn Blower. No. 497.
   114mm.   16.00
Ye Olde Devonshire Milk Can.
   78mm.   9.00
Monmouth Cap. No. 213. 60mm.   50.00
Tam o'shanter.   22.00
Thistle Vase. 47mm.   5.00
Welsh Hat with longest place name
   round brim. No. 6.
   3 sizes: 35mm.   12.00
         44mm.   11.00
         55mm.   14.00
Welsh hat, gilded buckle. No. 127.
   57mm.   14.00
Welsh Lady carrying a basket.
   Candlesnuffer. 110mm.   40.00
Welsh lady bust, fully coloured on
   ashtray base with hat forming
   match holder. 110mm. Can be
   found uncoloured.   30.00
Dutch Boy, standing coloured, salt
   pot. 128mm.   35.00
Dutch Boy, seated. 104mm.   50.00
Dutch Girl, seated. 104mm.   50.00

Seaside Souvenirs

Bathing Machine, No. 428, inscribed:	
Morning Dip. 62mm.	20.00
Boat. No. 434. 128mm long.	12.50
Child draped in towel, standing on	
a rock. 133mm.	30.00
Crab Pin Box and Lid. No. 426,	
detailed eyes. 100mm long.	20.00
Lifeboat. If inscribed: *Zetland, the*	
oldest lifeboat in the world saved 600	
lives. add £10.00. No. 381.	
125mm long.	20.00
Rowing Boat. No. 118. 130mm long.	12.50
Yacht. 115mm long.	16.50
Beachy Head Lighthouse, hollow	
base. No. 377. 130mm.	17.50
Eddystone Lighthouse. No. 136. 90mm.	10.00
Also found as Candlesnuffer.	
Also found inscribed:	
St. Catherines Lighthouse. 92mm.	22.00
Lizard Lighthouse. 110mm	22.50
Lighthouse salt pot, inscribed: *salt.*	
105mm.	13.00
Lighthouse pepper pot, inscribed:	
pepper. 120mm. No. 768.	13.00
Longships Lighthouse, model of.	
90mm.	7.00
Limpet shell *Pins* Tray on limpet	
shell base. No. 2587. 80mm long.	6.00
Crab ashtray or dish. 52mm long.	7.50
Lobster pintray with lid. No. 426.	
97mm long.	20.00
Whelk Shell. No. 451. 81mm long.	7.00

Countryside

Acorn, Model of. No. ll0. 56mm.	8.50
Can also be found as a pepper	
pot marked 'P'.	8.00

Animals

Bear, can be inscribed: *Model of Stoneware*	
Bear, a performing bear on hind	
legs with gilded muzzle. No. 205.	
106mm.	150.00
Cat, Cheshire. No. 17. 80mm.	10.00
Cat sitting, miniature, with long	
neck. No. 572. 68mm.	17.00
Cat, angry with arched back,	
inscribed: *Me backs up.* No. 195.	
100mm long.	15.50
Cat with long neck. No. 217.	
105mm.	16.00
Cat, sitting. No. 560. 55mm.	25.00
Cat, sitting, detailed fur.	
2 sizes: No. 75. 56mm.	25.00
No 245. 94mm.	65.00

Cat, standing with huge grin, erect	
bushy tail. Comic, black cartoon	
cat. 105mm long.	180.00
Cat, on oval lustre base. Inscribed:	
Good Luck. Cat coloured black.	
90mm. (Carlton mould).	26.00
Cat, Manx, standing. 80mm long.	35.00
Dinosaur Jug. No. 585. 78mm long.	10.00
Dog cream jug. No. 106. 60mm.	15.00
Dog cream jug. No. 555. 60mm.	15.00
Dog (no particular breed) sitting.	
55mm.	45.00
Dog (curly tail) standing. 65mm.	17.00
Dog, Basset/Dachshund. No. 296.	
132mm long.	65.00
Dog, Spaniel, sitting. No. 561.	
65mm.	40.00
Bulldog, lying, inscribed: *Another*	
Dreadnought. No. 238. 118mm long.	80.00
Bulldog, fierce standing, with verse. *Be*	
Briton Still to Britain True. No. 364.	
130mm long.	50.00
Bulldog, fierce standing, feet outwards.	
Inscribed: *'Another Dreadnought'.*	
135mm long.	35.00
Dog, crouched and barking.	
No. 253. 100mm long.	30.00
Dog, Scottie, wearing glengarry.	
No. 477. 86mm.	15.00
Dog, Scottie, wearing a tam-	
o'shanter. The larger size can be	
found fully coloured with black,	
green & orange tam.	
2 sizes: 63mm.	12.50
80mm.	16.50
Dog, crouching. No. 283. 170mm long.	45.00
Dog, sitting on spade shaped tray.	
·78mm.	20.00
Dog, Scottie, looking out of kennel.	
Can be found with inscription:	
The Black Watch or *Beware of the*	
dog. No. 154. 80mm long.	22.00
Dog, Spaniel, sitting. No. 584. 65mm.	15.00
Donkey, standing. No. 308.	
120mm long.	65.00
Elephant, sitting with trunk in the	
air. No. 218. 63mm.	22.50
Elephant, standing. No. 250. 65mm.	17.00
Elephant, standing, trunk raised.	
No. 253. 110mm long.	40.00
Can be found coloured green.	55.00
Elephant with howdah. No. 228.	
66mm. 75mm long.	30.00
Fish. No. 440. 104mm long.	10.00

Fish Jug. 70mm.	8.50
Fish Vase. No. 33. 88mm.	6.00
Frog, sitting, well detailed. No. 321.	
70mm.	65.00
Frog on a rock. Green.	
110mm long.	40.00
Grotesque animal No. 206. 100mm.	20.00
Hare, crouching, No. 235 or No. 245.	
70mm high	40.00
Hare, looking left, upright ears.	
No. 253. 80mm.	45.00
Hippo, with pointed teeth.	
113mm long.	80.00
Lion, sitting on square base. This	
was originally designed by	
Alfred Stevens for the British	
Museum. 105mm.	40.00
Lion, walking. Inscribed: *Be Briton*	
No. 123. or '*Another Dreadnought*'	
No. 288. 134mm long.	30.00
Without inscription.	22.50
Mouse (field mouse) eating. 48mm.	30.00
Mouse, nose to ground. No. 710.	
65mm long.	30.00
Pig, lying down. No. 544.	
80mm long.	15.00
Can be found inscribed: *Wunt be*	
druv.	
Pig, standing and fat. No. 109.	
2 sizes: 70mm and 100mm long.	20.00
Large size can be found	
inscribed: *Model of Irish Pig.*	35.00
Pig sitting on haunches, hands aloft.	
110mm.	150.00
Pig, standing, open mouthed.	
122mm long.	100.00
Pig, lying down. No. 559. Long nose.	
80mm long.	22.00
Pig, standing inscribed: *Model of*	
Sussex Pig. No. 198 and No. 281.	
78mm long.	40.00
Pig, standing, *Sussex Pig*, alert ears.	
No. 199. 67mm long. *Wunt be druv.*	25.00
Pig, sitting, long nose. No. 549.	
100mm long.	24.00
Pig, sitting, long nose. No. 215. 110mm.	35.00
Piglet with long ears. No. 33 or No. 99.	
65mm long.	20.00
Polar Bear. No. 236. 145mm long.	75.00
Rabbit, ears flat. No. 548. 66mm long.	10.00
Rabbit, crouching. No. 247 or 217.	
88mm long.	20.00
Rabbit, sitting, one ear up. No. 548.	
70mm long.	40.00

Rabbit, sitting on hind legs, upright.	
No. 242. 104mm.	40.00
Rhino, grotesque. No. 284.	
130mm long.	70.00
Seal.	
2 sizes: No. 571. 63mm long.	16.00
80mm long.	19.50
Snail. No. 252. 84mm long.	30.00
Teddy Bear. 90mm.	24.50
Tiger, sabre toothed, or Wild Cat	
No. 284 with inscription: *My word*	
if you're not off. 128mm long.	100.00
Toad. No. 331. 75mm.	22.00
Warthog or Wild Pig, open mouth.	
Grotesque. No. 244. 133mm long.	125.00

Birds (including Eggs)

Bird, coloured yellow, orange and	
black, shaped salt pot. 90mm.	50.00
Bird mustard pot, orange, yellow,	
red and black. 86mm long.	55.00
Bird alighting on edge of bowl.	
No. 248. 97mm.	30.00
Clara Cluck candlesnuffer. No. 384.	
87mm.	30.00
Duck, swimming. No. 562.	
65mm long.	13.50
Duck, conical beak open upwards.	
130mm.	30.00
Duck, standing on green base.	22.00
Can be found coloured. 170mm.	50.00
Duckling, standing on tree trunk,	
colouring on trunk and beak.	
186mm.	40.00
Duckling, comic, with a wasp on its	
beak.	40.00
Also found partly coloured.	
165mm.	50 00
Duck, lying down, could be dead.	
No. 237. 105mm long.	40.00
Duck, comical, airing wings on	
circular base. 155mm.	75.00
Egg with cock face, comb and tail	
on round base. 90mm.	22.00
Grotesque Bird. 100mm.	12.00
Grotesque Bird jug with long beak.	
80mm. No. 127.	12.50
Goose in full length cloak (Clara	
Cluck Candlesnuffer). 72mm.	30.00
Hen, sitting, red comb. No. 563.	
55mm.	10.00
Owl, comic. No. 33, No. 329, No. 324	
or No. 527. 60mm.	17.00
Penguin. No. 484. 70mm.	20.00
Penguin. No. 549. 76mm.	20.00

Penguin. No. 322. 80mm.   25.00
Penguin on heart shaped ashtray.
85mm.   20.00
Swan, black. 70mm high 100mm long.40.00
Swan, detailed plumage. No. 579.
60mm, 85mm long.   25.00
Swan Posy Vase. No. 435. 64mm.   10.00
Woodpecker *Pepper Pot*. No. 820.
65mm.   15.00

Great War
Highland Infantryman, with pack,
rifle and bayonet. Either glazed
or parian, both on round glazed
plinth. No. 530. 165mm.   190.00
Sailor, standing, arms folded,
unglazed on round glazed base.
(Very rare) No. 538. 160mm.   300.00
Nurse, with red cross on chest,
holding bandage. Can be found
inscribed: *Nurse Cavell*. No. 531.
165mm.   150.00
Wounded man in civilian clothes, on
crutches with one foot bandaged,
fully coloured, inscribed: *Blighty*,
glazed on a square base (rare).
130mm.   250.00
Biplane, with movable prop.,
2 different models exist:
(a) One has open struts between
the wings.   600.00
(b) The other model is identical
but has the struts filled in solid
between the wings. No. 633.
140mm long.
Both models have coloured
roundels and tail.   400.00
Monoplane, pointed wings,
can have revolving or fixed prop.
No. 523. 130mm long.   110.00
Monoplane, pointed wings and
revolving prop. No. 527.
130mm long.   125.00
Zeppelin with revolving 2-bladed
propeller, can be found with
inscription: *Zeppelin destroyed by
Lieutenant Robinson V.C. at Cuffley Essex
Sept. 3rd 1916.* No. 561.
175mm long.   225.00
Battleship, *HMS Iron Duke*, 2
funnels. No. 524. 165mm long.   110.00
Battleship, *HMS Lion*, 3 funnels. No.
524. 168mm long.   125.00
Battleship, *HMS Queen Elizabeth*, 3
funnels, 4 guns forward, 2 aft.
No. 615. 170mm long.   90.00

Battleship, *HMS Queen Elizabeth*, 2
funnels, 4 guns forward, 4 aft.
No. 524. 165mm long.   110.00
Battleship, *HMS Barham*. 2 funnels.
168mm long.   125.00
Battleship, *HMS Tiger*, 2 funnels. No.
525. 168mm long.   110.00
Battleship, *HMS Warspite*, 2 funnels.
168mm long.   125.00
British Minesweeper, Model of. No.
644. 150mm long. (very rare).   450.00
Torpedo Boat Destroyer, model of. Rare.
No. 615. 140mm long.   170.00
Submarine, inscribed: *E1*. Usually
found with inscription:
*Commander Noel Lawrence. Large
German Transport Sunk July 30th
1915. German Cruiser Moltke
torpedoed August 19th 1915.*
No. 525. 150mm long.   100.00
Ambulance with 'Rolls Royce' front,
can have three red crosses in grey
circles. No. 520. 115mm long.   75.00
A similar model exists with two
or three red or blue crosses
moulded in relief on back and
sides of ambulance.   75.00
Armoured Car (reputedly a 'Talbot'
but not named).125mm long.   125.00
Can also rarely be found named
Belgian Armoured Motor Car.   200.00
British Motor Searchlight. No. 123.
110mm long. (Scarce).   225.00
*Model of British Tank first used by
British Troops at the Battle of Ancre,
Sept. 1916* with inset steering
wheels and inscribed *HMS
Donner Blitzen, 515.* Long or short
rear facing guns.
2 sizes: No. 597. Short guns.
    138mm long.   50.00
    Long guns.
    138mm long.   50.00
    No.586. Short or long guns.
    160mm long.   55.00
Tank with no trailing wheels,
inscribed exactly as above. Short
forward and rear facing guns
protruding from side gun turrets.
Also a short gun protruding from
front of upper turret. Inscribed:
HMS Donner Blitzen.
2 sizes: No. 651. 135mm long.   45.00
    No. 643 or 651. 155mm long. 55.00

Tank with no trailing wheels inscribed: *HMS Donner Blitzen* and *515* on side only. Has a curved exhaust pipe on roof, and one small gun protruding from front of side turrets. It differs from the other tanks and is rather flat in appearance. No. 675. 108mm long. (Rare)   150.00

Field Gun, Model of, with fish tail. No. 616. 140mm long.   140.00

Howitzer. No. 526. 140mm long.   35.00

Howitzer. No. 518. 170mm long.   40.00

Machine Gun, 2 pieces, swivels on tripod. No. 602. 143mm long.   165.00

British Trench Mortar Gun. No. 613. 98mm long.   90.00

Shell, if inscribed: *Iron rations for Fritz.* Add £5.00.

4 sizes: No. 189. 69mm.	8.00
No. 581 or No. 556. 75mm.	10.00
No. 558 or No. 537. 110mm.	10.00
No. 170. 117mm.	10.00

(Shell 'salt' and 'pepper' pots also found. No. 663. 80mm).   each 10.00

Model of Stokes Bomb. No. 575. 24mm dia. at base (very rare). 105mm long.   275.00

Trench Mortar Bomb. Often found not named. No. 574. 86mm.   140.00

Hand Grenade. No. 576. 75mm.   30.00 Can be found inscribed: *Model of Mills Bomb.* No. 326 or No. 576. 84mm.   35.00

Floating Mine. No. 429. 55mm.   75.00

Anzacs Hat, Model of. No. 554. 90mm long.   35.00 Unnamed.   22.00

Balmoral Bonnet, Model of. No. 611. 74mm long.   25.00

French Trench Helmet, worn by the Dauntless French Poilu. No. 569. 82mm long. (Not named £50.00).   75.00

Glengarry. No. 508. 78mm long.   25.00

Glengarry, moulded thistle badge, ribbons and button in crown, coloured thistle to rear. No. 610. 94mm long.   30.00

New Zealand Hat, Model of No. 612. 80mm long.   25.00

Officer's Peaked Cap. No. 516. 72mm long.   20.00

German Steel Helmet. No. 506 or 566. 60mm long.   40.00

Rumanian Soldier's Steel Helmet, Model of, found with Bucharest Crest and Rumanian War declaration inscription. 82mm long.   85.00

R.F.C. Cap, Model of. Cap badge clearly moulded. No. 577. 80mm long.   85.00

Sailor's Hat, inscribed on band: *HMS Lion, HMS Queen Elizabeth, HMS Warspite, HMS Iron Duke* or *HMS Tiger.* Blue bow. No. 533. 71mm dia.   70.00

Tommy's Steel Helmet. No. 566. 82mm long.   40.00

German Picklehaube with tall spike. 88mm long, 65mm high. Very rare.   225.00

Bandsman's Drum. No. 489. 55mm dia.   12.50

Bell Tent. No. 118 and No. 483. 65mm.   20.00

Water Bottle. No. 219. 57mm.   13.00

Tommy in Dug Out, not named. No. 669. 85mm. Very rare.   200.00

Fireplace, inscribed: *Keep the home fires burning till the boys come home.* No. 629. 94mm.   25.00

Cenotaph, inscribed: *The Glorious Dead.* 130mm.   12.50

Folkestone War Memorial, May Their Deeds be held in reverence. 160mm.   80.00

Edith Cavell Memorial, Norwich, inscribed: *Nurse Cavell.* Red Cross on apron. No. 110. 168mm.   22.00

Lewes War Memorial. 142mm.   200.00

Home/Nostalgic

Babies Cradle on rocker. 74mm long.   15.00

Bellows. 140mm long.   14.50

Funnel Candlesnuffer. No. 437. 62mm.   12.50

Flat Iron. 65mm.   16.50

Kennel, inscribed: *Beware of the dog.* No. 397. 53mm.   10.50

Trivet for flat iron. No. 544. 70mm long.   9.00

Grandfather Clock, inscribed: *Nae man can tether time nor tide.* No. 622 and No. 110. 150mm.   25.00

Jardiniere on stand. No. 86. 77mm.   6.50

Horn Lantern. No. 455. 82mm.   10.00

Pillar Box, giant *ER* open slot. No. 504. 111mm.   25.00

Pillar Box, miniature. 56mm.   14.50

Stool, circular, 3 legged. No. 471.
33mm.   9.00
Suitcase with straps. No. 745.
58mm.   17.00
Sundial on wide square base. No 375.
93mm.   9.50
Watering Can. No. 455. 76mm.   10.50
Wheelbarrow. 120mm long.   12.50

Comic/Novelty
Billiken. 75mm.   7.50
Boy in nightshirt, holding candle.
Impressed on base *NIGHT.*
Candlesnuffer. 126mm.   65.00
Candlesnuffer in form of young boy
in nightwear, yawning and
stretching. No. 542. 85mm.   22.00
Caterpillar with human face in jersey,
with crossed legs grin on face,
red nose. No. 543. 74mm.   20.00
Also found coloured   30.00
Clown Candle Snuffer. No. 98.
85mm.   30.00
Choirboy, coloured. 104mm.   30.00
Cream Jug, dog shaped.   10.00
Edwardian Girl candlesnuffer
wearing bonnet, coat and muff.
77mm. No. 541, and 86mm. No. 175. 22.50
Elizabethan Lady, very large, huge
skirt, neck frill and cap. 140mm.   120.00
Extinguisher, Model of cone shaped.
No. 42. 65mm.   5.00
Hindu god sitting on rock, blue
beads. No. 28, No. 550 or No. 554.
90mm. (Blue beads add £5.00).   12.50
Huntley and Palmer's Biscuit hat pin
holder. No. 327 and 367.   50.00
Fisherman bending down into beer
barrel, *Waiting for the smacks*
inscribed on his bottom. 90mm.   50.00
Man in Blue Suit, sad expression, foot
in plaster, square base. Inscribed:
Blighty. 130mm high. Rare.   100.00
Policeman, short and fat. 103mm.   60.00
Policeman. Boy carrying truncheon,
salt pot. Inscribed: *SALT.* 130mm.   75.00
Tea pot in shape of man's head,
spout coming out of mouth. No.
332. 60mm.   26.00

Cartoon/Comedy Characters
Bonzo, dog (1920s cartoon
character). No. 927. 2 sizes: 80mm
& 96mm.   55.00

Felix the Cat, crouching. Black with
white face and yellow eyes.
80mm.   250.00
Tweedledum and Tweedledee, fully
coloured, pair of separate sitting
figures. 70mm.   each 40.00
Wilfred Wilfred, fully coloured.
Inscribed: *C3* on collar or *Wilful
Willie.* 120mm.   55.00
Winkie the Gladeye Bird. White.   20.00
Or coloured. 80mm long.   30.00
Winkie the Glad Eye Bird, not
named, as pepper pot. Fully
coloured. 70mm.   30.00
Winkie can also be found as salt
or mustard pots, in colour.   30.00

Alcohol
Beer Barrel. No. 406. 55mm.   6.00
Beer Barrel with separate stand.
No. 406. 50mm long. 57mm.   8.50
Old Beer Jug, model of No, 84. 80mm.   7.00
Bottle. No. 408. 90mm.   7.50
Bottle, inscribed: *Real Scotch.*
No. 409. 88mm.   9.00
Carboy No. 92. 80mm.   7.00
Soda Syphon.   14.00

Sport/Pastimes
Cricket Bag. No. 745. 95mm long.   16.50
Cricket Bat. 115mm long.   80.00
Golf Ball. No. 111. 40mm.   16.50
Golf Club head. No. 442. 70mm.   25.00

Musical Instruments
Bagpipes. No. 553. 115mm long.   50.00
Banjo. No. 748. 137mm long.   19.50
Double Bass. No. 306. 140mm long.   75.00
Upright Piano. No. 887.
83mm long.   22.50
Violin. No. 306. 136mm long.   75.00

Transport
Charabanc, (24 seater). No. 811.
134mm long.   75.00

Modern Equipment
Gramophone, square with large
horn. 102mm.   35.00

Footwear
Lancashire Clog, gilded studs.
No. 403. 83mm long.   6.50
Dutch Clog. No. 424. 70mm long.   6.00
Oriental Slipper. No. 312.
85mm long.   11.00

Hats

Straw Hat. No. 118. 92mm long.	19.00
Top Hat. 44mm.	6.50

Miniature Domestic

Barrel shaped Mug. 50mm.	5.00
Basket weave Mug. 60mm.	5.00
Cheese Dish, one piece. 40mm.	10.00
Cheese Stand, Model of, with lid. No. 200. No. 45. 55mm long.	25.00
Club Vase. No. 106. 59mm.	4.00
Jug. No. 102. 62mm.	4.00
Jug. No. 755. 60mm.	4.00
Jug, ribbed. No. 116. 60mm.	4.00
Kettle and lid. No. 494.	12.50
Star-shaped bottle. No. 503. 58mm.	6.00
Teapot with lid, diamond shaped. No. 202. 80mm.	16.50
Teapot with lid. 62mm.	12.50
Teapot, mans head. No. 376. 60mm.	15.00
Teaset on Tray No. 401.	30.00
Tray 106mm long.	7.00
Trinket Set on Tray No. 436.	30.00
Vase, 5 mouthed. No. 118. 93mm long.	4.00
Vase. No. 317. 35mm.	4.00
Vase, circular on two feet. No. 163. 88mm.	4.00
Vase. No. 107. 52mm.	4.00
Vase. No. 192. 56mm.	4.00
Vase, long-necked. No. 407. 65mm.	4.00

Domestic

Cone Candlesnuffer. 65mm.	6.00
Cream Jug. No. 37. 76mm.	5.00
Inkwell, square, with lid and pen rest. No. 433. 45mm.	14.50
Pins, Tray with wavy border. No. 231. 149mm long.	15.00
Tray, oval with wavy border. No. 436. 140mm long.	7.00

Miscellaneous

Bell, Model of, porcelain clapper. No. 5. 85mm.	9.50
Extinguisher, model of cone-shaped. No. 42. 61mm.	6.00
Greek Warrior's head Candlesnuffer with handle. 72mm.	45.00
Post and railings, posy vase. 140mm long.	8.00

Saxony

Made in
Saxony

Country of origin mark used by Wilhelm Kutzscher & Co, Schwarzenberger Porzellanfabrik, Schwarzenberg, Saxony. Many pieces were not factory marked and can be found listed in the unmarked section.

Unglazed/Parian
Robert Burns Bust of. 110mm.   20.00

Ancient Artefacts
Carlisle Salt Pot, not named.	4.00
Chester Vase. 55mm.	5.00
Hastings Kettle. 40mm.	5.00
Irish Bronze Pot. 45mm.	5.00
Old Roman Salt Pot, 14th Century,	
found near Carlisle by Permission of	
Tullie House Committee. 63mm.	5.00
Puzzle Jug with verse. 66mm.	6.00

Buildings - White
Hall Cross, Doncaster. 158mm.	35.00
Holy Trinity Church, Margate.	
100mm. An impressive model.	65.00
Iona Cathedral. 50mm.	45.00
Margate Clock Tower. 145mm.	20.00
Ross-on-Wye, *Town Hall.* 85mm.	45.00
Llandudno St Tudno's Church.	
60mm long.	45.00
Skegness Clock Tower. 123mm.	7.50
The Old Chapel on Lantern Hill,	
Ilfracombe, Devon. 55mm.	40.00
Wallingford, Town Hall. 90mm.	35.00
Weymouth Jubilee Clock Tower. 124mm.	18.00
Windmill, fixed sails. 85mm.	14.00

Monuments (including Crosses)
Banbury Cross. 146mm.	22.50
Captain Scott Memorial. 148mm.	25.00
Drake Monument. 125mm.	12.50
Largs Memorial.	16.50
Fishermens' Memorial, Hull.	12.00
Fishermens' Memorial, Southend.	15.00
Hull Soldier's War Memorial. 120mm.	25.00
Margate Surf Boat Memorial. 90mm.	70.00
The Monument, Laceby. 147mm.	38.50

Traditional/National Souvenirs
John Bull standing with Bulldog.	
102mm.	25.00
Gretna Priest, standing figure.	30.00
The Lincoln Imp. 115mm.	11.00
Manxman standing in top hat. 124mm.	20.00
Welsh Hat, with longest place name	
round brim. 44mm.	8.50
Welsh Lady, seated. 102mm.	24.50

Seaside Souvenirs
Beach Chair, wicker. 70mm.	12.50
Fisherwoman with bundle. 117mm.	25.00
Lifeboat. 135mm long.	12.00

Beachy Head Lighthouse	7.50
If with black band.	10.00
Corbiere Lighthouse Jersey. 103mm.	16.50
Lighthouse with open windows.	
115mm.	7.50
Lighthouse, narrow. 135mm.	9.50
Flamborough Lighthouse.	25.00
Mermaids, two on an oval base	
holding up a large shell. 105mm.	22.00
Needles Lighthouse. 125mm.	22.50
Scarborough Lighthouse. 125mm.	25.00
Sea Waves pin tray.	6.50

Figures
Man and woman in ornate garden seat,	
pillar either side. 62mm.	15.00
Shepherd and lamb by tree trunk, spill	
holder. 78mm.	15.00

Countryside
Four bar Gate and stile with	
milestone. 100mm long.	8.50

Animals
Cat on drum.	22.50
Cat singing, holding sheet music.	
66mm.	22.50
Cat, holding book *Sweet song.* 74mm.	22.50
Cat (Kitten), bandage around head	
with gilded bow. No. 939. 78mm.	35.00
Cat with Mandolin. 74mm.	22.00
Cat, Manx, drinking from jug.	
72mm long.	24.00
Cat in Gladstone Bag, right paw	
raised. Can be found inscribed:	
Good Morning. 55mm long.	22.00
Cat in Gladstone Bag, left paw	
raised, yawning. 55mm long. (pair).	22.00
Cat in Edwardian dress playing tennis.	
Two versions, one is holding racket	
further down, so that crest is over	
racket. 97mm.	100.00
Dogs, two King Charles Spaniels in	
Top Hat. 78mm.	15.00
Cow Creamer and lid. 148mm long.	17.00
Dog, Collie, standing. 120mm long.	15.00
Elephant with hunters and bearers.	
90mm.	20.00
Frog under Tulip, candleholder.	
100mm.	16.00
Hare, sitting. 95mm long.	12.50
Pig, ears forward, standing.	
90mm long.	20.00
Pig, sitting on haunches, ears	
forward. 76mm.	22.00

Spaniel sitting: 60mm.	15.50
Three Puppies in a Binocular case. 65mm.	22.00
Two Puppies and a Kitten in a basket. 65mm.	22.00
Polar Bear on ashtray. 85mm.	35.00
Shetland Pony. 102mm long.	30.00
Tortoise dish with shell lid. 75mm long.	10.50

Birds (including Eggs)

Hen and Cockerel on round base. 82mm.	15.00
Duck, airing wings, some colouring. 88mm.	14.00
Duck on round base, brown beak and feet. 98mm.	15.00
Egg, imprisoning a rabbit (he looks through a barred window). A large hare in tail coat standing beside it. 67mm.	45.00
Eagle on Perch. Impressive.	25.00
Seagull on rock, black edging on wings. 109mm.	22.50
Seagull on rock, huge spread wings. 130mm.	27.00
Seagull posy holder. 114mm.	8.00
Seagull on rock, raised tail, black edging to wings. 86mm.	17.50
Seagull on rock, black edging to wings. 96mm.	17.50
The above Seagulls can be found coloured, Add £10.00.	
Stork, Baby at feet beside tree trunk posy holder. 100mm.	12.00
Swan, open wings. 80mm.	6.00
Wagtail on tree trunk, black edging to wings. 110mm.	17.00
Can be found coloured.	28.00

Great War

Monoplane, fixed prop and pilot. 100mm long.	30.00
French Infantryman's Cap. 60mm long.	30.00
Clacton War Memorial, with inscription. 140mm.	22.50
Folkestone War Memorial. 160mm.	20.00
Great Yarmouth War Memorial. 130mm.	22.50
Margate War Memorial. 185mm.	45.00
Matlock Bath War Memorial. 150mm.	18.00

Home/Nostalgic

Basket, rectangular, 75mm long.	5.50
Coal Scuttle. 58mm.	5.00
Grandmother Clock. 85mm.	7.50
Lloyd Loom chair.	9.50
Mantle Clock with twisted side pillars. 92mm.	8.50
Pillar Box, inscribed: *I cant get a letter from you...* 72mm.	14.00
Shaving Mug. 54mm.	7.50
Watering Can. 67mm.	7.50
Wheelbarrow. 105mm long.	12.00

Comic/Novelty

Edwardian Lady chauffeur's companion with scarf and full length coat. 80mm.	50.00
Monk holding lantern. 113mm.	24.00

Alcohol

Toby Jug. 70mm.	10.00

Sport/Pastimes

Cricket Bag. 114mm long.	16.50
Football with gilded stitches. 60mm.	10.00

Musical Instruments

Harp with wide base. 90mm.	8.50

Transport

Hot Air Balloon. 67mm.	50.00
Steam Locomotive, inscribed: R.H. and D.R. (Romney Hythe and Dymchurch Railway). 100mm long.	80.00

Modern Equipment

Gramophone, with horn. 85mm.	22.50
Gramophone, with horn. 55mm.	17.00

Footwear

Ankle Boot with broad toe. 80mm long.	6.00
Ladies high, laced boot. 115mm long.	9.50
Lancashire Clog, buckle on front. 110mm long.	7.00

Miniature Domestic

Tea Pot and lid. 57mm.	9.50

Domestic

Pepper Pot. 75mm.	5.00
Salt Pot. 75mm.	5.00

Miscellaneous

Mans Head spill vase or pin cushion. 85mm.	8.50

S.C.H.L.

Scotch Porcelain

Trademark used by Shore, Coggins and Holt of Longton, Staffordshire. This mark was used from 1905-1910. The factory then became Shore and Coggins and used the Bell China mark (now Royal Doulton Group). The only pieces recorded carry the crest of Bolton Abbey.

Sport/Pastimes
Vase, or possibly hatpin holder, in
the form of cricket bat and
stumps. 103mm.   65.00

Trademark used for a Scottish retailer by an unknown manufacturer.
This china is fine and well produced, but the manufacturer is unknown.

Scotch Models
Parian/Unglazed
Bust of Scott, in tartan plaid on
circular glazed base. 108mm.   22.00

Traditional/National Souvenirs
Thistle Vase. 45mm.   5.00

Alcohol
Tankard. 62mm.   5.00

SDG

Shamrock China

Trademark used by an unknown Stoke potter for a Manchester retailer.
Only one small has been found with this mark to date.

5.00

Trademark used by Arkinstall and Sons. (Usual trademark Arcadian).
This mark was used by Arkinstall and Sons for the Irish market. It was thought to have been used by the Belleek factory, but I do not now think it was. It is similar to Colleen China.

Wares are often decorated with polychrome transfers including *Peasant Life in Ireland* and with illuminated lettering "The Top O'the mornin' to ye"

Shamrock Models
Ancient Artefacts
Canterbury Roman Ewer. 64mm.   5.50
Roman Vase found near Canterbury
original in Canterbury Museum.
No. 285. 65mm.   5.50
Grecian Bronze Pot found at Pompeii.
No. 138. 50mm.   5.50
Puzzle Jug. 68mm.   7.50
Shrewsbury Romano-Salopian Ewer
No. 613. 80mm.   5.50

Traditional/National Souvenirs
Bust of Irishwoman decorated with
  green shamrocks on shawl.
  Coloured features. Inscribed: *My*
  simple graceful Nora Cricna.
  87mm.   75.00
Shamrock. 90mm wide.   18.00

Animals
Frog, green eyes, gilded webbed
  feet, croaking. 75mm.   30.00

Model of Irish Pig, standing,
inscribed: *Wun't be druv* Can be
found inscribed: *The Dear Little
Shamrock....* No. 148. 60mm high,
70mm long.   40.00

Birds (including Eggs)
Cockerel, with orange face and
yellow beak. 100mm.   22.00

Miniature Domestic
Cheese Dish and cover.
76mm long.   12.50

Shamrock Crest China

Trademark used for a Belfast wholesaler by
R.H. & S.L. Plant (Ltd), Tuscan Works,
Longton. (Usual trademark Tuscan).
The initials N.P.O. were not used by any
known manufacturer and stand for
Northern Publishing Office, a Belfast
retailer. All pieces with this mark were
sold with Irish crests or transfers,
including Glenariff Glen, Newtownards,
The Honeycombe, Giants Causeway and
The Irish Jaunting Car.

Shamrock Crest Models
Ancient Artefacts
Irish Bronze Pot. 45mm.   5.00

Traditional/National Souvenirs
Irish Harp.   12.00

Seaside Souvenirs
Shell. No. 56. 85mm long.   10.50

Animals
Standing Pig.   19.50

J. Shaw

Birds (including Eggs)
Open Egg Shell. 65mm long.   8.00

Alcohol
Carboy. 68mm.   7.00

Miscellaneous
Jug.   4.00
Vase. 95mm.   4.00
Vase.   4.00

Trademark used by J. Shaw & Sons,
Longton, subsequently John Shaw & Sons
(Longton) Ltd. Willow Pottery, Longton
(see Hewitt Bros (usual trademark Willow
Art)).
This firm usually produced tableware and
fine bone china. Although most firms
producing small quantities of crested
ware usually stuck to 'smalls', the only
crested ware recorded from this firm are
the models below.

J. Shaw Models
Buildings - White
Shakespeare's Cottage.
    130mm long.   35.00

Countryside
Milk Churn and lid. 72mm.   7.00

Comic/Novelty
Biscuit impressed: *Huntley and
    Palmer.* Biscuit coloured on white
    shaped base. 68mm long. (Has
    been recorded with a Dolgelly
    crest).   45.00
Dr Beetle, standing figure with
    umbrella. 145mm.   80.00
Teddy Tails and Dr Beetle seated in
    armchair. 92mm.   100.00

Shell China

Trademark used by an unknown Staffordshire Pottery but resembles Arcadian or Willow.
This mark has only been recorded on three miniature models listed below.

Shell Models
Traditional/National Souvenirs
Welsh Hat. 55mm.   8.00

Miniature Domestic
Cheese Dish and cover. 45mm.   9.50

Comic/Novelty
Billiken. 70mm.   7.00

Shelley China

1890-1910. On small, decorative and domestic items.

1910-1923/4. On small, decorative and domestic items. The words 'LATE FOLEY' were incorporated 1910-1916.

ENGLAND

1912-1925.

1890-1910. On numbered models.

$\mathcal{S}^{HELLEY}$ C_{HIN_A}
LATE FOLEY

1910-1925. On numbered models.

$\mathcal{S}^{HELLEY}$ C_{HIN_A}

Shelley
CHINA
ENGLAND

1910-1925+.

Trademark used by Wileman & Co, Foley Potteries and Foley China Works, Fenton, Longton and subsequently renamed Shelleys Ltd.

The firm of Wileman and Co. was founded in or around the year 1860 by Mr J.F. Wileman and Mr J.E. Shelley. From 1883 the business was run entirely by the Shelley family; the founder and his son Percy Shelley, and later his grandsons. Wileman and Co. were well known and

respected manufacturers of fine china, specialising in tea and breakfast sets for the comfortable middle class market both at home and abroad. Several other firms used the tradename 'Foley' (notably E. Brain and Co.) and this can be confusing for the collector looking for early pieces. Obviously the tradenames were causing confusion in the 1900's for in 1910 the company decided to change its tradename to 'Shelley', using the name of the owners rather than the pottery. In its advertising to the trade the company announced, perhaps rather unfairly, 'The World Wide reputation of Foley china has caused many cheap imitations, and in future to protect the public the real genuine Foley china will always be indelibly marked Shelley'.

For sometime the tradename Shelley was accompanied by the title late Foley and one suspects that this was dropped from the markings on 'Crest China' before other domestic wares. The firm changed its name legally to Shelleys Ltd in 1925, but the new mark seems to have been used before this date.

The Shelley family produced commemorative and view ware before 1900, and seem to have begun producing Crest China as they called it in 1903 as a sideline. One suspects that this was in direct competition with W.H. Goss. Foley, and later Shelley fine crest china was sold in the best china shops, rooms and halls and not in bazaars, post offices, cafes and other dubious outlets. At first crests were applied to domestic wares (the same shapes can be found decorated in the usual styles of the day) and small trays and vases. Early models include simple small shapes such as books, hats, animals and some souvenir items of the South African War. All of these being rather more in line with the cheaper crested china firms than Goss, but by 1906 the Shelleys were producing small models of ancient artefacts, very like the Goss products. Over the next few years the firm produced the most interesting range of these, always in the delicate white china for which they were well known and with carefully painted crests.

With the coming of the war years, and the loss of skilled men to the battlefields of

France, the production of moulded models obviously became financially more important to the firm. (Models made during and after the Great War tend to be heavier and cruder than other products of the firm obviously the work of unskilled labour). In 1920 at the British Industries Fair the Shelley family showed 'Crest China' and advertised it in that year for the first time. Great War souvenirs and some novelty items were added to the range, but they never quite reached the vulgarity displayed by other manufacturers. Shelley stopped producing crested china much earlier than other firms, in fact they appear to have added very few items to their range after 1923 and do not mention its production in advertising after that date. Obviously they continued to produce the domestic ware which was always the speciality of the firm and made a feature of children's ware in the later 1920's as did many other manufacturers. Shelley Potteries Ltd. is now part of the Doulton Group.

The Shelley models are not very exciting for those who like the colourful and bizarre. A few half-hearted 'novelties' can be found, but basically 'respectable' and not to amuse on the mantelshelves of the 'working classes'. However, collectors of fine china are very drawn to Shelley/Foley pieces, especially to the named historic shapes which are so like Goss. (New collectors should be warned that the less common of these already change hands among seasoned collectors for more money than the common Goss models).

Early Foley/Shelley view ware is very beautiful, both monochrome (red, black and brown) and polychrome transfers can be found. Up to 80 designs of map decorations were produced between 1903 and 1910, all found on models marked FOLEY. Later Shelley transfers are rather disappointing being very highly coloured and not so attractive. The firm also produced models with transfer prints of a regional nature instead of crests. (A few early models marked FOLEY or SHELLEY/LATE FOLEY can be found with deep tinted pictorials printed all over. These are numbered but not named.) Some Crested China shapes have been found with all over floral decorations such as

the stylised cornflower. Foley/Shelley also produced commemorative ware and souvenirs of most Royal events from 1860 onwards can be found. Commemoratives, view ware and crested pieces were also made for the American, Australian, New Zealand and South African markets but examples of these are difficult to find in Britain.

The only military badges recorded are the *Royal Garrison Artillery, Royal Marines, RFC, Royal Artillery* and *2nd Life Guards*, but a 1914 War inscription can be found on some models. Commemoratives of the Boer War, although not crests, are of great interest to the military collector as they name generals and colonial supporters. (These are naturally marked Foley)

Some late Shelley models do carry 'Lucky Black Cat' transfers but these are rare so it seems likely that they were only made in a limited way. Some 'Lucky White Heather' pieces have been found and the firm made very few coloured crested models, 'How Ink is Made' being a noticeable exception. Other coloured models were made in the 1920's, including a striking range of birds. These however were not crested and are not listed here.

Very keen Shelley collectors are probably already aware of the wonderful range of crested domestic ware made by the firm. Collectors of 1920's and 30's china can find vases and bowls in lustred finishes and very evocative nursery ware designed by Hilda Cowham and Mabel Lucie Atwell.

Numbering System. This was the only firm to print (paint in the case of low numbers) a stock number on every model and to do so throughout that model's production. They appear to have begun to do so from around 1906 onwards, and so some early pieces marked Foley are not numbered. From registration numbers and trade names found on numbered models one can deduce the approximate date of original production. The following is offered as a rough guide to dating:

Models 1-120 designed 1903-1910.
Models 130-413 designed 1910-1923/24
Models 500-507+ designed after 1923/24.

Stock numbers 91-99, 121-129, 216-299 (with the exception of a Bulldog which is found numbered 238), 390-399 and 414-499 do not appear to have been used.

It seems that in four of the above five cases when a new series of models was added to the range the numbering recommenced at the nearest hundred above the last number used. The exception, the gap between stock numbers 121 and 129, seems to have been caused by the introduction of the new Shelley / late Foley mark.

Real Shelley addicts may like to make their own list of models in numerical order - if they do they will find that some 20 individual numbers have not yet been found. These unrecorded numbers must have been used and hopefully these models will eventually be recorded. A list of the unused numbers is given here 8, 9, 10, 12, 13, 14, 15, 17, 19, 37, 59, 75, 76, 77, 78, 79, 100, 152, 155, 156, 172, 193, 316, 356, 366, 383, 387. Almost certainly a numbered model in the above list is rare.

NB: These lists include pieces marked Shelley, Foley and Shelley late Foley.

Shelley Models
Unglazed/Parian

Bust of *Albert*, King of the Belgians. 1915. 118mm.	50.00
Bust of *Burns* on square glazed base. 140mm.	30.00
Bust of *The Right Hon. Winston Churchill First Lord of the Admiralty.* 125mm.	100.00
Bust of HM King George V. 2 sizes: 120mm.	55.00
130mm.	55.00
Bust of French, with inscription: *Field Marshall Sir John French, Commander in Chief of the Expeditionary Force.* 118mm.	65.00
Bust of Jellicoe, with inscription: *Admiral Sir John Jellicoe. In Supreme Command of the North Sea Fleet.* 118mm.	55.00
Bust of Joffre, with inscription: *General Joffre, Commander in Chief of the French Army* 1915. 130mm.	60.00
Bust of Kitchener, with inscription: *Field Marshall Earl Kitchener, Secretary of State for War.* 118mm.	50.00
Bust of *The Rt Hon David Lloyd George.* 2 sizes: 118mm & 130mm.	60.00

Sailor standing with hands on hips, square base. Inscribed: *Ready! Aye! Ready!* and impressed: *HMS Lion.* Coloured. 170mm.	125.00

Ancient Artefacts

Early Models (marked Foley) are sometimes found with no printed number or inscription. Models can be found with coloured transfer views, etc., instead of crests. All inscriptions begin: *Model of* so this will not be repeated throughout the list.

Ancient Cyprian Water Bottle. No. 140. 45mm.	10.00
Antique Tea Caddy - Queen Anne. No. 153. 70mm.	10.50
Aqua Mixel for pouring water over the hands of the priest. No. 137. 74mm wide.	8.50
Arabian Wine Vessel. No. 203. 75mm.	6.50
Caerswys Roman Vessel. No. 204 55mm.	6.00
Celtic Jar (an ancient). No. 200. 65mm.	7.00
Celtic Water Bottle. No. 205. 63mm.	6.00
Chester Roman Urn, inscribed: *A very rare Roman urn found near Chester now in possession of J.W. Salt Esq.* No. 118. 54mm.	6.00
Chinese Jar 12th Century. No. 304. 121mm.	14.00
Chinese Vase of great antiquity and beauty date about 5000 BC. Belongs to the nation. No. 115. 62mm.	6.00
Chinese Vase, about 500 AD. No. 213. 60mm.	8.00
Cinerary Urn of rare form. from Northants. No. 134. 40mm.	7.00
Cleopatra's Vase, inscribed: *An Egyptian vase taken from the tomb of Cleopatra.* No. 114. 50mm.	8.50
Colchester Famous Vase, inscribed: *Famous Colchester Vase in the museum.* No. 110. 48mm.	6.00
Cyprian Vase about 3000 BC. No. 206. 62mm.	8.00
Cyprian Water Bottle. No. 192. 76mm.	16.00
Derby Roman Vase, inscribed: *Roman Vase found at Little Chester, Derby.* No. 83. 65mm.	8.50

Dorset Cinerary Urn, inscribed: *Cinerary Urn with handles found at Dorset.* No. 132. 56mm. 6.50

Dover Cinerary Urn, inscribed: *Cinerary Urn found in Dover.* No. 141. 63mm. 8.50

Eastern Olive Jar. No. 208. 53mm dia. 8.00

Egyptian Vase, inscribed: *Ancient Egyptian Vase about 250 BC.* No. 84. 43mm. 7.50

Ely Saxon Vase, inscribed: *Ancient Saxon Vase,found in Ely.* No. 310. 88mm. 16.50

Exeter Vase. Unnamed Foley model. No. 117. 55mm. 6.00

Flemish Jug 14th century. No. 312. 70mm. 15.00

Gastrica Vase, inscribed: *Vase or bottle found in Gastrica. Ancient Cyprian pottery 900 BC.* No. 138. 51mm. 8.00

Glastonbury Bowl, inscribed: *Bowl from the ancient British lake village near Glastonbury.* No. 101. 50mm. 6.00

Glastonbury Vase, inscribed: *Vase from the Ancient British Lake Village near Glastonbury.* No. 104. 2 sizes: 50mm. 6.00
83mm. 12.00

Hanley Chinese Vase, inscribed: *Chinese Vase, originally in Hanley Museum.* No. 80. 63mm. 7.00

Hanley Egyptian Vase, inscribed: *Ancient Egyptian vase now in Hanley Museum.* No. 88. 63mm. 12.50

Herpes Jug, inscribed: *Jug from cemetery at Herpes, Charente.* No. 133. 45mm. 7.50

Hibernian Pot of rare antiquity. No. 313. 80mm. 16.00

Indian Wine Vessel from Temple, Delhi. No. 303. 162mm. 25.00

Irish Bronze Pot. No. 109. 35mm. 6.00

Italian Vase. 16th Century. No. 301. 100mm. 14.50

Italian Vase. 16th Century. No. 309. 100mm. 14.50

(The) Kai Ping Vase, date about 2500 BC. No. 119. 63mm. 8.50

Kang Hi Tea Caddy. No. 144. 63mm. 12.00

Kang Hi Vase, presented to George V No. 305. 120mm. 25.00

Kent Roman Urn, inscribed: *Roman urn from warriors grave, Kent.* No. 211. 52mm. 7.00

Lesser Pyramid Vase, inscribed: *Vase taken from a tomb under the Lesser Pyramid about 3500 BC.* No. 117. 57mm. 8.50

Letchworth Celtic Urn, inscribed: *Celtic Urn found in Letchworth.* No. 199. 80mm. 35.00

Lord Byron's Vase, inscribed: *Fine model of a Greek vase presented to this nation by Lord Byron. Now in South Kensington Museum.* No. 116. 57mm. 8.50

Loving Cup, 3 handled. Not found numbered. 40mm. 6.00

Lyme Regis Ammonite, model of. 88mm. 15.00

Malta Chatty. No. 89. 44mm. 9.00

Mayer Jug 1870, Model of No. 326. 71mm. 17.50

Newbury Leather Bottle, inscribed: *Leather Bottle found on battlefield of Newbury. 1644. Now in Museum.* No. 103. 60mm. 6.00

Notre Dame Candlestick, inscribed: *Altar Candlestick in church of Notre Dame.* No. 306. 115mm. 16.50

Penmaenmawr Urn, inscribed: *Ancient Urn found on Penmaenmawr.* No. 108. 48mm. 6.00

Persian Cafeterre (fine),15th Century. No. 302. 118mm. 16.50

Persian Scent Bottle 700 AD. No. 212. 55mm. 6.50

Persian Wallace Vase. No. 82. 55mm. 9.00

Persian Wine Server. 13th Century. No. 308. 105mm. 13.00

Phoenician Vase, original in Stoke-on-Trent Museum. No. 86. 57mm. 8.50

Phoenician Water Jar 1000 BC. No. 207. 65mm. 6.00

Pompeian Vessel in Burslem Museum. No. 87. 60mm. 12.00

Pompeian Wine Bottle, inscribed: *Wine Bottle taken from ruins Pompeii.* No. 135. 54mm. 17.00

Potters Vessel,found in Temple to Bhudda. No. 150. 54mm. 13.50

Puzzle Jug, with verse. No. 180. 65mm. 13.50

Roman Money Box, found at Lincoln AD 307. No. 131. 53mm. 9.50

Roman Tear Vase, 200 BC. No. 201. 63mm. 15.00

Roman Wine Vessel, 500 BC. No. 142.
51mm.   16.00
Sacred Vessel found in Bethlehem. No.
146. 51mm.   17.50
Salamis Lampshade, inscribed:
Ancient Cyprian pottery. No. 130.
60mm.   13.00
Salonika Vase, inscribed: Ancient
Greek vase found at Salonika by the
British troops when entrenching Jan
1916. No. 170. 70mm.   17.50
Scandinavian Water Bottle. No. 143.
83mm.   9.50
Sevres Vase,18th Century. No. 300.
88mm.   6.00
Sherborne Vase, inscribed: Model of
Roman Vase found in Sherborne. A
rather detailed, battered shape.
Reg. No. 456392. 95mm.   25.00
Silchester Urn, inscribed: Roman
Urn, from Silchester in Reading
Museum. No. 107. 50mm.   6.00
Silchester Vase, inscribed: Vase from
Silchester in Reading Museum. No.
102. 51mm.   6.00
Silver Rose Bowl. No. 147. 63mm.   13.00
Sofia Cup, inscribed: Very quaint cup
found with silver belt, Sofia,
Bulgaria. No. 139. 42mm.   14.50
Swindon Vase, inscribed: Vase dug
up near Swindon. No. 105. 58mm.   6.00
Tara Vase, now in the Vatican, Rome.
No. 113. 50mm.   10.00
Tibet Sacred Vase, inscribed: Sacred
Vase from Temple in Tibet. No. 209.
60mm.   8.00
Turkish Scent Jar. S.K. No. 202. 66mm.   8.00
Vatican Urn, inscribed: Golden Urn
in the Vatican. No. 145. 78mm.   16.00
Vestal Lamp, inscribed: Roman vestal
lamp. 500 BC. No. 149. 78mm.   19.50
Water Bottle, inscribed: Ancient
water Bottle of rare form. No. 136.
80mm long.   14.50
Water Bottle from tomb of Rameses II.
No. 210. 63mm.   14.00
Weymouth Vase, inscribed: Roman
Vase found at Jordan Hill,
Weymouth now in Dorset Museum.
No. 85. 56mm.   7.50
York Roman Ewer, inscribed: Roman
Ewer from original in Hospitium,
found in York. No. 81. 63mm.   10.00

Buildings - White
The Tower, Blackpool, Model of. No. 322.
2 sizes: 125mm.   19.50
135mm.   19.50
Blackpool Tower with buildings.
No. 412. 160mm.   22.50
Burns Cottage, Model of. No. 189.
68mm long.   22.50
Douglas Clock Tower - see
Monuments .
Dundee Arch. 92mm.   80.00
Forth Bridge. 130mm long.   45.00
Glastonbury Tor, not found
numbered. 85mm.   42.00
Manx Cottage, Model of (as Burns
cottage above. No. 198 - with
different inscription).
68mm long.   25.00
Monmouth Clock Tower-see Skegness
Clock Tower.
Ross-on-Wye, Town Hall, with Clock
Tower (not found numbered).
123mm.   70.00
Skegness, Clock Tower, can also be   22.50
found inscribed: Monmouth clock
tower. No. 371. 155mm.   40.00
Windsor Round Tower. No. 372.
88mm.   35.00

Monuments (including Crosses)
Attiwell Memorial Sleaford statue
(unglazed angel on base). 195mm. 145.00
Clacton-on-Sea Lifeboat Memorial,
A Lifeboat Hero 'Albert Edward'
Lifeboat Clacton-on-Sea. No. 318.
145mm.   40.00
Douglas Isle of Man. Queen Victoria
Jubilee Clock (Tower). 1887.
No. 388. 143mm.   65.00
King Alfred, Statue (not found
numbered).
2 sizes: 158mm   70.00
165mm.   70.00
Peel Monument. Inscribed: Peel
Monument Halcombe Hill
Ramsbottom. Built 1851 in
Commemoration of the Repeal of the
Corn Laws. No. 385. 123mm.
This is a square tower on a square
building, detailed brickwork.   140.00
Southport Lifeboat Memorial, with
inscription. No. 318. 140mm.   25.00
Rock of Ages, Cheddar, with verse
(not found numbered). 125mm.   16.00

Rufus Stone, with lengthy
inscriptions (not found
numbered).95mm.   12.50

Historical/Folklore
Bunyan's Chair (also found
inscribed: *The old armchair* or more
rarely: *In the Old Arm Chair at E'en
rest, free from all care with loved ones
blest)*. No. 347. 90mm.   19.00
Burn's Chair. No. 336. 86mm.   14.00
*Burn's Clock, Model of old Grandfather
clock in Burns Cottage, Ayr*. No.
307. 130mm.   22.00
Ducking Stool, two-piece,
Leominster. 120mm long.   70.00
Mary Queen of Scot's Chair (same
mould as Bunyan's Chair).
No. 347. 90mm.   19.00
Mother Shipton with black or white
hat and cat. With verse: *Near to
the Knaresboro Dropping Well. l
first drew breath as records tell*. No.
409. 110mm.   40.00
*Sir Walter Scott's chair at Abbotsford,
Model of*. No. 325. 68mm.   12.50

Traditional/National Souvenirs
Burns and Highland Mary on oval
base (not found numbered).
120mm.   35.00
Blackpool Ferris Wheel. No. 373.
117mm.   25.00
Legs of Man, model of. No. 351.
90mm.   25.00
Lincoln Imp, model of the, on
pedestal. No. 160 122mm.   22.50
Ripon Horn Blower, model of the,
with inscription: *The old time
custom of sounding the horn at 9pm
each day is still observed*. No. 158.
110mm.   16.00
Manx Legs triangular dish.
143mm wide.   17.00
Manx Loving Cup, 3 handles as legs
of Man. 80mm. (Foley mark
only).   25.00
Channel Island Milk Can, fixed lid.
No. 34. Unnamed. 60mm.   9.50
Kathleen Mavourneen, standing
figure of Irish lady Some
colouring. No. 405. 105mm.   100.00
Pat's Hat and Dudeen, model of.
(Irish Topper with pipe moulded
on top). No. 159. 53mm.   20.00

Highland Mary Statue. No. 411.   30.00
Tam-o'shanter (impressed) sitting
figure holding glass. 113mm.   40.00
Thistle Vase, can be found
inscribed: *Just a wee deoch an
Doris*. No. 181.
2 sizes: 50mm.   6.00
65mm.   7.00
Welsh Lady, seated, inscribed:
Cymru-Am-Byth. No. 404. 95mm
(rare).   60.00
Welsh Hat, model of the. Can be
found with longest Welsh place
name round brim. (Very
occasionally the hat can be found
painted black with a red hat
band). No. 154. 55mm.
Plain   16.50
Welsh name   22.50
Coloured   25.00
Swiss Cattle Bell. No. 314. 95mm.   25.00
Swiss Cattle Bell, not found
numbered, with 'Late Foley'
mark. 65mm.   17.00

Seaside Souvenirs
Bathing Machine. No. 320.
75mm long.   25.00
Lifebelt. No. 47. 100mm dia.   16.00
Lifebelt with cord on top. 92mm dia.   20.00
Lifeboatman, standing by Capstan,
inscribed: *A Life Saver*. Some
colouring. No. 410. 112mm.   70.00
Lifeboat, with gold anchor. No. 323.
Can be found inscribed: *Maud
Pickup*, add £7.00. 115mm long.   25.00
Boat, almost canoe shaped on two
supports, with hole at top
possibly for candle. 160mm long.
(Foley mark only).   22.00
Motor Boat with driver on waves.
No. 353. 112mm long.   35.00
Paddle Steamer, model of. No. 362.
160mm long.   100.00
Yacht in full sail, rarely named
Wallaroo. No. 401. 112mm.   25.00
Fisherman's Basket, inscribed: *A
good catch*. No. 186. 88mm long.   16.50
Beachy Head Lighthouse. No. 178.
100mm.   19.00
Bell Rock Lighthouse. No. 178. 102mm.   30.00
Eddystone Lighthouse. No. 73.
94mm.   12.00
Pharos Lighthouse. No. 73.
98mm.   13.00

Lighthouse on rock. 90mm.	9.50
Lyme Regis Ammonite. 98mm.	22.00
Scallop Shell. No. 166. 78mm wide.	14.00
Whelk Shell, inscribed: *What are the wild waves saying*. No. 168. 78mm long.	14.00
Can also be found inscribed. *Sheringham Whelk*. Add £10.00.	
Winkle Shell. Can be found inscribed: *What are the wild waves saying*. No. 169. 70mm long.	14.00

Countryside

Milk Can and lid. No. 34. 64mm.	10.00
Milk Churn. No. 46. 71mm.	13.00
Can be found inscribed: *Straight from the Coo*.	16.00
Pine Cone, closed, on its side. 90mm long.	7.00

Animals

Bear, Polar, walking. No. 67. 80mm long.	40.00
Camel, kneeling (1 hump). No. 64. 102mm long.	24.50
Cat, angry, inscribed: *Me backs up*. 2 sizes: No. 195. 90mm.	45.00
No. 198. 76mm.	70.00
Latter with pink ears and no tail.	
Cat, comical, and sitting with red bow and coloured face, can be found with either left or right ear up. No. 333. 132mm.	55.00
Cat, sitting. No. 68. 64mm long.	45.00
Cat, sitting, head slightly to one side, tail curled around, ruffled fur. No. 268. 96mm.	40.00
Cat, standing, with long body. No. 381. 120mm long.	80.00
Cheshire Cat, model of the Real, impressed: *Tim*. Can be found black. No. 148. 82mm.	45.00
Cow, Staffordshire Cow cream jug. No. 317.	25.00
Bulldog, seated, inscribed: *Another Dreadnought*. No. 233. 63mm.	35.00
Bulldog, black, in kennel, inscribed: *The Black Watch*	25.00
(Also found with bulldog not painted and no inscription). No. 316. 95mm.	20.00
Bulldog, seated. No. 324. 73mm.	27.00

Pup, standing on hand mirror, inscribed: *Some pup!* No. 382.	30.00
(This number 382 is also found on a large comical Pup, inscribed: *Some pup!* It has black ears and spots. 116mm).	120.00
Dog, sitting, alert terrier. No. 377. 100mm long.	50.00
Dog, Scottie, sitting. No. 505. 76mm.	55.00
Dog, Scottie, wearing purple tam-o'shanter. No. 506. 88mm.	60.00
Dog, Scottie, wearing black glengarry No. 507. 75mm.	65.00
Dogs, 2 Scotties sitting, one wearing tam-o'shanter and other wearing glengarry. Both hats beautifully coloured. Can be found inscribed: *Scots Guards*. Add £20.00 No. 386. 83mm.	80.00
Donkey, standing, *Gee Up Neddy*. 115mm long, 95mm high. No. 367.	100.00
Elephant, lying down. No. 70. Rd No. 447138. 80mm long.	30.00
Elephant, standing. No. 363. 70mm.	50.00
Fish Jug (tail forms handle). No. 350. 105mm.	22.00
Fox, sitting. No. 62. 78mm.	55.00
Hare, sitting, looking behind. No. 66. 90mm long.	70.00
Lion walking. No. 369. 162mm long.	70.00
Monkey, sitting, can be found inscribed: *Who hung the monkey?* No. 61. 64mm.	22.00
Mouse, sitting with paws raised. No. 65. 70mm.	70.00
Pig, standing with inscription: *You can push, you can shuv but I'm hanged if I'll be druv*. or *Putney on a Pig*. No. 74. 90mm long.	32.00
	50.00
Pig, sitting, with folded arms, can be found inscribed: *Very umble*	50.00
or *Sussex Pig, wunt be druv*. or *Putney on a pig*. No. 60. Rd. No. 447312. 80mm.	60.00
Piglet, standing. No. 90.	22.00
Toad. No. 71. 47mm.	25.00
Terrapin. No. 69. 85mm.	25.00

Birds (including Eggs)

Chick hatching from egg. 55mm.	11.00
Chick hatching from egg Pepper Pot. 67mm.	11.00

Duck, sitting. *A real prize Aylesbury Duck.* Beak may be coloured.
Reg. No. 582115. 85mm.   45.00
Goose, plump. No. 63. 93mm.   45.00
Penguin, with black and pink beak,
and holding newspaper. Also
found with black patches on back -
Add £25. No. 384. 100mm.   80.00
No. colouring.   60.00
Swan, open wings, with coloured
beak. No. 321. 85mm long.   25.00

Great War

Scottish Soldier, standing figure,
inscribed: *Scotland for ever.*
No. 402. 114mm.   150.00
Britannia, standing figure inscribed:
Rule Britannia. Gilded helmet.
No. 403. 108mm (rare).   170.00
Britannia. Very much larger
standing figure. *Rule Britannia*
inscribed on front and also *Peace.*
Naked child at side blowing trumpet.
No. 409. Very rare. 120mm.   400.00
Marianne, inscribed: *Vive la France.*
Some colouring. No. 406. 108mm
(rare).   140.00
Soldier, playing concertina outside
tent, inscribed: *Blighty is the place
for Me-e-e.* No. 341. 108mm long.   160.00
Medical Orderly *For King & Country,*
two red crosses on sleeves (Rare).
170mm.   500.00
Also found unglazed, fully coloured
as a soldier without red crosses or
inscription.   400.00
Biplane, usually found with a fixed
prop, but can be found with a
movable one. No. 344.
150mm long.   140.00
Bleriot Warplane, model of.
monoplane with fixed prop.
No. 311. 150mm long.   110.00
Zeppelin, model of. *L33* outpressed.
No. 332. 154mm long.   160.00
Battleship, not found named.
No. 319. 125mm long.   40.00
'AQUITANIA' 4 funnelled liner. An
armed merchant cruiser used
later as a troop transporter and
hospital ship. No. 357. 160mm
long. Very rare.   550.00
Submarine, inscribed: *E9.* No. 328.
150mm long.   65.00
Armoured Car, model of. No. 329.
120mm long.   70.00

Staff Car, Vauxhall. No. 361.
135mm long.   150.00
British Tank, model of, with trailing
steering wheels. No. 400.
115mm long.   30.00
Model of British Tank without trailing
wheels, with sponsons. No. 400A.
Rd. No. 658586. 100mm wide,
145mm long.   210.00
Tank Bank, as above but as
money box. No. 413. 140mm long.
Also found numbered 511.   110.00
Red Cross Van, model of. No. 330.
95mm long.   45.00
Howitzer. No. 340. 148mm long.   75.00
Field Gun. No. 331. 132mm long.   35.00
Trench Mortar, model of. Inscribed:
For freedom. No. 179 or No. 327.
63mm long.   22.00
9.2mm Shell, model of.
No. 175. 90mm.   14.00
With Lydd or New Romney crest.   22.00
German Zeppelin Bomb, model of.
No. 177. 85mm.   22.50
Mills Hand Grenade, model of.
No. 334. 78mm.   30.00
*Model of German Mine washed up on
the East Coast.* No. 188.   90.00
Can be found wrongly inscribed:
*Head of German torpedo
(Model of).* No. 187.
68mm (rare).   100.00
Head of German Torpedo, Model of.
No. 187. 70mm (scarce).   125.00
Bandsman's Drum. No. 57. 32mm.   12.50
Drum. No. 49. 60mm Dia.   12.50
Drum, burst No. 57. 31mm.   16.00
Bugle. No. 354. 112mm.   45.00
Field Glasses. No. 343. 83mm.   22.00
Peaked Cap. No. 54. 53mm dia.   12.50
Glengarry No. 176. 86mm long.   20.00
*Anti Zeppelin Candlestick as used
during the Great War - souvenir.*
No. 348. 83mm.   85.00
Fireplace, inscribed: *Keep the home
fires burning.* No. 338. 70mm.   22.50
Coal Hod, inscribed: *Coal rations;
Yours to a Cinder* or *Your rations to
a Cinder* No. 183. 55mm.   21.50
Cenotaph, flags in relief. No. 368.
2 sizes: 130mm.   20.00
157mm.   32.00
Florence Nightingale, sitting figure.
No. 408. 102mm.   125.00
Matlock Bath War Memorial, not
found numbered. 180mm.   55.00

Home/Nostalgic

Anvil, inscribed: *Every morning sees
some task to be done.* No. 183.
83mm long.   11.50
Armchair, inscribed: *The old armchair.*   12.50
(Also found inscribed: *Bunyan's
Chair).* No. 347. 90mm.   19.00
Baby's Cradle. (Often found not
numbered when marked *Foley).*
Found No. 50 and No. 503
(Shelley). 80mm long.   21.00
Bellows. No. 55. 95mm long.   17.50
Book. No. 56. 63mm.   16.50
Box of Matches, open to reveal
contents. Some colouring.
No. 190. 74mm long.   25.00
Cheese. 45mm.   12.50
Cigarette Case holding 6 gold-
tipped cigarettes. No. 349.   45.00
Clock, long case, inscribed: *Model of
14th Century clock in Wallace
collection.* Usually inscribed: *Wake
up and get to business,* or more
rarely: *The moving finger writes and
having writ moves on* (add £10.00),
*Burns Clock "Burns" Grandfather
Clock* (add £4.00). No. 307. 130mm. 24.00
Desk, roll-topped. No. 380.
80mm long.   30.00
Lace Iron. No. 504. 70mm.   30.00
Garden Roller. No. 358. 104mm long. 19.00
Handbag. No. 184. 85mm.   17.50
Kennel. No. 49. 55mm.   12.50
Lantern, inscribed: *Model of ye olde
lanterne* and *Ancient lights.*
No. 346. 105mm.   17.50
Pocket Watch and Matchbox Holder.
No. 379. 100mm.   45.00
Puzzle Jug. No. 180. 68mm.   10.00
Shaving Mug. No. 164. 54mm.   12.50
Sundial, octagonal with transfer of
dial face. No. 359. 120mm.   20.00
Swing Mirror on stand, silvered.
No. 376. 88mm.   50.00
Tobacco Pouch, 2 crossed pipes in
relief on front. No. 501.
98mm long.   30.00
Trunk. No. 167. 54mm.   12.00
Valise, half open. No. 58.
2 sizes: 73mm long.   14.50
120mm long.   19.50
Victorian Pillar Box, model of.
No. 157. 90mm.   40.00
Watering Can. No. 163. 63mm.   14.50
Water Pump. No. 51. 83mm.   17.00
Wheelbarrow. No. 355. 110mm long. 22.50

Comic/Novelty

Black Boy in bath, inscribed: *How
ink is made.* Partly coloured.
No. 374. 108mm long.   110.00
Black Boys head in Roman Vestal
lamp. 500 BC. No. 149. 93mm long. 65.00
Coal Hod can be inscribed: *Coal
rations yours to a cinder.* No. 185.
55mm.   13.00
Japanese Lady, standing, inscribed:
Yum, Yum, some colouring.
No. 407. 123mm.   150.00
Santa Claus, partly coloured,
carrying sack of coloured toys.
No. 378. 120mm.   300.00

Alcohol

Beer Barrel. No. 48. 63mm.   12.50
Beer Barrel on stand. No. 161. 65mm. 14.00
Bottle with cork, sometimes inscribed:
All Scotch. No. 214. 90mm.   10.00
No inscription.   8.50
Soda Syphon. No. 502. 96mm.   17.00
Toby Jug, with verse: *No tongue can
tell* etc. No. 335. 95mm.   19.00

Sport/Pastimes

Boxer, inscribed: *England's hope.*
Brown boxing gloves. No. 375.
120mm.   170.00
Golf Bag and Clubs. No. 197.
108mm.   75.00
Golf Ball. No. 210. 50mm.   20.00
Golf Ball on Tee. No. 215. 52mm.   17.00
Tennis Racquet with 3 Balls. No. 194.
116mm long.   25.00

Musical Instruments

Banjo. No. 72. 127mm long.   19.50
Piano, upright. No. 345. 76mm.   30.00

Transport

Charabanc, inscribed: *The Monach.*
No. 352. 125mm long.   55.00
Coal Truck, *Black Diamonds from...*
No. 389. 96mm long.   40.00
Cycle Lamp, very rarely found
inscribed: *Model of cycle oil head
Lamp.* No. 342. 83mm.   75.00
Locomotive. No. 365. 150mm long.   275.00
Motor Coupé. No. 360. 135mm long. 200.00
Open Motor Car. No. 361 - see WW1
Staff car.
Single Decker closed Motorbus 'K'
type. No. 370. 120mm long.   400.00
Double Decker Omnibus. No. 370.   450.00

Modern Equipment

Camera . No. 342.	45.00
Flash Lamp, model of. No. 191. 70mm.	15.00
Horn Gramophone. No. 337. 95mm.	40.00
Steamroller. No. 364. 130mm long.	450.00

Hats

Bishop's Mitre. No. 58. 70mm.	10.50
Top Hat, found numbered 11 and 35. 60mm wide.	7.50
Top Hat, giant. 75mm. 128mm long.	30.00
Trilby Hat, with black band. No. 500.	45.00

Footwear

Dutch Sabot. No. 36. 84mm long.	7.50
Leather highboot. No. 47. 69mm.	18.00
Lancashire Clog. No. 162. 98mm long.	14.00

Miniature Domestic

Cheese Dish and fixed lid. No. 196. 50mm. 75mm long.	20.00
Cup and Saucer. 38mm.	6.00
Tea Pot, fixed or separate lid, inscribed: *Take a cup o'tea*. No. 38. 55mm.	20.00

Domestic

Candleholder. No. 339. 107mm long.	17.00
Candleholder. 135mm long.	15.00
Coffee Pot with lid, ribbed and fluted. 140mm.	12.50
Hatpin Holder, circular base. 122mm.	17.50
Inkwell and pen rest. No. 165. 60mm long.	18.00
Jug. 80mm.	5.00
Pin Tray. 75mm dia.	5.00
Pin Tray, diamond. 92mm long.	5.00
Sugar Bowl. 65mm.	5.00
No. 171. Salt Pot.	11.00
No. 172. Mustard Pot. 48mm.	11.00
No. 173. Salt Pot, circular. 100mm.	11.00
No. 174. Pepper Pot, circular. 100mm.	11.00

Numbered Ornamental Wares

No. 1. Pin Tray.	5.00
No. 2. Vase.	5.00
No. 3. Dish with ribbed sides. 120mm dia.	8.00
No. 3 also a mug, 38mm. 120mm dia.	5.00
No. 4. 2 handled Loving Cup. 40mm.	5.00

No. 5. Fluted Trinket Tray. 70mm dia.	5.00
No. 6. Bell shaped jug.	6.50
No. 7. Vase, 2 handled with crinkle top. 56mm.	5.00
No. 10. Vase. 100mm.	5.00
No. 11. 2-handled pot. 35mm.	5.00
No. 16. Jug, with high looped handle. 63mm.	11.00
No. 18. Small Jug. 44mm.	5.00
No. 20. Jug. 65mm.	5.00
No. 21. Vase. 70mm.	5.00
No. 22. Vase, shaped. 38mm.	5.00
No. 23. 2-handled Vase. 50mm.	5.00
No. 24. Pot, with lid. 50mm dia.	9.50
No. 25. Vase,2 handles, with bulbous base. 60mm.	5.50
No. 26. Vase,2 handles. 40mm.	5.00
No. 27. Vase,2 handles, with crinkle top. 58mm.	6.00
No. 28. Jug, square. 35mm.	5.00
No. 29. Two-handled Vase. 64mm.	10.00
No. 30. Jug. 72mm.	5.00
No. 31. Cauldron. 2 handled. 35mm.	5.00
No. 32. Jug, small. 38mm.	5.00
No. 33. Vase,2 handles. 54mm.	5.00
No. 34. Milk Can and lid. 62mm.	9.50
No. 39. 3 handled Loving Cup. 36mm.	8.00
No. 40. Cream Jug. 55mm.	5.00
No. 41. Ewer. 63mm.	5.00
No. 42. Jug. 65mm.	5.00
No. 43. Vase, 2 handles. 54mm.	5.00
No. 44. Jug,2 handles. 50mm.	5.00
No. 45. Vase, crinkle top. 52mm.	5.00
No. 80. Jug. 74mm.	5.00
No. 106. Vase. 65mm.	5.00
No. 109. Irish Bronze Pot. (Unnamed). 36mm.	6.00
No. 111. Urn. 58mm.	5.00
No. 112. Taper Vase. 60mm.	5.00
No. 120. Box and lid, heart-shaped. 32mm.	7.00
No. 121. Pin Box and lid. 40mm.	7.50
No. 122. Pin Box and lid, square, with curved sides. 30mm.	8.00
No. 123. Pin Box and lid, square. 32mm.	8.50
No. 124. Pin Box, crinkle edge. 30mm.	9.50
No. 146. Jug. 66m.	5.00
No. 147. Silver Rose Bowl. 64mm.	9.00

No. 151. Bulbous Vase with 2
   handles and spout.   5.00
No. 181. Pin Box, waisted.
   50mm long.   5.50
No. 182. Horseshoe Dish. 97mm long. 7.00
No. 417. Ewer. 75mm.   5.00

Miscellaneous
Ewer with shamrock shape top.
   38mm.   6.00
Horseshoe. No. 182. 100mm.   17.50
Horse's Hoof. No. 52. (often found
   not numbered). 45mm.   7.50
Shield on stand, not found
   numbered. 52mm.   9.00
Urn with lid. 88mm.   5.00
Wall Pocket. 90mm.   6.00

Signal Series or
Signal China

Trademark used by Hewitt and Leadbeater,
   Willow   Potteries,   Longton   (Usual
   trademark Willow Art) for their Dublin
   agent.

'Smalls' only found with this mark,
   except for the following:

Signal Models

Traditional/National Souvenirs
Irish Harp with Shamrock decoration. 10.00

Home/Nostalgic
Anvil. 65mm long.   7.50
Fireplace, inscribed: *There's no place
   like home,* with black kettle and
   cauldron, red fire in relief. 65mm.   17.00

Miniature Domestic
Cheese Dish and cover.   9.50
Kettle & Lid. 57mm.   10.00

Skareb China

Trademark used for retailer J. Baker & Son, Bristol, by Arkinstall & Son, Arcadian Works, Stoke-on-Trent, (usual trademark Arcadian).

Several smalls and the models below have been found with this mark.

Skarab Models
Animals
Pig, kneeling. 70mm long.   20.00
Squirrel eating nut. 60mm.   30.00

Transport
Motor Spirit Can. 58mm.   22.50

Miniature Domestic
Cheese Dish, one piece. 65mm long.   9.50

Snowdon China

SNOWDON
CHINA

Trademark used for the Snowdon Mountain Tramroad and Hotels Co. Ltd. on china manufactured by Arkinstall & Sons Ltd. Arcadian Works, Stoke-on-Trent. (Usual trademark Arcadian).
For further details of this china and manufacturer see Arcadian China.
All crests found on china with this mark are either of Snowdon or Snowdon Mountain Tramroad & Hotels Co. Ltd. (This is a most striking red, white and black crest with the initials S.M.T.) or Owen Gwynedd. The china is very fine and well produced.

Snowdon Models
Traditional/National Souvenirs
Welsh Harp. 80mm.   9.50
Welsh Hat, model of, with longest
    Welsh place name round brim.
    52mm.   12.50
Welsh Tea Party, 3 Welsh ladies
    taking tea. Coloured. 50mm.   40.00

Animals
Black Cat sitting on a pouffe
    inscribed: *Good Luck*. 95mm.   30.00
Black Cat in boot. 62mm long.   60.00
Black Cats, three in bed. 66mm.   75.00

Great War
Cenotaph. 83mm.   10.00

Home/Nostalgic
Umbrella, open. 50mm dia.   17.50

Comic/Novelty
Bookmaker with greyhound and
  hare on ashtray. Some colouring.
  90mm long.   50.00

Modern Equipment
Camera folding. 60mm.   40.00

Miniature Domestic
Cheese Dish and cover, one-piece.
  68mm long.   10.00

Souvenir Series

Trademark used by an unknown manufacturer, possibly Hewitt and Leadbeater,
  usual trademark Willow, for a London
  wholesaler or retailer. See also H & S.
Pieces have been found with transfer prints
  of four flags of the Allies with the inscription: *We are fighting for a just cause* and also
  Imperial International Exhibition.

Souvenir Models
Seaside Souvenirs
Whelk Shell. 90mm long.   6.00

Animals
Pig. Inscribed: *The Pig that wont go.*
  95mm long.   19.50

Home/Nostalgic
Coal Scuttle. 53mm.   6.00

Footwear
Lancashire Clog. 85mm long.   6.00

S P Co. Ltd.

Spencer Art China

$$\text{SPENCER}$$
$$\text{ART}$$
$$\text{CHINA}$$
$$\text{FENTON}$$
$$\text{STAFFS}$$

Trademark used for a wholesaler or retailer in Manchester by an unknown manufacturer.

SP Models
Ancient Artefacts
Swindon Vase (not named).   4.00

Domestic
Pin Tray 75mm long Rectangular.   4.00
Stamp Box and lid. 63mm long.   7.50
Small Vase. 55mm.   4.00

Trademark used for a retailer by a Fenton manufacturer.
The models below all have Isle of Wight crests and are similar to Vectis/Victis models. One would assume that 'Spencer' was a retailer or wholesaler on that island. (No potter or pottery named Spencer was working in Fenton from 1900-1920.) The three Fenton manufacturers known to have produced a quantity of crested china were E. Hughes Ltd., A.G. Harley Jones and James Reeves. E. Hughes mostly made domestic ware so they were hardly likely to have produced the models below. The other two manufacturers could have used this mark but A.G. Harley Jones is possibly the most likely candidate as he used the term Art China in his marks (see Wilton China). One 'small' has been found with a Leeds crest, and one dog with Harrogate, which could have been used to fill other orders.

Spencer Art Models
Buildings - White
Osborne House. 150mm long.   100.00
The Old Village, Shanklin, Io W.
   100mm long.   100.00

Monuments (including Crosses)
Arch Rock, Freshwater Bay. 82mm.   40.00

Historical/Folklore
Mons Meg, Edinburgh Castle, model of.
130mm long.   22.00
Donkey in well at Carisbrooke Castle,
   with brown donkey. 92mm.   120.00

Animals
Calf. 102mm.   26.00
Cheshire Cat, inscribed: *Still*
    Smiling. 82mm.   12.50
Dog on hind legs. 75mm.   12.00

Alcohol
Barrel with open top. 45mm.   6.50

Sport/Pastimes
Rook chess piece. 48mm.   9.50

Sphinx

Trademark used by a foreign (French or German) manufacturer for the Belgian souvenir market.

The only model found has crest of Bruxelles.

Sphinx Models
Historical/Folklore
Coach and Horses with 3 figures,
    coloured, on base. 100mm long.   60.00

Sporting Series

SPORTING SERIES
G. V. & C.º
REG. APPLIED FOR

Trademark used by Arkinstall & Son Ltd., Arcadian Works, Stoke-on-Trent, usual trademark Arcadian.

Only one piece has been recorded with this mark, a spade trump with colour transfer of pheasants. It would appear that the Sporting Series was not a commercial success.   20.00

SR

ENGLAND

Mark used before 1913.

Trademark used by Samuel Radford (Ltd) High St, Fenton.
This china manufacturer established in 1879 did not produce a large range of crested china, but what they did was in porcelain and of very fine quality.

SR Models
Ancient Artefacts
Loving Cup, 3 handled. 35mm.   5.00

Countryside
Milk Churn and lid. 70mm.   7.00

Musical Instruments
Banjo. 110mm long.   22.00

Miniature Domestic
Cheese Dish and cover. 64mm long.   9.50
Shaving Mug. 55mm.   9.00

Standard China

Stanley China

Trademark used by an unknown British porcelain manufacturer.

Standard China Model
Domestic
Cup and saucer.   5.50

Mark used 1906-1930.

Trademark used by Charles Amison (& Co. Ltd), Stanley China Works, Wedgwood St, Longton.

The firm was established in 1889 and manufactured porcelain. (The factory closed in 1941 and was reopened in 1946, and continues to make Stanley fine bone china today.) Like most fairly successful firms, Amison made a small range of crested china wares when these were very fashionable. The models made seem to have sold well in the north of England.

No view ware or transfer devices have been recorded and the ware is very white and heavy.

Stanley Models
Ancient Artefacts
Puzzle Jug. 70mm.   6.50

Animals
Dog, bulldog sitting. Some
   colouring. 68mm.   20.00

Birds (including Eggs)
Parakeet, some colouring. 110mm.   17.00

Great War
Battleship. 119mm long.   25.00

Home/Nostalgic
Grandfather Clock Candle inscribed:
   Good Morning. 105mm.   17.50
Pillar Box. 76mm.   16.00

Footwear
Boot. 70mm. 106mm long.   7.50
Lancashire Clog.
  2 sizes: 125mm long   6.50
            135mm long.   7.50
Sabot. 80mm long.   6.00

Miniature Domestic
Cheese Dish and cover. 50mm.   9.50

Domestic
Pepper Pot. 80mm.   5.00
Pin Box and Lid, rectangular.
  56mm long.   6.00

Star Bazaar Art China

Trademark used for the Star Bazaar,
Douglas, Isle of Man, on china thought to
have been manufactured by Hewitt &
Leadbeater, Willow Potteries, Longton.
(Usual trademark Willow Art).
For details of Hewitt & Leadbeater see
Willow Art China.
This mark is only found on china with
Douglas or Isle of Man crests. Hewitt &
Leadbeater often used Art China in marks
designed for retailers, and the models
below could have been produced by
them.

Star Bazaar Models
Ancient Artefacts
Puzzle Jug. 70mm.   7.50

Traditional/National Souvenirs
Manx Man, John Bull mould with
  extra leg at back. 126mm.   95.00

Animals
Manx cat with collar, not named.
  63mm.   40.00
Manx cat, no collar. 60mm.   30.00
Pig, standing. No. 60. 81mm long.   20.00

Home/Nostalgic
Anvil. 50mm.   7.50
Hand holding tulip. 78mm.   7.00

Strand Art China

Strand China

Trademark used by an unknown English manufacturer, probably for a London retailer.

The only piece to have been recorded with the above mark is a 45mm five mouthed vase, valued at £4.00.

Trademark used for a London retailer by Podmore China Co, Elm Street, Hanley. (Usual trademark Podmore). This retailer obviously supplied towns all over the country as crests other than London are found.

Strand Models
Monuments (including Crosses)
Nelson's Column. 144mm.   40.00

Seaside Souvenirs
Lighthouse. 122mm.   9.00

Animals
Angry Cat, with arched back and
   tail. 100mm.   14.50
Dog in kennel, inscribed: *Black
   Watch*. 67mm.   12.50
Elephant, standing. 75mm.   20.00

Birds (including Eggs)
Penguin. 84mm.   14.50
Woodpecker.   20.00

Great War
Cenotaph, inscribed.
   3 sizes: 80mm.   9.00
             130mm.   10.50
             165mm.   17.50
Edith Cavell Memorial, London
   Inscribed: *Edith Cavell Brussels
   dawn October 12th 1915. Humanity
   sacrifice*. 142mm.   17.50

Home/Nostalgic
Thimble. 43mm. 17.50
Sack of Black coal inscribed: *If you*
can't afford a truck, buy a sack. 25.00

Transport
Charabanc. Inscribed: *Over the hills*
and far away. 124mm long. 40.00

Miscellaneous
Hand holding a tulip. 93mm. 7.00

Success (Art) China

Mark used by Hewitt & Leadbeater

Mark used by Hewitt & Leadbeater

Mark used by S. Hancock & Sons

Trademarks used by an unknown retailer, supplied by Hewitt & Leadbeater (usual trademark Willow Art), S. Hancock & Sons (usual trademark Corona) and possibly another manufacturer as well.

The fact that two quite different marks are found can either indicate that the tradename was used for a long time or that the name was used by more than one manufacturer.

The Art China mark would have been used by Hewitt & Leadbeater (see Willow Art China). The Garter mark is much more difficult, for several firms used this

device, including Hewitt & Leadbeater and S. Hancock and Sons. No models have stock numbers or inscriptions which give clues to the manufacturer but we can be fairly certain that it was S. Hancock & Sons.
The Salisbury Kettle listed below has a coloured transfer print of Beachy Head.

Success (Art) Models
Parian/Unglazed
Bust of *John Peel* with details of
verse. 136mm.   75.00

Ancient Artefacts
Lincoln Jack. No. 34. 52mm.   5.50
Salisbury Leather Kettle. 61mm.   7.00
Old Salt Pot in Carlisle Museum.
48 mm.   5.50

Traditional/National Souvenirs
Thistle vase with inscription: A *wee
Deoch-&-Doris*. 50mm.   7.50

Seaside Souvenirs
Lighthouse, black band. 105mm.   9.00

Great War
Torpedo. 145mm long.   65.00

Home/Nostalgic
Anvil. 58mm.   7.50
Grandfather Clock. 121mm.   17.50

Sussex China

Trademark used for an Eastbourne retailer by Sampson Hancock (& Sons), Bridge Works, Stoke. Pieces were sold with Sussex towns coats of arms. (Usual trademark Corona).
For further details of this china and manufacturer see The Corona China.
For the most part the models are identical to those found in the Corona range, except that there were two versions of Beachy Head Lighthouse made specially for this retailer. A Transfer of Pevensey Castle has been recorded. The models were probably made during the Great War.

Sussex China Models
Buildings - White
Bridge. Rarely found inscribed
Weymouth Bridge Add £15.00
130mm long.   19.50

Historical/Folklore
Ark. 90mm long.   8.00
Mother Shipton. 73mm.   12.00

Traditional/National Souvenirs
Laxey Wheel. 80mm.   40.00

Seaside Souvenirs
Lighthouse. 104mm.   9.50
Beachy Head Lighthouse, black band.
3 sizes:-102mm.   7.50
             118mm.   9.50
             150mm.   12.00

Animals
Mouse eating a nut. 40mm.	30.00
Staffordshire Bull Terrier. 79mm.	14.50
Teddy Bear, sitting. 85mm.	24.50

Great War
British Airship on base.
128mm long.	40.00
Lusitania. 163mm long.	125.00
Submarine, inscribed: *E4*.	
102mm long.	22.50
Submarine, inscribed: *E5*.	
125mm long.	26.00
Tank with inset wheels. 105mm long.	30.00
Torpedo. 150mm long.	65.00

Home/Nostalgic
Cigarette Case. 70mm long.	13.00
Grandfather Clock. 122mm.	16.50
Hip Bath. 95mm long.	12.50

Footwear
Lancashire Clog. 105mm long.	6.50

Musical Instruments
Harp. 90mm.	9.50

Sport/Pastimes
King, chess piece. 110mm.	40.00
Pawn, chess piece. 60mm.	35.00

Modern Equipment
Box Gramophone with arm on
record, no horn. 60mm square.	25.00

Domestic
Candlestick, column. 89mm.	4.00
Candlestick, square. 100mm.	5.00

Sussex China S.P. Co.

Trademark used for a Sussex wholesaler by Arkinstall & Son Ltd. Arcadian Works, Stoke-on-Trent. (Usual trademark Arcadian) and Sampson, Hancock (& Sons), Bridge Works, Stoke (usual trademark Corona).

S.P. Co. must have been a wholesaler in fancy goods or had a chain of shops because china models with this mark have crests from all over Sussex. Coloured transfer prints of Sussex views have been recorded but no other transfer devices, indicating that the mark was probably only used between 1914 and 1920.

One jug has been found with an Ashford crest, and a chess King with a Lydd crest, so Kent crests must also have been used.

Sussex S.P. Co. Models
Ancient Artefacts
Newbury Leather Bottle. 65mm.	5.50

Buildings - White
Cottage. 55mm.	10.50
Hastings Clock Tower. 157mm.	14.00

Traditional/National Souvenirs
Welsh Hat. 35mm.	10.00

Seaside Souvenirs
Houseboat. 58mm.	8.00
Lifeboat, inscribed: *Charles Arkcoll*	
115mm long.	30.00
Whelk Shell. 100mm long.	6.00

Countryside

Hay Stack, circular. 57mm.	9.50
Milk Churn and lid. 70mm.	8.00

Animals

Chimp. 75mm.	20.00
Dog, Staffordshire bull terrier, sitting. 72mm.	14.00
Mouse eating a nut. 44mm.	30.00
Pig, sitting. 63mm long.	20.00
Rabbit, lying, ears along back. 70mm long.	10.50
Tortoise. 70mm long.	9.00

Birds (including Eggs)

Swan. 62mm long.	8.50

Great War

British Airship found wrongly named *Model of Super Zeppelin*. 128mm long.	40.00
Battleship, 3 funnels and tiny gun fore and aft. 120mm long.	30.00
Red Cross Van. 85mm long.	40.00
Howitzer. 140mm long.	25.00
Mills Hand Grenade, model of. 62mm.	19.50
Colonial Hat. 88mm long.	18.00
Bell Tent. 64mm dia.	16.00
Drum. 51mm.	12.00
Ghurka Knife, model of. 110mm long.	25.00
Sandbag, model of. 73mm long.	22.50
Trench Dagger, model of. 102mm long.	70.00

Home/Nostalgic

Baby in Boottee. 80mm long.	15.00
Old Armchair, not named. 90mm.	10.00
Lantern. 90mm.	9.50

Comic/Novelty

Bean Pod, curved and split to reveal beans. 133mm long.	20.00
Policeman, no inscription. 140mm.	50.00
Suffragette Candlesnuffer. 72mm.	25.00

Sport/Pastimes

King, chess piece. 110mm.	35.00
Knight, chess piece. 63mm.	14.50

Musical Instruments

Banjo. 140mm long.	16.50
Double Bass. 151mm.	40.00
Piano, upright. 70mm long.	20.00

Footwear

Lancashire Clog. 100mm long.	6.50

Domestic

Pin Box and lid — circular. 64mm dia.	5.00

Sussex Ware

No details of mark available.

Trademark used for Cheesman & Co, Brighton by Hewitt & Leadbeater, Willow Potteries, Longton. (Usual mark Willow Art).
For further details of this china and manufacturer see Willow Art China. The sixth edition of the Goss Record published in 1906-7 carries an advert for the Goss Agent in Brighton, Cheesman & Co, 169 North Street, Brighton. In the advert the firm announces the sale of their 'Sussex Ware; including 'Ye Olde Sussex Pig', green with ivory decoration or brown with hop decoration. In 1905 when the new firm of Hewitt & Leadbeater was given a write-up in the *Pottery Gazette*, 'Hop Ware' was one of their newly invented lines. Hewitt & Leadbeater obviously went on to make heraldic china for Cheesman & Co. until well after the Great War.
No 'Ye Olde Sussex Pigs' have been recorded but would be a delightful novelty to look out for. They would probably not carry the Sussex China Garter mark.

A model of 'Ye Olde Sussex Pig' was reputedly made but so far has not been seen.   30.00

Sutherland Art China

1912-1941.

Trademark of The Alma Pottery, High Street, Longton and later of the Sutherland Works, Normacot Road, Longton.

A tea service has been found with the Triple Entente decoration, Rd No. 643369. Also inscribed: *The Allied Forces and For Freedoms Cause 1914*. A cream jug has been found with a 'RITA China Series' mark in addition to the one above, for further details see RITA China.

Sutherland Art China Models
Domestic
Cream Jug.   5.00
Cup & Saucer.   5.00
Sugar Bowl.   5.00

Swan China

Trademark used by Charles Ford, Cannon St, Hanley, subsequently a branch of J.A. Robinson & Sons Ltd. (Usual trademark Arcadian).

The original firm, known as T. & C. Ford at this address, was formed in 1854. By 1871 it was known as Thomas Ford, and in 1874 it became Charles Ford. (Presumably all these Fords were members of the same family.) Production of view ware and crested china seems to have begun at the turn of the century. Very shortly after this, in 1904, Mr Harold Taylor Robinson gained control of the firm and merged it with Robinson & Beresford in 1907. In 1910, Charles Ford was made a branch of J.A. Robinson & Sons Ltd. and production of Swan China was moved to the Arcadian Works. It is very difficult to distinguish original Charles Ford moulds from Arkinstall moulds, as both were used at the Arcadian Works and models were marked Swan or Arcadian. (Pieces are often found with both marks.) Early Swan models seem to be heavier than Arcadian China, these include miniature domestic items, small vases and animals. Later Swan and Arcadian models are identical. The Swan mark does not seem to have been used after 1925.

Early Charles Ford models can be found with views, monochrome only, and crests, often accompanied by suitable long and learned historic details concerned with the place or person. These do not appear on Arcadian China. An interesting range of all the crests of English Monarchs (about forty) can be found, each crest on a different small piece, with the relevant historical information printed on the reverse.

Polychrome view ware is the same as Arcadian, as are other transfer decorations including tropical birds, cockerels and Raphael Tuck cartoons. (These are always found with 'By special permission of Raphael Tuck & Sons Ltd.' printed on the base when marked Swan.)

Great War commemoratives and inscriptions are the same as Arcadian including crests of the Allies, but as yet the only military crests recorded are:

Black Watch
5th Dragoon Guards
East Surrey Regt.
Gordon Highlanders
Highland Light Infantry
Leicestershire Regt. 17th Foot
2nd Life Guards
Manchester Regt.
Northumberland Fusiliers
Prince Albert's own Hussars
Prince Consort's own Riffle Brigade
Queen's Bays
Queen's own Cameron Highlanders. 79th Foot
Royal Berkshire
Royal Engineers
Royal Field Artillery
Royal Flying Corps
Royal Horse Artillery
Royal Marines Gibraltar
Royal Irish Dragoon Guards
Royal West Surrey Regt.

A Lucky Black Cat transfer has been found, but these are not common. No Lucky White Heather devices have been recorded although a Pig has been found decorated with pink roses and shamrocks.

Numbering System. Original Charles Ford models carry painted stock numbers, but few of these have been recorded. Models made at the Arcadian Works have printed stock numbers which do not correspond to the numbers found on similar Arcadian pieces. Stock numbers are given where known in the following lists.

Swan Models
Unglazed/Parian
These busts can be found with
crests on their glazed bases, add
£10.00 if the bust carries the
correct Royal coat of arms.

Bust of King Edward VII on circular glazed base. 140mm.	50.00
Bust of Queen Alexandra, on circular glazed base. 140mm.	50.00
Bust of King George V, on circular glazed base. 135mm.	50.00
Bust of Queen Mary, can be found inscribed: *Queen Mary, born May 26th 1867*. 135mm.	50.00
Bust of *HRH Prince of Wales Born June 23rd 1894*, dressed as midshipman. 125mm.	80.00
Bust of Sir John Jellicoe on square glazed base. 175mm.	75.00
Bust of General Joffre, on square glazed base. 155mm.	75.00
Bust of Lloyd George, on circular glazed base. 135mm.	50.00
Bust of Lord Kitchener on square glazed base. 158mm.	70.00
Bust of Burns. 80mm.	35.00
Bust of Wordsworth on glazed base. 118mm.	22.50

Ancient Artefacts

British Bronze Pot. No. 160. 70mm.	5.50
Butter Pot, old, of 17th Century. 45mm.	5.50
Canterbury Leather Bottle. 40mm.	5.50
Canterbury Roman Ewer, inscribed: *Roman Ewer found near Canterbury original in Canterbury Museum.* No. 294. 64mm.	5.50
Canterbury Roman Vase. 65mm. No. 288.	5.50
Chinese Vase original in Hanley Museum. 58mm.	5.50
Club Vase. No. 582. 68mm.	4.00
Devon Oak Pitcher. 60mm. No. 192.	5.50
Dogger Bank Bottle. 70mm.	5.50
Eddystone Jug, inscribed: *old Spanish jug dredged up near Eddystone now in Atheneum, Plymouth.* No. 585. 58mm.	5.50
Egyptian Jug, about 400BC original in Stoke-on-Trent Museum. No. 162.	5.50
Egyptian Vase, inscribed: *Ancient Egyptian Vase 230BC.* No. 155. 42mm.	5.50

Egyptian Water Bottle. No. 156. 58mm long.	5 50
Fountains Abbey Cup. No. 709.	5.50
Glastonbury Vase. No. 642. 50mm.	5.50
Highland Whisky Bowl inscribed: *Model of Highland Whiskey Bowl.* No. 158. 90mm wide.	7.50
Highland Whisky Bowl. 134mm wide.	7.50
Horsham Jug inscribed: Model of Medieval Jug in Brighton Museum found at Horsham. No. 154. 70mm.	5.50
Irish Bronze Pot. No. 110. 35mm.	5.50
Kendal Jug. 75mm. No. 210.	5.50
Lincoln Jack from Original in Museum. 62mm. No. 50.	5.50
Loving Cup originated by Henry of Navarre, King of France. 3 handled.	
2 sizes: 40mm.	6.50
52mm.	6.50
Newbury Leather Bottle. 67mm.	5.50
Phoenician Vase, originally in Stoke on-Trent Museum. No. 217. 60mm.	5.50
Puzzle Jug, original in South Kensington Museum, with verse: *Try how to drink and not to spill.* No. 147 and No. 303. 70mm.	7.00
Puzzle Teapot. 86mm long.	13.50
Salopian Roman Ewer inscribed: *Roman Salopian Ewer found at Uriconium now in Shrewsbury Museum.* 70mm.	5.50
Shakespeare's Jug. 54mm.	6.50
Southwold Jar.	5.50
Upstones Jug, inscribed: *Ancient jug found near Upstones, Staffs.* No. 221. 62mm.	7.00
(Also found inscribed Ipstones). It seems Upstones was a spelling mistake.	
Winchelsea Vase. 82mm.	5.50
York Roman Ewer No. 57. 55mm.	5.50
York Roman Urn.	5.50

Buildings - Coloured

Shakespeare's House. 84mm long.	20.00

Buildings - White

The Tower Blackpool. 104mm.	16.50
Cottage on rectangular base. 78mm long.	12.00
First and Last Refreshment House in England. 73mm long.	14.50
Hamsfell Hospice. 70mm.	35.00
Ann Hathaway's Cottage, Shottery, near Stratford-on-Avon. 83mm long.	12.00

Highland Cottage, model of. 80mm.   20.00
Irish Cottage. 70mm long.   20.00
Irish Round Tower. 106mm.   16.00
Marble Arch. 65mm.   17.00
Southampton Bargate. 66mm.   30.00
Tower Bridge. 92mm.   40.00
Welsh Cottage, Model of. Same model
as Highland and Irish Cottages).
79mm long.   20.00

Monuments (including Crosses)
Barrow's Monument, Ulverston.
140mm.   30.00
Celtic Cross, not named. Usually
Irish crest. 125mm.   17.00
The Garden of Sleep at Cromer.
100mm high.   125.00
Iona Cross, not named. 120mm.   9.00
Lifeboat Memorial. 117mm.   16.00
Margate Surf Boat Statue.
120mm.   20.00
Plymouth Armada Memorial.
180mm.   30.00

Historical/Folklore
Ancient Coaching Hat, model of.
65mm long.   7.50
Davey Safety Lamp '1836'. 85mm.   16.50
Font, inscribed: *Model of ancient font
in Tideswell church dates back to the
14th century.* 90mm.   30.00
Stool, three legged rarely found
inscribed: *Jenny Geddes Stool.*
45mm.   18.00
Judge, bust, with inscription: *Defend
the children of the poor and punish
the wrong doer Copy of inscription
of New Bailey Court, London.* With
inscription add £15.00
3 sizes: 55mm.   20.00
60mm.   25.00
70mm.   35.00
Robinson Crusoe, holding Rifle.
120mm.   110.00
Mother Shipton, with verse: *Near to
Knaresboro dropping well.*
2 sizes: 76mm.   10.00
115mm.   18.00
Man sitting in Stocks. "*Time for
reflection AD1600*". 88mm.   20.00

Traditional/National Souvenirs
John Bull, bust.
2 sizes: 66mm.   17.50
86mm.   24.50

Cornish Pasty, inscribed: *This is a
Pasty don't 'ee see, will ee ave a
piece with me. There's more in the
kitchen.* 95mm.   15.00
Melton Mowbray Pie, The. Pie with
moulded pastry adornments and
verse. 50mm.   19.50
Ripon Horn blower with
inscription. 130mm.   14.50
Gretna Green Anvil. 65mm.   8.00
Scotsman bust *Tha can sit on the
Thistle noo* and *Stop yer tickling
Jock* verse. 90mm.   30.00
Irish Colleen. Bust.
2 sizes: 62mm.   25.00
85mm.   30.00
Irish Harp with Shamrocks. 112mm.   10.50
Thistle Vase, with verse: *Just a wee
deoch-&-doris* No. 14. 65mm.   5.00
Welsh Hat. 50mm.   9.50
Welsh Hat with longest place name
on brim. 50mm, 78mm dia.   14.50
Welsh Lady, bust, black hat, coloured
shawl. 83mm.   40.00
Welsh Leek, can be found with
inscription: *King Henry V. The
Welshmen did goot servace (at
Crecy) in a garden where leeks did
grow. Shakespeare.* 98mm.   7.00
Japanese Lady, sitting with fan.
No. 61. 62mm.   50.00

Seaside Souvenirs
Bathing Machine with '32' above the
door.
2 sizes: 60mm.   16.00
85mm well detailed.   25.00
Bell Rock lighthouse. 141mm.   30.00
Buchaness Lighthouse, Peterhead.
108mm.   30.00
Lifeboat with blue band and yellow
rigging. 113mm long.   22.50
Sometimes found named *James
Stevenson, Albert Edward, Elizabeth
Simpson, John Birch, Charles Arkoll,
Mary Batger* or
Nancy Lucy. Add £15.00.
*Novel Collecting Box for the Royal
National Lifeboat Institution Robin
Hoods Bay,* model of upright fish
standing on square base inscribed:
My diet is £.s.d. 128mm.   80.00
Lifeboatman bust. 85mm.   40.00
Lifebelt. 80mm dia.   12.50

Fishing Basket, found inscribed: *A good catch.* 50mm. 12.50
Beachy Head Lighthouse,
2 sizes: 102mm. 9.50
140mm. 14.50
Eddystone Lighthouse.
2 sizes: 105mm. 8.50
140mm. 12.00
Pharos Lighthouse, Fleetwood, model of.
2 sizes: 88mm. 14.50
130mm. 16.50
Lighthouse on circular base.
100mm. 7.00
Crab. 85mm long. 17.00
Scallop Shell. 70mm dia. 5.50
Scallop Shell *Menu Holder.* 62mm. 10.00
Shell candlesnuffer. 28mm. 10.00
Shell ink well, one open shell inverted on another inscribed: *We are always glad to hear from you.* 105mm. 12.50
Whelk Shell, inscribed: *Listen to the sea.* 85mm long. 6.00
Mussel Shells, top one upturned for *PINS.* 80mm long. 12.00
Judy Bust in mob cap with bow. 90mm. 70.00
Punch, bust, not named, some colouring. 83mm. 50.00

Countryside
Beehive on table. 78mm. 17.00
Hay Stack, circular. 58mm. 8.50
Hay Stack, rectangular. 50mm. 8.50
Milk Churn with lid. 63mm. 7.00
Pinecone. 90mm long. 6.00

Animals
Bear, Polar.
2 sizes: 100mm long. 75.00
136mm long. 75.00
Cat, angry, standing with arched back and green eyes. 63mm long. 16.00
Cat, Cheshire. 100mm. 8.50
Cat, climbing in boot, chasing mouse (peeping out of toe). 105mm long. 45.00
Cat, long necked and sitting. 12.00
Inscribed: *My word if you're not off.* 108mm. 16.00
Cat, sitting, and smiling (grotesque, rather similar to Cheshire Cat). 75mm. 9.50
Cat, sitting, with bow round neck. 56mm. 12.00

Cat, sitting, looking forwards, bow to neck. 66mm. 12.00
Black Cat, on scooter. 70mm. 200.00
Black Cat, sitting in octagonal dish. 100mm wide. 30.00
Black Cat, sitting, operating radio. 63mm. 130.00
Three Black cats on Sledge. 118mm long. 200.00
Black Cat in well. 60mm. 65.00
Black Cat playing piano. 52mm. 200.00
Bulldog, ferocious. 129mm long. 25.00
Bill Sykes Bulldog, inscribed: My *word if you're not off* 100mm long. 22.00
Dog, standing can be found inscribed: *Shetland Collie.* 95mm long. 29.50
Dog, Collie, lying down, inscribed: *Shetland Collie.* Add £10.00. 78mm long. 20.00
Dog, lying, with crossed paws. 108mm long. 26.00
Great Dane, sitting, wearing top hat, 1 ear raised, gold band around hat. No. 360. 112mm. 100.00
Dog, King Charles Spaniel, begging on cushion.
2 sizes: 68mm. 12.50
95mm. 16.50
Spaniel wearing black top hat, coloured with glass on green ashtray base. Reg. No. 67858. 70mm. 50.00
Dog, pup, with one ear raised. 68mm. 12.00
Dog, Pug, standing. 78mm. 14.00
Dog, Pug, sitting. 78mm. 16.50
Dog, puppy, sitting, inscribed: *Daddy wouldn't buy me a bow-wow.* 75mm. 22.50
Dog, *Scottish Terrier.* 66mm long. 20.00
Dog, Scottie, sitting wearing blue Tam o'shanter. 82mm. 20.00
Dog, standing looking left, curly tail, wearing disc on chain. 85mm long. 30.00
Donkey, inscribed: *Hee Haw.* 120mm long. 55.00
Elephant, African (big ears). 58mm. 25.00
Elephant, Indian, trunk modelled free from body, small ears, inscribed: *Baby jumbo.* 50mm. 30.00
If inscribed add £10.00.

Fish, open-mouthed.
108mm long. 6.50
Fish shaped dish. Inscribed: *A*
"Plaice" for everything. 14.50
Fish, curly, 98mm long. 10.50
Frog, open-mouthed and usually
green eyes.
2 sizes: 62mm. 17.00
80mm. 25.00
Hare. 73mm long. 16.00
Lion, walking. Found inscribed:
King of the Forest. 112mm. Add
£8.00. 20.00
Monkey, sitting, hand to mouth
wearing coat. 75mm. 20.00
Otter with fish in mouth.125mm long. 65.00
Pig, lying, decorated with pink
roses and shamrock collar.
118mm long. Rare. 75.00
Pig, lying down on its side, inscribed:
I wunt be druv. Rare. No. 356.
84mm long. 90.00
Pig, sitting and fat. No. 587, can be
found inscribed: *My word if you're
not off.* 90mm long. 22.50
Pig, standing, fat, inscribed: *Wunt be
druv.* 95mm long. 25.00
Pig, standing fat with floppy ears,
inscribed: *Wunt be Druv.* No. 298.
105mm long. 45.00
Pig, standing, with drooping ears.
No. 300, inscribed: *Wunt be druv.*
2 sizes: 90mm long. 25.00
105mm long. 40.00
Irish Pig, model of Alert ears.
Inscribed: *You can push...* 90mm long. 45.00
Sussex Pig, model of, standing thin
pig, inscribed: *You can push or you
can shuv but I'm hanged if I'll be
druv.* No. 148. 78mm long. 22.50
Pig, No. 293, coloured blue. 50.00
Piglet, standing, with erect ears,
inscribed: *WUNT BE DRUV.*
No. 277. 73mm long. 20.00
Also found decorated with
shamrocks and roses. Add £20.00.
Rabbit, crouching. 70mm long. 9.50
Shetland Pony. 105mm long. 40.00
Teddy Bear.
2 sizes: 68mm. 24.50
87mm. 30.00
Large size can be inscribed with
verse: *Come and be my Teddy Bear.*
Add £10.00

Tortoise. 72mm long. 12.00
Welsh Goat, model of, inscribed: *Yr
Afr Cymreig.* 100mm long,
118mm high. 55.00

Birds (including Eggs)
Canary. 90mm. 22.50
Chick breaking out of egg.
2 sizes: 63mm. 9.00
73mm long. 12.00
Larger size can be inscribed: *The
latest out.* Add £5.00.
Egg, with flattened base.
44mm. 8.00
Cock, standing, legs modelled
separately, inscribed: *Cock o'th'
North.* Some colouring to head.
100mm. 22.00
No inscription. 19.50
Can be found fully coloured, in
black with red face, white beak
and feathers outlined in gold
with no crest. Rd. No. 35594.
95mm. Add £10.00
Hen, roosting. 54mm. 9.50
Norwich Warbler, with whistle. 130mm. 30.00
Owl, baby 40mm. 16.50
Owl, long eared. 95mm. 30.00
Parrot inscribed: *Pretty Polly.*
2 sizes: 65mm. 14.00
75mm. 16.50
Swan. No. 12.
2 sizes: 70mm long. 8.50
83mm long. 10.00
Swan. No. 295. 55mm long. 8.50

Great War
British Soldier, model of, on oval
domed base. 135mm. 170.00
Scottish Soldier on oval domed
base, gun down. 140mm. 220.00
Despatch Rider, model of, on
motorbike. 120mm long. 90.00
Drummer Boy, model of. 145mm. 200.00
*Nurse and Wounded Tommy, model
of.* 108mm long. 190.00
Nurse, inscribed: *Soldier's friend.*
Red Cross on chest. 132mm. 80.00
Russian Cossack, model of, on
horseback. 122mm. 250.00
Sailor bust with hatband impressed
HMS Queen Elizabeth, hat tilted
down to left. 92mm. 47.50

Sailor, bust, found with hatband
impressed: *HMS Queen Elizabeth.*
Inscribed: *The handyman,* hat tilted
down to the right. 92mm.   47.00
Can be found inscribed: *Sailor
beware*   55.00
Usually found with Hearts of
Oak verse
Sailor, standing with hands on hips.
132mm.   115.00
Sailor, Winding Capstan, model of.
105mm.   125.00
Soldier, bust, inscribed: *Tommy
Atkins* with verse: *Soldiers of the
King* or *Territorial.* Some
colouring. 90mm.   40.00
With verse   50.00
Soldier with Respirator, bust
inscribed: *Model of new gas mask*
(rare). 95mm.   250.00
*Tommy Driving a Steam Roller over
the Kaiser,* inscribed: *To Berlin.*
120mm long. (Very Rare).   475.00
Tommy in Bayonet Attack, model of.
130mm.   170.00
Tommy and his Machine Gun, model of.
100mm long.   55.00
Tommy on Sentry Duty, model of.
110mm.   85.00
*Tommy Throwing Hand Grenade, model
of.* 125mm.   170.00
New Aeroplane, model of. Biplane
with fixed prop, and roundels in
relief. 120mm long.   170.00
New Aeroplane, model of, with
revolving prop. 135mm long.   75.00
Monoplane, V-winged,fixed 2 blade
prop. 117mm long.   150.00
British Airship with suspended engine.
128mm long.   125.00
Observer or Sausage Balloon, model of.
84mm.   75.00
Super Zeppelin, model of.
127mm long.   60.00
Battleship, inscribed: *HMS Queen
Elizabeth.*
2 sizes: 115mm long.   30.00
            160mm long.   40.00
Battleship, 3 funnels. 120mm long.   30.00
Torpedo Boat Destroyer, model of.
126mm long.   25.00
Submarine, inscribed: *E4.*
95mm long.   27.00
Submarine, inscribed: *E5.*
126mm long.   30.00

Armoured Car, model of.
95mm long.   50.00
Red Cross Van, red cross on each
side and rear. 'EH 139' printed on
radiator. 60mm high, 87mm long.   40.00
Tank, model of.
2 sizes: 115mm long.   17.00
            160mm long.   40.00
Can be found inscribed: *Original
made in Lincoln* for which add £15.00
Tank, model of, with inset steering
wheels. 115mm long. Can be
found inscribed: *Original Made in
Lincoln* - add £20.00.   40.00
Tank, model of, with one wheel.
145mm long.   350.00
Tank, model of, with trailing steering
wheels. Can be found inscribed:
Original made in Lincoln with
Lincoln crest and £20.00 should
be added for this. 144mm long.   40.00
Field Gun.
2 sizes: 112mm long.   22.00
            140mm long.   25.00
Field Gun with screen.
100mm long.   34.00
German Howitzer 140mm long.   25.00
Trench Mortar, model of.
70mm long.   21.50
Revolver, model of 83mm long.   77.50
Anti Aircraft Shell, model of.
98mm.   22.00
Cannon Shell.
3 sizes: 70mm.   5.50
            90mm.   8.50
            132mm.   30.00
The 90mm and 132mm sizes are
often inscribed: *Jack Johnson* - add
£10.00, or *Hartlepools Bombardment
Dec 16th 1914* - add £20.00.
Clip of Bullets, model of.
Sometimes inscribed. 57mm.   28.00
*Bomb dropped from Zeppelin,
model of.*   17.00
Bomb dropped on Bury St Edmunds.
75mm.   17.00
*Bomb which killed a chicken at
Southend, Model of.* (Rare)
75mm.   55.00
British Aerial Bomb, model of. 75mm.   55.00
Canister Bomb, model of. 60mm.   21.50
Plum Pudding Bomb, model of.
72mm long. (rare)   90.00
German Aerial Torpedo.
88mm long.   55.00

Hair Brush Grenade, model of.	
105mm long.	130.00
Mills Hand Grenade, model of.	
2 sizes: 62mm.	27.50
90mm.	55.00
Bandsman's Drum. 53mm.	12.50
Bell Tent, open base and flap. 70mm.	
Inscribed: *Camping Out.*	22.50
Capstan. 56mm.	14.50
Gurkha Knife, model of.	
110mm long.	25.00
Pair of Field Glasses, model of.	
78mm long.	17.00
Sandbag. 70mm long.	25.00
Tommy's Hut, model of.	
105mm long.	50.00
Trench Dagger. 102mm long.	70.00
Trench Lamp. 70mm.	21.00
Water Bottle, model of. 65mm.	17.50
Colonial Hat, model of.	
88mm wide.	16.00
Named.	20.00
Glengarry. 90mm long.	22.50
Officer's Peaked Cap, with coloured	
badge and hatband. 70mm dia.	19.50
If inscribed: *Territorials Cap* in	
blue and red.	30.00
Pith Helmet. 85mm long.	34.00
Tommy's Steel Helmet. 68mm dia.	42.00
Anti-Zeppelin Candle Holder.	
62mm.	22.50
Fireplace, inscribed: *We've kept the*	
home fires burning. 90mm.	20.00
Kitchen Range with pot. Inscribed:	
Keep the home fires burning.	
78mm long.	17.00

Home/Nostalgic

Anvil. 66mm.	7.50
Baby in Bonnet Handbell. 95mm.	47.50
Can be found without bonnet.	47.50
Bellows. 95mm long.	14.00
Chair, highbacked. 90mm.	9.50
Cradle. 70mm long.	12.00
Firebucket. 55mm.	5.00
Flat Iron. 81mm long.	16.50
Frying pan. 110mm long.	17.00
Grandfather Clock, narrow. 103mm.	17.50
Grandfather Clock, model of a	
usually found inscribed: *Make use*	
of time let not advantage slip.	
Shakespeare.	20.00
Can be found inscribed: *The time*	
of day or *Time and tide wait for no*	
man. 110mm.	22.00

Kennel inscribed *Beware of the Dog*	
54mm.	12.50
Lantern, horn. 85mm.	9.50
Pillar Box, inscribed: *GRV* and *If you*	
haven't time to post a line here's the	
pillar box. 63mm.	14.00
Saucepan and lid. No. 178.	
80mm long.	14.00
Stool,3 legged. 40mm.	9.50
Sundial, inscribed: *Life's but a*	
walking shadow. Square base. 83mm.	10.00
Table, square. 39mm.	7.50
Warming Pan, inscribed: *Model of old*	
Warming Pan and *Polly warm the*	
Bed 125mm long.	20.00
Water Pump. 90mm.	17.00
Watering Can. 78mm.	10.00
Wicker Basket, twisted handle,	6.50
inscribed: *Fruit Basket.* 63mm.	8.50

Comic/Novelty

'Arry, Bust of a Pearly King.	
83mm.	55.00
'Arriet, Bust of a Pearly Queen.	
82mm.	75.00
Billiken. 65mm.	7.50
Clown, bust, inscribed: *Put me*	
amongst the girls, some colouring.	
2 sizes: 80mm.	25.00
90mm.	25.00
Golliwog, fully coloured, verse to	
rear. 118mm. Rare.	400.00
Jester, double faced, happy and sad,	
and eyes open and closed. Can be	
found inscribed: *Ye jester awake, ye*	
jester asleep. Add £2.50.	
2 sizes: 65mm.	14.50
90mm.	20.00
Policeman on duty, with verse.	
Controlling The Traffic. 148mm.	55.50
Potato, gilded eyes. 77mm long.	30.00
Suffragette handbell, double-faced.	
Front, sour old lady, inscribed:	
Votes for women. Back pretty	
young girl, inscribed: *This one*	
shall have the vote. Some colouring.	
2 sizes: 70mm.	45.00
98mm.	65.00
Suffragette double faced bust. Same	
face and inscriptions as the	
handbell above. 98mm.	65.00
Some pieces can have brolly	
and necklace and be inscribed:	
Mrs Gamp with signature of	
Mrs Gamp on base.	

Cartoon/Comedy Characters

Ally Sloper, Bust with verse. Some colouring. 100mm.	40.00
Harry Lauder, bust, not named. Inscribed: *Stop ye're tickling Jock* and *Tha can sit on the thistle noo.*	
2 sizes: 83mm.	30.00
95mm.	47.00
Mrs Gummidge, standing figure, with inscription: *A lone lorn creetur and everything goes contrairy with her.* 112mm.	55.00

Alcohol

Beer Barrel, on stand. 40mm.	6.00
Monk, jovial and holding glass, with verse: *A jovial Monk am I.*	
2 sizes: 70mm.	12.50
112mm.	19.50
Soda Syphon. 100mm.	14.50
Beaker, inscribed: *Tak a thimblefull.* 40mm.	8.00
Toby Jug.	
2 sizes: 62mm.	14.00
75mm.	16.00

Sport/Pastimes

Cricket Bag. 80mm long.	16.50
Football. 50mm dia.	11.00
Golf Ball, inscribed: *The game of golf was first played in the year 1448.*	
42mm.	14.50
Golf Club head. 100mm long.	23.00
Caddie standing on golf ball.	
76mm.	40.00
Tennis Racquet. 90mm long.	22.00
Trophy, 2 handled. 49mm.	14.00
Knight chess piece. 62mm.	16.50
Rook chess piece. 55mm.	7.50

Musical Instruments

Banjo. 154mm long.	19.50
Guitar. 153mm long.	19.00
Harp. 105mm.	8.50
Piano, upright. 70mm long.	22.00
Tambourine. 70mm dia.	16.00

Transport

Car, Saloon, inscribed: *EH 139.*	
76mm long.	40.00
Open Tourer, inscribed: *EH 139.*	
110mm long.	40.00
Can of Petrol, impressed: *Motor Spirit.* 55mm.	22.00

Modern Equipment

Gramophone with horn. 112mm.	45.00

Hats

Bishop's Mitre. 55mm.	8.50
Fireman's Helmet. 82mm long.	35.00
Luton Boater. 78mm dia.	17.00
Monmouth Hat with verse.	
54mm.	50.00
Mortar Board. 66mm long.	40.00

Footwear

Oriental Shoe. No. 302.	
102mm long.	7.50
Ankle Boot. 83mm long.	7.00
Lancashire Clog. 92mm long.	6.00
Leather Highboot.	
2 sizes: 75mm.	20.50
105mm.	22.00
Queen Elizabeth's Riding Slipper from the original at Horman Hall, Thaxted, copyright. No. 213.	
100mm long.	40.00

Miniature Domestic

Cheese Dish, one piece. 50mm.	9.50
Cheese Dish and cover. 50mm.	9.50
Cup and saucer. 37mm.	6.00
Cup and saucer, fancy. 49mm.	7.50
Tea Pot with lid. No. 145. 40mm.	9.50
Tea Pot with lid, wide and low No. 165. 46mm.	11.00

Domestic

Hair Tidy and lid. 110mm wide.	6.50
Horses Hoof Inkwell + lid, with inscription: *We're aye prood to hear fra ye.* 90mm.	13.00
Trinket box and lid, heart shaped. No. 321. 60mm.	5.50
Wall Pocket, shield-shaped. 65mm.	5.00

Miscellaneous

Handbell, no clapper. 53mm.	5.00
Horses Hoof Vase. 60mm long.	5.00
Picture Frame. 203mm.	10.00
Mustard Pot and EPNS hinged lid with EPNS spoon. Inscribed: *MUSTARD.* 60mm.	7.50

Sylvan China

1919-1921.

Trademark used by Dura Porcelain Co. Ltd. Empress Pottery, Hanley.
This very short lived firm, established in 1919 and closed in 1921, seems to have been created to make crested souvenirs and dolls' heads to fill the market for cheap German wares that could no longer be imported. An advert for the firm in the *Pottery Gazette* of September 1920 illustrates some of their products including dolls' heads, and crested china boot, monoplane, red cross van, Florence Nightingale statue, hen and Shetland Pony. Some models appear to have been bought in from the Carlton Works. Presumably when German goods returned to Britain after the war they were still cheaper to import than the Dura Company could manage to produce them for - a constant problem for British manufacturers except during the war.
The china is actually quite reasonable and the crests are very well produced.

Sylvan Models
Ancient Artefacts
Puzzle Jug. 70mm.   7.50

Historical/Folklore
Burns Chair, model of. 89mm.   12.50
Mary Queen of Scots Chair, Edinburgh Castle, Model of. 76mm.   11.50

Traditional/National Souvenirs
Welsh Hat. 55mm.   9.00

Seaside Souvenirs
Whelk Shell *Listen to the Sea.* 100mm long.   7.00

Animals
Cat sitting on circular pouffe, inscribed: *Luck* in orange.
2 sizes: 65mm.   14.50
80mm.   14.50
Scottie Dog, black, looking out of Kennel. Inscribed: *Black Watch.* Green bow. 68mm.   15.50
Scottie Dog, sitting wearing tam-o' shanter. 76mm.   12.50
Scottie Dog, standing. 90mm long.   16.50
Pony, standing. 123mm long.   32.00

Birds (including Eggs)
Cockerel. 65mm.   16.00

Great War
Florence Nightingale, Lady of the Lamp. 1820-1910.   19.50

Home/Nostalgic
Fireplace, inscribed: *East or West home is best, Home Sweet Home.* Some colouring, vases and clock on mantlepiece. 95mm long.   25.00

Comic/Novelty
Billiken sitting on throne, inscribed: *The God of things as they ought to be.* 100mm.   9.50
Sack of black coal *If you can't afford a truck buy a sack.* 60mm.   20.00

Cartoon/Comedy Characters
Mr Pussyfoot, all water!! We don't think. This is a prohibishionist piece. 92mm.   50.00

Alcohol
Toby Jug with verse. 90mm.   16.00

Sport/Pastimes
Golf Ball, inscribed: *The ancient game of golf was first played in 1448.* 48mm.   14.50

Modern Equipment
Box Gramophone with Horn. 100mm. 30.00

Footwear
Clog. 76mm long.   6.50

Miniature Domestic
Cheese Dish and cover. 45mm.   9.50

Domestic
Hat Pins holder. 150mm.   12.00

Miscellaneous
Hand holding tulip. 90mm.   7.00

Syren China

Trademark used by Wiltshaw & Robinson
Ltd, Carlton Works, Stoke-on-Trent.
(Usual trademark Carlton).
For details of this china and manufacturer
see Carlton China.
This mark has only been found on the few
models listed below and one small vase.
As the duck is normally painted and
rather more delicate when marked
Carlton, one suspects that this mark was
used for a cheap range for a small retailer
or a mark used by the company on wares
which were not good enough to be
marked Carlton.

Syren Models
Animals
Cat seated on upright piano.
  95mm.   40.00
Cat seated on rocking chair. 95mm.   25.00

Birds (including Eggs)
Comic Duck on green base.
  108mm.   40.00
Owl wearing mortarboard. 72mm.   25.00

Comic/Novelty
Oval Dish with two bananas in
  relief. 120mm long.   20.00

Cartoon/Comedy Characters
Felix, walking on armchair. All white.
  75mm.   135.00

Sport/Pastimes
Sports Trophy. 132mm.   17.50

Talbot China

Trademark used for a retailer by Sampson
  Hancock (and Sons), Bridge Works, Stoke.
  (Usual trademark Corona).
For further details of this china and
  manufacturer see The Corona China.
The models listed below are obviously from
  the Corona range. H.B. and G. must have
  been a retailer, with almost all of the models
  recorded having Castle Coombe Crests,
  so it is probable that he had a shop in that
  area. The only other crests are of Ventnor
  and Burnham-on-Sea perhaps used to fill
  orders.

Talbot Models
Seaside Souvenirs

Bathing Machine. 68mm.	12.50
Lighthouse. 105mm.	8.50
Whelk Shell. 102mm long.	6.50

Buildings White

Blackpool Tower. 122mm.	12.00

Historical/Folklore

Noah's Ark. 95mm long.	9.00

Animals

Cow creamer. 130mm long.	10.00
Fish vase. 60mm.	5.00
Pig, standing. 45mm.	17.00
Tortoise. 70mm long.	13.00

Home/Nostalgic

Armchair, padded. 62mm.	15.00
Desk Top. 55mm long.	10.00
Grandfather Clock. 125mm.	18.00

Pillar Box. 70mm.	14.50
Sofa. 95mm long.	14.50

Musical Instruments

Harp. 95mm.	9.50

Modern Equipment

Gas Cooker. 70mm.	12.00

Sport/Pastimes

King chess piece. 115mm.	35.00
Queen chess piece. 112mm.	35.00

Taylor and Kent

TAYLOR & KENT
LONGTON
ENGLAND

1912+

Mark found on models exported to Australia.

TAYLOR & KENT
LONGTON
ENGLAND

1950+

Trademark used by Taylor and Kent (Ltd), Florence Works, Longton. (Usual trademark Florentine).

For details of this china and manufacturer see Florentine China.

Taylor and Kent only used the crown mark on coloured buildings without crests. I suspect these were finished to a higher standard than the Florentine range and so the company were happy to have their name on them. The first mark was registered in 1912 so it is probable that these models were made before the Great War. Taylor and Kent made some models of buildings after 1930 but these have a slightly different mark, with the addition of a new trade name for the china.

A small jug has been recorded with the T & K the Coronation of George & Mary in 1911.

The final mark dates from 1950 so this must be the very last manufacturer of crested china.

Taylor and Kent Models
Buildings - Coloured
Ann Hathaway's Cottage.

4 sizes: 50mm long.		17.50
70mm long.		20.00
115mm long.		26.00
135mm long.		30.00

Shakespeare's House.

2 sizes: 70mm long.		17.50
115mm long.		26.00

Birds (including Eggs)
Swan, posy holder. 81mm.   7.00

Home/Nostalgic
Baby in hip bath. 100mm long.   12.50
Watering Can. 70mm.   9.00
Saloon Car, windows gilded on one
  side only. Inscribed: *Commemorative*
  of Duke & Duchess of Yorks visit to
  Australia 1927 and exported to that
  country.   40.00

Transport
Saloon Car bearing unusual
  commemorative of the Duke &
  Duchess of York's visit to
  Australia 1927. 88mm.   45.00

Miniature Domestic
Cheese Dish and cover. 70mm long.   9.50

Domestic
Egg Cup. 45mm.   6.00

Temple Porcelain

TEMPLE

PORCELAIN

BRITISH MAKE

Trademark used by an unknown manufacturer. It closely resembles products of the Nautilus Porcelain Co of Glasgow.

Crests from all over the south of England and Wales are found on crested china with this mark. Most items found are 'smalls' and the models listed below appear to be produced by the Nautilus Porcelain Company.

The china is for the most part quite fine and the crests are reasonably well produced. No view ware or any other transfer devices have been recorded.

Temple Models
Ancient Artefacts
Beer Bowl, 3-handled 74mm dia.   5.50
Loving Cup. Three handled. 39mm.   6.00
Puzzle Jug. 70mm.   7.50
Staffordshire Tyg, one handled,
  not named. 63mm.   4.00

Traditional/National Souvenirs
Indian Canoe, high sides. 135mm long. 17.00

Animals
Pig, fat and standing. 67mm.   20.00

Home/Nostalgic
Bellows. 105mm long.   13.00
Bucket with upright handle. 70mm.   6.00
Coal Scuttle, shell shaped, on two ball
  feet.   5.50
Cradle. 62mm long.   9.50
Lantern. 67mm.   8.50

Lantern, Policeman's Bulls-eye. 68mm.   9.00
Milk Churn and lid. 75mm.   7.00
Half-open Suitcase. 62mm long.   6.00

Alcohol
Carboy.   7.00

Sport
Curling Stone.   25.00

Musical Instruments
Tambourine. 73mm dia.   12.00

Footwear
Oriental Slipper. 98mm long.   7.50

Miniature Domestic
Cheese Dish and cover. 50mm.   9.50

Domestic
Oval Trinket Box. 80mm long.   6.00

Thistle China
T.C. & P.G.

Trademark used for L.M. Mack, Ayr, by
Hewitt & Leadbeater, Willow Potteries,
Longton. (Usual trademark Willow Art).
For details of this china and manufacturer
see Willow Art China.

China with this mark has always been recorded with Scottish crests, often the crest of Ayr. The models listed below and 'smalls' are from the Willow Art range.

T.L.K.

Thistle Models
Parian/Unglazed
Bust of *Burns*. 150mm (with Ayr
crest).   40.00

Buildings - Coloured
Model of Burns cottage, inscribed:
*Robert Burns The Ayrshire Bard was
born at Alloway, near Ayr on Jan
25th 1759. He died on 21st July 1796
at Dumfries where he was buried.*
107mm long.   40.00

Monuments (including Crosses)
Burns, statue.
  2 sizes: 108mm.   22.00
            177mm.   30.00

Animals
Rat, with curled tail.
  80mm long.   35.00

Great War
Monoplane with fixed prop.
  146mm long.   75.00
New field gun with screen and sight
  groove. 109mm long.   40.00

Home/Nostalgic
Bucket. 76mm.   8.00

Alcohol
Carboy in Basket. 70mm.   7.00
Champagne cooling bucket. 52mm.   12.00

Musical Instruments
Bagpipes. 114mm long.   50.00

Hats
Top Hat matchstriker. 45mm.   7.00

Miniature Domestic
Cheese dish and cover, rectangular.
  77mm long.   9.00

Mark used by an unknown British manufacturer. One Jug, 60mm has been recorded with a colour transfer of George V and Mary. Inscribed: *Crowned June 22nd 1911*.

T.M.W. & Co Ltd. & S Ltd.

This mark can also be found with the initials TMW & S Ltd.

Trademark used for a wholesaler by Hewitt and Leadbeater (usual trademark Willow Art). No known potters used the initials T.M.W.

The models listed below have been found with a number of different crests, indicating that this was a wholesaler's mark. (The mark seems to be a print of a Bargate which may provide a clue.)

T.M.W. Models
Historical/Folklore

Mother Shipton. 105mm.	12.00

Traditional/National Souvenirs

Welsh Leek. 55mm.	7.00

Seaside Souvenirs

Bathing Machine, inscribed: *A Morning Dip.* 78mm.	16.50
Yacht in full sail. 117mm.	19.50

Animals

Bull, *King of the Herd.* 115mm long. (Willow).	75.00
Cat, sitting. 65mm.	12.00
Bulldog with black collar, sitting. 55mm.	30.00
Scottie Dog, wearing blue, red and black glengarry. 60mm.	14.50
Terrapin. 85mm long.	12.00

Birds (including Eggs)

Fluffy Chick. 65mm.	20.00
Swan. 65mm long.	9.00

Great War

Bugle. 72mm.	24.50

Home/Nostalgic

Pillar Box, inscribed: *GR* and If you haven't time... 80mm.	18.00

Alcohol

Barrel. 33mm.	5.00
Tankard, foaming, Candlesnuffer. Inscribed: *Here's Health.* 55mm.	7.00

Tourist Art China

TOURIST
ART

CHINA
FRANK DUNCAN LTD
AUCKLAND

Trademark used for Frank Duncan Ltd. Auckland, New Zealand, between 1921 and 1929, by Hewitt & Leadbeater Ltd. Willow Potteries, Longton. (Usual trademark Willow Art).

For details of this china and manufacturer see Willow Art China.

Models with this mark are invariably Kiwi miniatures. The crests found include New Zealand and Wellington. The New Zealand crest is often accompanied by the inscription: 'A Souvenir from Auckland' or 'Wellington'. A vase and the lighthouse below have been found with transfer prints of a view of the 'New Bath Building Rotorua, N.Z.' Fortunately this view is recognisably a product of Willow Potteries. Other New Zealand transfer views have also been found. Hewitt and Leadbeater were the only firm to outline their views with a black scroll border, so the mark can be identified. Frank Duncan Ltd was no doubt a New Zealand fancy goods wholesaler.

Tourist Art Models
Buildings - Coloured
Model of Maori Whare from Rotorua
   N.Z. Brown coloured. 85mm.   170.00

Buildings - White
Model of Maori Whare. 50mm.   110.00

Traditional/National
Tiki Figure.   50.00

Seaside Souvenirs
Lighthouse. 110mm.   10.00
Shell Pintray. 64mm diameter.   6.00

Animals
Black Cat with bottle. 70mm.   90.00

Birds (including Eggs)
Kiwi on base, beak to ground. 66mm. 50.00

Home/Nostalgic
Wheelbarrow. 110mm long.   20.00

Alcohol
Barrel on stand. No. 35. 58mm.   7.50

Transport
Tram, single decker *"Life on the ocean
wave"* 100mm long.   170.00

Domestic
Trinket Tray.   7.00

Towy China

Treasure China

```
TOWY CHINA
BRITISH
MAKE
```

See Bronwen Treasure China

Trademark used for a Welsh retailer by
Hewitt and Leadbeater Ltd. Willow
Potteries, Longton. (Usual trademark
Willow Art).
This mark has only been found on a Welsh
Hat with an unrecognisable crest which
has not been named on the model but is
obviously Welsh. The hat fortunately
is not only identical to the Willow
Art model but carries the same stock
numbers, so one can confidently assume
that this mark was used for a Welsh retailer
by Hewitt and Leadbeater.

Towy Models
Traditional/National Souvenirs
Welsh Hat. No. 75. 57mm.   10.00

Tresarnian Ware

Trevelyan China

TRE
SARNIAN
WARE

F.B.& C°L™
TREVELYAN CHINA
MANCHESTER

Trademark used by an unknown foreign manufacturer.
The only piece seen with this mark is a bud vase with six heart-shaped openings and the Guernsey coat of arms. Probably made in Saxony.

5.00

Trademark used by F.B. & Co. Trevelyan China Manchester. A one-handled mug with a black transfer printed view of Edylf Gate, Bridlington has been recorded. See also ECHO CHINA for another mark used by this wholesaler

16.00

Tre-Pol-Pen Series

Triood

Trademark used for an unknown English manufacturer, probably for a Cornish retailer.
Only one model recorded.

Traditional/National Souvenirs
Cornish Pasty, inscribed: *Will ye ave a piece of my pasty.* 95mm long.   14.50

From 1919.

Trademark used by Hoods Ltd. International Works, Fenton. Products are identical to The Corona China.
Hoods Ltd was established in 1919 and manufactured earthenwares. Obviously the firm made crested china souvenirs of the Great War very early in their history and probably only made a range of such wares until the early twenties, when Germany competition returned. The models produced are very ordinary and do not carry inscriptions. The range includes domestic items and 'smalls', which, like the models tend to be rather heavy.
Crests recorded are from all over the Midlands and south of England. One military crest, *The Worcestershire Regiment,* has been found.

Triood Models
Ancient Artefacts
Salisbury Kettle. 105mm.   5.50
Welsh Milk Can. 70mm.   5.50

Buildings - White
Bottle Oven, (Inside of). 81mm.   16.50
Clifton Suspension Bridge.
  120mm long.   75.00
Micklegate Bar, York. 110mm.   19.50

Traditional/National Souvenirs
Welsh Hat. 49mm.   9.00

Seaside Souvenirs
Lighthouse. 108mm.   6.50

Animals
Collie Dog, sitting.   22.00
Elephant, standing trunk down.
  50mm high, 75mm long.   20.00
Pig, standing, ears forward.
  85mm long.   16.00
Rabbit, ears raised. 62mm long.   9.50

Birds (including Eggs)
Swan posy holder. 58mm.   7.00

Great War
Airship on base. 130mm long.   35.00
Monoplane with movable prop.
  150mm long.   75.00
Battleship. 120mm long.   30.00
Submarine, impressed: *E4*.
  104mm long.   24.50
Red Cross Van. 100mm long.   40.00
Tank, with inset steering wheels.
  102mm long.   24.50
Field Gun. 130mm long.   24.00
Bell Tent, with open flaps. 86mm.   19.00
Ghurka Knife. 135mm long.   20.00
Pickelhaube. No. 58. 52mm.   40.00

Home/Nostalgic
Cigarette Case. 70mm.   14.00
Grandfather Clock. 125mm.   16.50
Iron Trivet. 74mm long.   8.00
Jardiniere on stand, fixed. 80mm.   7.00
Tobacco Pouch. 75mm long.   13.50
Writing Slope. 50mm long.   12.50
Water Bottle, rectangular. 66mm.   10.00
King Chess piece. 110mm.   30.00
Pawn Chess piece. 63mm.   25.00

Comic/Novelty
Jug in shape of Man's smiling face.
  80mm.   7.00

Musical Instruments
Harp. 92mm.   10.00
Upright Piano. 62mm.   20.00

Modern Equipment
Gas Cooker. 70mm.   13.00

Footwear
Hob Nail Boot. 70mm long.   6.50
Ladies Shoe. 90mm long.   7.50
Lancashire Clog. 95mm long.   7.00

Miniature Domestic
Cheese Dish, one piece. 58mm.   9.50
Cheese Dish and cover. 82mm long.   9.50
Club speciman vase. 72mm.   4.00
Coffee Pot with lid. No. 205. 70mm.   9.50

Domestic
Candlestick, round base. 85mm.   4.00

Tudor Arms China

Trademark used by a wholesaler for ware by Hewitt & Leadbeater Ltd. Willow Potteries, Longton. (Usual trademark Willow Art), and by Sampson Hancock of Hanley. (Usual trademark Corona Pottery).

Most models with this mark have Welsh Crests and it is possible that C.J. and Co. were Cardiff wholesalers. The only military badge recorded is that of the R.F.C. All models listed below are from either the Willow Art or Corona range and stock numbers where they occur are the same.

Tudor Arms Models
Buildings - White
Bottle Oven. 85mm.   17.50
Lloyd George's Home.
   102mm long.   45.00

Historical/Folklore
Model of Burns Chair. 88mm.   12.50
   Corner seat version.   17.00
Gladiators Helmet. 80mm.   22.00
The Man in the Sun. 100mm.   45.00

Traditional/National Souvenirs
Welsh Hat, with blue ribbon and
   longest place name around brim.
   No. 75. 57mm.   9.50

Seaside Souvenirs
Bathing Machine. 65mm.   13.00

Animals
Black Cat in Boot. 88mm long.   45.00
Bulldog, standing.
   125mm long.   15.00
Dog, Alsatian, standing. 82mm.   25.00
Elephant, walking. 52mm.   20.00
Fish Vase. 70mm.   6.00

Great War
Tank with trailing wheels.
   125mm long.   22.50
Lusitania (as Corona model).
   165mm long.   125.00
Submarine, E4. 97mm long.   22.50
Bell Tent with open flaps. 80mm.   16.00
Kit Bag with verse: *Pack up your
   troubles in your old kit bag.*
   74mm.   24.50

Home/Nostalgic
Church Bell, inscribed: *Curfew must
   not ring tonight.* 70mm.   9.50
Coal Scuttle, helmet shaped. 53mm.   7.00
Watering Can. 72mm.   9.00

Alcohol
Toby Jug, standing, truncated at hem
   of frock coat. 73mm.   15.00

Footwear
Boot. 112mm long.   7.00
Button-up Boot. 74mm long.   9.00

Miniature Domestic
Bagware Tea Pot with lid. 68mm.   9.50

Domestic
Hatpins holder, fluted 132mm.   12.00

Tuscan China

R.H. & S.L. PLANT
ENGLAND

R.H. & S.L. PLANT
ENGLAND

Trademark used by R.H. and S.L. Plant (Ltd), Tuscan Works, Longton.

Mr Richard Hammersley Plant was born in Longton in 1847 and began work at the Daisy Bank Pottery at the age of seven. He was employed there for twenty five years, eventually becoming the Manager. In 1880 he started his own business with his brother which was known as R.H. and S.L. Plant. Mr R.H. Plant died in 1904, and his two sons and his brother carried on the business which is still in existence today. Messrs Plant were known for their tea and breakfast wares produced for the home, colonial and foreign markets. They were represented in London by Messrs Mogridge and Underhay, 10, Barletts Buildings, Holborn Circus, EC. In 1906 R.H. and S.L. Plant added Arms Ware in 'superb ivory porcelain', with the arms of all Nations, the Colonies and the United Kingdom', to their range using the Tuscan trademark. In 1908 they were advertising 'Heraldic Ware' in Tuscan China, adding that arms of towns could be applied to small fancy pieces and teaware.

During the Great War the company obviously made china miniatures a speciality and by 1916 were also producing

'Present from . . . Ware' and 'Nursery Rhyme Ware'. In 1919 the firm could offer 'Heraldic Ivory China, Heraldic Bone China, View Ware, Nursery Rhyme Ware and Present from . . . Ware'. Like so many high and medium class china manufacturers they had to turn to cheaper wares during the war years. By the 1920 British Industries Fair the company was showing 'High Class Services' as well as 'Seaside Ware'. The firm continued to produce Heraldic Wares until at least 1925 but no mention is made of them however in adverts after that date.

Tuscan China is quite fine and well produced, but the majority of crested china made by the firm appears to have been domestic ware, little of which survives as it would have been in constant use. However, an impressive range of animals with bead eyes was made identical to those made by the Grafton factory. Indeed, some animals appear to be from Grafton moulds. A large number of small pots and vases have survived and unless numbered, these have not been listed as they are of interest only to collectors specialising in crests of specific areas or towns. Miniatures and 'smalls' can be found with views and other 'twenties' transfer decorations, but no 'Lucky Black Cats' or 'Lucky White Heather' transfers have been recorded. Some Chinese figure and mille fleur designs were produced, completely covering the piece.

Foreign and colonial crests were also made. Great War Commemoratives can be found on 'smalls' and models, these being *Flags of the Allies* transfers with the inscription: *Freedom and Honour.* ('Tuscan' advertised ashtrays decorated with planes and flags in 1938 but it is not known if these were ever made.)

In the thirties the firm made a range of coloured animals and 'Crinoline Ladies' and these appeal to collectors of the Goss and Arcadian Ladies, but obviously they have nothing whatsoever to do with crested china.

Numbering System. Stock numbers do appear on the base of some models and can be painted in any colour. These are recorded in the following lists where known. Paintresses' marks are painted initials or dots and dashes.

Tuscan Models

Ancient Artefacts

Loving Cup,3 handled. No. 82. 39mm.	6.00
Nose of Brasenose. 95mm long.	13.00
Roman Lamp. 84mm long.	5.50

Buildings - White

Newquay Look-Out-House with three portholes, some colouring. 100mm.	60.00
Tower of Refuge, Isle of Man. 93mm.	40.00

Historical/Folklore

Diakonon, mythical grotesque figure of squat man with flat head which bears the crest. Found with Southsea crest. No. 156. 60mm.	20.00
Coronation Chair, ornate. 80mm.	7.50
The Chertsey Abbey or *Curfew Bell*, *cast circa 1370*. With wooden clapper. Rarely on wooden base. 88mm.	20.00
No base.	14.50
Peter Pan statue, not named. 140mm.	65.00
Miners Dish, inscribed: *Model of the Ancient Miners Dish cast in the 3rd year of the reign of K. Henry VII. Now in the Barmoor Court, Wirksworth, Derbyshire.* 142mm long.	75.00

Traditional/National Souvenirs

Cornish Pasty. 95mm long.	12.00
Monmouth Cap. 70mm dia.	50.00
Welsh Hat. 50mm.	10.00
Can be found with longest place name around brim.	12.50
Welsh Lady jug. Can be found named: *CYMERWCH DOGON O LEFRITH.* 82mm.	22.00
With inscription.	27.50

Seaside Souvenirs

Lifeboat. 125mm long.	16.50
Lighthouse, not named. 100mm.	12.00
Withernsea Lighthouse, with details. 110mm.	22.50
Crab. 88mm long.	20.00
Whelk Shell. 118mm long.	6.00
Whelk Shell, detailed moulding. No. 36 or No. 56. 84mm long.	6.00

Countryside

Milk Churn and Lid.	6.00
Pine Cone. 75mm.	5.00

Animals

Bear, Polar, sitting on hind legs. 98mm.	45.00
Camel with two humps, kneeling. No. 118. 125mm long.	40.00
Cat in Boot. 88mm.	20.00
Cat, fat and angry with tail in air. 80mm.	17.00
Cat, Cheshire with one bead eye. 91mm.	21.00
Cow, said to be Indian, lying down. 155mm long.	19.00
Dog, Bulldog. 72mm long.	18.00
Dog, Bulldog, running. 120mm long.	65.00
Dog, Bulldog in kennel. 70mm.	16.00
Dog, Hound, running. 200mm long.	30.00
Dog, Spaniel, sitting. 53mm.	12.50
Donkey, lying down, yellow bead eyes. 125mm long.	40.00
Elephant, sitting and comical, with yellow bead eyes. 80mm.	32.00
Elephant with howdah, with orange glass eyes. 80mm.	150.00
Fish, large, open mouth, looking upwards, wavy tail. 2 sizes: 120mm long.	6.50
130mm long.	6.00
Fish, curled. 105mm long.	7.50
Fish, open mouthed, can have glass eyes. 120mm.	15.00
Fox, running. Yellow bead eyes. 145mm long.	110.00
Frog, red bead eyes. 55mm.	22.00
Hippopotamus, inscribed: My *word if I catch you bending.* Brown and black bead eyes. 58mm.	75.00
Lion, (Daily Sketch), white. 130mm.	65.00
Monkey, sitting. Glass eyes. No. 120. 85mm.	18.00
Monkey, hanging by tail from branch of tree. 155mm.	95.00
Mule. 130mm long.	40.00
Pig, ears point forward. 80mm long.	26.00
Pig, running, red bead eyes. 87mm.	25.00
Rabbit sitting on hind legs, front paws in air, ear laid back, red glass eyes. 77mm.	100.00
Racehorse. 140mm long.	40.00
Sloth on tree trunk, bead eyes. 110mm long.	70.00

Snail. 85mm long.	14.50
Squirrel holding nut. 70mm.	20.00
Terrapin. 95mm long.	16.00
Tortoise / Turtle, standing with bead	
eyes. 108mm long.	30.00

Birds (including Eggs)

Bird Bowl, grotesque. 98mm long.	16.00
Bird Jug, long beak. 80mm.	18.00
Egg, cracked open and lying on	
side. 65mm long.	9.00
Chick hatching from egg. 77mm long.	12.50
Chicken, plump. 55mm.	16.00
Finch, coloured, on flower holder	
rock. 140mm.	40.00
Penguin. 88mm.	22.50
Swan. 60mm.	9.50

Great War

E4, Submarine. 118mm long.	26.00
Kit Bag, with no inscription. 63mm.	22.00
Bandsman Drum. 33mm.	12.50
Bell tent. 54mm.	16.00
Tommy's Steel Helmet. 73mm long.	25.00

Home/Nostalgic

Anvil. 60mm.	7.50
Baby, naked, lying on tummy	
105mm long.	65.00
Bellows. 106mm long.	14.50
Feeding Bottle. 80mm long.	8.50
Grandfather Clock, inscribed: *Time*	
for tea 5 o'clock. 128mm.	18.50
Inkwell Vase. 55mm.	7.00
Lemon, open top. No. 35. 75mm long.	12.50
Marrow with green stalk. 75mm.	25.00
Loaf of Bread. 62mm.	22.00
Pillar Box Candlesnuffer. 79mm.	16.00
Shaving Mug. No. 180. 57mm.	9.50
Tomato with green leaves. 60mm dia.	25.00
Watering Can. 72mm.	9.00

Comic/Novelty

Boy Scout, saluting. 140mm.	160.00
Girl dressed as clown, hands out-	
stretched, on square base. 130mm.	35.00
Boy dressed as clown on square	
base, hands in pockets. 130mm.	35.00
Boy in nightshirt and nightcap,	
candlesnuffer. Could be Wee	
Willie Winkie.	
2 sizes: 60mm.	20.00
90mm.	24.00

Cartoon/Comedy Characters

Pa Piggins Daily Sketch character.	
Coloured on white square base,	
wearing blue bowler hat, checked	
trousers and grey jacket with	
primrose in lapel. 132mm.	140.00
Snooker or the Kitten Cat, cat sitting	
on square base putting on crown.	
Can be found coloured and	
unglazed. (Daily Sketch Cartoon	
Character). 130mm.	100.00

Alcohol

Bottle. No. 104. 87mm.	8.00
Carboy. No. 11. 70mm.	7.00
Wine glass. 75mm.	8.00

Transport

Racing Car. 135mm long. Inscribed	
Dennis Two Seater, Petrol	
Consumption Nil.	200.00
or *Gamage two seater Petrol*	
Consumption nil, 110 tax on this car.	200.00

Footwear

Button Shoe. 108mm long.	18.00
Ladies buttoned decorative heeled	
shoe. 103mm long.	20.00
Oriental Shoe, pointed toe.	
100mm long.	7.00

Hats

Monmouth Cap. 70mm diameter.	50.00
Top Hat matchstriker. 45mm.	6.50

Miniature Domestic

Cheese Dish and cover. 2 pieces.	
50mm.	9.50

Numbered 'smalls'

No. 5. Cone Vase. 65mm.	4.00
No. 6. Vase. 60mm.	4.00
No. 10. Ewer. 70mm.	4.00
No. 21. Vase.	4.00
No. 22. Vase. 30mm.	4.00
No. 24. Jug. 45mm.	4.00
No. 42. Crinkle top vase. 42mm.	4.00
No. 57. Ewer. 58mm.	4.00
No. 58. Ewer.	4.00
No. 59. Vase. 43mm.	4.00
No. 71. Vase. 63mm.	4.00
No. 72. Jug. 63mm.	4.00
No. 89. Vase. 55mm.	4.00
No. 97. Vase. 50mm.	4.00

No. 100. Urn. 65mm.   4.00
No. 101. Ewer.   4.00
No. 110. Jug. 51mm.   4.00

Miscellaneous
Bamboo hat pin holder. 100mm.   8.50
Bamboo Vase. 100mm.   5.00
Hammer head match striker.
 88mm long.   20.00

Tuskar Rock China

Trademark used for a Wexford retailer by an unknown manufacturer of delicate porcelain, probably Arkinstall and Son, (usual trademark Arcadian).

The models below have been found with Rosslare or Wexford crests, Tuskar Rock lighthouse being off Rosslare, Ireland.

Traditional/National Souvenirs
John Bull, Bust of. 67mm.   25.00
Pearly Queen with ostrich feathers
 on her hat, inscribed: *Harriet*.
 Reg No. 448566. 70mm.   80.00

Miscellaneous
Urn. 41mm.   4.00

Union Crest China

Union K

Trademark by an unknown manufacturer although it does resemble Carlton China.

Historical/Folklore
Model of Ancient Coaching Hat.
No. 217. No details of size.   9.50

Alcohol
Highland Whisky Bowl. 120mm dia.   7.50

Trademark used by the German firm Klosterle (near Carlsbad), the former Graflich Thun'sche Porzellanfabric.
The use of the term Czechoslovakia indicates that this mark, used on domestic ware, was produced after the Great War, when anything German was shunned by the British public. One interesting item recorded is a card box with the four suits on the sides. Another is a crinkle top rose with a Frome crest. K must be an indication of date, mould or model pieces. Can also be found with T.

Domestic ware.   £4.00 upwards

Sport/Pastimes
Card Box, with four suits on the
sides.   20.00

Unity China

UNITY

CHINA

Possibly a trademark used by Sampson Hancock & Sons, Bridge Works, Stoke (usual mark Corona), or a mark used by a wholesaler who bought in models from the Corona factory.

The following transfer prints have been found on various models all encircled by Flags of Allies, with bunting around rim and inscribed 'Unity':
Admiral Jellicoe
General Joffre
General French
Earl Kitchener
King George V

Unity Models

Animals
Bulldog, standing with flags and
bunting and portrait of Admiral
Jellicoe. 114mm long.   60.00

Birds (including Eggs)
Swan posy holder. Flags of Allies
and bunting around rim. Central
transfer print of *General Joffre*
encircled by Flags of Allies and
inscribed: *Unity*. 90mm.   40.00

Hats
Top Hat. 70mm.   9.50

Miniature Domestic
Cheese Dish. 50mm.   9.50

Unity China

UNITY

CHINA

Trademark used by the German firm of Max Emanuel and Co., Mitterteich. (Bavaria). (Usual trademark Mosanic).
See Maxim China for further details of this manufacturer.

This mark is identical to one used by Max Emanuel and Co., on pink view ware china, with the addition of the words Unity China. If, as I suspect, this mark was used after the Great War the use of the word Unity is very apt, if not, a little tactless, as no mention of the country of origin is made.

Universal Series

Trademark used by an unknown manufacturer but bears a remarkable resemblance to Ivora ware and Porcelle China, which was made for William Ritchie and Son Ltd. 24/26/28 Elder Street, Edinburgh, by Birks, Rawlins & Co. (usual trademark Savoy). The porcelain is more cream than white, and reasonbly fine. All pieces found bear Scottish crests.

Universal Models
Great War
Bandsman's Drum. 57mm dia.   12.50

Footwear
Oriental Slipper. 95mm long.   7.50

Vale China

Mark used from 1928-37.

Trademark used by H.J. Coldough, Vale Works, Longton. For all further details of this china, see Royal Vale entry.

Vectis/Victis Models

VECTIS MODELS NIGH VENTNOR I.O.W.

VICTIS MODELS NIGH VENTNOR I.O.W.

Trademark used for Nigh, a fancy goods dealer in the Isle of Wight by J.A. Robinson and Sons, subsequently Cauldon Ltd. (Usual trademark Arcadian).
For details of this china and manufacturer see Arcadian China.
There seems to have been some indecision in the Arcadian Works as to how to spell Vectis, which is of course the Roman name for the Isle of Wight. The models with this mark could have been made by any of the branches of J.A. Robinson, which included Arkinstall ('Arcadian'), Robinson and Leadbeater (R. and L.) and Wardle's Art

Pottery Ltd. The parian models listed below would almost certainly have been made by R. and L.
All the models are souvenirs of the Isle of Wight, and carry Isle of Wight crests. A number of 'smalls' have been recorded with the coloured transfers of tropical birds on Arcadian and Cauldon wares.

Vectis Models

Parian/Unglazed
Osborne House, Isle of Wight. 48mm.
140mm long.   100.00
Sleep of Innocence. Osborne House,
Cowes. I.O.W. Two babies lying on
a couch, glazed or unglazed.
2 sizes: 106mm long.   145.00
        114mm long.   165.00

Ancient Artefacts
Cadogan Teapot, not named. 50mm. 12.00

Buildings - Coloured
The Old Village, Shanklin, I.O.W.
100mm long.   150.00

Buildings - White
Carisbrooke Castle Gateway, I.W.
96mm.   120.00
Cottage on rectangular base, no
inscription. 50mm.   9.50
Old Church, Bonchurch.
105mm long.   130.00
The Old Village, Shanklin, I.o. W.
100mm long.   100.00
Osborne House, Cowes, I.O.W
48mm. 140mm long.   100.00

Monuments (including Crosses)
Arch Rock, Freshwater Bay, I.O.W.
80mm.   40.00
Maiwand Memorial Forbury Gardens,
Reading. 98mm.   24.50
Tennyson Monument, Freshwater,
I.O.W. 145mm.   75.00

Traditional/National Souvenirs
Donkey in Wheel, donkey coloured,
Carisbrooke Castle. 90mm.   120.00
Map of Isle of Wight. A coloured map
standing upright on an oval
ashtray 106mm long.   50.00
Sleep of Innocence, Osborne House,
Cowes, I. O. W. See Parian/
unglazed section.

Seaside Souvenirs
Bathing Machine. *Morning Dip 7 a.m.*
  65mm.   14.00
Lighthouse. 107mm.   12.00
Needles Rock and Lighthouse.
  130mm long.   45.00

Animals
Calf, often found with *Isle of Wight
  Calves* transfer and verse.
  100mm long.   30.00
  No verse.   24.50
Elephant, walking. 79mm long.   26.00
Lion, walking. 145mm long.   24.50

Great War
Nurse Cavell statue. 160mm.   20.00
Field Glasses. 65mm.   19.00

Birds (including Eggs)
Brooding Hen. 50mm.   8.50
Parrot. 66mm.   12.00

Home/Nostalgic
Coal Bucket.   6.00

Domestic
Hatpin holder, swirl pattern. 130mm. 12.00

Venetia China

Trademark used by Charles Waine (and Co),
Derby Works, Longton (usual trademark
Venetia China).

Charles Waine and Co. worked in Longton,
manufacturing china from 1891 to 1920,
but only used the initials C.W. until 1913.
The firm made a range of 'smalls' and
small models probably at the turn of the
century when many other established
firms added crests to their shapes. One
commemorative decoration has been
found on several pieces, this being a
coloured transfer view of the 'Imperial
International Exhibition'. Venetia is rather
heavy and gritty more like earthenware
than china, the view and crests are
adequate but by no means exceptional.

Venetia Models
Ancient Artefacts
Loving Cup, 3 handles. 40mm.   5.50

Seaside Souvenirs
Lighthouse on rocky base. 114mm.   8.50

Animals
Manx Cat. 80mm.   30.00
Dog with raised tail, possibly a Husky.
  83mm.   20.00
Pig, fat standing. 96mm long.   40.00

Birds (including Eggs)
Swan posy bowl. 80mm.   6.00

Home/Nostalgic
Coal Scuttle. No. 35. 80mm.   6.00

Miniature Domestic
Cheese Dish and cover. 55mm.   9.50
Circular Cheese Dish and cover.
 71mm dia.   9.50
Tea Pot with lid.
 2 sizes: 58mm.   9.50
        76mm.   12.00

Victoria Arms China

Trademark used on china produced by
Hewitt & Leadbeater Ltd. (Usual
trademark Willow Art).

Victoria Arms Models
Historic/Folklore
HRH Prince of Wales in his
 investiture costume, standing on
 base. 88mm long.   150.00

Great War
Tank with trailing wheels, inscribed:
 Model of British Tank.
 130mm long.   22.00
Kit Bag, drawn string. 70mm.   25.00
Kitchen range, with pot on fire,
 inscribed: *Keep the home fires
 burning.* Some colouring. 78mm
 long.   19.50

Victoria China

J. R .C

Mark used approx 19101924.

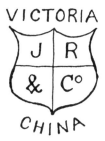

Marks used approx 1910-1924.

Trademark was thought to have been used on crested wares by James Reeves, Victoria Works, Fenton. However, it is probable that J.R. & Co was a china wholesaler who purchased ranges from J.A. Robinson (Usual mark Arcadian). Taylor & Kent (Usual mark Florentine) and Sampson Hancock (Usual mark Corona).

James Reeve was established in 1870 and produced tableware and ornamental earthenware. It seems likely that the firm began making some miniatures just before the Great War and continued to do so as the craze for war souvenirs grew and the supply of skilled operatives diminished. The firm continued in business until 1948, but seems not to have made crested ware and other miniatures after the mid-Twenties. They obviously saw such production as a sideline, as they never advertised it or bothered to register the mark used on their range.

Victoria china is rather heavy as one would expect from an earthenware manufacturer but it is quite well finished. Some models showed a marked similarity to Botolph China. Other models shows a great similarity to Florentine China (Taylor and Kent) but there is no known connection between the two firms. No view ware, 'Lucky White Heather' or 'Lucky Black Cats' have been recorded with this mark but two different coloured transfers entitled 'Welsh Costume' have been found on Welsh Hats. J. Reeves seemed to have found a good market in Wales, many Welsh crests and models have been recorded. Some military badges have also been recorded.

Army Service Corps
Australian Commonwealth
5th Battalion Bedfordshire Regiment
Brecknockshire Regiment
Cambridgeshire Regiment
1st City of London Brigade
6th Battalion Duke of Wellington's West
   Riding Regiment
Herefordshire Regiment
5th Battalion (Weald of Kent) "The Buffs"
1st Battalion Hertfordshire Regiment
18th Battalion London Irish Rifles
4th Battalion Norfolk Regiment
5th Battalion Norfolk Regiment
4th Battalion Northamptonshire Regiment
Northumberland Fusiliers
4th Battalion Surrey Regiment "The Queens"
Royal Fusiliers, 1st City of London Brigade.
5th Battalion Suffolk Regiment
5th Battalion Royal Sussex Regiment
   S. Africa 1900-1902 Cinque Ports.
5th Battalion, the Welsh Regiment
2nd Battalion West Riding Brigade R.F.A.
4th Battalion West Riding Regt
5th Battalion West Riding Regiment
West Yorkshire Regiment
King's own Yorkshire Light Infantry
No other commemoratives have been found
with this mark.
Numbering System. No stock numbers are
found on crested models. The painted
numerals, dots and dashes found on the
base are paintresses' marks. A few items
of crested domestic ware have been
recorded and some of these carry
stock numbers, e.g. Salt Pot 148 and
Candlestick 144. It is possible that the
firm offered a range of these items, but
very few have survived.

Victoria Models
Ancient Artefacts
Carlisle Salt Pot. 70mm.	5.50
Chester Roman Vase, named.	
58mm.	5.50
Fountains Abbey Cup. 50mm.	5.50
Puzzle Jug. 67mm.	6.50
Salisbury Jack. 47mm.	5.50
Tyg. l handle. 70mm.	5.50

Buildings - White
Blackpool Tower, with buildings.	
142mm.	10.50
Bottle Oven. 82mm.	16.00
Old Pete's Cottage, I.o.M.	
48mm high, 75mm long.	30.00

Monuments (including Crosses)
Iona Cross. 108mm.	12.50
Ripon Market Cross. 120mm.	20.00
Wallace Tower, Stirling. 120mm.	40.00

Historical/Folklore
Man in Pillory. 105mm.	17.00
Miner's Lamp. 84mm.	16.00
Mother Shipton. Sometimes found	
named. 70mm.	10.00
Suffragette handbell. 72mm.	25.00

Traditional/National Souvenirs
Blackpool Ferris Wheel. 108mm.	17.00
Laxey Wheel. Isle of Man. 95mm.	40.00
Legs of Man, inside life belt. 90mm.	16.00
Legs of Man, flat. 80mm wide.	17.00
Ripon Horn. 90mm.	17.50
Ripon Hornblower. 90mm.	16.00
Bust of Scotsman wearing tam-	
o'shanter and plaid. 63mm.	20.00
Welsh Bardic Chair 86mm.	
(identical to Old Arm Chair.)	19.50
Welsh Harp. 90mm.	10.00
Welsh Hat with thin blue ribbon	
band. 48mm and 58mm.	9.00
Welsh Hat, two different moulds	
one with twisted cord band, and	
the other with blue band with	
gold tassels. Can be found with	
Llanfair...etc. around brim.	
62mm.	9.00
Inscribed	11.50

Seaside Souvenirs
Baby seated on rock. 109mm.	18.00
Bathing Machine. 65mm long.	12.00
Bathing Machine with figure on	
steps. 75mm.	18.00
Yacht in full sail. 126mm.	16.50
Canoe. 102mm long.	9.50
Houseboat, rectangular.	
90mm long.	12.50
Fisherman, bust. 87mm.	17.50
Fisherwoman, bust. 87mm.	17.50
Lighthouse. 97mm.	6.50
Lighthouse, unnamed	
Flamborough. 110mm.	30.00
Whelk Shell, rarely inscribed: *Listen*	
to the sea. 95mm long.	6.00

Countryside
Acorn on plinth, pepper pot. 75mm	9.00
Milk Churn and lid. 70mm.	6.00

Animals

Bear, Polar, *Sam.* 96mm long.	60.00
Cat, with long neck. 115mm.	14.00
Cat, sitting, furry mane. 110mm.	22.00
Cat, The Cheshire. Inscribed: *Always*	
smiling. 80mm.	9.50
Cat, Manx. 80mm long.	25.00
Bulldog in kennel. 70mm long.	16.00
Bulldog, sitting. 55mm.	20.00
Dog, King Charles Spaniel in cradle.	
90mm long.	16.00
Dog, King Charles Spaniel, begging	
on cushion. 70mm.	12.50
Dogs, two King Charles Spaniels in	
Top Hat. 70mm.	17.00
Puppy sitting. 88mm.	12.50
Donkey, walking. 92mm long.	25.00
Elephant, kneeling. 80mm long.	20.00
Fish, inscribed: *Caught at...*	
102mm long.	6.50
Fish Vase. 115mm.	6.00
Frog cream jug. 75mm.	8.50
Frog, singing, hands on chest, open	
mouth. 95mm.	65.00
Hare, ears down. 77mm long.	16.50
Monkey, crouching, hands to	
mouth. 88mm.	18.00
Mouse playing Mandolin. 90mm.	25.00
Pig, kneeling. 70mm long.	16.00
Pig, standing. Sometimes inscribed:	
The pig that won't go. 88mm long.	16.50
Piglet, standing. 70mm.	16.00
Rabbit with upright ears.	
75mm long.	12.00
Rabbit, 98mm long.	12.00
Seal with ball. 73mm.	19.50
Teddy Bear, sitting. 98mm.	25.00
Toad. 39mm.	18.00

Birds (including Eggs)

Canary on rock. 100mm.	12.50
Chick hatching from egg.	
65mm long.	9.00
Hen, roosting. 92mm long.	9.50
Kingfisher, with long beak. 80mm.	30.00
Owl.	
2 sizes: 70mm.	16.50
95mm.	18.50
Parrot. 76mm & 93mm.	10.50
Pelican jug. 63mm.	7.50
Swan.	
2 sizes: 70mm.	7.50
90mm long.	8.50
Swan posy bowl. 80mm long.	6.00

Great War

Despatch Rider. 120mm long.	90.00
Tommy and his Machine Gun.	
97mm long.	55.00
Bust of Sailor. 90mm.	40.00
Sailor winding capstan. 133mm.	100.00
Airship on base. 128mm long.	35.00
Monoplane with roundels and	
4-bladed movable prop.	
170mm long.	110.00
Battleship, two guns fore, one aft.	
120mm long.	30.00
Lusitania, 165mm long.	145.00
Torpedo Boat Destroyer. 110mm long.	25.00
Submarine, inscribed *E4.* 104mm long.	22.50
Submarine, inscribed *E9.*	
147mm long.	30.00
Armoured Car (Arcadian).	
94mm long.	40.00
Red Cross Van. 102mm long.	40.00
Red Cross Van, with painted not	
moulded crosses. 90mm long.	40.00
Renault Tank. 82mm long.	80.00
Tank, with inset steering wheels.	
100mm long.	35.00
Tank, wide, with large side turrets.	
120mm long.	40.00
Field Gun. 127mm long.	25.00
Trench Mortar. 65mm.	21.00
Torpedo, fixed prop. 155mm long.	55.00
Bullet. 75mm.	7.00
Mills Hand Grenade, not named.	
Rd. No. 657211. 60mm.	25.00
Capstan. 55mm.	14.00
Colonial Soldier's Hat.	
73mm long.	19.50
Officer's Peaked Cap. 65mm long.	17.50
Drum. 38mm.	14.00
Field Glasses. 80mm long.	17.50
Ghurka Knife. 143mm long.	25.00
Grandfather Clock, usual model but	
with clock transfer at 3.25. With	
inscription: *World War 1914 1919.*	
Peace signed 3.25pm June 28 1919.	
110mm.	85.00
Bell Tent, hexagonal, open flap.	
89mm.	22.00
Kit Bag, open. 70mm.	22.00
Pith helmet. 56mm.	30.00
Sandbag. 74mm long.	25.00
Water Bottle. 64mm.	17.00
Cenotaph. 135mm.	16.50
Florence Nightingale statue. 148mm.	25.00
Matlock Bath War Memorial. 185mm.	85.00
Ripon War Memorial. 118mm.	85.00

Home/Nostalgic

Baby in Bootee. 80mm long.	14.00
Baby in bath. 100mm long.	16.50
Broom Head. 105mm long.	19.50
Coal Bucket. 62mm.	6.00
Cradle. 80mm long.	12.00
Dolly tub with clothes. 80mm.	26.00
Flat Iron. 60mm.	14.50
Garden Roller. 85mm long.	12.50
Girl in Bonnet, salt pot. 93mm.	12.50
Gladstone Bag. 45mm.	8.00
Grandfather Clock. 120mm.	16.00
Grandmother Clock. 85mm.	16.50
Lamp. 100mm long.	10.00
Lantern. 86mm.	10.00
The Old Armchair, with inscription. 83mm.	12.50
Pillar Box, inscribed: *I cant get a letter from you, so send you the box.* 70mm.	16.00
Policeman's Lamp. 70mm.	10.00
Portmanteau. 55mm.	8.00
Sundial on large square base, inscribed: *Tempus fugit.* 109mm.	16.50
Shaving Mug. 30mm.	9.50
Tobacco Pouch. 72mm long.	12.50
Watering Can. 70mm.	9.50
Writing Desk. 55mm.	15.00

Comic/Novelty

Boy's face, smiling on cream jug. 73mm.	11.00
Boy's head, smiling on match holder shoulders. 75mm.	14.50
Boy on Scooter. 106mm.	30.00
Jack in the Box. 95mm.	28.00
Pierrot playing banjo, some colouring. 120mm.	40.00
Screw, inscribed: *You could do with a big fat screw (wage rise).* 76mm.	40.00
Suffragette Handbell, two sided. One side ugly old lady, inscribed: *Votes for women.* Reverse, a pretty young girl, inscribed: *This one shall have a vote.*	
2 sizes: 72mm.	45.00
108mm.	60.00

Cartoon/Comedy Characters

Ally Sloper bust, not named. 83mm.	35.00
Harry Lauder, bust. 63mm.	30.00

Alcohol

Carboy. 72mm.	8.50
Champagne Bottle in ice bucket inscribed: *Something good – a bottle of the boy.* 83mm.	20.00
Whisky Bottle.	9.50

Sport/Pastimes

Boxing Glove. 69mm long.	30.00
Cricket Bag. 115mm long.	16.50
Pawn chess piece. 60mm.	25.00
Rook Chess Piece. 55mm.	10.00

Musical Instruments

Banjo. 137mm long.	20.00
Grand Piano, with closed lid. 80mm long.	24.00
Upright Piano. 63mm.	22.00
Tambourine. 68mm dia.	12.50

Transport

Charabanc, with driver. 115mm long.	40.00
Motor Horn, inscribed: *Pip Pip.* 90mm long.	25.00
Saloon Car. 80mm long.	40.00

Modern Equipment

Cash Register. 47mm.	22.00
Gas Cooker. 70mm.	13.00
Gramophone, square without horn. 58mm.	25.50
Radio Horn. 95mm.	30.00

Footwear

Ladies 18th Century Shoe. 92mm long.	8.50
Lancashire Clog.	
2 sizes: 85mm long.	7.00
100mm long.	8.50
Oriental Shoe with pointed turned up toe. 95mm long.	9.00

Miniature Domestic

Candleholder, circular. 45mm.	5.00
Cheese Dish and cover. 50mm.	9.50
Coffee Pot with lid.	
2 sizes: 69mm.	9.50
125mm.	9.50
Cup and Saucer, diamond shaped. 50mm.	5.50
Tea Pot with lid. 60mm.	9.50
Tea Pot with lid, ball shaped. 75mm.	9.50

Miscellaneous
Candlestick with snake entwined.
  106mm.   12.50
Hair Brush Trinket Box and lid.
  140mm long.   14.00
Lily Vase. 115mm.   6.50
Mustard Pot and lid, on 3 small
  feet, with spoon. 70mm.   9.50

Victoria

Trademarks used by two German manufacturers, Charles Schmidt and Co, Carlsbad (Bohemia), and Moschendorf, Hof, Bavaria (usual trademark Gemma). For further details of manufacturer see Gemma. This mark is usually found on domestic wares but the models listed below have been recorded. The ware is very fine and one would assume that Schmidt and Co made this china in another works or offered it as an alternative range to Gemma. This china is often found in pearl lustre. It can also be found coloured in maroon and green with gilded flowers on a variety of domestic shapes. Some Canadian crests have been recorded.

Victoria Models.
Seaside Souvenirs

Bathing Hut. 80mm.	12.50
Yacht, yellow/brown lustre.	
No. 2276. 105mm long.	16.50
Conch Shell on 4 stubby feet.	
100mm.	6.50

Birds (including Eggs)

Hen, pepper pot, red comb & beak.	
70mm.	12.00
Swan posy bowl. 58mm.	6.50

Home/Nostalgic

Grandmother Clock, lustre. 88mm.	8.00
Watering Can. 78mm.	8.50
Wheelbarrow. 100mm long.	7.00

Musical Instruments

Grand Piano, removable lid. 103mm.	14.00

Footwear

Sabot. 84mm long.	5.00

Sport (including Pastimes)

Boxing Glove. 65mm long.	20.00

Miniature Domestic

Cauldron. 58mm.	4.00
Cheese Dish and cover. 30mm.	8.00
Cup and Saucer with lithophane of	
Blarney Castle. 60mm.	35.00
German Beer Mug. 50mm.	5.00
Jug and Bowl set. 69mm.	9.50

Domestic

Cheese dish and cover, oyster shell	
pearl lustre. 164mm long.	15.00
Inkwell and lid. 40mm.	9.50
Pin Box and lid, heart-shaped.	
84mm long.	7.00
Salt Pot. 80mm.	4.00
Tea Pot & Lid. 120mm.	9.00

Victorian Porcelain

Vignaud

For details of this manufacturer, see Robinson & Leadbeater.

For details of trademarks used by this French china manufacturer, Vignaud, of Limoges, France see Limoges.

Viking China

W

BRITISH MADE

Pieces were bought in for resale in the Isle of Man by D.W. Kee from Hewitt and Leadbeater, Willow Potteries, Longton (see Willow Art), and Taylor & Kent (Ltd.), Florence Works, Longton. (Usual trademark Florentine).

Viking China Models
Animals

Cat, standing. 60mm.	19.50
Manx Cat. 90mm long.	40.00

Miscellaneous

Jug. 55mm.	4.00

Trademark used by H.M. Williams and Sons, Bridge Pottery, Longton.

This firm, established in 1858, according to an advert in the *Pottery Gazette*, were well known for their china tea and dinner sets. They used the mark above on cheaper wares from 1900 and probably for only a short time. (The mark is shown in an advert in the *Pottery Gazette* in 1903.) Their range of crested china is quite well produced, but by no means exceptionally so, and most of the items found could be described as 'smalls'. Many models are recorded with the commemorative transfer *The Triple Entente* which consists of shields of the flags of France, Great Britain and Russia. Add £5.00 for this decoration.

W Models
Ancient Artefacts

Loving Cup, 3 handles. 55mm.	5.00
Salisbury Kettle. 102mm.	5.00

Animals

Cat, long necked. 112mm.	16.00
Cat, Manx. 60mm.	24.50
Frog cream jug. 60mm.	14.50
Pig, standing. 100mm long.	20.00
Pig's Head, hollow. 88mm long.	50.00
Rabbit, sitting. 86mm.	10.00
Seal.	22.00

Birds (including Eggs)

Pelican cream jug. 58mm.	8.50
Owl, Comic. No. 547.	17.00
Swan posy bowl. 80mm long.	6.00

Home/Nostalgic

Oil Lamp. 58mm.	10.00
Policeman's Lamp. 71mm.	14.00
Portmanteau. 80mm long.	8.00
Shaving Mug. 55mm.	9.50
Watering Can. 55mm.	14.50

Sport/Pastimes

Cricket Bag. 110mm long.	16.50

Footwear

Ladies Shoe with high heel. 90mm long.	8.50

Miniature Domestic

Cheese Dish. 45mm.	9.50
Tea Pot with lid. 70mm.	9.50

Miscellaneous

5-mouthed Vase.	4.00

W & Sons

"W&Sons," "MIKADO" WARE Rᴰ No 438118

One of only two pieces known is a ewer with pale green trim and handle displaying colour transfers of Japanese scenes. This is remarkably similar to a series of vases produced by Moore Bros. of St. Mary's Works, Longton with a sprig of holly and crest and the motto: Carpe Diem. Manufacturer unknown but probably Moore Bros. W & Sons could also be a retailer.

Mikado Ware Models

Ewer, pale green trim with Japanese scenes. 75mm.	30.00

Miniature Domestic

Cheese dish and cover, two-piece. 80mm long.	30.00

Wade

Warwick China

No details of mark available except that mark incorporates 'Wades'.

Trademark used by Wade & Co, Union Pottery, Burslem, subsequently Wade, Heath & Co. (Ltd).
This company which went on to make coloured cartoon models in the thirties and later Wade miniature animals and Disney characters, (Hat Box series), did not surprisingly make a large range of crested china. The odd items found with their name are domestic pieces, the crest almost appearing to have been added as an afterthought. The firm before 1927, when it became Wade, Heath and Co., manufactured earthenwares so the crested wares tend to be heavy and useful rather than ornamental.

A small range of earthenware domestic wares was produced.
£4.00 upwards

Trademark used for W.H. Smith and Sons by Arkinstall and Son Ltd. Arcadian Works, Stoke-on-Trent.   (Usual   trademark Arcadian).
For further details of the china and manufacturer see Arcadian China.
This range of china made for W.H. Smith is of a higher quality than one normally associates with Arcadian China and the crests   are   boldly   and   beautifully produced. The models are, however, made from Arcadian moulds and if one can judge from the models recorded, seem to have been made before and during the Great War, but not afterwards.
Numbering System. Numbers can either be printed or written and are usually in the style of a fraction. the lower numbers occur on many different models and could possibly be an order number. The following lower numbers have been recorded: 010, 01^1/2, 06^1/2, 09, 012, 014, 015 and 030. The upper numbers appear to be stock numbers and where recorded they coincide with Arcadian stock numbers. Stock numbers where known are given in the lists below.

Warwick Models
Ancient Artefacts
Ancient Tyg, model of. 70mm.   5.50
Cambridge Roman Jug. 58mm.   5.50
Canterbury Roman Urn, inscribed:
Roman Urn found near Canterbury,
original in Canterbury Museum.
70mm.   5.50

Chester Roman Vase. 60mm.   5.50
Egyptian Vase, about 230BC. 41mm.   5.50
Highland Whisky Bowl. 90mm dia.   5.50
Lincoln Jack, from original in Museum.
   62mm.   5.50
Newbury Leather Bottle. 65mm.   5.50
Norwich Urn, inscribed: *Model of*
cinerary urn found at Norwich. No.
135. 50mm.   5.50
Roman Lamp. 90mm long.   5.50
Reading Vase, inscribed: *Model of*
vase from Silchester in Reading
Museum. 53mm.   5.50
Winchelsea Roman Cup, inscribed:
Roman cup found near Winchelsea.
51mm.   5.50

Buildings - White
Rowton Tower, with inscription: *King*
Charles I stood on this tower Sept
24th 1645 and saw his army defeated
on Rowton Moor. 105mm.   40.00

Historical/Folklore
The Brading Stocks, man sitting in
stocks. 82mm.   30.00
Yorick's Skull, inscribed: *Alas poor*
Yorick. 57mm.   16.00

Traditional/National Souvenirs
Prime Cheddar Cheese, with slice out.
60mm.   12.50

Seaside Souvenirs
Fishing Basket, inscribed: A *good*
catch. 70mm long.   10.00
Lighthouse. 148mm.   14.50

Animals
Bear, Polar. 96mm.   40.00
Bear, Teddy, sitting. 90mm.   30.00
The Cheshire Cat. Inscribed: *The*
smile that won't come off. 100mm.   19.00
Dog, Collie. 95mm.   29.50
Dog, King Charles Spaniel begging
on cushion. No. 60. 70mm.   12.00
Elephant, standing, trunk curled
inwards. 60mm.   30.00
Otter, holding fish in mouth.
120mm long.   65.00
Pony, Shetland. 105mm long.   25.00
Rhinoceros. 90mm long.   95.00

Birds (including Eggs)
Chick breaking out of egg.
63mm long.   9.00
Hen, roosting. 54mm.   8.50
Egg shaped salt pot, inscribed: s
56mm.   4.00
Egg shaped pepper pot, inscribed:
p. 56mm.   4.00

Great War
British Airship on stand.
128mm long.   35.00
E4 Submarine. 95mm long.   27.00
Red Cross Van, red cross on each
side and rear. *'EH 139'* inscribed
on radiator. 85mm long.   40.00
Pith Helmet. 80mm long.   30.00
Field Glasses. 78mm long.   17.00
Bell Tent with open flap inscribed:
Camping Out 65mm.   22.50
Anti-Zeppelin Candleholder.
62mm.   17.00

Home/Nostalgic
Grandfather Clock. 113mm.   17.50
Lantern, inscribed: *Watchman What*
of the Night. 82mm.   16.00
Sundial on square base.   8.50
Thimble, inscribed: *Tak A Thimble*
Full. 40mm.   20.00
Three-legged stool. 42mm.   8.50

Alcohol
Highland Whisky Bowl. 90mm dia.   5.50

Sport/Pastimes
Cricket Bag. 80mm long.   16.50
Ashtray with central raised heart/
club /diamond / spade indicator.
The more we are together the merrier
we will be.   30.00
Rook chess piece. 55mm.   7.50

Musical Instruments
Banjo. 155mm long.   20.00

Miniature Domestic
Cheese Dish and cover. 50mm.   9.50

Domestic Wares
Candlesnuffer, cone. 65mm.   5.50
Pair – salt and pepper pots,
octagonal. Inscribed: *Salt* and
Pepper. 88mm.   5.00

Warwick Ware

Mark used by an unknown British manu-facturer.
Only one item has been found so far, candlestick holder in the form of Silver tankard on tray, inscribed: *The more we are together, the merrier we will be* with lucky white heather motif. Registration applied for.
100mm.   40.00

Waterfall Heraldic China

F C   CH
COPYRIGHT

F.C.C
H.

Trademark used for a Northern wholesaler by Hewitt and Leadbeater, Willow Potteries, Longton. (Usual trademark Willow Art).
For further details of this china and manufacturer see Willow Art China.
All crests and model souvenirs of monuments and buildings found with this mark are northern. The most

commonly found crests are Withernsea, Grimsby, Hull and Filey, indicating that the models were sold in northern towns, resorts and ports. Most models are identical to those found in the Willow Art range but some models were obviously made especially to be sold in Hull, Grimsby and Hedon.
Stock numbers where they occur, coincide with Willow Art numbers.

Waterfall Models
Ancient Artefacts

Lincoln Jack, not named. No. 44. 60mm.	5.50
Portland Vase, not named. 53mm.	4.50
Puzzle Jug. 68mm.	6.50

Buildings - White

Grimsby Hydraulic Tower. 165mm.	50.00
Grimsby Hydraulic Tower designed by Sir W. Armstrong. Erected first stone laid 1849. Finished 1854. Height 320ft. Width 28ft. Tank capacity 30,000 gallons. On square base. 150mm.	70.00
Wilberforce House, Hull. 115mm long.	125.00

Monuments (including Crosses)

Hull Fishermans Memorial, with inscription.	
2 sizes: 135mm.	20.00
160mm.	24.00
Hull South African War Memorial, with inscription. 165mm.	35.00
Kilnsea Cross, Hedon with inscription: *Erected at Ravenspurne 1339 by King Henry IV. Re-erected at Hedon.* 140mm. Rare.	200.00
Rufus Stone with inscription. 110mm.	7.50
The Monument, Laceby, with inscriptions. 154mm.	40.00
Sir William de la Pole, Statue of, with long inscription. 160mm.	35.00
Charles Henry Wilson, First Baron Nunburnholme, statue, inscribed on front: *The largest private shipowner in the world. Born 1833. Died 1907. 32 years a member of parliament for Hull and a great benefactor to the city. Erected by public subscription, in the year AD 1912. 154mm.*	75.00

Historical/Folklore

James V Chair, Stirling Castle, Model of. No. 200. 100mm.	16.50
Mary Queen of Scots Chair. 82mm.	12.50
Mons Meg Edinburgh Castle. 134mm long.	20.00
Skull. 60mm long.	12.00

Traditional/National Souvenirs

Bagpipes, can be found with turquoise ribbon. 118mm long.	50.00
Cornish Pasty. 108mm long.	12.00
Dutch Boy. 80mm.	12.50
Welsh Hat. 53mm.	9.00

Seaside Souvenirs

Grimsby fisherman, bust. 83mm.	45.00
Lifeboatman, bust, inscribed: *Hull Fisherman.* 83mm.	55.00
Lighthouse, not named. 115mm.	10.00
Spurn *Lighthouse,* with inscriptions. 130mm.	30.00
Withernsea Lighthouse, with inscription. 2 sizes: 113mm & 130mm.	22.00

Countryside

Acorn. 62mm.	10.00
Milk Can and lid. 60mm.	7.00

Animals

Bear, Teddy, sitting. 76mm.	24.00
Cat, Cheshire, inscribed: *Still smiling.* 95mm.	14.50
Cat, chubby standing with tail in air. 80mm.	22.00
Cat, sitting, with shield. No. 62. 75mm.	19.50
Cat with arched back. 65mm.	20.00
Cat, sitting, medallion on chest. 72mm.	22.00
Black Cat on Boot. 90mm long.	75.00
Dog, Bull Terrier, standing. 60mm.	12.50
Dog, Collie, standing. 85mm.	16.00
Dog, King Charles Spaniel, begging on cushion. 95mm.	16.00
Elephant, walking. 52mm.	20.00
Fish with open mouth. 103mm long.	8.00
Lion, walking. 120mm long.	24.50
Pig, sitting on haunches, upright ears, inscribed: *You may push me. You may shuv. But I'm hanged if I'll be druv.* 75mm.	30.00

Pig, large, sitting laughing.
Inscribed: *You may push...* No. 137.
105mm long.   30.00
Tortoise. 70mm long.   10.00

Great War
Nurse. Inscribed: *A Friend in Need.*
130mm.   70.00
Standing Sailor, *Our Brave Defender.*
128mm.   70.00
Despatch Rider. 115mm long.   90.00
Airship observation balloon
inscribed: *BETA.* 85mm long.   90.00
Monoplane, with revolving prop.
150mm long.   85.00
Battleship H.M.S. Queen Elizabeth.
165mm long.   60.00
Battleship, impressed: *HMS Lion.*
140mm long.   40.00
Submarine impressed: *E4.* 116mm
long.   24.50
Submarine *E5.* 124mm long.   25.00
Red Cross Van. Red cross on side.
84mm long.   40.00
British Tank, Model of
92mm long.   22.50
British Tank, Model of with trailing
wheels. 130mm long.   22.50
Armoured Car. 95mm long.   40.00
Field Gun. 120mm long.   30.00
Field Gun, with screen.
115mm long.   35.00
Howitzer. 115mm long.   30.00
British Aerial Torpedo.
102mm long.   40.00
Glengarry, some colouring.
83mm long.   22.00
Bell Tent, open flap. 68mm.   22.00
Trench Lamp. 70mm.   18.00
Kitchen Range, with cooking pot,
inscribed: *Keep the Home Fires...*
No. 199. 80mm long.   20.00

Home/Nostalgic
Coal Scuttle. 65mm long.   6.00
Flower Basket. 70mm.   6.50
Grandfather Clock.
2 sizes: 104mm.   14.00
          125mm.   16.50
Watering Can. 75mm.   8.50

Comic/Novelty
Baby saluting. Inscribed: *One of the
B'hoys.*   30.00
Billiken, not named. 73mm.   7.50
Bust of a Judge.   20.00

Alcohol
Beer Barrel on stand. 58mm.   6.50
Beer Tankard, silver on circular
ashtray base, inscribed: *The more
we are together the merrier we will
be.* 100mm dia.   25.00

Sport/Pastimes
Cricket Bat. 115mm long.   80.00
Golf Ball. 45mm.   12.00
Knight chess piece. 62mm.   16.50
Rook chess piece. 55mm.   7.00

Musical Instruments
Bagpipes. 117mm long.   50.00

Hats
Mortar Board. 65mm long.   30.00

Footwear
Ladies Shoe with blue bow.
114mm long.   13.00
Slipper Wall Pocket. 152mm long.   12.50

Miniature Domestic
Cheese Dish and cover, circular.
45mm.   9.50
Coffee Pot with lid. 70mm.   9.50
Cup & Saucer. 35mm.   5.00

Domestic
Trefoil Cruet with lids. 60mm.   4.00

Miscellaneous
Horse's Hoof. 60mm long.   8.50

Waterloo Ware

Trademark probably used by a retailer for items thought to be produced by Sampson, Hancock & Sons, Stoke. (Usual trademark Corona).

Waterloo Ware Models
Buildings - White
Bottle Oven, inside of. 84mm.   25.00

Great War
Ghurka Knife. 135mm long.   25.00

Waverley China

Trademark used for Wyman & Sons Ltd. by Arkinstall & Son, Ltd. Arcadian Works Stoke-on-Trent.   (Usual   trademark Arcadian).

Alternative factory mark used for an agent in Glasgow.

For further details of china and manufacturer see Arcadian China.
This mark has only been found on 'smalls' and ancient artefacts, and was probably only used before the Great War.

Waverley Models
Ancient Artefacts
Arundel, model of vase found near.
  64mm.   5.50
Dorothy Vase, Model of. bagware
  vase. No. 100. 48mm.   8.50

Glastonbury Bronze Bowl. 2
  models. No. 74. 40mm. No. 100.
  41mm.   5.50
Hastings Kettle. No. 237. 62mm.   5.50
Highland Whisky Bowl. 30mm.   7.00
Newbury Leather Bottle. No. 100.
  65mm.   5.50
St. *Davids Vase,* inscribed: *Vase found*
  at St. Davids. 69mm.   6.00

Wedgwood

✳✳✳
WEDGWOOD
✳
ENGLAND

Used after 1900.

WEDGWOOD
ETRURIA ENGLAND

c1900.

Trademark used by Josiah Wedgwood (and
  Sons Ltd), Etruria.

The famous firm of Wedgwood
  made a few small vases and jugs
  with crests at the turn of the
  century. The china is very fine and
  the crests are beautifully enamelled.
  These heraldic wares were
  obviously also exported, as crests
  of Le Havre and Monaco have
  been recorded.   15.00

There is also a series of small vases
  with gold ramshead handles with
  coloured transfers of soldiers.
  The regiments are named on the
  back of the vases. 60mm.   from 30.00

A 43mm three-handled loving cup
  with a gilded handle has also
  been recorded.   20.00

Wellington China

Wembley China

Trademark of J.H. Cope & Co., Wellington Works, Longton, Staffs. from 1924-1947. The firm produced high quality porcelain.

Domestic
Cup, saucer and plate, Lucky White Heather from Brecon.   Set 12.00

Trademark used on china for sale at the British Empire Exhibition of 1924 and 1925 by the Cauldon Group of Companies. (Usual trademark Arcadian). All pieces therefore carry B.E.E. crests and are priced accordingly. Some Wembley China pieces are rather grey and 'gritty'.

Wembley Models
Parian/Unglazed
George V bust on glazed
  plinth inscribed: *A souvenir*
  from Wembley, with inscription:
  King George V - Born June 3rd
  1865 Ascended the throne
  May 6th 1910.
  2 sizes: 125mm & 140mm.   85.00
Edward VII bust in trilby on glazed
  plinth. 125mm.   55.00
Prince of Wales, (Edward VIII)
  bust on glazed plinth, with
  inscription: *HRH The Prince*
  of Wales, Born June 23rd 1894.
  135mm.   85.00

Ancient Artefacts
Chinese Vase. 65mm.   12.00

Buildings - White
Big Ben. 140mm.   40.00
Burns Cottage. 112mm long.   47.50
Cottage on base. 92mm long.   25.00
St. Nicholas Chapel, Ilfracombe.
  95mm long.   28.00
Wembley Stadium, fully inscribed.
  130mm long.   100.00

Historical/Folklore

Miner's Lamp. 70mm.	25.00
Mother Shipton. 115mm.	20.00
Man in Stocks. 88mm.	32.00

Traditional/National Souvenirs

Thistle Vase. 70mm.	9.50
Welsh Hat. 52mm.	20.00
Welsh Tea Party. 98mm.	55.00

Seaside Souvenirs

Bathing Machine. 65mm.	26.00
Yacht. 125mm.	30.00
Trawler with sails set on both masts.	
125mm long.	35.00
Lighthouse, not named.	
2 sizes: 110mm.	15.00
140mm.	20.00

Countryside

Beehive on table. 78mm.	28.00
Haystack, circular. 55m.	20.00
Pine Cone, closed inside. 90mm.	20.00

Animals

Cat with long neck, sitting. 108mm.	18.00
Black Cat, sitting on armchair.	
55mm.	32.00
Fawn. 50mm.	50.00
Fish, 100mm long.	12.00
Frog, with open mouth. 62mm.	22.00
Hen, brooding. 63mm long.	24.00
Hippopotamus. 90mm long.	80.00
Kangaroo. 75mm.	100.00
Lion, walking. 85mm long.	35.00
Monkey sitting. 69mm.	28.00
Pig, sitting and smiling.	
63mm long.	30.00

Birds (including Eggs)

Cock, red comb and yellow beak.	
90mm.	23.00

Great War

Nurse and Wounded Tommy.	
108mm long.	190.00
Sailor winding capstan, Model of.	
105mm.	125.00
Tommy, driving a steamroller over	
the Kaiser. 120mm.	500.00
Soldier Bust, unnamed Tommy	
Atkins. Some colouring. 90mm.	40.00
Observer or Sausage Balloon. 82mm.	75.00
Minesweeper. 125mm long.	85.00
Armoured Car, model of. 95mm long.	50.00

Red Cross Van.	
2 sizes: 90mm long.	50.00
100mm long.	50.00
Tank, Model of. 115mm long.	30.00
Field gun with screen and sight	
hole. 107mm long.	40.00
Howitzer. 135mm.	30.00
Trench dagger. 105mm long.	70.00
Capstan. 56mm.	20.00
Pair of Field Glasses, Model of.	
78mm long.	30.00
Colonial Hat. 86mm long.	28.00
Officer's Peaked Cap. 65mm dia.	25.00
Cavell Memorial, inscribed: *Nurse*	
Cavell. 160mm.	30.00

Home/Nostalgic

Fireplace, no inscription but much	
colouring. 90mm.	25.00
Grandfather Clock. 108mm.	22.00
Kennel. 50mm.	12.50
Lantern, horn. 85mm.	12.00

Comic/Novelty

Billiken. 60mm.	15.00
Hand holding Pig's trotter.	
110mm long.	14.50
Policeman on duty. 145mm.	50.00
Suffragette Candle Snuffer, with face	
of young girl/old woman. 72mm.	30.00

Sport/Pastimes

Curling Stone. 49mm.	25.00
Bishop chess piece. 72mm.	25.00

Musical Instruments

Banjo. 153mm long.	25.00
Guitar. 155mm long.	25.00

Transport

Car, open tourer, (2 seater).	
110mm long.	45.00

Hats

Boy Scout's Hat. 73mm dia.	30.00

Miniature Domestic

Jug. 55mm.	10.00
Tea Pot, one piece. 48mm.	15.00

White Horse China

The White House

Trademark used for the Royal Mail Steam Packet Company by an unknown manufacturer, but resembling Carlton China and Arcadian.
Found with colour transfer printed views of ships at sea, including *RMSP ASTURIAS, THE ROYAL MAIL STEAM PACKET COMPANY, RMSP AMAZON, THE ROYAL MAIL STEAM PACKET COMPANY* and *RMSP ORINOCO, THE ROYAL MAIL STEAM PACKET COMPANY.*

The above display transfer prints of ships.

White Horse Models
Ancient Artefacts
Roman Pot in Lewes Castle.   5.50

Historical/Folklore
Carlisle Ancient Stone Roman Altar,
  Model of. 122mm. (Bears the arms
  of Reading.)   35.00

Animals
Squirrel eating nut. 68mm.   30.00

Hats
Coaching Hat, not named. No. 124.
  39mm.   12.50

Trademark used for a Lancashire retailer by an unknown manufacturer (possibly Arcadian).
Only one small and two animals have been found with this mark. A.H. and S.M. Manchester was not a manufacturer so one can assume that the White House, Manchester, was a retail outlet.

White House Models
One small recorded.   4.00

Animals
Upright Cat playing flute.
  70mm.   40.00
Squirrel eating nut. 68mm.   30.00

W.H.H. and S.

Seaside Souvenirs
Corbiere Lighthouse, Jersey. 100mm.	16.00
Eddystone Lighthouse. Pepper Pot.	
107mm.	12.50

Animals
Dog, Spaniel, sitting. 60mm.	12.50
Elephants, two on a sledge on slope.	
76mm.	75.00

Birds (including Eggs)
Duck posy bowl, yellow beak.	
83mm long.	11.50

Great War
Monoplane with revolving	
propellor. 145mm long.	75.00
Plymouth War Memorial. 175mm.	65.00

Sport
Cricket Cap. 70mm long.	50.00

Miniature Domestic
Cheese Dish and cover. 76mm long.	9.50

Trademark used by a Plymouth, Devon retailer by Hewitt & Leadbeater. (usual trademarks Willow Art or in this case Devonia Art China).
The initials W.H.H. and S.P. are retailer s initials. The P under the mark stands for Plymouth, although a Jersey crest has been found.

W.H.H. and S. Models
Ancient Artefacts
Puzzle Jug. 66mm.	7.00

Buildings - White
Clock Tower, not named. 125mm.	10.50

Monuments (including Crosses)
Sir Francis Drake, statue. Plymouth.	
163mm.	16.00
Plymouth Armada Memorial.	
175mm.	35.00

Why Not China

Wilco Series

For all details of this manufacturer see Wy
Not crest china.

Trademark used by Wilkinson & Co., a
Derbyshire retailer, by Hewitt and
Leadbeater. Willow Potteries. Longton.
(Usual trademark Willow Art).

Wilco Models

Ancient Artefacts
Chester Roman Vase. 57mm.   5.50

Animals
Rabbit, crouching with alert ears.
     No. 97. 60mm long.   12.50

Miniature Domestic
Cheese Dish and cover. 50mm.   9.50

Williamsons

Willow Art and Willow China

Trademark used by H.M. Williamson and
Sons, Bridge Pottery, Longton.
For more details see W.
This mark was used by Williamson and Sons
on domestic china with the usual patterns,
and has also been found on domestic
ware with crests. It also appears on the
two models listed below.

Early mark 1907-1925.

A range of crested domestic ware.

Williamson Models
Ancient Artefacts
Guernsey Milk Can, with lid.
105mm. (Found with a Guernsey
crest).   12.50

WILLOW
ART CHINA
LONGTON

Alcohol
Tankard. 75mm.   5.00

Early mark 1907-c1910.

Early mark 1907-25.

Can have STAFFORDSHIRE added, or MADE IN ENGLAND, as below

Can be found with "ware" rather than "china". Used between 1925-1930.

Mark used between 1907 and 1925. (Models with these marks can also be found impressed H & L 1907-1920 and Hewitt Bros. 1920-1925).

WILLOW CHINA

Mark found on late coloured models from 1925.

Early mark 1907-19

Mark found on domestic ware, 1925-1930.

H & L

Impressed mark 1905-1919.

H. BROS
WILLOW
ENGLAND

Impressed Mark 1919-25.

Trademark used by Hewitt and Leadbeater, Willow Potteries, Longton, subsequently, Hewitt Bros, and eventually Willow Potteries Ltd. a branch of Cauldon Ltd. Hewitt and Leadbeater joined in partnership in 1905 as manufacturers of 'artistic and useful specialities in great variety'. Mr Edwin Leadbeater was the son of the senior partner of Robinson and Leadbeater (R. and L. makers of Parian busts), and brought his experience to the new business. Arthur Hewitt was his brother-in-law. Edwin Leadbeater, as already mentioned (see: Leadbeater Art China), always received a good press from the *Pottery Gazette* and so we have more information about the products of the Willow Pottery than any other 'arms ware' firm.
As well as flower holders and vases in many shapes and colours, the new firm

produced ecclesiastical and art statuary in plain white, antique ivory and art colours. (These were marked H. and L.) The firms early ornamental wares are very beautiful, vases were made in the form of open flowers, the most striking being an arum lily with green leaves. 'Hop Ware' and 'Vine Ware' were also made, these vases and jugs having moulded bunches of green hops on dark green grounds or purple grapes and green vine leaves on cream grounds. They are delightful and delicate. (These early items are very rare and carry the earliest Willow mark.)
But 'Heraldic Ware' was one of the firm's leading lines from the beginning and its production helped Hewitt and Leadbeater to establish themselves. The company supplied miniatures with crests, views and other decorations including poppies. The range at this time was called 'Daisy Arms China' but this title does not appear on the models. By 1914, the firm was heavily involved in the production of heraldic novelties, and were said to specialise in models of churches, crosses and buildings of historic interest, also introducing models of a car, battleship, aeroplane, soldier, sailor and nurse to their range. A quote from the *Pottery Gazette* of December 1914, will give some idea of the firm's production.
'For a town such as Stratford, for instance, they have a model of Shakespeare's house in five sizes, Ann Hathaway's Cottage in five sizes, three distinct bust models of Shakespeare embracing in all ten different sizes, Shakespeare's font and desk, and a bust of Ann Hathaway in three sizes'.
Models of a racehorse and jockey were produced for the Newmarket agent, Mr P. S. Hobbs. On race days the result of a race would be rushed back to the shop by a boy on a bicycle and the girls would quickly paint in the colours of the winner on the jockey.
(The Parian models would have been marked H. and L. Not all the Ann Hathaway's cottages have been found.)
The war years were very kind to this firm as they could easily manufacture the cheap souvenirs usually supplied by the German china industry. Hewitt and Leadbeater produced a range of topical interest, but cannot be said to have made

many original Great War souvenirs. They did begin to produce dolls' heads but this seems to have been short-lived. They had become well known in the trade as specialists in the production of miniatures and parian, but their real speciality in terms of originality was coloured buildings. These sold cheaply at the time but are becoming particularly sought by collectors today. Although Goss cottages change hands for hundreds of pounds, the Willow Art coloured buildings are much more interesting and typical of the period, showing the same good eye for design and colour that was used on the early decorative vases. By 1920 the firm offered a range of 200 different miniatures from stock and offered to make copies of any building of which a photograph or postcard was supplied.

In November 1919 Edwin Leadbeater left the firm to start a pottery business on his own account. (See: Leadbeater Art China for details.) The remaining Mr Hewitt took his brother into partnership and the firm at Willow Pottery became known as Hewitt Bros. Hewitt Bros. continued to use the same tradename on heraldic china and described themselves as 'Novelty Potters'. They produced the usual post-war memorials, figures and comic items. In 1922 they introduced their 'Teddy Tail' and 'Black Cat China'. Teddy Tail transfers, from the original drawings by M. Charles Folkard, creator of the cartoon for the *Daily Mail,* were applied to nursery ware. (Very few, if any, of these mugs and plates have survived.) Black Cat transfers, from the original drawings by Mr H.H. Hosband were applied to domestic ware such as plates, hair tidies, trinket boxes and small vases.

Hewitt bros. did not survive the Depression but it is difficult to understand why the firm came to grief so early, except that they produced only novelties which were the last things people could afford. By 1925 Mr Harold Taylor Robinson had bought the firm and had formed a new company. Willow Potteries Ltd., using the tradename 'Willow Crest'. Willow Potteries Ltd. became part of the Cauldon group almost immediately. By 1927 Willow China was produced along with Arcadian at the Arcadian Works. It is difficult to tell if the

late models were originally Hewitt Bros. or Arkinstall moulds. The Willow mark was not used after 1930 but many recognisably Willow buildings are found marked Goss England, so the Willow moulds obviously were being used after that date.

The *Pottery Gazette* of December 1914 tells us that 'Willow Art Arms Ware, is of a warm, ivory caste, of an excellent body and well treated both as regards the potting and the painting. Praise indeed! Very few exceptionally fine pieces of Willow Art arms ware are found, for the most part the ware is heavy and the painting of crests is just about adequate. This heraldic china sold well because it was cheaply produced and novel. The early wares, especially the parian and coloured buildings made by the firm however, would have sold on their technical merit, and early view ware is found on very fine china.

Very little view ware has been recorded. Early coloured views are found on small dishes and vases, they are pleasant but unremarkable. More exciting are monochrome (brown) pictorials found on small Willow Art pieces, with the earliest factory mark, occasionally finished in yellow lustre, and coloured transfers of a regional nature which include Peeping Tom (Willow Art) and Kiaora from Maoriland, Tiki, New Zealand, (Willow).

Willow Art was exported too, so foreign crests are found: Australia, New Zealand and Gibraltar have been recorded. A Jerusalem crest is often found but this is an indication that the model was purchased from the Jerusalem and Oriental Bazaar, Great Yarmouth and not from the Middle East.

Agents or retailers names are usually printed within rectangular boxes.

The following military badges were also produced by Hewitt and Leadbeater:

Army Cyclists Corps
Army Ordnance Corps
Army Service Corps
Canadian Forces
Canadian General Service Corps (Maple Leaf)
Coldstream Guards
Gloucestershire Regiment
Grenadier Guards
Hendon Flying School

13th Hussars
King's Own Yorkshire Light Infantry
Leicestershire Regiment
1st Life Guards
2nd Life Guards
Lincolnshire Regiment
Loyal North Lancs Regiment
Machine Gun Corps
North Staffordshire Regiment
Northumberland Fusiliers
Notts & Derby Regiment
Royal Air Force
Royal Army Medical Corps
Royal Army Ordnance Corps
Royal Artillery
Royal Engineers
Royal Field Artillery
RE Longmoor Camp (2 versions - Edward
    VII cipher and George V cipher)
Royal Military College, Camberley
Royal Flying Corps
Royal Naval Air Service
Royal North Lancashire Regt.
Royal Sussex Regiment
Queen's Royal West Surrey Regiment
Royal West Surrey Regiment, 2nd Foot
Royal West Surreys, the Queen s
Scots Guards
Somerset Light Infantry
York & Lancaster Regiment
Flags of the Allies Great War commemora-
tives are found inscribed: *United We Stand.*
Other Willow Art commemoratives found
are *Franco British Exhibition 1908* and *BEE.*
Willow Art and Willow China can be found
decorated with red poppies and 'Lucky
Black Cat' transfers. Willow Art 'smalls'
can be found with a pale blue transfer of
a Kingfisher and edged in blue, these
have the inscription *Happy Days at . . .*
Numbering System. Willow Art models in
general production, not made for a
specific retailer, do sometimes have painted stock numbers, and these have been
listed where they are known. Paintresses
marks are usually initials found under
these numbers.
Some late models usually marked Willow
have impressed stock numbers, for example
the Willow black cat on a pouffe is
impressed 539. These numbers are very
difficult to spot and equally difficult to read
clearly as they are usually covered in thick

glaze and more often than not have the
trademark printed over them. They have
not yet been recorded, it is hoped that as
clear examples are found they will be noted.

Models can be found marked Willow or
Willow Art.

Willow Art and Willow Models
Parian/Unglazed
All the busts can be found
    impressed H. and L. (Hewitt and
    Leadbeater).
Bust of Albert King of the Belgians,
    not named, on square glazed
    base. 170mm.   80.00
Bust of *Ann Hathaway* on square
    base. 135mm.   45.00
Bust of Burns impressed: *Burns* and
    impressed on the reverse *H. Bros*
    on square unglazed base with a
    crest. 150mm.   40.00
Bust of Burns impressed: *Burns H & L,*
    circular plinth. 175mm.   40.00
Bust of Burns, on circular glazed
    base. 140mm.   30.00
Bust of *Chamberlain,* round plinth.
    170mm.   30.00
Bust of General Foch. 165mm.   40.00
Bust of French, not named, on
    square glazed base. 170mm.   80.00
Bust of Sir John French, square base,
    unglazed. 168mm.   95.00
Bust of General Roberts in uniform,
    square base, unglazed. 168mm.   95.00
Bust of Gladstone, not named, on
    circular glazed base. Can be
    found with crest of W.E.
    Gladstone on glazed base when
    £10.00 should be added. 160mm.   30.00
Bust of *Grace Darling.* 152mm.   80.00
Bust of *Highland Mary* on square
    base. 140mm.   45.00
Bust of Jellicoe, wearing peaked cap,
    named, on circular glazed base.
    165mm. (Rare).   110.00
Bust of Kitchener 170mm.   95.00
Bust of *Tom Morris.* Crest
    St. Andrews and golfing
    inscriptions. 150mm.   300.00
Bust of John Peel with full
    inscription, circular base.
    140mm.   75.00
Bust of *Peeping Tom,* unglazed.
    134mm & 155mm.   30.00

Bust of Sir Walter Scott, not named,
on circular glazed base.

2 sizes: 130mm.   30 00

163mm.   40.00

Bust of Shakespeare, on circular
base. 120mm.   17.50

Bust of *Smuts* in military uniform,
unglazed. 150mm.   130.00

Mr Pickwick, Pickwick Papers. Unglazed
Dickensian figure. 119mm.   65.00
Can also be found decorated in a
brown wash.

Scold's Bridle, on circular base, with
verse, from Walton on Thames.
112mm.   65.00

Bill Sykes and his dog, standing
figure on base. Coloured beige,
no crest. 128mm.   55.00

Girl Doll, head marked *Willow
England*, fixed glass eyes, head /
shoulder height. 285mm. Whole
doll.   130.00

Girl Doll, in pink robe, fully
coloured, with real hair. 185mm.   145.00

Ancient Artefacts

Beccles Ringers Jug, with full
inscription. 67mm.   17.50

Chester Roman vase, not named.
55mm.   5.50

Lincoln Jack, not named. No. 74.
53mm.   5.50

Loving Cup. 2 and 3 handled.   6.50

Persian Wine Server, not named.
105mm.   5.50

Phoenician Water Jug, not named.
66mm.   4.50

Plymouth Jug, not named. No. 24.
47mm.   4.50

Pompeii Lamp. 95mm long.   5.50

Puzzle Jug with verse: *Try how to
drink.* 70mm.   7.00

Puzzle Teapot (Lady Cadogan's
teapot), with verse to rear. 65mm.   19.00

Buildings - Coloured

Coloured buildings can be found
glazed or unglazed. Some of
these models can also be found
white.

Ann Hathaway's Cottage.

5 sizes: 50mm long.   18.00

60mm long.   18.00

65mm long.   25.00

105mm long.   30.00

130mm long.   40.00

Battle Abbey Gateway. 139mm long.   82.50

*Bell Hotel, Abel Fletcher's House in
John Halifax Gentlemen.*

3 sizes: 57mm long.   50.00

84mm.   65.00

124mm.   7.00

Bell Hotel Tewkesbury on ashtray
base. 76mm long.   40.00

John Bunyan's Cottage. 75mm long.   82.50

Burns Cottage, Model of. 108mm long.   40.00

Burns House, inscribed: *The poet
occupied this house from 1793 until
his death 21st July 1796.* 90mm.   145.00

Cat and Fiddle. 92mm.   150.00

Feathers Hotel, Ludlow.

2 sizes: 52mm long.   75.00

112mm long.   125.00

Godalming Old Town Hall.
100mm.   125.00

Harlech Castle. 200mm long.   195.00

*Harvard House, Stratford-on-Avon,
purchased and restored by
Miss Marie Corelli for Mr
Edward Morris and by him
presented to Harvard University,
Cambridge 1909. Mass. U.S.A.*
and on the base *to be obtained
only from Fred Winter, High Street,
Stratford-on-Avon.*
Brown timbered building.
142mm.   250.00

Knox's House, inscribed: *Model
of the house in Edinburgh where
John Knox the Scottish reformer
died 24th Nov 1572.*
102mm.   145.00

Leicester Hospital, Warwick.
157mm long.   235.00

Mason Croft, The House of Miss
Marie Corelli. 90mm long.   150.00

John Milton's Cottage. 60mm long.   150.00

*Famous Old Blacksmiths shop and
marriage room, Gretna Green.*
85mm long.   40.00

Old Chapel, Lantern Hill, Ilfracombe.
76mm long.   90.00

*Old Curiosity Shop. No. 14,
Portsmouth Street.* 80mm long.   140.00

*Old Maids Cottage, Lee near
Ilfracombe.* 59mm long.   65.00

Old Ostrich Inn, Colnbrook. 80mm.   250.00

*Historical, Old Mint House, Pevensey
1342 AD.* 120mm long.   160.00

*The Olde Trip to Jerusalem Inn,
1199 AD*, inscribed: *Home
Brewed Ales.* 106mm long.   250.00

St. Bennet's Abbey, Norfolk Broads on
pintray base. 70mm.   100.00
St. Bernards Monastery, Coalville.
102mm long.   135.00
St. Ann's Well, Gt. Malvern.
167mm long.   150.00
St. Nicholas Church, Great Yarmouth.
140mm long. Also found unglazed.   115.00
Shakespeare's House.
6 sizes: 52mm long.   16.00
65mm long.   17.50
110mm long.   30.00
125mm long.   40.00
130mm long.   40.00
157mm long.   45.00
210mm long.   50.00
Stokesay Castle Gate House.
100mm.   150.00
Tan House, Little Stretton.
120mm long.   125.00
Upleatham Church. 90mm.   100.00
Waltham Abbey Tower, grey
unglazed, black windows.
100mm.   125.00
Whittington Inn, with inscription.
100mm long.   110.00
Wilberforce Museum with inscription.
Coloured grey 115mm long.   115.00

Buildings - White
Old Castle, Ballybunion. Ruins on
rectangular base. 102mm.   80.00
Bath Abbey, West Front. 110mm.   40.00
Battle Abbey Gateway, front. 95mm.   40.00
Bell Hotel, Abel Fletchers House in
John Halifax Gentleman.
2 sizes: 84mm long.   25.00
124mm long.   30.00
Bell Hotel, Abel Fletchers House in
John Halifax Gentleman, on ashtray
base. Some colouring.
75mm long.   40.00
Big Ben. 146mm.   25.00
Blackpool Tower. 125mm.   13.00
Blackpool Tower, with buildings.
150mm.   20.00
Blackpool Tower, with buildings,
impressed: *Variety, Dancing,*
Concert. 165mm.   30.00
Bourne Abbey, West Front.
108mm.   65.00
John Bunyan s Cottage, Model of
75mm long.   22.00

Burns Cottage, Ayr, Model of, with
inscription.
2 sizes: 66mm long.   16.00
105mm long.   27.50
Burns Mausoleum, Dumfries. 95mm.   75.00
Bury St. Edmunds, Abbey Gate.
80mm.   75.00
Canterbury Cathedral, West Front.
125mm.   40.00
Canterbury, West Gate. 90mm.   30.00
Carillon Tower, Loughborough. 159mm.   65.00
Carnegie's Birthplace, inscribed: *The*
birthplace of Andrew Carnegie.
85mm long.   75 00
Castle Hill Tower, Huddersfield.
115mm.   50.00
Chantry Front Wakefield, Model of
95mm long.   125.00
Chatham, Town Hall, Model of
146mm.   70.00
Chesterfield Parish Church, Model of,
found with inscription. 125mm.   50.00
Citadel Gateway, Plymouth. 110mm.   30.00
Clifton Suspension Bridge, Model of,
with long inscription.
120mm long.   80.00
Conisborough Castle, The Keep.
95mm.   100.00
Cottage, inscribed: *Built in a day 4th*
June 1319.
2 sizes: 43mm long.   26.00
92mm long.   35.00
Crofter's Cottage. 55mm long.   30.00
Fair Maids House, Perth. 65mm high,
78mm long.   75.00
First and Last House in England.
83mm long. With green door.   20.00
First and Last House in England, with
annexe. 95mm long.   30.00
Gretna Green Marriage Room.
60mm long.   20.00
Grimsby Hydraulic Tower, with
inscriptions. 165mm.   50.00
Hampton Court Palace, flat frontage
on ashtray base. 108mm long.   60.00
Hamsfell Hospice, Grange over Sands.
(Often found not named). 72mm.
An odd square building with
outside stairs and flat roof, and
with impressed Greek inscription
over door.   75.00
Hastings Castle Ruins. 100mm.   40.00
Hastings Clock Tower. 165mm.   17.50

Hay Castle, Brecon. 94mm.	55.00
Hop Pole Hotel, flat frontage on ashtray base, with long quotation referring to the inn from Chapter 50 The Pickwick Papers by Charles Dickens, on ashtray 60mm long.	40.00
King Charles Tower, Chester, with outer steps. 100mm.	47.50
John Knox s House, with inscription 110mm.	50.00
Lancaster, Castle Gateway 90mm.	55.00
Leicester Clock Tower. 175mm.	50.00
Lincoln Cathedral, West Front. 100mm and 118mm long.	35.00
Lincoln Cathedral, West Front, on ashtray base. 110mm.	30.00
Lincoln, Stonebow. 104mm long.	50.00
Lloyd George's Home, inscribed: *The Old Home of the Right Hon. D. Lloyd George Esq. M. P. Llanystymdwy near Criccieth.* 2 sizes: 75mm long.	45.00
102mm long.	55.00
Loch Leven Castle, Kinross. 75mm.	75.00
Old London Bridge on ashtray base. 105mm long.	70.00
The Marble Arch. Unglazed. 98mm long.	25.00
Margate *Jubilee Clock Tower.* 120mm.	20.00
Mickelgate Bar, York. 116mm.	24.00
Monnow Bridge, Monmouth. 92mm.	40.00
Morpeth Castle, Model of. 78mm.	75.00
Nottingham Castle, Model of 92mm long.	55.00
Old Bridge House, Ambleside. 88mm.	75.00
Old Nottingham Inn, Ye Olde Trip to Jerusalem, 1199 AD, Model of. 95mm.	75.00
Old Ostrich Inn, Colnbrook. 80mm.	60.00
Park Tower, Barnsley. 137mm.	65.00
Peterborough Cathedral, West Front. 80mm long.	45.00
Peveril Castle. 115mm long.	55.00
Pump Room, Harrogate. 75mm.	47.50
St. Ann's Well, Buxton. 120mm.	65.00
St. Ann's Well, Great Malvern 102mm long.	65.00
St. Benet's Abbey, Norfolk Broads, castle ruins on pintray base. 70mm.	40.00
St. Botolph's Church, Boston. 112mm.	55.00

St. Denny's Church, Sleaford. 2 sizes: 95mm & 140mm.	65.00
St. Nicholas' Church, Great Yarmouth. Unglazed. 143mm long.	65.00
St. Paul s Cathedral. 140mm.	30.00
Saville Fountain, Saville Gardens, Windsor. No. 730. 140mm.	75.00
Saxon Church, Bradford on Avon. 74mm.	75.00
Shakespeare s House. 2 sizes: 120mm long.	14.00
160mm long.	17.00
Skegness, Clock Tower. 2 sizes: 125mm.	18.00
165mm.	45.00
Skegness, Pier Entrance. 85mm long.	85.00
Solomon's Temple, Grinlow Tower, inscribed: *Erected on site of a prehistoric barrow, Buxton.* 88mm.	90.00
Temple Bar, Waltham Cross. 100mm long.	80.00
Tennysons House, Mablethorpe. 85mm long.	100.00
Tudor Gabled House, Taunton AD 1800 also *AD 1578.* 100mm.	75.00
Upleatham Church, Redcar 88mm.	40.00
Uttoxeter Market Place, Conduit, Scene of Dr. Johnson's Penance. 123mm.	40.00
Wainhouse Tower, Halifax. 130mm.	125.00
Wallingford, Town Hall. 84mm.	75.00
West Malling, Abbey Tower 94mm.	125.00
Westminster Abbey, West Front. 3 sizes: 70mm.	20.00
114mm.	24.00
130mm.	28.00
Whittington Inn, with inscription. 100mm long.	47.50
Wilberforce House, Hull. 86mm.	125.00
Windmill, with sails. 85mm.	40.00
Windsor Castle. 125mm long.	25.00
Windsor Castle, Round Tower 2 sizes: 68mm.	25.00
83mm.	28.00
Worcester Cathedral. 144mm long.	40.00
Worksop, Priory Gate House. 88mm.	75.00

Monuments (including Crosses)

Ancient Runic Cross, Bakewell. 110mm.	47.50
Arwenack Monument, erected by Martin Killigrew. AD 1787, Falmouth. 120mm.	40.00
Ashington Boer War Memorial. 135mm.	75.00

Ancient Runic Cross Bakewell. 115mm.   20.00
Banbury Cross. 140mm.   40.00
Bovey Tracey, Old Cross. 140mm.   70.00
Bradlaugh's Monument, Northampton.
142mm.   50.00
Bruce Statue, Stirling. 160mm.   60.00
Burns Statue, standing, right hand
on chest. 176mm.   30.00
Burns Statue, seated on rock, with
dog, pipe and tam-o'-shanter, all
on plinth. 167mm.   35.00
Burns and Highland Mary.
2 sizes: 117mm.   50.00
130mm.   55.00
Bunyan Statue. 165mm.   20.00
Bunyan Statue on heavy base.
170mm.   20.00
Burmah Cross, Taunton. inscribed:
Burmah 1885-6-7 and *Somerset
Light Infantry.* 118mm.   75.00
Burton Statue, inscribed: *Michael
Arthur, first Baron Burton.*
128mm.   30.00
Caister-on-Sea Lifeboat Memorial.
Moulded in relief: 1903 and
Caister Lifeboat on lifebelt.
162mm.   35.00
Andrew Carnegie, statue.
150mm.   30.00
Cleethorpes Fisherman's Memorial
with inscription: *Erected by Public
Subscription to the memory of
George Henry Smith (skipper) and
William Richard Leggatt (Third
Hand) etc. unveiled August 30th
1908.* 155mm.   30.00
Cleopatra's Needle, with lions.
128mm   135.00
Old Cornish Cross, Model of
100mm.   19.50
Drake, Statue, Plymouth.
160mm.   16.00
*Druids Well, Sutton Park, Sutton
Coldfield.* 45mm.   70.00
Flodden Cross, inscribed: *Flodden
1513, to the brave of both nations.*
136mm.   25.00
*Sir John Franklin, discoverer of the
north-west passage, born at Spilsby
April 1786. Died in the Arctic
Regions June 1847.* Statue.
163mm.   85.00
*General Sir Redvers Buller's Cross at
Crediton, model of.* 115mm.   75.00

Gibbet Cross, Hindhead, inscribed:
*Post Tenebras Lux In Luce Spes In
Obrtu Pax Post Obitum Salus.*
136mm.   12.00
Gladstone Statue, Blackburn.
130mm.   40.00
The Globe, Swanage. 85mm.   30.00
Hall Cross, Doncaster. 133mm.   110.00
*Hector Macdonald Memorial,
Dingwall.* 112mm.   75.00
Highland Mary Statue, Dunoon, on
plinth. 150mm.   35.00
Huddersfield, Market Cross.
150mm.   125.00
*Tom Hughes Monument, Rugby
School.* 140mm.   40.00
Hull Fisherman's Memorial.
2 sizes: 135mm.   20.00
160mm.   24.00
Hull South African War Memorial,
with inscription: *Erected to the
memory of the men of Hull who fell
in the late South African War.*
165mm.   35.00
Keppels Column 1778. 140mm.   50.00
King George Stone, Kingstown.
135mm.   80.00
Laceby, The Monument.
2 sizes: 120mm.   25.00
155mm.   40.00
*Lytham St. Anne's Lifeboat Memorial,
erected in honour of 13 brave Men,
who lost their lives while attempting
to save the crew of the German barque
Mexico. December 6th 1886.*   50.00
Lowestoft Fisherman's Memorial.
130mm.   26.00
*Maiwand Memorial, Forbury Gardens,
Reading.* Lion sometimes coloured
black or brown, add £5.00.
100mm.   25.00
Margate Surf Boat Memorial. 135mm.   20.00
Margate Surf Boat Memorial, (Rock)
inscribed: *IN MEMORY OF NINE
HEROIC MEN WHO LOST
THEIR LIVES BY THE
CAPSIZING OF THE MARGATE
SURF BOAT "FRIEND TO ALL
NATIONS" IN ATTEMPTING TO
ASSIST A VESSEL IN DISTRESS
AT SEA 2ND DEC 1887.*
2 sizes: 110mm.   100.00
130mm.   100.00
Martyrs' Memorial, Coventry, 2
piece cross. 134mm.   125.00

The Monument. 160mm.	125.00
Nelson's Column. 160mm.	90.00
Isaac Newton, statue. 165mm.	40.00
Peter Pan, statue. 140mm.	80.00
Queen Victoria's Statue, Blackburn.	40.00
Queen Victoria's Statue, Wakefield.	
115mm.	40.00
Queen Victoria's Statue, Windsor.	
2 sizes: 65mm.	35.00
167mm.	55.00
Richmond Market Cross. 137mm.	25.00
Rock of Ages, usual verse &	
inscription. 80mm.	10.50
C.S. Rolls Memorial, inscribed:	
*Memorial to the late Hon*ble	
C.S. Rolls. 128mm.	40.00
Rufus Stone. 110mm.	7.50
Ruskin Memorial, Friars Crag.	
2 sizes: 150mm.	20.00
180mm.	24.00
Sailor's Stone, Hindhead. 95mm.	15.00
St. Albans Clock Tower. 120mm.	30.00
St. Alban, Statue of. 146mm.	65.00
Saville Fountain, Saville Gardens,	
Englefield Green. 140mm.	85.00
Saxon Soldier, statue on square	
base. 125mm.	90.00
Scone, The Cross. 142mm.	100.00
Toad Rock, Tunbridge Wells. 83mm.	20.00
Todmarden Memorial (obelisk on	
4-sided base). Also known as the	
Stoodley Pike. 130mm.	70.00
Wallace Statue. 141mm.	85.00
Wallace Statue, model of. Figure with	
arm outstretched, sword in other	
hand on stone plinth. 155mm.	125.00
Sir William de la Pole, Statue of,	
inscribed on back: *"Sir William*	
De-La-Pole Knight Bannaret First	
Mayor of Hull. AD 1332-5"	
on left: *"Lord Myton of Holderness*	
Baron of the Exchequer. Founder	
of the Charter House at Hull.	
Died April 21st 1366."	
on right: *"Statue of Sir William-De-*	
La-Pole presented to the Corporation	
of Hull by Alderman Robert Jameson	
Sheriff of Hull 1808-9." 160mm.	40.00

Historical/Folklore

Archbishops Chair, Canterbury	
Cathedral. 93mm.	14.00
Inscribed.	18.50
Bangor Abbey Bell, inscribed: *Model*	
of the old bell, Bangor Abbey, Co.	
Down. Rare. 85mm.	45.00

Bishop's Jester, Wells Cathedral. Fully	
coloured. No crest.	
2 sizes: 110mm.	60.00
125mm.	60.00
Bunyan's Chair, Model of.	
90mm.	19.00
Bunyan's Cushion, Model of.	
105mm long.	40.00
Burns at the plough. Rectangular plinth.	
100mm long.	60.00
Burns Chair. 85mm.	12.50
Can be found as corner seat, also	
inscribed: *Dumfries.*	18.00
Daniel Lambert, sitting on chair With	
long inscription. 118mm.	125.00
Devil looking over Lincoln.	
115mm.	19.50
The Ducking Stool, with inscription	
as Arcadian. Can be found	
coloured brown with no crest.	
2-piece. 120mm.	85.00
Father Christmas carrying sack of	
toys. 110mm.	200.00
Font, not named. 2 sizes: 55mm &	
87mm.	16.50
Gladiators Helmet. 80mm.	25.00
James V Chair, Stirling Castle.	
No. 200. 100mm.	14.50
Joan of Arc. 150mm.	100.00
John Knox Chair, Edinburgh. brown	
no crest. 122mm.	47.50
Lady Godiva on horseback, on base.	
80mm.	30.00
Man in the Moon. Can be found	
with yellow face. No. 311. 55mm.	30.00
Man in the Sun. 94mm.	47.50
Mary Queen of Scots Chair, Edinburgh	
Castle, Model of. 75mm.	10.50
Mons Meg, Edinburgh Castle.	
130mm long.	20.00
Mother Shipton.	
2 sizes: 80mm.	10.00
105mm.	13.00
Peeping Tom, bust. 130mm.	25.00
Queen Phillipa's Record Chest.	
92mm long.	20.00
Ripon Hornblower. 120mm.	16.00
A Rubbing Stone for Asses, a 17th	
century puzzle printed on a brick	
wall. 100mm long.	45.00
Shakespeare's Font, no plinth.	
Inscribed: *Model of Font in which*	
Shakespeare was Baptised. 85mm	
dia. 40mm.	17.50

Shakespeare's Font, on hexagonal
plinth. Inscribed: *Model of Font in
which Shakespeare was Baptised.*
128mm.   22.00
*Sir Walter Scott's Chair, Abbotsford,
Model of.* 80mm.   14.50
Skull, can be inscribed: *Alas poor
Yorick.* 60mm long.   16.00
Skull, brown. 60mm long.   22.00
Sword, ornate in scabbard.
135mm long.   70.00
Sundial, Tideswell Church, Model of.
110mm.   25.00
Trusty Servant, with verse on both
sides, fully coloured. 132mm.   150.00
Trusty Servant bust, on fluted column.
Coloured. 113mm.   100.00

Traditional/National Souvenirs
'ARRIET, Bust of Pearly Queen.
92mm.   55.00
'ARRY, Bust of Pearly King.   40.00
John Bull, standing. 120mm.   55.00
Banbury Cake. 105mm wide.   70.00
Bolton Trotter 135mm long.   12.00
Blackpool Big Wheel.
2 sizes: 88mm.   20.00
100mm.   22.00
Blackpool Big Wheel, rectangular
base. 120mm.   19.50
Cheddar Cheese, slice out,
inscribed: *Prime Cheddar Cheese.*
34mm high, 67mm dia.   12.50
Also found 55mm high, 42mm dia.   12.50
Chertsey Abbey Bell *Curfew must not
ring tonight.* 75mm.   15.00
A Cornish Pasty.
2 sizes: 90mm long.   12.00
100mm long.   14.00
Chester Imp, The. 80mm.   40.00
Englishman, bust, wearing black
hat. No. 114. 76mm.   25.00
Leaking Boot. Cleethorpes Standing
figure of young boy holding boot
aloft (attached to his hand by
string). 145mm.   75.00
Lincoln Imp. 63mm.   10.50
Lincoln Imp, on pedestal. 102mm.   8.50
Manx Man, John Bull as above but
with an extra leg added at rear.
Same colouring. 120mm.   95.00
Map of Isle of Wight,
coloured map. 60mm.   45.00
Melton Mowbray Pie with verse.
55mm.   30.00

Reading Biscuit, impressed: *Huntley
& Palmer* can be found with
verse: *Than Reading biscuits there
are no finer, Here's a good one
reproduced in china.* (Add £8).
Coloured biscuit. 85mm long.   50.00
Coloured biscuit on ashtray base.   50.00
Can also be found on stand.   50.00
Can also be found as hatpin
holder, on stand with verse.   50.00
River Thames Pleasure Punt,
175mm long.   100.00
With coloured cushions add £30
Yarmouth Bloater 121mm.   12.00
Irish Harp. 105mm.   10.00
Irishman, bust. No. 115. Wearing
Black hat. 78mm.   25.00
Bagpipes. 118mm long.   50.00
Blacksmiths Anvil, Gretna Green,
often found not named, with
inscription.
3 sizes: 45mm.   6.00
70mm.   7.50
76mm.   7.50
Gretna Priest, standing on
square base. 136mm.   45.00
The Old Priest's Chair, Gretna
Green. No. 163. 82mm.   30.00
Jimmy Strength, with inscription: *A
well known Border character whose
name was James Stuart a descendant
of the Royal Family of that name. He
was famous for his age and great
strength and died in his 123rd year.*
Figure on square plinth. 114mm.   90.00
Scotsman, bust. No. 116. Wearing
coloured tam-o'shanter. 80mm.   25.00
Scotsman matches holder. Comic
fully coloured figure. Inscribed:
Matches. 90mm.   65.00
Souter Johnny, sitting figure, with
verse. 130mm.   30.00
Coloured.   40.00
Tam-o'shanter, sitting figure, with
verse. 135mm.   30.00
Coloured.   40.00
Thistle vase.
2 sizes: 50mm.   4.00
68mm.   4.50
Leek Vase. 98mm.   7.00
Welsh Hat, Model of, with longest
place name. 52mm. (Arcadian
mould).   11.50

Welsh Hat, can have blue hat band.
Can be found with longest Welsh
place name printed round brim.
57mm.   9.00
Inscribed: 11.50
Welsh Harp, very delicate. 90mm.   9.50
Welsh Lady, bust, with black hat.
No. 117. 110mm.   25.00
Welsh Leek. 55mm.   7.00
Welsh Tea Party, a figure group, on
square ashtray base some
colouring. 50mm.   50.00
Dutch Boy. 80mm. Can be found
fully coloured, when £10.00
should be added.   12.50
Dutch Girl. 80mm. Can be found
fully coloured, when £10.00
should be added.   12.50
(A pair to the Dutch Boy).

Seaside Souvenirs
Bathing Machine, inscribed: *A
morning dip.*
2 sizes: 65mm.   16.00
          80mm.   18.50
Lifeboat, coloured ropes, if found
inscribed: *A.E. Davies* or *Mark
Lane* add £15.00. 118mm long.   22.50
Motorboat, with driver, at sea.
115mm long.   19.50
Paddlesteamer. 154mm long (rare). 100.00
Rowing Boat on rocks.
109mm long.   16.00
Yacht in full sail. 122mm.   19.50
Fisherman's Basket with handle
77mm long.   6.50
Fish Basket without handles. 80mm
long.   8.00
A Yarmouth Fish Swill, basket.
40mm.   14.00
Lifeboatman standing by capstan.   45.00
Lighthouse, not named. No. 135.
105mm.   7.00
Lighthouse, octagonal. No. 145.
110mm.   10.00
Lighthouse on rocks with brown
rowing boat. 133mm.   30.00
Beachy Head lighthouse, with black
band. 2 sizes: 100mm & 136mm.   12.00
Flamborough Lighthouse. 110mm.   30.00
North Foreland Lighthouse. 135mm. 40.00
Scurdyness Lighthouse pepper pot.
108mm.   17.00
Spurn Lighthouse, with details of size
and power. 125mm.   22.50

Withernsea Lighthouse, with details
of size and power. 110mm and
127mm.   22.00
Crab. 83mm long.   20.00
Mermaid, seated on rock, combing
hair, holding gilded mirror.
Impressed No. 374. 105mm.   30.00
Oyster Shell posy holder 89mm.   5.50
Shell menu holder on coral base.
No. 360. 90mm.   9.00
Scallop Shell resting on coral. 70mm
wide.   9.00
Scallop Shell hatpin holder on coral
base. 92mm.   10.50
Stick of Rock, pink stick with resort
printed (very realistic), so far
Great Yarmouth, Southsea and now
Clacton have been recorded. Has
been found as a salt and pepper
pot. 75mm.
White   70.00
Pink   150.00
Truck of Sand, same model as truck
of coal but with coal painted
yellow, can be inscribed: *Sand for
the kiddies from...* or *A truck of sand
from...* 90mm long.   80.00
Whelk shell, inscribed: *Listen to the
sea.* 110mm.   7.00

Countryside
Milk Can with lid. 60mm.   7.00
Pinecone. 90mm.   6.00
Treetrunk hat pin holder. 80mm.   12.50
Treetrunk Vase. 80mm.   9.50
Treetrunk, horizontal, with ivy. Open
top. 72mm long.   9.50

Animals
Bear, inscribed: *The Bear of
Bromsgrove,* with Bromsgrove
arms. 95mm long.   90.00
Boar, standing on rocky base.
102mm long. Two varieties of
base may be found.   80.00
Cat, angry, with tail in the air. Blue
bow. 80mm long.   22.00
Cat, in boot, white or blue bow.
88mm long.
White bow.   22.50
Blue bow.   28.50
Cat, Cheshire, with coloured face.
Inscribed: *Always Smiling* or more
rarely: *Cheshire Cat, 'still smiling'.*
2 sizes: 68mm.   10.00
          95mm.   14.50

Cat, Manx, walking, detailed fur.
100mm long.   40.00
Cat's head on base. 60mm.   65.00
Cat, sitting, bow round neck.
80mm.   12.00
Cat, sitting, blue or red bow.
60mm.   30.00
Cat, sitting, large red bow, and red
and green eyes. 70mm.   25.00
Cat, sitting, looking left, crest on
shield. 74mm.   14.50
Cat, sitting, detailed thick coat, and
tail around paws. Candlesnuffer.
57mm.   20.00
Cat, standing, chubby, sometimes
with blue bow. 70mm.   22.00
Cat, standing (long back), green
eyes and red tongue. 117mm long.   40.00

Black Cats
Black Cat on Cushion. 100mm.   30.00
Black Cat on diamond ashtray
inscribed: *Ashtray* and *Good Luck.*
120mm long.   30.00
Black Cat on Pouffe, inscribed: *Good
luck.* Can be found with red or
blue bow. 85mm. Impressed. No.
539. 80mm, 90mm and 95mm.   30.00
Black Cat on pepper pot. 90mm.   25.00

Smaller Arcadian type Black Cats.
Black Cat on pillar box. 56mm.   75.00
Black Cat, playing bagpipes. 60mm.   95.00
Black Cat with bottle. 70mm.   75.00
Black Cat in boot, blue bow.
95mm long.   75.00
Black Cat on Jug. 60mm.   65.00
Black Cat, wearing kilt and sitting
on a curling stone.   100.00
Black Cat, playing bagpipes, and
wearing kilt, standing on thistle
ashtray. 88mm long.   100.00
Black Cat on telephone. 65mm.   115.00
Black Cat, playing a harp. 60mm.   95.00
Black Cat, wearing kilt and
glengarry, standing on golf ball.
70mm.   125.00
Black Cat, standing beside thistle
vase. 57mm.   95.00
Black Cat, wearing a Welsh hat,
standing beside a leek. 67mm.   95.00
Black Cat, sitting in cup, inscribed:
*May your cup of Good Luck brim
over.* 90mm.   85.00

Bear, Polar, sitting on haunches.
2 sizes: 82mm.   40 00
        96mm.   55.00
Bear, Polar, standing. 83mm.   45.00
Bear, Teddy, sitting. No. 112. 65mm
and 75mm.   24.50
Bull, Highland, inscribed: *King of the
Herd.* 115mm long.   80.00
Calf, standing. 100mm long.   35.00
Cow, kneeling. 105mm long.   60.00
Deer, sitting.
2 sizes: 64mm.   40.00
        115mm long.   55.00
Dog, Bulldog, sitting, feet moulded
separately. Black collar and red
mouth. 55mm.   30.00
Dog, Bulldog, sitting, feet integrally
moulded. 54mm.   25.00
Bulldog, standing. 92mm long.   20.00
Dog, Bulldog, black, emerging from
kennel, inscribed: *The Black
Watch.* 70mm long.   25.00
Dog, Bull Terrier, standing. 60mm.   16.50
Dog, Collie, sitting. 78mm.   30.00
Dog, Collie, standing. No. 484. 85mm.   30.00
Dog, Dachshund, sitting, long ears
and rather comic. 75mm long.   50.00
Can be found with red mouth,
black patches and puzzled, painted
eyes.
Dog, Foxhound. 69mm.   60.00
Dog, Labrador, walking.
90mm long.   24.50
Dog, The Manx three legged, often
found not named.   50.00
Inscribed: *Prince Toby Orry.*
70mm.   75.00
Dog, walking rather like St. Bernard.
No. 511. 95mm long, 50mm high.   35.00
Dog, Scottie, sitting wearing a
glengarry.
4 sizes: 60mm.   14.50
        85mm.   17.50
        90mm. No. 309.   17.00
        100mm.   19.50
Dog, Scottie, sitting wearing a dark
blue tam-o'shanter. 80mm.   16.00
Dog, Scottish Terrier, standing.
No. 116. 90mm long.   18.50
Donkey in harness. No. 294.
115mm long.   65.00
Elephant, large. 110mm long.   45.00
Elephant, with trunk in the air,
curled back against the head. No.
336. 90mm long.   50.00

Elephant, walking. Can be
inscribed: *Baby Jumbo*. No. 113.
52mm. (Coloured add £10). 20.00
Elephant Jug. 70mm. 14.50
Fish Ashtray, in shape of plaice.
78mm long. 13.50
Fish, curved. 75mm long. 8.00
Fish, straight. 130mm long. 7.00
Fish, straight, with open mouth.
115mm long. 9.00
Fox, walking. 100mm. 80.00
Hare, sometimes found with red facial
features. 77mm long. 19.50
Kangaroo on rectangular base.
115mm. 100.00
Lion, crouching. Red open mouth.
82mm long. 30.00
Lion, crouching. Red open mouth,
on base, roaring at a tiny mouse
on a green apple, inscribed: *Much
ado about nothing.* 115mm. 80.00
Lion, walking. (Different moulds).
3 sizes: 85mm long. 25.00
110mm long. 25.00
125mm long. 25.00
Lion with mane and 'furry' legs.
164mm long. (Pair with Arcadian
Lioness). 90.00
Lion, walking on diamond-shaped
ashtray base. Inscribed: *Who burned
the tablecloth?* 105mm long. 40.00
Monkey, holding coconut. 85mm. 25.00
Three Wise Monkeys, sitting on wall,
with inscription. 124mm. 16.00
Three Monkeys on diamond shaped
ashtray. Monkeys inscribed: *See
not evil, speak not evil, hear not evil.*
130mm long. 20.00
Mouse. No. 99. 62mm long. 25.00
Pig, standing, thin ears pointing
forwards. 97mm long. 25.00
Pig, sitting on haunches can be
found inscribed: *You may push etc.*
No. 177 or No. 137.
2 sizes: 60mm. 25.00
72mm. 30.00
Pig, standing. Very fat, with double
chin. No. 54 or No. 211.
96mm long. 24.50
Pig, standing fat, ears pointing
forward. No. 60. 82mm long. 22.00
Pony, inscribed: *A Native of Shetland.*
108mm long. 40.00
Rabbit, lying down. 54mm long. 9.50

Rabbit, sitting, alert or laid back
ears. 60mm long. 9.50
Ram, with curly horns.
90mm long. 65.00
Rhinoceros, standing. 87mm long. 90.00
Stag, lying down. 115mm long. 40.00
Toad, grotesque. 80mm long. 100.00
Tortoise. 88mm long. 10.00
Tortoise, realistic. 95mm long. 40.00
Tortoise, standing wearing a blue
hat/helmet. Rd. No. 70961. 62mm. 80.00
Isn't this Rabbit a Duck?: On its base a
rabbit, turned on its side, a duck.
75mm. 30.00

Birds (including Eggs)
Bird, crested (reputedly a tit) posy
holder. 77mm long. 12.00
Bird on plinth. 103mm. 12.50
Bird posy holder. 104mm long. 12.50
Canary on rock, reputedly the
Norwich canary, can be found
coloured yellow on green base,
98mm.
White 19.00
Coloured 30.00
Chicken, very fluffy. No. 325.
65mm. 20.00
Chicken pepper pot. 70mm. 11.00
Chicken Salt pot. 70mm. 11.00
Chicken, yellow, emerging from
egg, inscribed: *Every little helps
mother will be pleased.* 50mm. 30.00
Cock. 46mm and 100mm. 14.00
Goose. 96mm. 20.00
Goose, comical, with long neck,
some colouring. 155mm. 55.00
Pelican, with inscription: *A
wonderful bird is the pelican, his
beak will hold more than his belican.*
75mm. 55.00
Royston Crow on oval base, coloured.
No. 44. 70mm. 60.00
Swan, can be found with yellow
beak, add £1.00. 60mm.
White beak. 8.50
Swan, with head on breast. 58mm. 9.50
Swan posy holder.
2 sizes: 65mm. 7.00
93mm long. 7.00
Turkey. 57mm. 30.00
Wise Owl with verse: *An aged owl
sat in an oak* etc.
2 sizes: 98mm & 115mm. 24.50
Larger size can be found fully
coloured & unglazed. Add £30.

Great War

Airman, standing to attention. 140mm.	250.00
Air Force Officer, a hero holding medal. 140mm. Scarce.	250.00
Can rarely be found coloured.	325.00
Nurse, inscribed: *A friend in need.* 130mm.	70.00
Sailor standing. Inscribed: *Jack Ashore.*	70.00
Sailor, at attention, inscribed: *Our brave defender.* 130mm.	70.00
Soldier, with rifle, inscribed: *Our brave defender.* Always found with gun broken off at top. It is still classed as perfect. 132mm.	70.00
Monoplane, with fixed propeller. Inscribed: *Model of New Aeroplane.*	75.00
Monoplane with revolving prop. no colourings. No. 67. 150mm long.	85.00
Monoplane with revolving prop., coloured roundels on wings, and stripes on tail. No. 57. 150mm long.	140.00
Aeroplane Propeller. No. 216 and No. 214. 150mm long.	35.00
Can be found with RAF, RNAS or RFC crest.	50.00
Airship (Observation Balloon), inscribed: *Beta.* 80mm long.	90.00
Battleship. 4 funnels. 127mm long.	30.00
Battleship, impressed: *HMS Lion.* No. 213. 140mm long.	40.00
A rare variety with black mast and red striped funnels has been seen.	85.00
Liner converted to a troop Carrier. No. 213. 140mm long.	95.00
Can rarely be found inscribed: *HMS Lion.*	170.00
Can also be found with 2 forward facing guns mounted on forward deck (rare).	200.00
Submarine, impressed: *E5.* 116mm long.	25.00
Submarine, inscribed: *E4.*	
2 sizes: 95mm long.	25.00
118mm long.	25.00
Red Cross Van, red cross on side. No. 812. 84mm long.	40.00
British Tank, Model of. No. 207. 92mm long.	22.00
Both of the above tanks can be found either with side guns moulded flat against tank, or with side guns standing proud protruding from side turrets.	

British Tank, Model of With trailing wheels. 130mm long.	20.00
Can be found with a Lincoln crest inscribed: *Model of 'British Tank' original of which was made in Lincoln.*	40.00
Field Gun. 120mm long.	30.00
Field Gun, with screen. 115mm long.	35.00
Howitzer. 115mm long.	30.00
British Hand Grenade. 86mm.	20.00
Cannon Shell. 70mm.	6.00
Cannon Shell *Pepper* Pot. No. 222. 88mm.	6.00
Cannon Shell *Salt* Pot. No. 223. 86mm.	6.00
Bandsman's Drum, with cording. 60mm.	12.50
Bell Tent, with open flaps. 70mm.	22.00
Bugle.	
2 sizes: No. 370. 70mm.	24.50
No. 379. 115mm.	45.00
Field Glasses. 83mm.	20.00
Kit Bag with verse: *Pack Up your troubles in your old kit bag.* No. 220. 74mm.	24.50
Airman's Cap. 82mm long.	120.00
Forage Cap. 83mm long.	20.00
Glengarry. Some colouring. 83mm long.	22.00
If with Scottish crest.	24.00
Officer's Peaked Cap. No. 100. 70mm dia.	20.00
Officer's Peaked Cap, inscribed *Souvenir of Canadian Forces 1915*	45.00
Pickelhaube (German spiked helmet). No. 58. 50mm.	30.00
Tommy's Steel Helmet. No. 221. 76mm long.	40.00
Trench Lamp. 70mm.	17.00
Fireplace, inscribed: *Keep the home fires burning.* Some colouring. 100mm long.	20.00
Kitchen range, with pot on fire, inscribed: *Keep the home fires burning.* Some colouring. No. 199. 78mm long.	20.00
Edith Cavell. Statue, London, inscribed: *Brussels dawn Oct 12th 1915. Sacrifice, Humanity.* No. 281.	
4 sizes: 110mm.	20.00
130mm.	20.00
150mm.	20.00
160mm.	22.00

Edith Cavell, Nurse. Patriot and
martyr, memorial Statue. Norwich.
2 sizes: 155mm. — 35.00
170mm. — 40.00
The Black Watch Memorial,
Edinburgh. Scottish soldier on
square base, often not named.
127mm. — 75.00
Cenotaph, inscribed: *The Glorious*
Dead MCMXIV-MCMXIX with
green wreaths.
4 sizes: 70mm. — 8.00
145mm. — 10.50
155mm. — 14.50
184mm. — 14.50
The 155mm size has dropped flags
on stepped base, with green wreath
with purple ribbons.
Chatham *Naval War Memorial.*
160mm. — 80.00
Coalville War Memorial. 135mm. — 140.00
Dover Patrol memorial. 130mm. — 40.00
Dumfries War Memorial, inscribed:
Black Watch. 130mm. — 85.00
Florence Nightingale Statue, Model of.
Can be found inscribed: *Florence*
Nightingale 1820-1910. No. 225.
3 sizes: 120mm. — 22.50
160mm. — 25.00
Folkestone Road of Remembrance
Memorial. 77mm. — 50.00
Folkestone *War Memorial May Their*
Deeds be held in reverence. 160mm. — 80.00
Great Yarmouth War Memorial. With
inscription. 174mm. — 45.00
Ilkeston War Memorial, with
inscription. — 170.00
Langholm, War Memorial. Angel,
unglazed on glazed base. 180mm. — 190.00
Loughborough War Memorial, Carillon
Tower 155mm. — 60.00
Matlock Bath *War Memorial,* inscribed.
2 sizes: 182mm. — 40.00
155mm. — 75.00
Scarborough Lighthouse, with
inscription: *This lighthouse was*
damaged in the bombardment by
German warships on Wednesday
December 16th 1914. 132mm. — 140.00
Scarborough Lighthouse, with
rectangular buildings, depicting
shell damage. Inscribed: *This*
Lighthouse was damaged in the
bombardment by German Warships
on Wednesday December 16th 1914.
110mm. — 170.00

Southsea. *Royal Naval War Memorial.*
160mm. (Chatham, Plymouth and
Southsea War Memorials are
identical in design). — 55.00
War Memorial with one soldier
leaning over another, found with
a York crest. 165mm. — 65.00
Worthing War Memorial, inscribed:
Duty Nobly done 1914-1918.
170mm. — 70.00

Home/Nostalgic

Ali Baba Basket, very detailed.
75mm. — 6.00
Anvil on base, can be found
inscribed: *A Sussex Legend,* with
verse, but more usually
Blacksmith's Anvil.
4 sizes: 35mm. — 7.50
45mm pointing right. — 7.50
55mm pointing left. — 7.50
75mm. — 7.50
Baby's Bottle. No. 42. 90mm long. — 10.50
Bag, open with four feet. — 10.00
Basket, oval with handle. 70mm long. — 6.50
Basket of Milk, six bottles with
brown tops. 64mm. — 24.50
Bell. 58mm. — 6.00
Bell, inscribed: *Curfew must not ring*
tonight. No. 107. 65mm. — 9.50
Book, *Model of* No. 71. 57mm. — 12.50
Chest and lid. 90mm long. — 7.50
Child smiling, bust. 60mm. — 19.50
Chinese Lantern. 80mm. — 10.50
Coal Scuttle, helmet shaped.
53mm. — 8.00
Desk, rolltop. 80mm long. — 17.00
Dressing table mirror, with one
drawer. 87mm. — 19.50
Fireplace, inscribed: *There's no place*
like home. 70mm. — 17.00
Fireplace / Range with saucepan.
Sometimes inscribed: *May yer*
fireside aye be cheers and yer kail-pat
aye be fou. Copyright Allan Junior.
75mm long. — 20.00
With verse. — 25.00
Flat Iron. 64mm. — 16.50
Flat Iron with trivet. (2 pieces).
66mm. — 25.00
Garden Roller. 51mm. — 19.50
Garden Trug. 75mm long. — 7.50
Ginger Jar with fixed lid. — 5.00

Grandfather Clock, found inscribed:
Make us of time let not advantage
slip. Shakespeare, or more rarely:
Nae man can tetha time or tide.
Burns. Add £5.00. Can also be
found in brown. Add £20.00.
112mm.   19.50
Grandfather Clock, slimmer version.
Time 11.35. 130mm.   20.00
Hammer Head *"Matches" My*
Speciality is striking. 85mm long.   22.00
Hand mirror with reflective
silvering. 150mm long.   25.00
Jardinière, 2-piece. 130mm.   7.50
Lantern, horn. 106mm.   10.00
Oil Lamp. 95mm long.   6.50
Old Armchair with verse. 88mm.   9.50
Pail, with moulded rope handle.
63mm.   6.50
Pillar box, G.R., in red and blue,
with open slot. Inscribed: *If you*
haven't got time to post a line here's
the pillar box. 78mm.   17.50
Pillar Box, outpressed G.R. open
slit.
  2 sizes: 90mm.   22.50
            105mm.   35.00
Pipe. 2 sizes: 76mm & 93mm long.   30.00
Shaving Mug. No. 125.
  2 sizes: 55mm.   9.50
           70mm.   10.50
Sundial, circular with round base,
with inscription: *I mark not the*
hours. 118mm.   10.50
Sundial, circular on square base,
No. 205, with inscription: *I mark*
not the hours. 98mm.   7.50
Sundial on octagonal base.
125mm.   13.00
Suitcase, open. 60mm.   8.00
Thimble, *Just a Thimble full.* 52mm.   12.00
Tobacco Jar with crossed coloured
pipes on lid. Inscribed: *tobacco.*
115mm.   22.00
Umbrella. 50mm.   17.50
Valise, half-open. 77mm long.   7.50
Watering Can. 75mm.   9.50
Wedding ring, gold, in open box.
60mm. Inscribed: *"Safety First".*   40.00
Wheelbarrow. 105mm long.   19.50

Comic/Novelty
Alarm Clock. Inscribed: *Many are*
called but few get up. 65mm.   30.00
Billiken, The god of luck, often found
unnamed. 73mm.   7.00

Billiken, The god of luck, sitting on
high backed chair. 100mm.   9.50
Biscuit Lid trinket box on tray base.
Impressed: *Oval High Tea.* Biscuit
coloured. 75mm long.   40.00
Box of Matches, half-open.
75mm.   25.00
Boy's smiling head. 64mm.   11.00
Boy Scout. *Be Prepared.* 110mm.   160.00
Boy on Pig's back, boy fully
coloured. 94mm long. Rare.   300.00
Broadbean pod splitting open,
occasionally inscribed: *Good old*
bean. 130mm long.   24.00
Fan, open, hat pin holder. 90mm.   30.00
Fat Lady on weighing scales,
scale registers 20 stone,
inscribed: *Adding weight.*
Blue Bonnet.
90mm.   80.00
Mr Pecksniff, standing Dickensian
figure. 115mm.   40.00
Policeman salt pot, blue helmet,
black boots. 80mm.   65.00
Regimental Sergeant-Major Pepper
Pot. 84mm.   45.00
Sack of Meal with Mouse, inscribed:
May the mouse ne'er leave yer meal-
poke wi' a tear- drop'n its e'e.
63mm.   17.50
  With brown or grey mouse.   22.00
Sailor, comical, some colouring.
95mm.   55.00
Sailor Toby Jug, coloured. 68mm.   30.00

Black Boys
All of these boys are fully coloured
with red or blue stripped pyjamas
but sit on white boxes etc. All
uncommon.
Black Boy, standing with hands in
pockets. 94mm.   100.00
Black Boy, playing drum. 70mm.   120.00
Black Boy, in bath of ink, inscribed:
How ink is made. 110mm long.   110.00
Black Boy, in bed with spider,
inscribed: *A little study in black*
and fright. Boy can have red or
blue pyjamas. 70mm long.   140.00
Black Boy in bed, face coloured,
inscribed: *Just a little Study in*
black and white. 62mm long.   100.00
Black Boy, eating slice of melon,
sitting on soap box. 80mm.   150.00

Black Boy with yellow pumpkin
and lid. 80mm.   160.00
Black Boy, at table eating a boiled
egg which has a chicken popping
out. 70mm.   140.00
Two Black Boys, heads popping out
of box, inscribed: *Box of chocolates*.
Can be found with boys painted
as white children, yellow hair
and blue eyes or brown hair, dirty
faces and is often found
not coloured at all. 60mm.
Coloured   75.00
No colouring   30.00
Black Boy, holding container for
Cigarettes. 102mm.   120.00
Black Boy, holding container for
matches. Inscribed: *Matches*.
100mm.   120.00
Black Boy and Girl sitting on tree
trunk. Some Colouring. 68mm.   120.00
Black Boy peering out of shower,
coloured trousers hanging from
top. Rare. 67mm.   170.00

Children
Girl and Boy sitting in armchair,
both fully coloured. 60mm.   200.00

Little Birds
From Arcadian moulds. Head fully
coloured, eggs white.
Flapper's head hatching from egg,
inscribed: *A little bird from...*
50mm long.   40.00
Black Boy's head hatching from egg,
inscribed: *A blackbird from*
50mm long.   55.00

Comic Ashtrays
Jester, fully coloured, on heart shaped
tray decorated with other card
symbols. 65mm.   55.00
Scotsman, really grotesque, sitting
on white bench on white ashtray.
95mm.   35.00
Scotsman can be found coloured.   47.50
Bookie with coloured hare and
greyhound on octagonal ashtray
base. 70mm.   45.00

Comic/Novelty
Man in the sun. 100mm.   70.00
Mr Pickwick standing. 114mm.   40.00
Petrol Pump attendant saluting.
Inscribed: *Petrol Sir*. 97mm.   125.00

Baby, with arms outstretched,
inscribed: *Cheerio*. Some
colouring on face. 120mm.   30.00
Baby, saluting, inscribed: *One of the
b'hoys*. Can be found with
A.W.W.H. on chest. Some
colouring on face. 3 sizes: 125mm,
150mm & 160mm.   55.00
Hammer Head, Matchholder, can be
found inscribed: *My speciality is
striking* or *Matches*. Add £2.00.
80mm long.   22.00

Cartoon/Comedy Characters
Dr. Beetle Charlie Tolkard's character
in the *Daily Mail* (impressed).
142mm.   125.00
Harry Lauder, bust. Brown hat with
thistle. 80mm.   22.00
Can be found named.   30.00
Martin Chuzzlewit Shakespeare figure
of Mr Pecksniff, brown trousers,
green jacket, blue waistcoat.
115mm.   40.00
Teddy Tail, impressed. 142mm.   125.00
Two Cartoon Characters sitting in
Armchair. 90mm. (Thought to be
Dr. Beetle and Sunny Jim!)   150.00
Coloured with striped chair.   200.00
"Sunny Jim", glazed bust (name
impressed).   95.00
Winkie, not named, inscribed: *Glad
Eyes* on beak. 60mm.   22.00

Alcohol
Barrel. 50mm.   6.00
Barrel on stand. No. 35. 58mm.   6.50
Barrel with opening on one side.
54mm long.   5.50
Barrel Jug with grapevine in relief.
Known as vine jug. 90mm.   17.00
Beer Bottle with red hand. 98mm.   12.50
Beer Bottle and Tankard on
horseshoe ashtray, with
inscription: *The more we are
together the merrier we'll be*. Silver
Tankard . 85mm.   13.50
Bottle, syphon and glass on
horseshoe tray, inscribed: *Scotch
and Soda*. Menu holder on back.
65mm high,110mm long.   14.50
Beer Bottle and Tankard on square
ashtray. 78mm wide. Verse as above. 14.50
Bottle. No. 104. 90mm.   7.50
Can be inscribed: *One Special
Scotch*.   8.50

Bottle, red triangle to rear. 87mm.   10.00
Drunk in Top Hat and Tails draped
  drunkenly around a female statue
  (bust on column). Inscribed:
  How cold you are tonight. On blue
  or white ashtray base.
  96mm.   125.00
Drunks, two staggering, bottles in
  hand on ashtray, inscribed:
  *Another little drink wouldn't do us
  any harm.* Sometimes coloured.
  92mm.   55.00
Hand, holding beaker, inscribed:
  Good health. 50mm.   12.00
Man, Mr Pickwick character (As in
  Arcadian range) on rim of beaker.
  75mm.   55.00
Monk holding tankard. 155mm.   20.00
Stud, lapel with miniature bottle
  attached, inscribed: *The More We
  are together, the Merrier we will be.*
  31mm. Rare.   30.00
Tankard candlesnuffer, foaming
  inscribed *The more we are
  together...* or *Here's Health.* 58mm.   9.50
Thimble, inscribed: *Just a thimbleful.*
  50mm.   20.00
Thistle vase, with verse: *A wee Deoch
  an Doris.* 56mm.   6.00
Toby Jug. 78mm.   16.50
Whisky Bottle, inscribed: *One Special
  Scotch* or *One Special Irish* (add £3.00).
  63mm.   8.00
Whisky Bottle, with cork, usually
  inscribed: *One Special Scotch.* No.
  64. 88mm.   8.00
Whisky Bottle inscribed: *Here's a
  bottle and an honest friend, what
  wad ye wish for mai man?*   15.00

Whisky Bottle and Soda Syphon on
  Tray, inscribed: *Scotch and Soda.*
  88mm dia.   14.50
Whisky Bottle, Soda Syphon and
  Tumbler on horseshoe ashtray.
  With inscription: *The more we are
  together, the merrier we will be* or
  Scotch and Soda. Some colouring.
  (willow).
  2 sizes: 87mm long.   17.00
            115mm long.   17.00

Sport/Pastimes
Golfer s Caddie holding golf bag,
  figure coloured. 110mm.   125.00
Golf Clubs in Bag. 108mm.   75.00

Football. 50mm dia.   9.50
Jockey on Racehorse on oval glazed
  base found in different coloured
  silks. Can be found coloured but
  unglazed. 2 sizes: 104mm
  & 112mm.   95.00
Racehorse, impressed. 102mm.   75.00
Racehorse on circular base.
  115mm.   75.00
Bridge Trump indicator. Coloured
  suit symbols on circular base,
  spinning cover allowing only one
  suit to be seen. Very ornate. Rd.
  No. 693774. No. 1015. 104mm dia.   30.00
Diamond Trump. 65mm.   6.00
  Sometimes inscribed: *Trumps* – add £2.00
  Spade, Heart and club indicators
  were also made, but these are less
  common.
Playing Cards, box and lid. 154mm long. 15.00

Musical Instruments
Bagpipes. 118mm.   50.00
Banjo. 160mm long.   19.50
Guitar. 163mm long.   19.50
Lute. 159mm long.   45.00
Piano. open keyboard. 80mm.   22.50
Piano, upright. 65mm.   22.50

Transport
Car, open 4 seater. 2 sizes: 114mm
  No. 213 & 140mm long.   50.00
Car, open 2 seater. 116mm long.   40.00
Car, open 2 seater, very detailed
  model with spare wheel on side
  running board. This is a Morris.
  108mm long.   90.00
Charabanc. 125mm long.   45.00
Tram, single decker, open top.
  Inscribed: *"Life on the Ocean Wave"*
  No. 333. 112mm long.   170.00
Tram, double decker, open top.
  Inscribed: *Life on the ocean wave.*
  No. 333. 108mm long.   170.00
Can of Petrol, impressed: *Motor
  spirit.* 55mm.   17.50
Car Horn, No. 41. 70mm.   25.00
A truck of coal from ... Wagon of black
  coal.
  2 sizes: 75mm long.   40.00
            90mm long.   40.00
  Also found with coal painted
  grey or brown and inscribed: *A
  truck of iron ore from...*   47.50

Modern Equipment

Camera, folding. 60mm.	40.00
Horn Gramophone, square. No. 27.	
95mm.	25.00
Horn Gramophone on round base.	
2 sizes: 60mm.	30.00
85mm.	35.00
Radio Horn, can be found inscribed:	
Hello... (name of town) calling.	
55mm.	25.00
70mm.	25.00
With inscription.	40.00

Hats

Crown. 60mm.	25.00
Luton Boater. 90mm long.	16.50

Footwear

Boot. 112mm long.	11.00
Edwardian Shoe, blue bow.	
No. 118. 110mm long.	10.50
With white bow.	8.50
Ladies heeled shoe and bow. No. 128.	
115mm long.	8.00
Ladies Riding Shoe, square toe and	
blue tie. 115mm long.	16.00
Lancashire Clog, yellow buckle.	
88mm long.	6.50
Sabot. No. 334. 75mm long.	6.00
Slipper wall pocket, blue bow. 2	
sizes: 152 & 178mm long.	12.50

Miniature Domestic

Complete Tea Set on rectangular	
tray, comprising teapot & lid,	
2 cups & saucers, milk jug, sugar	
bowl & tray. 102mm long.	25.00
Cheese Dish, one piece. 45mm.	9.50
Cheese Dish and cover. 45mm.	9.50
Coffee Pot with lid. 70mm.	9.50
Tea Pot with lid. 60mm.	9.50

Interesting Domestic Items with Crests

Bagware Milk Jug. No. 161. 55mm.	5.00
Bagware Vase. No. 232. 73mm.	5.00
Basket Dish. 45mm.	6.00
Cards, box and lid. Rectangular but	
shaped. 120mm long.	12.00
Cheese and lid, rectangular, ornate	
club shaped dish. 40mm.	9.50
Column Candlestick with snake	
around column. 120mm.	7.50
Hairpins, box and lid.	
115mm long.	7.00

Hat Pins, curved fluted holder.

2 sizes: 110mm.	16.00
125mm.	16.50
Horseshoe ashtray. 80mm.	6.50
Horseshoe ashtray with menu	
holder and rectangular slot	
possible for matches. Rd. No.	
708047. 110mm long.	15.00
Horseshoe Base menu holder.	
113mm.	8.50
Muffin Dish and lid. No. 82.	
70mm dia.	8.50
Napkin Ring, ornate. No. 310.	
45mm dia.	8.00
Pin Box and lid, horseshoe shaped.	
62mm.	5.00
Pin Box, oval, with safety pin in	
relief on lid. 90mm long.	7.50
Pin Box, heart-shaped, ornate	
moulding. No. 394. 90mm long.	7.50
Preserves Jar and lid. 75mm.	10.50
Trefoil Cruet with lids. 65mm.	6.50
Trinket Box, oval on eight collar	
stud feet with moulded cufflinks	
placed between each stud. Border	
of moulded cufflinks and tie pin	
in relief on lid. 90mm long.	12.00
Hexagonal Salt Pot. 100mm.	4.00
Pepper Pot. 75mm.	4.00
Bagware Teapot and lid. 108mm.	10.50
Bagware Milk Jug. No. 179. 80mm.	6.50
Salt Shaker, silver top. 98mm.	12.00

Miscellaneous

Cauldron, 2 handles. 36mm.	4.00
Cauldron, on three feet. 60mm.	4.00
Bell. 60mm.	8.50
Hand holding a tulip. No. 74.	
80mm. (With ring on finger).	7.00
Vase with moulded key pattern.	
No. 277. 118mm.	8.50

Willper Heraldic China

Wilton China

Trademark used by Sampson Hancock & Sons, The Garden Works, Hanley. (Usual trademark Corona).

Only a few pieces have been seen to date.

Ewer with Chester crest. 53mm.	4.00
Squat Jug. 60mm.	4.00
Vase. 60mm.	4.00

Seaside Souvenirs
Lighthouse. 102mm.	10.00

Alcohol
Toby Jug. 77mm.	12.00

cl923-1934. Also found with MADE IN ENGLAND under.

**WILTON
ART
CHINA**

in gilt 1932-1934

Found on models with Felix transfer or inscription.

Trademark used by A.G. Harley Jones at Wilton Pottery, Fenton. This firm specialised in lustre ware.

Mr A.G. Harley Jones started his business in Fenton in 1905, and until 1920 seems to have concentrated on producing ornamental wares. After 1920 he diversified production, adding general earthenwares and crested china to his range. In 1923 he advertised 'Wilton heraldic china' and registered the mark in 1927. M. Harley Jones was quite successful before 1920, expanding his business and extending his premises. After this date he seems to have had great difficulty in surviving, snatching at any craze or passing whim in the china trade to make money. This makes his wares very appealing to collectors as he produced a small but very original and innovative range of crested china models, tending towards the vulgar but reeking with nostalgia. Unfortunately he turned to crested china at the end of its popularity and even this new venture could not stem the tide of his insolvency. His turnover dropped from £22,062 in 1927 to £8,915 in 1932. By 1933 he had turned his hand to making glazed tile fireplaces but to no avail: he was declared bankrupt in June 1934. The account of his bankruptcy proceedings is a sad record of business losses from 1927 onwards, enlivened only by the Official Receiver's questions regarding a marriage deed made on the eve of his bankruptcy settling his household effects on a lady he married three days later. The Official Receiver doubted whether the settlement held good in law.

Wilton China is for the most part rather heavy and is better described as pot . This does not however mean that models are not attractive: they are particularly modern, amusing and often unique to this pottery. There are obviously very few ancient artefacts or Great War souvenirs in the range as there was little call for these after 1923, but the novelty and comic items produced are particularly exciting. Mr Harley Jones shows the same awareness of public taste as the manufacturers of Carlton China and he also made many models in lustre ware. Unlike Carlton he does not seem to have made models of Felix the Cat but he used a transfer print of him with the inscription: *Felix the film cat* on many different models and small vases. He did make models of that other popular twenties animal 'Bonzo Dog'. Lucky Black Cat transfers, transfer prints of a regional nature such as Welsh Tea Party groups and the Devil at Devil's Bridge and view ware (both monochrome, red, black or blue and polychrome) can all be found. One Canadian crest has been found. A few lucky white heather devices but not commemorative pieces have been recorded.

Numbering System. No stock numbers were printed or painted on Wilton models. Painted numbers, such as 018 or 012 are found on a large number of different models and must be the paintresses marks.

Wilton Models

Ancient Artefacts

Ancient Tyg,1 handle. 70mm.	5.50
Bronze Pot, not named. 35mm.	4.00
Loving Cup, 3 handles. 39mm.	7.00

Buildings - Coloured

These can be found with crests

Ann Hathaway s Cottage. 55mm long.	25.00
Ann Hathaway's Cottage, on ashtray base. 73mm long.	40.00
Ann Hathaway's Cottage nightlight. 106mm long.	30.00
Feathers Hotel. 1600. Ludlow. 100mm long.	100.00
Shakespeare's House. 53mm long.	25.00

Buildings - White

Ann Hathaway's Cottage, in pearl
  lustre on oval base. 57mm long.   20.00
Ann Hathaway's Cottage, sometimes
  on ashtray base in lustre.
  73mm long.   20.00
Ann Hathaway's night light in
  pearl lustre. 106mm long.   22.00
Blackpool Tower, found in lustre.
  92mm.   13.00
Blackpool Tower. 175mm.   16.50
Blackpool Tower and buildings.
  175mm.   22.00
Christchurch Priory. 108mm long.   65.00
Cottage, Thatched. (Probably
  unnamed Ann Hathaway's
  Cottage.) 56mm long.   15.00
Feathers Hotel, Ludlow. 100mm.
  (Lustre).   45.00
Lichfield Cathedral, can be lustre.
  85mm.   50.00
Peterborough Cathedral, West Front of.
  90mm long.   25.00
Shakespeare's House. 53mm long.   12.50
Tamworth Castle. 130mm long.   55.00

Monuments (including Crosses)

Liberty Statue.180mm.   135.00
Toad Rock near Hathersage.
  95mm long.   30.00

Historical/Folklore

Dick Whittington and cat on ashtray
  base, inscribed: *IV miles to London*
  on milestone and *Turn again*
  Whittington on ashtray. 110mm.   125.00

Traditional/National Souvenirs

Blackpool Big Wheel.105mm.   14.50
  Found with the Felix transfer and
  Pathe trademark, inscribed: *Felix*
  the cat comes to Blackpool.   45.00
Blackpool Tower and Wheel on
  ashtray base. 90mm.   26.00
Irish Harp, with green shamrocks.
  105mm.   9.50
Thistle Vase. 60mm.   4.00
Welsh Hat.
  2 sizes: 35mm. (miniature)   10.50
          70mm. (Wide brim).   12.50

Seaside Souvenirs

Bathing Machine with girl in
  doorway. Can be found with
  some colouring, lustre or
  inscribed: *Morning Dip' 7a.m.!*
  100mm.   25.00
Fisherman's Creel, fish on lid
  inscribed: *A good catch*. Sometimes
  with separate lid. 88mm long.   14.50
Sailing Yacht, 125mm.   23.50
  Can be found in lustre.
  Inscribed: *Saucy Sue*.   30.00
Beachy Head Lighthouse. 100mm.   10.00
Lighthouse, inscribed: *Sailor beware*.
  Found in lustre. 155mm.   16.00

Bathing Belles/Twenties Flappers

Bathing Belle lying across back of
  an ashtray. Inscribed: *Breezy Bright*
  and Bracing. 108mm long.   65.00

Countryside

Horseshoe. 105mm.   9.00

Animals

Cat, sitting. 65mm.   14.00
Cat, angry. Raised tail, coloured
  bow and face. Inscribed: *My word*
  if you're not off. 115mm.   28.00
Cat on pouffe candlesnuffer,
  outpressed *Luck* in orange. 62mm.   22.00
Cat, sitting, red bow. Can be found
  in lustre. 60mm.   20.00
Cat, sitting, inscribed: *Luck*. Red
  tongue. 102mm.   20.00
Black cat on lid of fishing creel,
  inscribed: *I'm here just for luck.*
  80mm.   40.00
Cat, comical, sitting looking
  forward, looped tail as handle,
  painted face. Can be found
  inscribed: *My word if you're*
  not off. 107mm.   30.00
Black cat on lid of hexagonal trinket
  box. 95mm.   60.00
Black cat on cheese, mouse at base.
  80mm.   47.50
Bulldog, standing, inscribed: *What*
  we have we hold. 130mm long.   25.00
Terrier Dog, sitting, can be found in
  lustre. 85mm.   22.00
Dog, begging. 72mm.   15.00
Dog, Pug, 57mm.   16.50
Pig, inscribed: *You may push....*
  80mm long.   22.50

Birds (including Eggs)

Cock. (Lustre), red comb. 70mm long.	18.00
Cockerel Pepper Pot, red comb.	
Inscribed: *Pepper.* 70mm.	14.00
Cockerel Salt Pot, red comb.	
Inscribed: *Salt.* 70mm.	14.00
Hen Pepper Pot. Inscribed: *Pepper.*	
80mm.	14.00
Duck, sitting. Found in lustre.	
50mm.	12.50
Goose, wearing hat, on round base.	
(Lustre). 65mm.	50.00
Goose, yellow beak. (Lustre). 58mm.	17.00
Turkey, yellow beak. 55mm.	16.00

Great War

Sailor, seated and holding	
submarine. Blue cap band. Can be	
found in lustre. 75mm	
White.	75.00
Coloured.	110.00
Battleship, tall top mast and no	
forward guns. 115mm long.	110.00
Fieldglasses. 83mm.	20.00
Folkestone War Memorial,	
inscribed: *Road of Remembrance.*	
78mm.	55.00
Hay War Memorial. 150mm.	150.00
St. Anne's *War Memorial.*	
152mm.	120.00
Thetford *War Memorial.* 150mm.	125.00
Walsall War Memorial. 115mm.	125.00

Home/Nostalgic

Book with clasp. 65mm.	12.50
Fireplace with clock and dogs on	
mantlepiece, kettle & teapot on	
hob. Inscribed: *Loves Old Sweet*	
Song. 90mm.	27.00
Grandfather Clock, inscribed: *Make*	
use of time let not advantage slip.	
130mm.	16.50
Sundial, inscribed: *What o'clock* and	
Serene I stand among the flowers and	
only count life's sunny hours.	
146mm.	14.00
Garden Roller. 98mm long.	18.00

Comic/Novelty

Bookmaker, standing figure,	
inscribed: *6 to 4 the field.*	
80mm.	80.00
Broke to the wide, man standing with	
head and shoulders bowed.	
85mm.	80.00

Little girl measuring herself against	
a large, sitting St. Bernard dog on	
round base. Inscribed: *I'se Biggest*	
(Lustre). 90mm.	70.00
Open Razor ashtray, inscribed: *Got*	
me through many a scrape, found in	
lustre. 106mm long.	50.00
Rider, lady standing wearing	
jodhpurs and hat, smoking a	
cigarette. 97mm.	170.00
Toff, coloured figure, smoking,	
wearing jacket with baggy	
trousers and trilby. Standing on	
horseshoe ashtray base. 108mm.	
108mm wide. Inscribed: *'Bey Jove".*	165.00
Tramp holding glass of beer, sitting	
by milestone, inscribed: *Its better*	
to be alive with eighteen pence than	
dead with a thousand pounds.	
76mm.	70.00
Truck of Coal, inscribed: *Black*	
Diamonds. Black coal, sometimes	
found unpainted. Found in	
lustre. 98mm long.	25.00

Cartoon/Comedy Characters

Bonzo Dog. (Lustre). Pink and black	
face. 48mm.	50.00
Can also be found sitting on a	
lustre ashtray base. 110mm long.	40.00
Mutt and Jeff, on rectangular base.	
105mm long.	95.00

Sport/Pastimes

Bishop chess piece. 70mm.	35.00
Castle Chess Piece. 57mm.	8.00
Pawn chess piece. 55mm.	30.00
Spade Trump indicator. 66mm.	7.00

Alcohol

Barrel. 52mm.3.00	5.50
Barrel of Beer, on stand. 55mm.	6.50
Whiskey Bottle. 98mm.	9.00

Musical Instruments

Piano, upright with open keyboard.	
65mm high, 98mm long.	22.00

Modern Equipment

Horn Gramophone, inscribed: *His*	
Master's Voice. 104mm.	30.00
Radio operator, inscribed: *Listening*	
in. Some colouring. Found lustre.	
80mm.	110.00
Telephone, upright. 105mm.	26.00

Footwear
Lancashire Clog, with verse: *There's many a factory lass wi clogs on her feet.* 120mm long.   9.00

Domestic
Ashtray, semi circular or circular with colour transfer of a cigarette. 95mm long.   17.00
Sometimes inscribed: *Who burnt the cloth?*   22.00
Cigarettes, octagonal holder. 64mm.   7.50
Matches, octagonal holder. 64mm.   7.50
Pastry cutter, clover shaped. 90mm long.   9.50

Miniature Domestic
Cheese Dish, 1 piece. 50mm.   8.50
Cheese Dish and cover, horseshoe shaped. 45mm high, 90mm long.   12.50

Miscellaneous
Thimble. 43mm.   17.50

Wil-Wat China

WIL-WAT
W.W
G
CHINA

Trademark used for a retailer by Alfred B. Jones and Sons Ltd. Grafton China Works, Longton. (Usual trademark Grafton). For further details of this china and manufacturer see Grafton China. Fortunately for the researcher, models with this mark are found with the Grafton mark printed alongside. WWG must have been a retailer, the G in the mark probably represents Grimsby as all pieces found have Grimsby or Cleethorpes crests, but it is difficult to draw any conclusion about when the models were made. The two models made specially for this retailer do not carry stock numbers but the fish does, presumably being taken from the Grafton range.

Wil-Wat Models
Monuments (including Crosses)
The Monument, Laceby. 150mm.   40.00

Traditional/National Souvenirs
Leaking Boot, Cleethorpes (Statue of boy, boot joined to hand by string).156mm.   90.00

Animals
Fish, straight, with open mouth. 100mm long.   9.50
Rabbit. 65mm long.   12.50

Wordsworth Art China   W and R

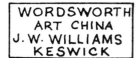

Trademark used for the retailer J.W. Williams, Keswick. The inclusion of the word 'Art' in the trademark suggests that it may have been produced by Hewitt and Leadbeater, Willow Potteries, Longton. (Usual trademark Willow Art).

Two items have so far been recorded, these being a 70mm ewer and a 38mm jug, both with Keswick crests, valued at £4.00 each.

Trademark used for a London wholesaler by Hewitt and Leadbeater, Willow Potteries, Longton. (Usual trademark Willow Art). For details of this china and manufacturer see Willow Art China. Models and 'smalls' with this mark usually carry crests of the south of England. All models are found in the Willow Art range and seem to have been made during the Great War.

W and R Models
Ancient Artefacts

Cirencester Ewer. 73mm.	5.50
Lincoln Jack. No. 34. 52mm.	5.50

Historical/Folklore
Model of Mary Queen of Scots Chair,
Edinburgh Castle. 80mm.	12.50

Seaside Souvenirs
Lighthouse, not named. 110mm.	9.00

Animals
Cat, sitting, badge on chest. 72mm.	19.50
Cat, standing, chubby. 70mm.	22.00
Cat on boot. 70mm.	25.00
Elephant, walking. No. 113. 52mm.	20.00
Hare, sitting, ears laid back. 74mm long.	19.50
Pig, standing. 85mm long.	20.00
Teddy Bear sitting. 80mm.	22.00

Birds (including Eggs)
Swan posy holder. 65mm long.	9.00

Great War

Soldier with rifle, inscribed: *Our*
brave defender. 132mm.   70.00
Monoplane with moveable
  propeller. 150mm long.   85.00
Battleship, impressed: *HMS Lion.*
  140mm long.   40.00
Tommy's Steel Helmet. 75mm dia.   42.00

Home/Nostalgic

Anvil. 60mm.   8.50
Book. 58mm.   12.00
Coal Scuttle, helmet shaped.
  50mm.   9.00
Grandfather Clock. Inscribed: *Make*
  use of time... 125mm.   16.50
Watering Can. 75mm.   12.50

Comic/Novelty

Billiken, not named. 73mm.   8.50

Alcohol

Beer Bottle. 42mm.   8.50

Transport

Car, open 4 seater.
  114mm long.   40.00

Footwear

Ladies Riding Shoe with square toe.
  115mm.   13.00
Ladies Edwardian Shoe with white
  bow. 110mm long.   9.00

Miniature Domestic

Coffee Pot with lid. 69mm.   9.50

Miscellaneous

Hand holding tulip. No. 74.
  80mm.   7.00

W.R. & S.

Trademark used by William Ritchie and Co.
Ltd. 24, 26 and 28 Elder Street, Edinburgh.
(Usual trademark Porcelle).
For details of this wholesaler and retailer see
Porcelle.
This mark is identical to the Porcelle mark
but the word Porcelle and the visor have
been omitted.

W.R. & S. Models

Seaside Souvenirs

Whelk Shell. 100mm.   7.00

Animals

Elephant with howdah. 68mm.   30.00

Birds (including Eggs)

Penguin. 75mm.   20.00
Swan, opening wings. 58mm.   12.50
Swan posy bowl. 58mm.   9.50

Great War

Officer's Peaked Cap.   16.50
Bell Tent. 74mm.   20.00

Hats

Top Hat. 45mm.   7.50

Wy Not? Crest China

Mark can also be found as Wy Knot or Why Knot.

Trademark used for a wholesaler by Hewitt and Leadbeater, Willow Potteries, Longton. (Usual trademark Willow Art). Mark also used by Robinson and Leadbeater Wolfe Street, Stoke-on-Trent (usual trademark Robinson and Leadbeater. For details of this china and manufacturer see Willow Art China and Robinson and Leadbeater. This mark is often badly printed and can be read as IVY NOT. Crests on models with the mark are from all over England and Wales, and all the models are from Willow Art moulds, so it is impossible to suggest what the last D in the initials underneath the mark stands for. Stock numbers were found coincide with Willow Art numbers.

Wy Not Models
Ancient Artefacts
Loving Cup, 3 handles. 39mm.	6.00
Puzzle Jug, with inscription. 68mm.	8.50
Winchester Leather Jack, not named. 50mm.	4.00

Buildings - White
Knaresborough Castle. 95mm.	80.00

Monuments (including Crosses)
Bunyan's Statue. 163mm.	20.00
Lord Byron's Monument. 165mm.	50.00

Historical/Folklore
Bunyan's Chair. 90mm.	19.00
Bunyan's Cushion. 100mm long.	40.00
Burn's Chair, Dumfries. 83mm.	12.50
James V Chair at Stirling Castle, Model of. 102mm.	14.50
Mary Queen of Scots Chair, Edinburgh Castle, Model of. 75mm.	12.50
Medieval Man's head candlesnuffer, with handle. 74mm.	40.00
Sir Walter Scotts Chair, Abbotsford, Model of. 85mm.	14.50
Skull, inscribed: A Prehistoric Skull. No. 171. 60mm long.	22.50

Traditional/National Souvenirs
Welsh Hat. 57mm.	8.00

Animals
Bear, Teddy. 75mm.	22.50
Cat, sitting, blue bow. No. 62. 2 sizes: 60mm.	14.00
75mm.	16.50
Cheshire Cat, inscribed: Still Smiling. 88mm.	14.50
Dog, sitting, badge on chest. 80mm.	16.50
Dog, Collie, standing. 85mm.	30.00
Elephant, walking. 52mm.	20.00
Mouse (very fat, often described as a guinea pig).62mm.	25.00

Great War
Nurse, inscribed: A friend in need. 130mm.	70.00
Sailor, inscribed: Our brave defender, and carrying a flag on his chest instead of a crest. The flag transfer is inscribed: Good Luck. The boys in blue. 130mm.	100.00
Soldier, inscribed: Our brave defender. Only example known has Union Jack on chest and inscribed: Bravo!. Kitchener's Army. (A Willow Art decoration).	100.00
Battleship,4 funnels. 127mm long.	30.00
Red Cross Van, red crosses on side. 84mm long.	40.00
Field Gun. 120mm long.	30.00
Field Gun with screen. 115mm.	35.00
Pickelhaube. 50mm.	30.00
Kit Bag, 74mm.	19.50
Tommy's Steel Helmet. 76mm long.	40.00
Kitchen Range. Inscribed: Keep the Home Fires Burning. 78mm long.	20.00

Home/Nostalgic

Book. 58mm.	10.50
Grandfather Clock, inscribed: *Make*	
use of time... 124mm.	18.50
Iron and Trivet. 70mm long.	25.00
Shaving Mug. 55mm.	9.50

Comic/Novelty

Billiken. 70mm.	8.50

Footwear

Lancashire Clog, with yellow	
buckle. 88mm long.	7.50
Shoe with laces. 116mm long.	11.00

Miniature Domestic

Cheese Dish and cover. 50mm.	9.50
Tea Pot with lid. 68mm.	9.50

Miscellaneous

Hand holding a tulip. 81mm.	7.00

Zuyder Zee China

COPYRIGHT

Trademark is found on pieces with colour scenes and amusing rhymes and ditties, often Dutch but not always.
It would appear that Zuyder Zee China was manufactured for export to The Netherlands by J.A. Robinson & Sons of Stoke (usual trademark Arcadian).

Zuyder Zee Models

Jug, 75mm, with colour transfer	
Music Hath Charms, also inscribed	
A Cheerful wife is the Joy of Life.	25.00
Fluted Vase 75mm, colour transfer	
of children hand in hand 'called	
Flying Dutchman' and 'Industry	
is the parent of success'.	25.00

Manufacturers' marks appearing as symbols

Unmarked Models

Thistle above shield see Charles Waine & Co.

Trademark used by either Josef Vater of Austria during the second half of the 19th century, or more probably by Ackerman & Fitze of Germany after 1908.
One cup and saucer with the above mark has been reported. It is painted in various colours and has the crest of Guernsey.
5.00

MANUFACTURED FOR M.S.ANDERSON PERTH

Mark of unknown manufacturer. One 50mm jug with the arms of Perth has been recorded.
5.00

Many models found unmarked are recognisably pieces from the major firms which for some reason escaped from the pottery without the trademark. Some factories, such as Grafton, did not mark pieces with firing flaws, but most firms did not mark all their perfect ware. However, Grafton pieces usually bear their painted stock numbers. Models with no crest could well be travellers samples. Unmarked models of known origin are not listed below. Many models in the original listings in earlier Price Guides have turned out to be Savoy. Certain shapes did not have enough room on the base to carry a factory mark, such as candlesnuffers with hollow bases. Possible factories have been put in parentheses where known. A trained eye can tell which pottery made an unmarked piece in most cases.
There are however quantities of unmarked crested china which cannot be attributed to any one manufacturer. This china could have been made by several firms known to have made crested wares but do not appear to have used a trademark. These firms include:
George Proctor and Co., High Street, Longton. Advertised arms ware in 1907 but their initials G.P. and Co. L. have not been found on recorded marks.
Barkers and Kent Ltd., The Foley Pottery, Fenton. Were said in 1921 to be doing much to fill the gap left by the German manufacturers. An illustrated article in the *Pottery Gazette* shows a range of Great War souvenirs and animals. The initials B. and K.L. used by the firm are not found in known marks.
Biltons (1912) Ltd., London Road Works, Stoke-on-Trent. Biltons had at one time made little else except teapots, but when they lost male operatives during the Great War they changed to making 'small fancies' (why women could not be taught to make teapots has perhaps more to do

with male vanity than their own capability). 'Small fancies' included models of soldiers, sailors, nurses, pierrots, pierrettes and animals. They were offered coloured, but look very suitable for the application of crests. Biltons did register marks but none have been found on crested china.

C.J. Bisson and Co., 82 Liverpool Road, Stoke-on-Trent. During the Great War the firm specialised in heraldic china and the company also owned The British Doll Manufacturing Co. Both of these lines were tackled to take advantage of the lack of German competition. C.J. Bisson do not seem to have registered a mark but a photograph of their range of heraldic novelties shows Great War souvenirs, a piano, and animals.

As these firms were earthenware manufacturers the models would tend to be reasonably heavy.

Many German firms also manufactured crested china for the English souvenir market and chose not to use a trademark, especially after the Great War. German wares tend to be somewhat whiter, or greyer and of poorer quality than British made wares. They often have impressed four figure numbers.

These include:

Max Emanuel, The Mosanic Pottery, Mitterteich, (usual trademark Mosanic).

Moschendorf, Hof, Bayern (usual trademark PM and Rex).

Hutschenreuther, Probstzella, Thuringia (Trademark P).

Klösterle, Carlsbad (usual trademark Union K).

However, many of the models listed below are known to have been produced by Wilhelm Kutzscher and Co., Schwarzenberger Porzellanfabrik, Schwarzenberg, Saxony, (usual trademark, St George China, Impero, Saxony and Princess).

Generally, pieces which have neither factory mark nor inscription are less desirable than those which do and are sometimes worth slightly less. This is not as important with rare items or with medium range wares.

Values for pieces with firing defects and therefore not finished off, i.e. mis-shapen, having no crest, colouring, or gilding are about half to three-quarters of the full value.

Busts

Bust of General Booth, can be found inscribed: *Salvation Army*. Glazed.

2 sizes: 75mm.	35.00
86mm.	40.00

Bust of Charles Dickens.

2 sizes: 110mm.	50.00
210mm.	65.00

Bust of Admiral Beatty, unglazed.

165mm.	80.00

Bust of *Robert Burns*, glazed. 108mm.   20.00

Bust of *Jellicoe* on column base,

unglazed. 164mm.	75.00

Bust of *Kitchener* on square base.

120mm.	40.00

Bust of *Redmond*, glazed. 110mm.   40.00

Parian/Unglazed

Brandenburg Gate, Berlin.

62mm.	115.00

Cartmel Priory Church.

100mm long.	60.00

Mow Cop Castle, Staffordshire. (Tunstall Pottery).

2 sizes: 130mm long.	80.00
238mm long.	150.00

St Pauls, stone coloured.

87mm long. (probably Savoy)	100.00
145mm long.	125.00

Solomons Temple (Grinlow Tower). Inscribed: *Erected on the site of a Historic Barrow*. 85mm.   45.00

York Minster, West Front. 128mm.   35.00

Ancient Artefacts

Brading Roman Vase. No. 141.

52mm.	5.00

Lewes Vase. Unnamed. No. 305.

40mm.	4.00

Loving Cup. 3 handles. 36mm.   5.00

Loving Cup. 3 handles. Silver and

black. 69mm.	10.50

Puzzle Tankard.

4 sizes: 41mm.	6.00
47mm.	6.00
51mm.	6.00
53mm.	6.00

Puzzle Jug. 70mm.   7.00

Salisbury Kettle. 110mm.   4.00

Winchester Bushel. 102mm dia.   13.50

Buildings - Coloured

Abbot Reginalds Gateway and old Vicarage Evesham. 130mm long.   125.00

Abel Fletchers, Bell Hotel.	
120mm long.	65.00
Birthplace of Dr Andrew Carnegie.	
75mm high, 83mm long.	80.00
Boston Stump. 65mm long.	40.00
Craigwell House, Bognor.	
115mm long.	75.00
Canterbury Weavers, The. No. 141.	85.00
Dan Winter's Cottage, where the first	
orange Lodge was formed in Co.	
Armagh, Ireland. A Money Box.	
Unglazed. 128mm long.	50.00
Dundee, Royal Arch. (Shelley).	
95mm.	125.00
Fair Maids House, Perth. 80mm	
long. (Willow).	145.00
The Feathers Hotel, Ludlow.	
112mm.	125.00
Folkestone Parish Church AD1138.	
103mm long.	80.00
Gabled House, not named.	
Nightlight. 135mm long.	75.00
The Keep, Hawarden. Unglazed.	
140mm long.	90.00
Hampton Court Palace. 80mm.	75.00
Hardys Cottage. 40mm,	
55mm long.	95.00
Harvard House, with long	
inscription: *Restored by Marie*	
Carelli... 145mm.	170.00
Ann Hathaways' Cottage,	
Stratford-on-Avon, Nightlight.	
No. 1404. 110mm long.	30.00
Irish Cottage, Money Box.	
1110mm long.	35.00
Ledbury, Old Market House.	
97mm long.	75.00
Market Harborough Old Grammar	
School.	
2 sizes: 126mm.	125.00
150mm.	125.00
Monnow Gate, Monmouth. 48mm.	50.00
Knaresborough Castle.	75.00
Old Falcon Tavern, Bideford on Avon.	
115mm.	75.00
Old Lantern Chapel, Ilfracombe.	
74mm long.	45.00
Old Town House, Dunbar. 130mm.	75.00
Pete's Cottage, Isle of Man.	
57mm long.	75.00
Plas Newyd House, impressed: *The*	
House of the Ladies of Llangollen.	
115mm long.	85.00
Priory Church, Christchurch.	
Unglazed. 223mm long.	125.00

Pump Room and Baths. Trefriw Wells,	
plus long inscription.	
95mm long.	150.00
Shakespeare's House.	
2 sizes: 65mm long.	16.00
157mm long.	25.00
Shanklin, IoW, The Old Village.	
98mm long.	160.00
Stokesay Castle, Gate House.	
116mm long.	150.00

Buildings - White

Archway, wooden door, large iron	
hinges, steps up to door. 105mm.	20.00
Battle Abbey Gateway. 96mm.	25.00
Beverley, North Bar. 90mm.	30.00
Big Ben. 135mm.	17.00
Birmingham Town Hall.	
2 sizes: 95mm long.	25.00
128mm long.	30.00
Blackpool Tower with buildings,	
impressed: *The Tower of Blackpool.*	
120mm.	17.00
Bootham Bar, York. 135mm.	30.00
British Government Pavilion B.E.E.	
Wembley 1924-5. 60mm.	80.00
Castle, (unknown). 76mm.	50.00
Church, with Hastings crest.	
115mm.	60.00
Conduit, Uttoxeter Market Place.	
120mm.	45.00
Cottage, single storey. 66mm.	12.50
Eastbourne, The Wish Tower. This is	
one of the Martello Towers built	
about 1806. Napoleon at that time	
threatening an invasion of England.	
May Bonaparte says every heart, land	
in Pevensey level and fight him square	
and drive him to the devil. Ancient	
Toast. In form of base and lid with	
black cannon on top as knot.	
100mm dia, 102mm high.	105.00
Folkestone, Parish Church. AD1138.	
106mm long.	50.00
Garden of Sleep, inscribed:	
On the grass of the cliff, at the edge	
of the steep	
God planted a garden, a garden of	
sleep!	
'Neath the blue of the sky in the	
green of the corn.	
It is there that the regal red poppies	
are born!	
Brief days of desire, and long dreams	
of delight,	

They are mine when my poppy-land
cometh in sight
O heart of my heart!
Where the poppies are born
I am waiting for thee - in the hush of
the corn.
110mm long.   75.00
Great Yarmouth Clock Tower, not
named. 125mm.   10.50
Guildford, The Castle. 100mm.   45.00
Lincoln Stonebow. 85mm.   30.00
Old throne of the Right Hon. D. Lloyd
George Esq. MP Llanystymdwy near
Criccieth. 76mm long.   50.00
Mickelgate Bar, York. 98mm.   40.00
Ripon Cathedral, West Front.
80mm long.   50.00
Rowton Tower, Chester.
88mm long.   40.00
Royal Arch, Dundee front. (Willow
Art). 94mm.   80.00
St Albans, Clock Tower (very small)
74mm.   20.00
St Tudno's Church, Llandudno with
open pillars. 52mm.   40.00
Scarborough Castle Ruins.
75mm long.   60.00
Whitby Abbey Ruins. 75mm.   90.00
Windmill, fixed sails. 80mm.   16.00
Windmill on stilts on square base,
fixed sails in form of scent bottle.
78mm.   20.00
Wrekin Cottage (Foreign). 62mm.   20.00
York Micklegate Bar. 92mm.   45.00
York Minster, West Front. 114mm.   30.00
York Minster, WestFront. 128mm.   40.00

Monuments (including Crosses)
Ashington Boer War Memorial.
138mm.   80.00
Banbury Cross 145mm.   20.00
Black Watch South African War
Memorial. Scotsman on plinth with
rifle standing at ease. Inscribed: *Am*
Freice adan Dubh. To the memory of
officers, non-commissioned officers and
men of the Black Watch who fell in the
South African War 1899-1902. 168mm.110.00
Bradlaugh's Monument, Northampton.
2 sizes: 110mm.   65.00
140mm.   75.00
Brixham Clock Tower. 120mm.   22.50
Captain Scott Statue. 150mm.   17.00
Celtic Cross. 110mm.   12.00
Cleethorpes Clock Tower. 136mm.   24.00

Captain Cook's Monument. 135mm.   30.00
Hall Cross, Doncaster.
2 sizes: 156mm.   40.00
185mm.   40.00
Keswick Monument with grid on lid,
(Grafton). 100mm.   80.00
King Edward VII statue (wrongly
named, actually Drake!). 125mm.   17.00
Larg's Tower, inscribed: *Battle of*
Largs Memorial. 166mm.   22.00
Margate Surf Memorial with
inscriptions.
3 sizes: 80mm.   20.00
144mm.   25.00
330mm. (rock).   100.00
The Metal Man, Tramore. 150mm.
(Saxony).   75.00
Parnells Memorial. 165mm.   85.00
Ruskins Memorial, Friars Crag.
Fully inscribed, grey, unglazed.
180mm.   35.00
St David's Old Market Cross. No. 742.
95mm.   25.00
St Winifreds Statue, Holywell.
135mm.   25.00
Sir John Franklin discoverer of the
North West Passage. Born at Spilsby
April 1786. Died Arctic Regions
June 1847. 165mm.   50.00
Skegness Clock Tower. 120mm.   8.00
South Shields Lifeboat Memorial.
125mm.   16.00
Swanage Globe.
2 sizes: 54mm white.   15.00
65mm coloured.   22.00
Swanage Globe, brown bisque on
square ashtray base. Impressed
The Great Globe Swanage. 80mm.   30.00
Swanage Globe. 65mm base,
85mm long.   30.00
Weymouth Jubilee Clock Tower.
125mm.   17.00

Historical/Folklore
Bass Rock, in relief on square plaque.
125mm long.   40.00
Baby in wraps, perhaps Moses in
bullrushes. 66mm long.   16.50
Banbury Lady on Horse. 130mm.   30.00
Auld Brig O'Doon, Ayr. Picture in
relief on wall plaque.
125mm long.   30.00
Exterior of Burn's Cottage, in relief
on plaque. 128mm long.   30.00

Devil looking over Lincoln. 114mm.	17.50
Edwardian Lady carrying black cat	
and basket. 106mm.	35.00
If named *Mary Bull*	50.00
Execution Block. 100mm long.	14.50
Plaque, rectangular with picture of	
Fair Maid's House, 1860 in high	
relief. 130mm long.	30.00
Giant's Causeway. *Wishing Chair.*	
105mm.	95.00
Idol or grotesque imp or lucky	
charm. 90mm long.	15.00
Jacobean Font at Newport, IoW. Model	
of. 70mm.	24.50
Knaresborough Dropping Well.	
77mm.	23.00
Knight's Armour, torso decorated in	
relief. 70mm.	70.00
Knight's Helmet and Visor, with	
reclining animal on top. 80mm.	35.00
Man in the Sun. 100mm.	47.50
Monmouth Cap with verse. 45mm.	40.00
Mother Shipton, fully coloured.	
110m.	20.00
Sanctuary Chair, Beverley Minster.	
68mm.	20.00
Scold's Bridle, bust of old woman	
wearing bridle, with story of	
gossiping women. Can be found	
coloured. 64mm.	
White.	40.00
Coloured.	65.00
Skull. 44mm.	17.00
Sword in scabbard, ornate. 135mm.	40.00
Trusty Servant. Coloured figure on	
white base. 130mm.	150.00
Ulphus Horn, Original in York	
Minster, Model of. 110mm long.	30.00
Viking or Saxon King standing on 3	
stepped base, axe in hand and	
scrolls in the other. 150mm.	45.00
Dick Whittington and cat, figure	
with very large sitting cat	
holding shield. 100mm.	70.00

Traditional/National Souvenirs

John Bull, bust. 75mm.	10.00
John Bull, standing, with dog.	
106mm.	25.00
John Bull, standing, no dog. 120mm.	17.00
Bolton Trotter. 132mm long.	10.00
Bolton Trotters, two joined as a pair.	
107mm long.	13.50
A Plate o' Bolton Trotters, Three pigs	
trotters on a plate.	17.00

Cheddar Cheese, Model of, with	
inscription: *This famous cheese has*	
been made in and around Cheddar	
for centuries, and to this day no	
country in the world has been able to	
equal it. 60mm dia. (Grafton).	16.00
Cheddar Cheese, inscribed: *Elind*	
Burritt Esq USA says 'far surpasses	
anything I saw in the Mammoth	
Cave of Kentucky. 40mm.	20.00
Jersey Milkmaid. 80mm.	30.00
Lincoln Imp, on pedestal. 110mm.	8.50
Lincoln Imp, wall hanging, crest on	
back. 125mm.	17.00
Manx Man, 3-legged. 126mm.	50.00
Melton Mowbray Pie, with pastry	
roses and leaves. 55mm.	23.50
Bust of Burns, glazed. No. 589.	17.50
Gretna Priest, inscribed: *The famous*	
Gretna Priest from the celebrated	
Blacksmiths shop, Gretna Green.	
118mm. (Saxony).	30.00
Highland Mary, statue. 150mm.	25.00
Scotsman playing bagpipes on	
pedestal. 138mm.	45.00
Scotsman standing in kilt, flower	
vase. 109mm. (Arcadian). No	
crest.	50.00
Souter Johnny, sitting in chair	
(Saxony). 95mm.	24.50
Tam-o'shanter, sitting in chair.	
2 sizes: 94mm.	24.50
130mm.	30.00
Jug with thistle pattern in relief.	
51mm.	5.00
Miniature Toby Jug Welsh Lady,	
coloured. 42mm.	22.00
Welsh Lady in chair. 100mm.	23.00
Welsh Lady Bust glazed, black hat,	
coloured shawl, verse to rear.	
82mm.	26.00
Welsh Hat. 55mm.	7.00
Welsh Hat, very tall. 70mm.	10.50
Dutch Girl, bust, flowers in relief on	
base.	16.00

Seaside Souvenirs

Ship's Binnacle (looks like a	
lighthouse with four pierced	
windows). 95mm.	6.50
Canoe. 110mm long. (Florentine).	10.50
Lifeboat. 98mm long.	14.00
Lifeboat. 125mm long.	17.00
Lighthouse. 100mm.	6.50
Barnsness Lighthouse. 120mm.	17.00

Eddystone Lighthouse. Three-piece
salt, pepper and mustard cruet.
Can be found with two spoons
with flags.   18.00
Lighthouse on rocks with steps,
130mm.   7.00
Lighthouse with 3 open windows.
115mm.   7.00
Lighthouse, tiny. Candlesnuffer.
70mm. (Grafton).   10.00
Lighthouse, candlesnuffer.
2 sizes: 65mm. (Willow).   8.00
106mm.   9.00
Teignmouth Lighthouse. 125mm.   17.00
Beachy Head Lighthouse. 124mm.   11.00
Un-named Rock, no crest, original
could be off the Devon coast.
40mm.   13.00
Lifeboatman bust, 2-piece. 120mm.   30.00
Lifeboatman on rock base. 120mm.
(Carlton).   30.00
Fisherman holding rope. 113mm.   17.00
Fisherman/Lifeboatman Bust on
round plinth. 105mm.   19.50
Fisherman's Head Pot with hat
forming lid. 115mm.   35.00
Mermaid with fish. 84mm.   30.00
Lobster trinket box & lid.
100mm long.   12.50
Waves, group of. 95mm long.   12.50
Nautilus Shell, held up by two
mermaids. 106mm.   17.00
Whelk Shell.
2 sizes: 84mm long.   5.00
95mm long.   5.00
Whelk Shell, inscribed: *Found at
Ryde.* 75mm long.   6.00
Yacht. 128mm.   14.00
Bathing Belle, poking head out of
change tent. 80mm. (Carlton).   40.00
Bathing Belle on rubber duck. 80mm.   24.00
Wicker Bathing chair. No. 1411 pale
beigh. 67mm.   14.00

Figures
The figures listed below are those
which do not belong under any
other heading.
Baby, on rug, naked. 130mm long.   75.00
Baby in wraps - see Historical/
Folklore
Baby, with arms outstretched and
coloured hair. 95mm.   30.00
Boy, feeding birds, standing next to
a large basket on a base. 80mm.   30.00

Child candlesnuffer, standing,
impressed *MORNING,* holding
cup. 125mm.   70.00
Girl carrying basket of eggs at foot
of steps, cock standing on top
step. 80mm.   35.00
Girl on stool, with dog on floor.
(Beige/lustre). 108mm.   30.00
Girl sitting on horse beside tree
trunk. 110mm.   25.00
Edwardian Child pepper pot. 84mm.   14.00
Edwardian Lady holding cat and
basket, possibly Mary Bull.   40.00
Housekeeper or cook wearing mob
cap and apron, carrying keys and
a ladle. 120mm. (Saxony).   45.00
Milkmaid holding milk churn.
120mm.   70.00
Man in Nightdress with candle and
poker, shouting and angry. 155mm.   50.00
Man, standing wearing bowler hat
with book in one hand, umbrella
in the other. 118mm.   27.00
Man, Down and Out, inscribed:
Broke to the wide. 80mm. (Wilton).   75.00
Nurse candlesnuffer, fat, holding
baby. 110mm.   75.00
Schoolboy, standing hands in pocket
looking to the right. *Coachy* on cap
fully coloured. 115mm.   80.00
Two Lady Grape Treaders, with
skirts rolled up, standing in
barrel of grapes. 105mm. (Saxony).   40.00
Washer Woman, holding basket of
washing. 118mm. (Saxony).   40.00
Woman carrying case and bottle.   25.00
Monk carrying lantern and basket.
2 sizes: 114mm.   22.50
135mm. (Saxony).   24.50

Countryside
Acorn. 55mm.   8.50
Axe in Tree Stump. 75mm.   16.50
Butterfly with open wings and wire
legs. 90mm long. (German).   20.00
Daffodil Cup & Saucer. 38mm.   10.00
Four bar gate with stile and
milestone. 96mm long.   10.50
Milk Pail and lid with match striker
base. 66mm.   10.00
Pine Cone. 85mm.   6.00
Strawberry with leaf. 65mm.   12.00
Tree Trunk spill holder, with shepherd
and lambs in front. 75mm.   20.00
Tree Trunk spill holder, with one
lamb and shepherdess with sickle.
75mm.   20.00

Animals

Bear, Polar, on ashtray base. 82mm.	25.00
Bear, playing a Mandolin. (German)	30.00
Bear, Polar perched on ledge looking down upon ashtray base. 82mm.	30.00
Bull's head cream jug. 78mm.	10.00
Camel kneeling on rectangular base. 122mm long.	22.00
Camel, kneeling. 80mm long.	22.00
Kitten, standing.	17.50
Black Cat, sitting up, no crest, yellow eye and orange mouth, comical face. *Good Luck* in orange. 133mm.	30.00
Cat, angry with arched back, coloured face. 70mm.	16.00
Cat on Drum. 90mm. (Saxony).	22.50
Cat, in holdall, can be inscribed: *Good Morning* with right paw raised, yawning or *Good Night* with left paw raised, yawning. 55mm long. (Saxony).	24.50
Cat on pouffe, outpressed: *LUCK*. 73mm. (Willow Art).	26.00
Cat, Cheshire with arched back, and coloured facial features. 74mm.	50.00
Cat, with toothache, bandage round jaw tied with three bows. 95mm.	30.00
Cat, dressed, with toothache, ruff around neck, bandage around head, left paw raised. 105mm.	30.00
Cat, singing from long sheet of music. 65mm. (Saxony).	22.50
Cat, singing, red mouth, green bow. 75mm. (Grafton).	50.00
Cat, reading from book. 74mm. (Saxony).	22.50
Cat, sitting, looking up, gilded face. 67mm.	14.50
Cat, sitting, coloured face. 100mm.	19.50
Cat, sitting in quilted padded armchair. 68mm.	22.00
Cat, sitting, comical, right ear down, left ear up. 2 sizes: 110mm.	10.00
120mm.	12.00
Cat, Egyptian, with long ears. 90mm long.	30.00
Cat, thin and foreign looking, sitting. 70mm.	14.50
Cat, long necked. 115mm.	12.00
Cat, posy bowl.	20.00
Cat, comic, sitting in trinket dish. Bow at neck, tail upright. 45mm	50.00

Cat, standing, plump, black features. 89mm.	20.00
Cat, standing in long skirt, holding tennis racquet. 100mm.	50.00
Cat and Rabbit, in high Boot, inscribed: *A jolly place for a jolly couple*. 83mm. (Saxony).	22.00
Cat, from Alice in Wonderland, long legs, tail wrapped around legs. 100mm. (Florentine).	30.00
Cat, furry kitten with open mouth. 90mm.	40.00
Cat and kitten either side of posy bowl. 105mm long.	15.00
Cat (tiny) sitting on oval candleholder with loop handle (probably Podmore or Sylvan) 115mm long.	30.00
Cat and Kitten, sitting by open square box on ashtray base. 72mm.	23.00
Cat, sitting, left paw raised. 75mm.	19.50
Cat, Cheshire, sitting, ear up. 128mm.	15.00
Cat, Manx. 90mm long.	30.00
Cat, Manx, standing drinking from jug, sometimes inscribed: *Mothers favourite*. 70mm long. (Saxony).	24.50
Cat with mouse. 77mm.	24.50
Cat, standing, hands on hips, tail forming third leg. 86mm.	22.00
Cat scent bottle and lid. 90mm. (Grafton).	45.00
Cats, three, in linen basket. 68mm.	30.00
Cheshire Cat, 90mm.	7.50
Cheshire Cat, long neck, looking left, 1 green eye,1 winking red eye. 115mm.	14.50
Cougar, on oval base, roaring showing teeth. No. 934. 125mm long.	65.00
Cow lying down, with gold horns, inscribed: *The Jersey Cow*.	
3 sizes: 108mm long.	20.00
120mm long.	20.00
140mm long.	20.00
Cow standing, gold horns, smaller sizes inscribed: *The Jersey Cow*.	
2 sizes: 93mm long.	22.00
108mm long.	22.00
(Pair with above).	
Cow Creamer, inscribed: *The Jersey Cow* standing, gold horns. Comes with lid, the tail forming the handle. 145mm long.	24.00
Cow cream jug.	
2 sizes: 110mm long.	20.00
125mm long.	20.00
Dinosaur jug. 85mm long.	7.50

Dog, Bulldog, extremely thin,
sitting. 95mm long.   20.00
Dog, Collie, sitting. 80mm.   22.00
Dog wearing dress and overcoat,
green colouring on hat. 92mm.   60.00
Standing Chauffeur Dog, goggles
on cap, smoking pipe, wearing
long overcoat. 84mm.   50.50
Dog, standing, chauffeur dog,
dressed in long travelling coat
and flat cap, tied with scarf under
chin. (Pair to the chauffeur
above).82mm.   55.00
Dog, Bulldog. 110mm long.   16.00
Dog, black bulldog in kennel.
67mm.   12.00
Dogs, two bulldogs, one seated and
the other standing. 57mm.
(Saxony).   20.00
Dog, Bull Terrier, sitting next to a
bucket. 80mm.   27.00
Dog, Dachsund. 73mm long.
(Willow).   45.00
Dogs, two Pharos Hounds, on
oblong base. 76mm long.   75.00
Dog, Collie, lying down.
110mm long.   22.50
Dog, sitting, one ear raised.
69mm.   12.00
Dog, standing, tail as support.
80mm.   22.00
Dog, Terrier. 61mm.   9.50
Dog, Scottie, wearing Tam-
o'shanter.   9.50
Dog, King Charles Spaniel.
67mm.   16.00
Dog, comical pup, sitting, brown
patches. 61mm.   24.00
Dog, Pointer, walking. 125mm long.   23.00
Dog, Pointer, with spring tail (often
missing). 90mm long.   30.00
Without tail.   20.00
Dog, three legged *Prince Toby Orry*
from I.O.M.   60.00
Dog, Staffordshire Bull Terrier, long
neck. 110mm.   20.00
Dog, with toothache, head bandaged
sitting. 90mm.   30.00
Dog, Labrador, sitting half out of
kennel. (Saxony). 98mm.   30.00
Dogs, two, and cat in basket.
2 sizes: 63mm.   22.00
              70mm.   25.00
Dog, Pug, lying down. 96mm long.   20.00
Dog, Spaniel with droopy ears.
60mm.   13.00

Dog, King Charles Spaniel, wearing
ribbon, lying on cushion.
82mm long.   20.00
Pair of Spaniels in top hat. 82mm.   20.00
Dog, probably a Retriever, lying on
oblong base. 120mm long.   22.00
Dog, sitting Labrador puppy, large
paws. 70mm.   20.00
Dog, sitting, paw on rat. 78mm high,
95mm long.   30.00
Dog Coal Scuttle. 80mm. (Saxony).   16.50
Donkey, inscribed: *Carisbrooke
Donkey.* 100mm long. (Saxony).   30.00
Donkey. 90mm long.   15.00
Donkey, inscribed: A *Malvern
Donkey.* 95mm long.   30.00
Donkey, inscribed: WE ARE TWO.
95mm long.   20.00
Elephant, gigantic, with gold tusks.
Trunk raised. 130mm.   70.00
Elephant, trunk looped upwards.
85mm long. (Florentine).   26.50
Elephant, Indian, standing.
2 sizes: 63mm long.   22.00
          100mm long.   26.00
Elephant, kneeling. 95mm long.   20.00
Elephant, standing, trunk looped up.
80mm long. (Carlton).   30.00
Elephant, circus, with front feet on
stool. 102mm.   80.00
Elephant, circus, doing handstand
on stool. 74mm.   80.00
Elephant heads, 2 on vase as
handles. 76mm.   7.50
Elephant No.346. 50mm.   24.00
Elephant, walking. 70mm high,
110mm long.   40.00
Two Elephants on Toboggan going
down hill. 70mm.   55.00
Elephant with Hunters and two
Indian Bearers. 95mm.   50.00
Frog on hind legs, arms on chest,
open mouth. 85mm.   22.50
Giant Frog, with huge open mouth.
80mm.   30.00
Frog with bead eyes. 72mm.   20.00
Frog cream jug. 100mm long.   9.50
Fish, inscribed: *Yarmouth Bloater.*
120mm long.   8.00
Fish match holder/striker   10.00
Fish salt pot, with black markings to
face. 108mm long.   8.50
Fish, open mouth, raised head.
110mm long.   12.50
Fish with open back for pin cushion.
118mm long.   6.00

Fish, gilded tail. 112mm long.	6.00
Guinea Pig. 60mm long.	30.00
Horses and Bulldogs heads in	
rectangular frame. 103mm.	25.00
Kangaroo. 95mm.	75.00
Lambs (two) by hollow tree trunk	
spill holder. See countryside.	
Lion, walking. 135mm.	18.00
Lion, on rectangular base. 116mm.	9.50
Lion, male, standing, open mouth,	
looking left. 110mm long.	25.00
Lion, wearing coat and trousers	
holding telescope. 132mm.	75.00
Monkey, wearing coat.	
80mm. (Grafton).	15.00
Monkey with bead eyes. No.245.	
70mm. (Grafton).	15.00
Mouse. 60mm.	25.00
Mouse playing Mandolin. 90mm.	30.00
Pig, standing, ears forward. 80mm	
long.	17.50
Pig, standing. 73mm long (Arcadian).	18.00
Pig, hairy, standing with holes in	
nostrils. Inscribed: *The pig that*	
won't go. 85mm long.	16.50
Pig, sitting on haunches, wearing	
picklehaube & iron cross (Arcadian).	
93mm.	110.00
Pig sitting on haunches, Pepper Pot.	
70mm.	20.00
Pig, sitting, ears flat out. 70mm.	22.00
Pink Pig posy holder.	18.00
Pig, standing, with hands on hips	
and pink ears. (Gemma).83mm.	30.00
Pig money box, with gold coin in	
mouth. 87mm long.	30.00
Shetland Pony inscribed: *A Native of*	
Shetland. 80mm.	21.50
Sheep with gilded bell, standing.	
65mm.	0.00
Rabbit, crouching. 65mm.	10.50
Rabbit, miniature, crouching, ears	
erect. 30mm.	12.50
Large Rabbit, crouching, right ear	
up. 60mm high. 90mm long.	14.50
Rabbit on sledge. (Saxony).	
93mm long.	35.00
Rabbits, two arm in arm on wide	
base. 72mm wide.	30.00
Rabbits, two cuddling on ashtray.	
54mm.	30.00
Rhino, very grotesque. 155mm long.	30.00
Seal with ball on nose. 73mm.	24.50
Sheep, pale green lustre with	
coloured view of Christchurch	
Oxford. 65mm.	30.00

Squirrel, large, in shape of milk jug.	
90mm.	16.50
Teddy Bear. 79mm.	22.50
Tortoise pin box and lid.	
2 sizes: 80mm long.	9.50
128mm long.	14.50
Vole. No.163. 60mm long.	50.00

Birds (including Eggs)

Bird, fledgling, with tiny wings	
outstretched. 59mm.	17.00
Bird on rock, black tinges to wings.	
65mm.	17.00
Blackbird on perch. 118mm long.	12.50
Canary on a perch. 110mm long.	12.50
Chick, yellow, hatching from egg,	
pepper pot. 55mm.	13.00
Chick, yellow, hatching from egg,	
salt cellar. 60mm.	13.00
Chicken, very plump, on circular	
base. 67mm.	10.00
Chick, hatching from egg. 72mm.	8.50
Cockatoo on plinth, brown beak.	
173mm.	30.00
Cockerel, pepper pot. 71mm.	9.50
Crested Tit posy holder.	
80mm long.	10.00
Crow, Royston. White (Arcadian).	25.00
Duck ashtray, some colouring.	
95mm long.	17.00
Duck, plump, pecking on circular	
base. 59mm.	15.00
Duck, plump yellow beak & webbed	
feet, on round base. 75mm.	15.00
Duck, ewer with handle. 130mm long.	9.50
Duck pepper pot. 77mm.	12.50
Ducks, 2 with coloured beaks and	
feet on oval stand. 185mm. (an	
enormous model).	50.00
Duckling, airing wings, comical.	
69mm.	16.50
Duck, on circular base.	
2 sizes: 60mm.	16.00
103mm.	22.00
Larger size has brown beak and feet.	
Duck, circular base, some colouring.	
2 sizes: 95mm.	14.00
106mm.	16.00
Duckling with brown beak and feet,	
wings raised, beak upwards and	
open, on circular base. 85mm.	16.00
Duck posy bowl. Circular base, gold	
beak. 92mm.	14.50
Eagle on rock, colour on beak and	
feet. 130mm.	32.00
Egg. 65mm upright.	7.00

Fledgling birds,2 sitting on base
sharing one open beak. Can be
found coloured.(Grotesque). 110mm.
White.   8.50
Coloured.   19.50
Goldfinch on Rock, looking forward.
109mm. Not numbered. Some
colouring. 110mm.   26.00
Goldfinch on Rock, bird looking left.
No. 698. Some colouring. 108mm.   26.00
Goldfinch on Rock. No.859.
105mm long.   22.00
Hen, brooding. 65mm long.   8.50
Hen and Cockerel on circular base.
Red combs. 82mm.   17.00
Hens, two on circular base. 80mm.   17.00
Hen trinket box & lid. 86mm long.   12.00
Kingfisher. 60mm.   30.00
Owl, on plinth with verse. 115mm.   17.50
Owl on three books. 121mm.   25.00
Owl, pepper pot. 90mm.   20.00
Owl, long-eared, perched on rock.
110mm.   22.50
Owl, tiny, perched on two sectioned
dish (Saxony).   10.00
Parakeet, fully coloured on plinth.
215mm.   25.00
Parrot on vase. 78mm.   12.00
Pelican. l00mm.   17.50
Penguin, holding book, beak open.
122mm. (Shelley).   90.00
Pigeon with puffed up chest,
standing on ashtray base. 75mm.   22.00
Stork, nesting beside chimney pot
with baby in nest. l00mm.   25.00
Stork on one leg (Carlton). 100mm.   15.00
Swan, head back. 72mm.   7.50
Swan trinket box and lid. 69mm.   8.00
Warbler on tree stump. 130mm.   26.00

Great War
Cossack, standing figure on
rectangular base. 126mm.   95.00
Jack Ashore, boy sailor on round
base, coloured face. 153mm.   60.00
Sailor bust, parian on round glazed
base. Inscribed: *HMS Tiger.*
No. 532. 135mm (Savoy).   50.00
Soldier, standing with tree stump
support one hand clenched the
other in pocket. No. 576. 110mm.
(Grafton Prince of Wales)   40.00
Airship with moulded propellers
and two gondolas. 130mm long.   40.00
Monoplane, with pilot. 98mm long.   40.00
Lion Battleship. 143mm long   50.00

Submarine, *E4.* 102mm long.   22.50
Renault Tank. 105mm long.   80.00
Bury St Edmunds Bomb. 80mm   17.00
Bomb, standing on 4 feet. 83mm.   12.00
Shell, pepper pot. 110mm.   20.00
Bugle. 70mm. (Willow Art).   27.50
Boot with puttee. 73mm. (Grafton).   25.00
Mess Pot. 55mm.   65.00
Military Cap ashtray, crest inside
hat. 126mm long.   14.50
Peaked Cap. 60mm.   12.50
German spiked helmet, gilded
strap. 55mm.   35.00
Pith Helmet. 55mm long.   35.00
Telegraph Station (Grafton). 90mm
long, 66mm high.   70.00
Cenotaph,147mm.   7.50
Clacton-on-Sea War Memorial, with
inscription. 145mm.   30.00
Dingwall War Memorial, not
named. 125mm high,
160mm long.   70.00
Folkestone War Memorial.
138mm.   40.00
Great Yarmouth War Memorial &
inscription. 150mm.   20.00
*Hawick '1514' Memorial unveiled (sic)
June 4th 1914.* Rectangular upright
plaque with Hawick War
Memorial in relief. 145mm. Rare.   110.00
Llandudno War Memorial, not
named. 183mm.   55.00
Margate War Memorial. 190mm.   80.00
Matlock War Memorial. 155mm.   65.00
Matlock-Bath War Memorial.
150mm.   20.00
Matlock-Bath War Memorial.
188mm. (Florentine).   75.00
Otley Churchyard, War Memorial
Cross.123mm.   75.00
Retford, War Memorial 1922. 177mm.   140.00

Home/Nostalgic
Anvil on base. 58mm.   7.50
Armchair padded and three-legged.
66mm.   19.50
Armchair, basket weave. 67mm.   14.50
Armchair, padded with blue forget-
me-nots around back rest. 62mm.   22.50
Armchair, Jacobean style. 64mm.   12.00
Ornate French Chair. 84mm.   14.50
Armchair, upholstered. 85mm.   14.00
Basket with coloured fruit. 85mm.
(Carlton).   20.00

Bell. 65mm.	6.00
Bucket with moulded rope handle.	
67mm.	6.00
Butter churn. 65mm.	7.00
Coal Scuttle. 70mm.	5.00
Cradle on rockers. 45mm.	10.00
Flat Iron, box style, possibly a	
money box. 65mm.	8.00
Fob Watch on horseshoe shaped	
trinket tray. 150mm.	13.50
Grandfather clock, inscribed: *Make*	
Use of time... 13mm.	20.00
Grandfather clock.	
2 sizes: 104mm.	16.00
129mm.	18.00
Grandmother clock. 86mm.	10.00
Handbag. 84mm.	16.00
Hip Bath. 90mm long.	9.50
Jardiniere,2-piece.160mm.	7.00
Kettle on primus stone. 78mm.	12.50
Kitchen Funnel, silver rim. 64mm.	16.50
Mantle Clock. 94mm.	16.00
Mantle Clock. 85mm. (different mould)	16.00
Photograph Frame, cardboard	
backing. 94mm. (Gemma).	18.00
Pillar Box, fat. 85mm.	14.00
Pillar Box, miniature. (Savoy)	
No. 504. 58mm.	14.50
Pillar Box. 70mm.	13.00
Ring. 64mm dia.	22.00
Shaving Mug. 37mm.	9.50
Shaving Mug, taper sides. 53mm.	10.00
Shaving Mug, ornate, pearl lustre.	
55mm.	11.50
The above model has been found	
with a colour transfer of 'Mr	
Peggotty' with inscription.	
Shaving Mug, angular handle. 44mm.	9.50
Suitcase, closed 80mm long.	7.00
Suitcase, gilded straps. 57mm.	7.00
Trunk. 60mm long.	7.50
Tub of washing. 87mm.	22.00
Umbrella. 38mm. (Arcadian).	16.50
Watering Can, oval shaped with no	
rose on spout. 87mm.	9.50
Watering Can. 77mm.	9.50
Water Bottle, rectangular. 66mm.	10.00

Comic/Novelty

Arriet (impressed on back). Bust of	
Pearly Queen. 93mm.	40.00
Apple Salt Pot. 50mm.	22.00
Baby in Bootee. 80mm long.	14.50
Baby in Coracle. 50mm.	16.50
Bean Pod, open. 125mm long.	25.00

Biscuit. Impressed *Huntley & Palmer*	
coloured biscuit. 53mm dia.	40.00
Biscuit. Impressed: *Huntley &*	
Palmer white, on base. Top can be	
pierced for hatpins. 88mm high.	40.00
Biscuit, beige. 57mm dia.	35.00
Clown playing Banjo, some colour.	
120mm.	40.00
Jack in the Box with open lid.	
92mm. (Florentine).	28.00
Suffragette Handbell, double faced,	
old / young woman. Coloured	
and inscribed: *Nature has endowed*	
women with so much power that the	
law gives them very little. Dr.	
Johnson. 107mm.	50.00
Leg of Mutton. 80mm long.	20.00
Man and woman, sitting, cuddling,	
in ornate alcove with balustrade.	
(Saxony). 54mm.	20.00
Man, with earphones and beer mug.	
60mm.	22.50
Map of Isle of Thanet on ashtray base.	
Some colouring. Rare. 60mm.	140.00
Sailor, comic. *HMS Lion.* 85mm.	60.00
Scout, standing, staff in hand,	
retriever dog sitting on his right,	
paws and head looking over	
shield bearing crest. 110mm.	70.00
Tomato pepper pot on leaf base.	
42mm.	20.00
Vaulting Horse, square looking	
bulldog with legs joined by 3	
poles. 80mm long. Some	
colouring. (Saxony).	22.00
Womans Head (flapper) on Turtle	
trinket box. 80mm long.	22.50
Womans Head tea pot, some	
colouring. 66mm.	16.50

Cartoon/Comedy Characters

Crested faced man white or fully	
coloured. 80mm.	35.00
Coloured.	60.00
Felix, standing Cat on oval base, no	
colouring. 87mm. (This is a really	
nice Felix.)	150.00
Mrs Gamp. Seated figure, with	
brolly. 114mm.	80.00
Harry Lauder bust. 58mm.	22.00
Sunny Jim bust. 85mm.	45.00
Bust of Man with walrus	
moustache, button nose and large	
ears. Comical character – identity	
unknown! 80mm.	25.00

Alcohol

Barrel, upright. 53mm and 65mm.	5.00
Thistle Ashtray with soda syphon, silvered top, beaker and 4-sided bottle with red top. 76mm long.	18.50
Man in Bowler Hat, sitting, holding beer glass.	50.00
Bust of drunk in hat, red spotted nose, crooked grin candlesnuffer. 85mm.	30.00
Bottle, inscribed: *Lacon's Fine Ales.* 90mm.	30.00
Carboy. 70mm.	7.00
Champagne Bottle in Ice Bucket. 80mm.	15.00
Whiskey and Soda on horseshoe ashtray. 115mm long.	16.50

Sport/Pastimes

Boxer, fists up. (Florentine). 118mm.	170.00
Cricket Stumps & bat, spillholder. 105mm.	80.00
Footballer, with ball, no colouring. 130mm.	80.00
(Savoy range advertised a coloured version of this model)	
Football, leather. 55mm.	10.50
Cat holding golf club on golf ball plain white. Registration applied for (Willow). 70mm.	80.00
Golf Ball, pepper pot on circular base. 50mm dia.	14.00
Golf Caddie, holding golf bag. Hand in front of mouth as if shocked at bad shot. 65mm.	100.00
Rugby Ball. 74mm long.	12.50
The Sprinter. Comic figure with cork-screw legs – wound up for action. l00mm.	60.00
Tennis Court Liner in form of a wheelbarrow. 90mm long.	20.00
Tennis Racquet with single ball attached. 135mm long.	19.50
Tennis Racquet, detailed strings. (Grafton). 118mm long.	20.00
Trophy. 100mm.	9.50
Artist's Easel on stand. 60mm.	2.00
Bridge Trumps. 60mm.	
Club.	6.00
Diamond.	6.00
Heart.	9.00
Spade.	6.00
Rook Chess Piece. 48mm.	12.00

Musical Instruments

Drum set with cymbals and drumsticks. 65mm. (St. George).	14.50
Harp. 93mm.	10.00
Lute (Irish) Good Luck with shamrocks and harp. 159mm.	40.00
Piano, grand. 63mm.	16.00
Piano, upright. 63mm.	14.00
Tambourine. 70mm.	11.00

Transport

Aeroplane with pilot, size varies, usually 100mm long. (Almost certainly German).	40.00
Bust of Bleriot, inscribed: *Messieur Bleriot. 1st man to cross the Channel in an Aeroplane. June 25th 1909.* Grafton. 90mm.	85.00
Car with chauffeur. 85mm long.	40.00
Hot Air Balloon, square basket. 2 sizes: 65mm.	50.00
90mm.	50.00
Petrol can impressed: *Motor Spirit.* 67mm.	19.50
Sleigh, ornate. 105mm long.	25.00
Tram. 100mm long.	170.00
Charabanc 18 seater with driver. 125mm long.	35.00

Modern Equipment

Cash Register. 44mm. (Saxony).	16.00
Typewriter inscribed: *My little typewriter.* 44mm. (Saxony).	20.00
Identical model to the above.	
Typewriter Inkwell. 80mm. (Foreign).	16.00
Gramophone, square. No horn. (Saxony). 55mm.	22.00
Gramophone with horn. 60mm.	30.00
Gramophone in cabinet. 91rnm.	80.00

Hats

Boater, Straw. Coloured petersham band. Unglazed. 107mm long.	22.00
Also found coloured inside, with white band.	20.00
Chauffeur's Large Peak Cap. 125mm long.	16.00
Fireman's Helmet. 63mm.	35.00
Fireman's Helmet vase. 48mm.	22.00
Knight's Helmet forming pin box and lid. 80mm.	17.00
Opera Hat. 36mm.	20.00
Top Hat, very wide brim. 60mm.	7.50
Top Hat, with antlers across brim. 65mm.	15.00

Top Hat, with umbrella across brim.
Some colouring. 65mm.   12.00
Top Hat match striker, not glazed
underneath. 42mm.   6.50
Top Hat match striker, inscribed:
*The Rapid Patent Silk Hat Ironing
Machine.* 45mm.   30.00
(Obviously an advertising item)
Trilby. 96mm long.   24.00

Footwear
Dutch Sabot. 70mm long.   5.00
Boot with Spat. 80mm long.   7.50
Boot, ten open lace holes. 105mm long. 7.50
Boot, old. 60mm long.   12.00
Boot, old, leaning to the left. 118mm
long.   12.00
Boot, open, with pierced eyelets.
78mm long.   7.00
Bootee, with bow, 6 eyelets.
92mm long.   12.00
Oriental heeled shoe, curled up toe.
176mm long.   20.00
Oriental Slipper with turned up toe.
100mm long.   12.00
Riding Boot with Spur. 90mm.   15.00
Ladies Court Shoe, frilled tongue
inset straps & button. 85mm long.   9.00
Ladies heeled Shoe, frilled tongue.
107mm long.   7.50
Ladies Shoe, frilled edge.
113mm long.   9.50
Ladies Shoe, high heel and front
buckle. 115mm long.   9.00
Ladies Shoe, gilded heel and toe.
150mm long.   11.00
Ladies Shoe, frilled tongue and
edge. 145mm long.   12.50
Ladies Boot, pressed eyelet holes.
2 sizes: 83mm long.   8.00
          105mm long.   10.00
Lancashire Clog. 112mm long.   7.50
Sabot with turned up toe, can be
found in grey lustre. 93mm long.   6.00
Shoe with side fastening.
80mm long.   9.00
Slipper wall pocket. 65mm wide.   12.50

Miniature Domestic
Bagware Vase. 41mm.   4.00
Candle Snuffer cone. 45mm.   6.50
Cheese Dish and cover. 64mm long.   7.50
Cheese Dish and cover in shape of
horseshoe. 45mm.   19.50
Cheese Dish and cover, inscribed:
Cheshire Cheese. 78mm long.   16.00

Cheese Dish and fixed cover.
64mm long.   8.50
Cheese Dish and cover. 85mm long.   7.50
Cheese Dish and cover, shield
shaped base. 60mm.   8.50
Dressing table set comprising: two
scent bottles and stoppers, three
rouge pots and lids, ring tree and
two candlesticks, all on
rectangular tray. 155mm long.   Set 30.00
Horseshoe Ashtray. 68mm long.   4.00
Hot Water Jug with lid. 98mm.   8.50
Kettle and lid. 80mm.   8.50
Sheaf of Corn Jug. 79mm.   12.50
Teapot and lid. 75mm.   8.50
Miniature coffee set comprising:
coffee pot and lid, sugar basin,
milk jug, two cups and saucers on
rectangular tray. 155mm long.   33.00
Miniature tea set comprising: teapot
and lid, sugar basin, milk jug,
two cups and saucers on
rectangular or circular tray.   30.00
Bellows Box and lid. 120mm long.   9.50
Cake Slice pin box and lid.
138mm long.   14.00
Tankard, silver rim.   16.50

Domestic
Eye Bath.   4.00
Column Candlestick, two-handled.
82mm.   3.00
Funnel Candlesnuffer. (Savoy).   12.50
Funnel, silver rimmed. 64mm.   16.00
Plate with pierced rim. 230mm dia.   15.00
Ring holder. 88mm.   10.00
Ribbon Plate. 175mm dia.   15.00

Miscellaneous
Beaker with lithophane of
Shakespeare. 90mm.   30.00
Gourd. 70mm.   9.50
Horseshoe. 66mm.   5.00
Loving Cup,3 handled, with
lithophanes of King Edward,
Queen Alexandra, King George,
Queen Mary or Dover Castle. 39mm. 40.00
Lithophane match holder/striker
with lithophane of King Edward
VII or Chamberlain. 43mm.   30.00
Southwold Jug with lithophane of
George V or Queen Mary. 60mm.   30.00

ILLUSTRATED SECTION

In the following pages will be found illustations from virtually every theme and all major factories.

Any similar item from another factory will be worth approximately the same as one shown here.

By using this easy-to-use section, one should be able to determine an idea of correct retail price.

All prices exclude VAT and are for pieces in perfect condition.

Index to Illustrations

Arcadian Josepl Chamberlain £40.00

Arcadian Lloyd George £50.00

Arcadian George V £47.50

Arcadian Edward VII in Trilby £65.00

Grafton Roberts £65.00

Arcadian Kitchener £75.00

Arcadian Joffre £75.00

Arcadian Edward VII £47.50

Swan Queen Alexandra £47.50

Willow Burns £40.00   Willow Scott £30.00   Carlton Wordsworth £25.00

Carlton Ruskin £40.00

Shelley Kitchener £50.00

Grafton George V £55.00

Grafton Lloyd George
£55.00

Shelley Burns £30.00

Grafton Kitchener £40.00

Arcadian Albert King of the Belgians £65.00

Swan Queen Mary £50.00

Swan George V £50.00

Shelley Sir John
French £65.00

Carlton Edward VII
Wearing Trilby
£55.00

Shelley Celtic Ancient
Jar No. 200 £7.00

Shelley Eastern Olive
Jar No. 208 £8.00

Shelly Notre
DameCandlestick
£16.50

Shelley Greek
Salonika Vase
£17.50

Carlton Etruscan Vase
£5.50

Shelley Indian Wine
Vessel No. 303 £25.00

Arcadian
Chinese Vase
£5.50

Shelley Italian
15th Century
Vase £14.50

Arcadian Pompeii
Lamp £5.50

Arcadian Winchester Bushel £40.00

Shelley Roman
Money Box £9.50

Foley Exeter
Vase £5.00

Carlton
Merthyr Vase
No. 382 £5.50

Arcadian
Lichfield Jug
£6.00

Florentine Puzzle
Jug £7.50

Foley Vase
No. 25 £5.00

Shelley Persian
Cafeterre £16.50

Shelley
Arabian Wine
Vessel £6.50

Arcadian
Ewer £4.00

Foley Kent
Roman Urn
£5.00

Foley Ewer
No. 41 £5.00

German Puzzle
Tankard £10.50

Wilton Feathers Hotel
Ludlow £100.00

Unmarked Irish Cottage
Money Box £35.00

H & L Mason Croft
£150.00

Willow Old Curiosity Shop
£140.00

Mosanic Pump
Room Harrogate
£40.00

Mosanic Building Each Around
£40.00-£50.00

Willow Old
Maids £65.00

Unmarked Mow Cop Castle
Staffs £125.00

Savoy Exeter Cathedral £125.00

Leadbeater Christchurch Priory Church £150.00

Willow Ann Hathaways's
Cottage Various Sizes
£18.00-£40.00

Willow Pevensey Old Mint
House £160.00

Gretna Blacksmith's Shop
£40.00

Willow Art Old Ostrich Inn
Colnbrook £250.00

Willow The Tan House Little
Stretton £125.00

Willow Burns Cottage £40.00

Willow Shakespeare's House Various
Sizes £16.00-£50.00

Willow Gretna
Blacksmith's Shop £40.00

Arcadian Westminster Abbey £30.00

Willow Upleatham £100.00

Regency Clifton Suspension Bridge £75.00

Royal Arms China Thatched Cottage £12.50

Willow Worcester Cathedral £40.00

Tuscan Newquay Look-out £60.00

Willow Lancaster Castle £55.00

Carlton Wembley Stadium £95.00

German Windmill Fixed Sails £14.50

Saxony St.Tudno's Church 45.00£

Willow Art Godalming Town Hall £125.00

Arcadian Wimborne Minster £65.00

Arcadian Portsmouth Guildhall £40.00

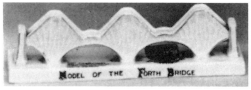

Unmarked Carlton Forth Bridge £40.00

Burns' Cottage Interior £30.00

Willow Chatham Town Hall £70.00

Willow Canterbury Cathedral £40.00

Alexandra St. Paul's £40.00

Grafton Toll Gate House £65.00

Arcadian The Globe Swanage £40.00

Guildford Castle £45.00

Willow Windsor Round Tower £25.00

Grafton Smallest House in Wales £25.00

Wy Not Knaresborough Castle £60.00

Carlton Dutch Cottage Canvey Island £130.00

Foreign Lantern Hill Chapel Ilfracoombe £20.00

Arcadian Kent Hop Kiln £47.00

Willow Art First & Last House £20.00

Wilton Ann Hathaways Cottage £20.00

Arcadian Brick Cottage
£15.00

Willow Monnow Bridge
£40.00

Alexandra Tower Bridge £45.00

Norfolk Crest
Shakespeare's House £12.00

Swan Tower Bridge £40.00

Arcadian Boston Stump £47.50

Arcadian Big
Ben £22.05

Grafton Southampton
Bargate £35.00

Carlton The Alderley
Beacon £100.00

Willow Abbey Gate,
Bury St. Edmunds £75.00

Brit. Man. Brick
Cottage £10.00

Podmore Lincoln Cathedral £30.00

Carlton Arundel Castle
Keep £115.00

Carlton Ripon
Market Cross
£18.00

Willow Nottingham Castle £55.00

Saxony Skegness
Clock Tower £7.50

Savoy Portsmouth Town Hall
£80.00

Carlton
Lighthouse £16.50

Grafton Bath Abbey £45.00

German Bandstand
£10.00

Carlton Hastings Castle £30.00

Carlton Bishop's
TowerPaignton
£47.00

Victis Shanklin Old Village £100.00

Botolph Big
Ben £17.50

Saxony Llandudno Church
£45.00

Arcadian Marble Arch £20.00

Carlton York
Micklegate Bar
£35.00

Arcadian Windmill
£40.00

Arcadian Rochester
Castle £47.50

Willow Canterbury
West Gate £30.00

Devonia Drake
Statue £16.50

Saxony Fisherman's
Memorial
Southend £15.00

Thistle Burns
Statue £30.00

Saxony Captain
Scott Memorial
£25.00

Willow   Foreign
MargateSurf   Lifeboatman
Boat Memorial   on Rocky Base
£20.00   £14.50

Arcadian King
Alfred's
Statue £55.00

Clarence Crest,
Baron Burton
Statue £30.00

Willow Laceby
Memorial
£40.00

Willow Queen
Victoria Statue,
Blackburn £40.00

Willow Edith
Cavell Statue
£30.00

Willow Hull
Fisherman's
Memorial £24.00

Arcadian Richmond
Market £30.00

Willow Flodden
Cross £25.00

Willow C.S.Rolls
Memorial £40.00

Devonia Art
Derry's Clock
Plymouth £18.00

Willow Gibbet
Cross,
Hindhead
£12.00

Willow Ruskin
Memorial £24.00

Willow Florence
Nightingale
Statue £25.00

Willow Bunyan
Statue £20.00

Willow Grimsby
Hydraulic Tower
£50.00

WHH and S.
Plymouth Armada
Memorial £35.00

Willow Isaac
Newton Statue
£40.00

Carlton Fisherman
'Son of the Sea'
£40.00

Arcadian Maiwand
Memorial Reading
£25.00

Shelley Rufus
Stone £12.50

Corona Ruskin
Memorial £17.50

Carlton Queen
Eleanor's Cross
Northampton
£80.00

Boy Scout and his Dog £45.00

Arcadian Bust of Judge £35.00

Shelley Lincoln Imp £22.50

Carlton Jenny Jones £40.00

Arcadian Bust of Peeping Tom of Coventry £17.00

Alexandra Burns and Highland Mary £30.00

Gemma Coronation Chair £6.00

Regis Mary Queen of Scots Chair £10.50

Carlton Suffragette Handbell £65.00

Unmarked Bust of General Booth £40.00

Carlton Ripon Hornblower £16.00

Saxony John Bull and his Dog £25.00

Wy-not? Crest Burns' Chair £12.50

Savoy Cornish Pasty £12.50

Shelley Pat's Hat and Dudeen No. 154 £20.00

Willow Archbishop of Canterbury's Chair £18.50

Willow 'Alas Poor Yorick' Skull £16.00

Grafton Prime Cheddar
Cheese £12.50

Arcadian English Folksong
Bride and Chest £55.00

Carlton Crown
£20.00

Shelley Seated Welsh Lady £60.00

Carlton Cheddar
Cheese (Wedged)
£16.00

Arcadian Bust of John Bull £30.00

Grafton Welsh
Lady Toby
Jug, Coloured
Ethnic Series
£70.00

Willow Souter
Johnny £30.00

Arcadian
Coaching
Hat £7.50

Kingsway   Regis Dutch Arcadian Mother
Dutch Girl   Boy £16.50   Shipton £10.00
£16.50

Arcadian Coal Miner's
Lamp '1836' £22.00

Carlton Biddenden
Maids £80.00

Arcadian Lincoln
Devil £16.00

Carlton
Yorkshireman
£35.00

Carlton Caveman
with Club £130.00

Willow Daniel
Lambert £125.00

Shelley Legs of Man
No. 351 £25.00

Willow Art
Tam O'Shanter £30.00

Arcadian 'Colleen' on
Ashtray £55.00

Carlton Tam O'Shanter
£24.50

Carlton Ulphus
Horn £45.00

Arcadian Irishman on
Shamrock Ashtray
£100.00

Arcadian Welsh
Ladies Tea
Party £58.00

Lucky Charm £8.00

Podmore Chester Imp £30.00

Edwardian
Lady, Cat and
Basket £30.00

Tall Welsh Hat £10.00

Kingsway Handbell
£9.00

Grafton
President
Wilson's
Grandfather's
Chair £14.00

Saxony Gretna
Priest £30.00

Arcadian Henry V
Cradle £75.00

Podmore Bunyan's
Chair £16.00

Shelley Sir Walter
Scott's Chair
No. 325 £12.50

Willow Scott's Chair £14.50

German Ornate
Chair £12.50

Arcadian High Backed
Chair £9.50

Willow James V
(Stirling) Chair £14.50

Willow Burn's (Dumfries)
Chair £18.00

Shelley Bunyan's
Chair £19.00

Tuscan Coronation
Chair £20.00

Carlton Old Arm
Chair £15.50

Crown Rocking
Chair £22.50

Rialto Carved
Chair £12.50

Foreign Upholstered
Armchair £14.50

Carlton Armchair
£14.50

Saxony Lloyd Loom
Chair £9.50

Foreign Padded
Armchair £7.00

Botolph Bather and Bathing
Machine £16.50

Grafton Whelk Shell £6.00   Shelley 'Sheringham Whelk' £14.00

Swan (RNLI) Fish
Collection Box
£80.00

Arcadian Fish £5.00

German Girl on Seaside
Donkey £17.00

Florentine Legs of Man
Lifebelt £16.00

Shelley Lifeboat No. 323 £25.00

Foreign Coracle
(Tied to Stump) £6.50

Brit. Man. Houseboat
(Ark) £10.00

Arcadian Donkey £50.00

Carlton Motor Boat on Waves,
with Driver £27.50

Arcadian 'Plaice' Ashtray £14.50

Carlton Fishing Boat £32.50

Willow Blackpool Big
Wheel £20.00

Grafton Oyster Shell
(Coral Legs) £7.00

Saxony 'Sea Waves' £6.50

Botolph Whelk Shell
£6.50

Arcadian Scallop
Inkwell £12.50

Florentine Basket
Beach Chair £12.00

Willow Blackpool Tower with
Buildings £20.00

Excelsior Laxey Wheel
£40.00

Foreign 'Bathing Belle'
on Globe £35.00

Grafton
Lighthouse
Miniature
£10.00

Arcadian Fish Basket £12.50

Grafton Girl on Sand with Bucket
and Spade £135.00

Grafton
Eddystone
Lighthouse
£10.00

German Yacht with
Waves £11.00

Coronet Punch
and Judy £65.00

Foreign Frog on Whelk Shell
£15.00

Arcadian Lifebelt £12.50

Arcadian Curled Fish £11.50

Carlton Bathing Belle
£150.00

Foreign Bathing Beauty
on Shell £35.00

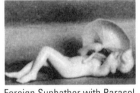

Foreign Sunbather with Parasol
£35.00

Gemma Lighthous
£6.50

Shelley Fish Basket No. 186 £16.50

Willow Art Shell Hatpin Holder £10.50

Arcadian Bathing Machine £16.00

Arcadian Lighthouse £16.00

Grafton Boy on Sand with Toy Yacht £125.00

Foreign Liner £17.00

Whelk Shell £6.50

Grafton Lighthouse £12.50

Foreign Bell-Hop on Suitcase £20.00

Foreign Clock Tower £7.50

Shelley Scallop Shell No. 166 £14.00

Swan Fish Basket £12.50

Carlton Bandstand £39.50

Podmore Margate Clocktower £15.00

Willow Beachy Head Lighthouse £12.00

Dainty
Lighthouse
£12.50

Brit. Man.
Lighthouse
£6.50

Milton
Octagonal
Lighthouse
£10.50

Grafton
Lighthouse
(Black Band)
£14.50

Queens
Lighthouse
(Rocky Base)
£12.50

Carlton
Lighthouse
'Sailor Beware'
£16.50

Willow
Lighthouse
£7.00

Arcadian
Beachy
Head
£10.50

Saxony
Beachy
Head
£7.50

Beachy
Head
Lighthouse
£12.50

Saxony
Beachy Head
(Banded)
£10.00

Shelley Pharos
Lighthouse
No. 73 £13.00

Carlton
Flamborough
Head Fog Siren
Building £60.00

Shelley Motor Boat on Waves No. 353 £35.00

Saxony The Needles
Lighthouse £22.50

Kingsway Lifeboat £14.50

Willow Paddle Steamer £100.00

German Mother Hen
and Chicks £30.00

German Parakeet
and Cockatoo £24.50

Willow
Canary £30.00

Podmore
Penguin
£13.50

Ugly Duckling £9.50

Carlton Chick in Egg
£10.00

Savoy Duck £13.50

Carlton Turkey on
green base £40.00

Grafton Hen £20.00

Arcadian Cock o'th'
South £23.00

Corona Mouse
eating Nut
£25.00

Arcadian Sussex
Pig £20.00

Arcadian Duck/Rabbit
£30.00

Florentine Pig £19.50

Canary on
Perch £12.00

Bird on Rock £13.00

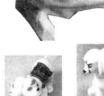

Arcadian Pelican £35.00

Arcadian Peacock £22.00

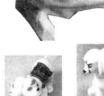

Grafton Dogs With Two Heads
Each £95.00

Clifton Chick
Emerging From an
Egg £11.00

Coronet Swan Posy Holder
£6.00

Carlton Owl
(with Mortar
Board) £25.00

Carlton Roosting Hen
£11.00

Arcadian Parrot £14.50

Arcadian Cockerel £25.00

Gemma Swan £

Arcadian Owl
(Verse) £15.50

Florentine Baby Bird
Cream Jug £7.50

Florentine Pelican
Cream Jug £7.50

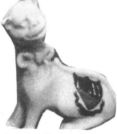

Arcadian Cheshire Cat £14.50

Alexandra Cat in Boot £26.50

Grafton Cheshire Cat (smiling)
£12.00

Wilton Cat
on Pouffe
£22.00

Devonia Labrador £24.50

Unmarked Tortoise
Pin Box £9.50

Carlton Racehorse £100.00

Foreign Cat
Sitting £10.00

Saxony Cat on
Drum £22.50

Arcadian Angry Cat
Arched Back £14.50

Florentine Pekingese in Cradle
£16.50

Savoy Dog Cream Jug
£10.50

Cat and Rabbit
in Boots £22.00

Corona Large
Cat with ruff
£30.00

Florentine Puppy
(Large/Sitting) £12.50

Foreign Cat on Trinket Box
(Beige Lustre) £16.50

Florentine Spaniels
in Hat £17.00

Carlton Puppy in Slipper £80.00

Grafton
Monkey
£15.00

Saxony Cat,
Playing Mandolin
£22.00

Carlton Ape
with orange
face £27.00

Gemma Manx Cat £30.00

Gemma Pug £22.00

Shelley Bulldog
in Kennel No. 316
£20.00

Gemma Dog and Fly
£20.00

Saxony Puppies
and Kitten in
Basket £22.00

Carlton Puppy and Horn
Gramophone 'His Masters
Voice' £70.00

Savoy
Miniature
Cat £17.00

Carlton Dog with Banjo
£35.00

Sylvan Cat on
Pouffe £14.50

Grafton
Bulldog Standing
£20.00

Alexandra Bulldog Standing £16.50

Willow Art Cat with Bow
£12.00

Carlton Scottie
wearing Tam
O'Shanter £18.00

Gemma Dog Lying £26.50

Spaniel £14.50

Norfolk Crest Dog
wearing Medallion £22.00

Grafton Terrier £27.50

Spaniel on Cushion
£22.00

Arcadian Bill Sykes
Bulldog £25.00

Arcadian Long-Necked
Cat £12.50

Gemma Comical
Cat £25.00

Carlton Cat
Wearing Black
Top Hat £30.00

Three Black Cats on a Sledge
£210.00

Black Cat on
Telephone £115.00

Black Cat Radio
Operator £110.00

Black Cat on wall
£80.00

Black Cat on a Milk
Churn £65.00

Black Cat on a swing
£75.00

Black Cat with
Umbrella £165.00

Arcadian Black Cat
on Yacht £165.00

Black Cat on a
Bicycle £210.00

Black cat in a Well
£65.00

Arcadian Black
Cat on Jug £65.00

Black Cat on a Pillar
Box £75.00

Arcadian Black Cat
Climbing Milkchurn
£65.00

Arcadian Black
Cat with Bottle
£75.00

Arcadian Black Cat
on Vertical
Horseshoe
£95.00

Five Black Cats
on House £190.00

Arcadian Three wise
Monkeys £15.00

Grafton Bear and
Ragged Staff £40.00

Grafton Snail £17.50

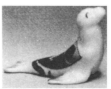

Grafton Seal £22.50

Willow Monkey
holding Coconut
£25.00

Carlton Black Cat on
Oval Hat Box £30.00

Arcadian Shetland Pony £25.00

Arcadian Open Mouthed Fish
£6.50

Arcadian Rabbit
£10.00

Willow Art
Rabbit, Alert Ears
£9.50

Arcadian Tortoise
£12.00

Arcadian Crab £17.00

Arcadian Teddy Bear
95mm £30.00

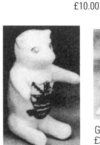

Arcadian Small
Teddy Bear
70mm £24.50

Grafton Frog Sitting
£35.00

Arcadian Lion £30.00

Unmarked Polar Bear
Ashtray £30.00

Kingsway Wise
Old Owl £30.00

Shelley Walking Bear
No. 67 £40.00

Shelley Scottie
No. 506 £60.00

Carlton Duck on
Green Base £40.00

Grafton Labrador Puppy
£35.00

Arcadian Squirrel
£30.00

Corona Bear (Large and Furry) £24.50

Queens Indian Elephant £20.00   Albion Toad £30.00

Saxony Frog Under Tulip Candlestick £16.00

Pearl Arms Elephant Cream Jug £14.50

Arcadian Frog £18.00   Griffin Camel Kneeling £17.00

Grafton Fish Open Mouth £7.00

German Lion £10.00

Foreign Goldfinch on Rock £22.00

Savoy Clara Cluck Candlesnuffer £30.00

Corona Swan Posy Holder £6.00

Foreign Rabbit on Sledge £30.00

Grafton Dog on Ashtray Swains Studdy Series £70.00

Arcadian Standing Pony £25.00

Brit. Man. Fledgeling Jug £7.50

Grafton Kitten £27.50

Arcadian Yellow Chick on Egg £30.00

Grafton Spaniel £17.50

Willow Mouse £25.00

Willow Long-Eared Hare £19.50

Grafton Red Fox and Pheasant
No. 434 £65.00

Grafton Duck, Open
Posy Holder £35.00

Queens Grotesque
Animal £10.00

Saxony Eagle
on Perch £25.00

Savoy Mouse £30.00

Willow Sitting Deer
£40.00

Gemma Cat
in Bowl
£35.00

Arcadian Rabbit
or Duck £30.00

British Manufacture
Fish Vase £5.00

Frog
Huge Open
Mouth £15.00

Carlton Turkey,
Coloured
£50.00

Standing Donkey
'We are Two' £50.00

Willow Ram with curly
Horns £65.00

Grafton Sitting
Comic Cat
(Yellow Bow)
£30.00

Willow Crouching
Lion £80.00

Grafton Duck Swimming
No. 377 £20.00

Savoy Walking Lion £30.00

Crown Brooding
Hen £11.00

Saxony Swan Open
Winged Posy Holder
£6.00

Carlton Monkey
£24.00

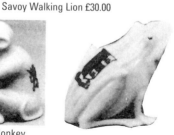

Savoy frog £65.00

Dainty Sitting
Pup £16.50

Arcadian
Chick Salt Pot
£7.00

Arcadian Tommy on Sentry Duty £85.00

Arcadian Russian Cossack on Horseback £250.00

Arcadian British Cavalry Soldier on Horseback £235.00

Arcadian Tommy and His Machine Gun £55.00

Arcadian Nurse and Wounded Tommy £190.00

Arcadian Nurse £80.00

Arcadian Salior £115.00

Willow Art Kitchen Range £20.00

Arcadian Bust of British Territorial Soldier £9.00

Grafton The Bomb Thrower £175.00

Arcadian Bugler Boy £215.00

Arcadian British Soldier £175.00

Arcadian Observer
Balloon £75.00

German Monoplane
with Pilot £25.00

Arcadian Monoplane £75.00

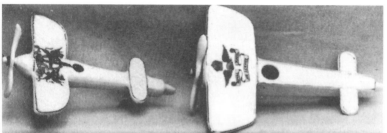

Savoy Model of
British Motor
Searchlight £225.00

Carlton Monoplane £95.00

Willow Monoplane £85.00

Savoy Monoplane £110.00

Arcadian Bi-Plane £170.00

Arcadian Nurse
Cavell £37.50

Shelley Zeppelin £160.00

Arcadian Monoplane with coloured
roundels £95.00

Swan British Aerial
Bomb £55.00

Carlton Biplane with coloured roundels
£400.00

Arcadian Bury St.
Edmunds Bomb £12.0(

Grafton Battleship £75.00

Corona Submarine
E.4. £22.50

Carlton Battleship HMS Warspite £125.00

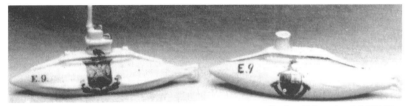

Carlton Submarine E.9. £70.00

Grafton Submarine E.9. £47.50

Alexandra Torpedo £55.00

Corona British Airship £35.00

Savoy
Highland
Infantryman
£190.00

Swan HMS Queen Elizabeth £40.00

Corona 'Lusitania' £120.00

Carlton RMS Lusitania £150.00

Grafton HMS Iron Duke £100.00

Savoy Submarine E.1. £100.00

Carlton HMS Humber Monitor £55.00

Arcadian
Hair Brush
Grenade
£160.00

Carlton HMS Queen Elizabeth £110.00

Arcadian Torpedo Boat
Destroyer £30.00

Carlton Minesweeper £65.00

Willow Liner converted
to Troopship £95.00

Carlton H.M.S. Australia £125.00

Savoy Battleship HMS Lion £125.00

Shelley Submarine E.9.
£65.00

Willow Art Airship
Beta £90.00

Carlton Battleship HMS Tiger £110.00

Swan Tommy's Hut £50.00

Carlton
Munitions
Worker £140.00

Arcadian Sailor
winding Capstan
£125.00

Arcadian Bust of
a Sailor £47.50

Savoy Armoured Car £125.00

Shelley Armoured Car
No.329 £70.00

Grafton Motor Tractor
as used on
the Western Front
£300.00

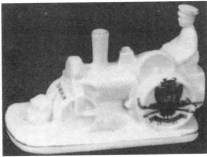

Arcadian Tommy driving Steamroller over the Kaiser
£500.00

Arcadian
Sheringham
Bomb £170.00

Carlton Vickers Tank £260.00

Willow Tank with Trailing Wheels
£20.00

Arcadian Tank 160mm long
£40.00

Coronet Tank £40.00

Savoy HMLS Donner Blitzen Tank
£55.00

Grafton Tank £35.00

Carlton Fiat Tank
£450.00

Arcadian Armoured Car
£50.00

Grafton Desert Gun £85.00

Corona Renault Tank £95.00

Shelley Red Cross
Van £45.00

Corona Red Cross
Van £40.00

Savoy Two-Piece Machine Gun £165.00

Savoy Howitzer £40.00

Carlton Field Gun with
screen and sight hole £45.00

Arcadian Howitzer £25.00

Willow Art Field Gun with screen £35.00

Swan Field Gun with screen £34.00

Grafton Mills Hand
Grenade with Pin
£30.00

Grafton 'French 75' £75.00

Arcadian Trench Mortar £22.50

Shelley Howitzer £75.00

Arcadian Field Gun £25.00

Carlton Machine Gun £45.00

Arcadian Despatch Rider £95.00

Arcadian German Aerial Torpedo £55.00

Grafton Water Bottle £15.00

Aynsley Hand Grenade with Flames £40.00

Carlton German Incendiary Bomb £30.00

Swan Clip of Bullets £30.00

Corona Shell £10.00

Willow Kitbag £24.50

Grafton Cannon Shell £12.50

Arcadian Sandbag £25.50

Swan Anti-Aircraft Shell £22.00

Arcadian Canister Bomb £20.00

Arcadian Field Glasses £19.00

Arcadian Mills Hand Grenade 62mm £27.50

Arcadian Anti-Zeppelin Candlestick £22.50

Carlton Cannon Shell £12.50

Shelley 9.2mm Shell £14.00

Swan Jack Johnson Shell £18.50

Swan Trench Dagger £70.00

Carlton Blackpool
War Memorial
£65.00

Arcadian Woodhouse
Eaves War Memorial
£160.00

Arcadian Lewisham
War Memorial £80.00

German Clacton-
on-Sea War
Memorial £22.50

Arcadian Killin
War Memorial
£170.00

Carlton
Tunbridge Wells
War Memorial
£160.00

Arcadian Folkestone
War Memorial £80.00

Arcadian Folkstone War Memorial
£80.00

Unmarked
Llandudno War
Memorial £55.00

Unmarked
Margate War
Memorial £80.00

Devonia Cheddar
War Memorial
£170.00

Podmore
Blackpool War
Memorial £155.00

Foreign Matlock
Bath War
Memorial £14.00

Willow Matlock
Bath War
Memorial
£75.00

Arcadian Bishops
Stortford War
Memorial £125.00

Arcadian
Burnham on
Crouch War
Memorial £125.00

Devonia Art
Plymouth War
Memorial £125.00

Carlton Brighton War
Memorial
£110.00

Arcadian Burford
War Memorial
£170.00

Carlton Douglas
War Memorial
£85.00

Willow Nurse
Edith Cavell
Norwich Memorial
£25.00

Arcadian Dover
War Memorial
£65.00

Arcadian Dover
Patrol Memorial
£45.00

Foreign Southsea
War Memorial £20.00

Gemma Rocking
Chair £12.50

Arcadian Three-
Legged Stool £9.50

Willow Ornate Hand
Mirror £25.00

Willow Art
Grandfather
Clock £19.50

Foley Bellows
£17.50

Carlton Warming
Pan £15.00

Grafton Winged
Armchair £18.00

Arcadian Cradle £13.00

Brit. Man. Suitcase
£6.00

Florentine Flat Iron £14.50

Gemma Three
Legged Stool
£7.00

Carlton Book with
Gilded Clasp £12.50

Arcadian Woven Straw
Basket £6.00

Foreign Tiny Basket £6.00

Gemma Four-Legged
Stool £8.00

Victoria Broomhead £19.50

Arcadian Narrow
Grandfather
Clock £17.50

Carlton Valise £10.00

Willow Coal Scuttle
£8.00

Wilton Grandfather
Clock £16.50

Carlton Square
Sundial £12.50

Arcadian Alarm
Clock £24.50

Arcadian Gramophone
Cabinet £100.00

Shelley Valise No. 58 £14.50

Gemma Bucket £4.00

Gemma
Grandmother
Clock £8.50

Tuscan Crusty
Bread Loaf £22.00

Willow Dressing Table
Mirror £19.50

Arcadian Dustpan £10.00

Carlton Shaped
Clock £22.00

Carlton Time
Glass £22.00

Gemma Ornate Mantle
Clock £10.50

Gemma Helmet Coal
Scuttle £6.50

Florentine Cradle on
Rockers £12.00

Crown Circular
Sundial £12.50

Willow Sundial
£7.50

Shelley Handbag
No. 184 £17.50

Foreign Mantlepiece
Clock with Side
Wings £7.00

Queens Narrow
Grandfather
Clock £22.00

Cyclone
Suitcase £9.00

Foreign Mantle Clock with Rope Twist Columns £7.00

Podmore Grandfather Clock £16.50

Florentine Grandfather Clock £15.00

Carlton Grandfather Clock £22.00

Brit. Man. Grandfather Clock £15.00

Shelley 14th Century Clock No. 307 £24.00

German Grandfather Clock £10.00

Corona. Grandfather Clock £16.00

Arcadian Grandfather Clock £20.00

Porcelle Grandfather Clock £18.00

Savoy Sundial £9.50

Florentine Pillar Box 'I can't get a Letter so send you the Box' £14.50

Arcadian Sundial 'Life's but a Walking Shadow' £13.50

Shelley Victorian Pillar Box No. 157 £40.00

Willow 'GR' Pillar Box £22.50

Willow Grandfather Clock £19.50

Warwick Sundial £8.50

Arcadian Village Pump with Trough £16.50

Foley Water Pump No. 51 £17.00

Willow Art Anvil £7.50

Signal Anvil £7.50

Florentine Sofa £12.50

Kingsway Hammerhead Match Holder £24.00

Arcadian Umbrella £17.50

Willow Book £12.50

Shelley 'Ancient Lights' Lantern £17.50

Coronet Carboy £7.00

Savoy Kennel £10.50

Willow Yarmouth Fish Swill Basket £14.00

Shelley Garden Roller No. 358 £14.00

German Oval Post Box £15.00

Gemma Wheelbarrow £7.00

Triood Writing Slope £12.50

Premier Coal Scuttle £7.00

Foley Cradle on Rocker £15.00

Arcadian 'GR' Miniature Post Box £16.00

German Open Carpet Bag £6.00

Shelley Milk Churn No. 46 £16.00

Botolph Policeman's Lamp £10.00

Shelley Sundial £20.00

Grafton Axe in Tree Stump £12.00

Arcadian Fireplace 'There's No Place Like Home' £14.50

Unmarked Wall Plaque Ayr-Brig O'Doon £30.00

Arcadian Devonshire Dumpling £22.50

Brit. Man. Brick Cottage £10.00

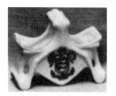

Gemma Garden Trug £4.50

Willow Watering Can £9.50

Arcadian The Old Armchair £10.50

Willow Chest and Lid £10.00

Arcadian 'Ally Sloper' £40.00

Podmore Mr. Pussy Foot £50.00

Carlton 'Bonzo' Dog £30.00

Arcadian Bust of Harry Lauder £30.00

Carlton Winkie the Gladeye Bird £23.00

Swan Clown £25.00

Grafton Chinese God Fu Hing £60.00

Arcadian Girl in Egg £40.00

Podmore Wilfred Wilfred £55.00

Carlton John Citizen 'Housing Unemployment, Taxes' £125.00

Foreign Boy Feeding Birds £20.00

Carlton Jester £22.50

Arcadian Black Boy and Crocodile £165.00

Arcadian Black Boy in Bed with Spider £105.00

Arcadian Black Girl making Ink in Bath £155.00

Arcadian Black Boy playing Banjo £150.00

Florentine Baby on
Rock £18.00

Foreign Boy and Flag
£22.00

Willow Peeping Tom
Bust £25.00

Monk with Lantern
£25.00

Arcadian Baby Sitting
in Round Bath £50.00

Arcadian Baby Girl
by Hip Bath £85.00

Willow Art Mermaid
on Rock £30.00

Arcadian Black
Boy in
Egg £55.00

Arcadian Jester £14.50

Victoria Fat
Screw £40.00

Arcadian Black Boy and
Girl on Tree Trunk £120.00

Arcadian Black Boy
with Pumpkin (Lid
Missing) £155.00

Arcadian Sailor and
Parrot Mustard £65.00

Willow Man in the
Moon £30.00

Arcadian Bathing Belle
with Feet in Pool £75.00

Cyclone Schoolboy
on Scooter £300.00

Arcadian Fat Lady weighing on Scales £80.00

Savoy fat Policeman £60.00

Arcadian Japanese Girl £47.00

Foreign Beauty on Shell £35.00

Arcadian Sailor Toby £40.00

Grafton Dutchman Holding Cheese £20.00

Botolph Pillory £17.00

Willow RSM Pepper Pot £45.00

Shelley Matches No. 190 £85.00

Carlton Boy Blowing Bubbles £75.00

Arcadian Sailor Toby Jug £47.50

Wilton Tramp and Tankard ect. £70.00

Grafton Baby £30.00

Cyclone Baby Bath £13.00

Victoria 'Jack-in-the-Box' £28.00

Brit. Man. Baby in Bootee £14.00

Arcadian Policeman on Point duty £55.50

Arcadian Jovial Policeman 'Stop' £34.50

Carlton Baby 'Mothers Darling' £135.00

Regency Cigarette Case £13.00

Arcadian Soda
Syphon £15.50

Carlton Hand and Glass £14.50

Arcadian Scotch and Soda £15.50

Carlton Drunkard by
Lamp Post £75.00

Grafton
Soda
Syphon
£13.00

Carlton Jovial
Monk £17.00

Podmore Beer Barrel £6.50

Arcadian Toby Jug £16.00

Grafton Man in
Beer Barrel £38.50

Arcadian Tankard
Overflowing £8.50

Willow Art
Beer Barrel £6.00

Willow Bottle and Tankard
on Horseshoe £13.50

Savoy Barrel and stand
two-piece £8.50

Grafton Champagne Bottle £10.00
Willow Scotch Bottle £8.50
Arcadian Miniature Corked Botle £7.00

Arcadian Man with
Tankard £65.00

Arcadian Jovial Monk
with glass £12.50

Shelley Beer Barrel
No. 48 £12.50

Willow Thames Punt £100.00

Panorama
Footballer Trophy
'RN Accountants'
£125.00

Carlton 'Put and Take'
Ashtray £65.00

Carlton Boy Jockey
on Ashtray £50.00

Grafton Footballer
£95.00

Grafton Girls on Punt £77.50

Carlton Golfer on Ashtray £150.00

Arcadian
Cricket
Bat £80.00

Grafton Tennis
Player Suzanne
Lenglen £160.00

Brit. Man. Canoe £9.00

Carlton Cricket
Batsman on
Ashtray £200.00

Arcadian
Caddie
and Golf
Clubs £85.00

Arcadian Chess
Rook £7.50

Sussex
Chess
Knight
£16.00

Corona
Chess
Knight
£16.00

Corona
Chess
Bishop
£30.00

Heraldic Chess
King £40.00

Alexandra
King £40.00

Arcadian Golf
Club £23.00

Kingsway Golf
Ball £9.50

Carlton Curling Stone
£24.50

Carlton Keeper in Goal £160.00

Shelley Golf Ball
on Tee No. 215
£17.00

Small Football
£10.50

Carlton Roller Skate £45.00

Large Football £10.50

Shelley Tennis Racquet and Balls
No. 194 £25.00

Botolph Tennis Racquet £17.50

Norfolk Cricket
Cap £60.00

Florentine Boxing
Glove £30.00

Arcadian Tennis
Racquet £16.50

Grafton
'The Colonel'
£55.00

Carlton Jockey on Racehorse
£110.00

Swan Cricket Bag £16.50

Savoy gilded
Golf Club £25.00

Foreign Jockey Cap
£15.00

Civic Cricket Bag £16.50

Large Rugby Ball £10.50

Arcadian Billiard Table, Cue and 3 Balls £125.00

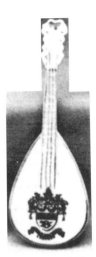

Willow Lute £45.00

Wilton HMV Horn Gramophone £30.00

Devonia Bagpipes £50.00

Victoria Radio Horn £30.00

Florentine Grand Piano £20.00

Arcadian Tambourine £16.00

Victoria Upright Piano (open Lid) £22.00

Arcadian Harp £10.50

Shelley Bugle £45.00

Willow Guitar £19.50

Florentine Square Gramophone £25.00

Saxony Harp £8.50

Saxony 55mm Horn Gramophone £17.00

German Ornate Grand Piano £14.50

Arcadian Banjo £20.00

Arcadian Upright Piano (Closed Lid) £22.50

Foreign Ornate Sleigh £35.00

Carlton Motor Cycle
and Sidecar £100.00

Foreign Coronation Coach
Inkwell £30.00

Foreign Girl in Car Laden
with Luggage £30.00

Carlton Gondola £22.50

Arcadian Taxi-Cab
EH 139 £75.00

Arcadian
Petrol Pump
Attendant
£95.00

Foreign Hot
Air Balloon
£40.00

Arcadian Motor
Spirit Can
£22.00

Willow Coal Truck £40.00

Carlton Stephenson's
Locomotion No. 1 £40.00

Florentine
Charabanc with Driver £40.00

Carlton Locomotive £160.00

Carlton Coal Truck
'Black Diamonds' £40.00

Florentine Saloon
Car £40.00

Arcadian Charabanc 7734 £50.00

Podmore Charabanc
XL 100 £40.00

Savoy Ambulance
£75.00

Shelley Coupe No. 360 £200.00

Shelley Vauxhall Motor Car
No. 361 £150.00

Carlton Saloon Car DN 999 £100.00

Grafton 'Dreadnought'
Charabanc £55.00

Botolph Saloon Car £40.00

Limoges Open Car £30.00

Swan Open Tourer EH 139 £4.00

Botolph Red Cross
Van EH 139 £40.00

Diamond Red Cross Van £70.00

Foreign Motor Car Open
Top £15.00

Caledonia Heraldic Open 4-Seater
Tourer £47.00

Podmore 18-Seater Charabanc £40.00

Carlton Luggage Trolley £45.00

Foreign Open Tourer
Chauffeured £20.00

Carlton Open Sports Car
DN 999 £50.00

Willow Square
Gramophone with Horn
£25.00

Carlton Radio
Operator £140.

Carlton Gramophone
with Horn £40.00

Podmore Horn
Gramophone £30.00

Willow
Radio Horn
£25.00

Carlton Box
Gramophone with Dog
"HMV' £70.00

Florentine Hexagonal
Gramophone with
Horn £40.00

Corona Square
Gramophone £25.00

Carlton Treadle
Sewing Machine
£30.00

Arcadian
Folding Camera
£40.00

Carlton Stick
Telephone
£30.00

Carlton
Gramophone
Cabinet £75.00

Corona Gas Stove
£13.00

Willow Radio
Horn £25.00

Gemma Cash Register
£16.00

Victoria
Radio Horn
£30.00

Carlton Cash Register
£30.00

Foreign Treadle Sewing
Machine £17.50

Arcadian Boy Scouts Hat £22.00

Arcadian Top Hat
£6.50

Carlton Crown
£25.00

Arcadian Welsh Hat with
Inscription 52mm £12.00

Gemma Bowler Hat
£20.00

Carlton Forage Cap £22.00

Foreign Top Hat with
Umbrella £9.50

Florentine Welsh Hat £70.00

Wilton Welsh Hat
£12.50

Savoy Balmoral Bonnet
£25.00

Shelly Trilby Hat £45.00

Gemma Fireman's
Helmet £40.00

Unmarked Straw Boater £22.50

Savoy New Zealand
Hat £25.00

Willow Crown
£25.00

Shelly Pat's Hat
& Dudeen £20.00

Gemma Welsh Hat
£10.00

Arcadian Luton Boater
£22.50

Arcadian Top Hat £6.50   Grafton Coaching Hat £7.50

Foreign Sabot
(Coloured floral) £10.00

Grafton Oriental
Shoe £10.00

Arcadian Riding
Boot £25.00

Saxony Ladies
Boot £9.50

Arcadian Slipper
Wall Pocket
£8.50

Side Fastening
Boot £8.50

Gemma Ladies Shoe,
Frilled Tongue £7.50

Florentine Bootee £10.00

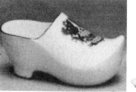

Foley Dutch Sabot £7.50

Temple Oriental Slipper £7.50

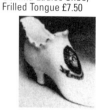

Edwardian Shoe
£6.50

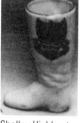

Shelley Highboot
£18.00

Porcelle Ankle
Boot £6.00

German Boot £8.00

German Ladies Boot £6.50

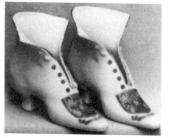

Saxony Ankle Boots £6.00 each

Willow Long Shoe £8.50

Corona Lancashire Clog £6.00

Pair Carlton Lancashire Clogs £17.00

Grafton Boot
with Puttee
£23.50

Gemma Shoe
with Eyelets
£6.50

Willow Sabot
£6.00

Gemma Pierced
Dish £8.50

Gemma Coffee Pot
£8.50

Gemma Meat Dish
& Cover £5.00

Carlton Saucepan £8.00

Carlton
Cylinder
Vase
£4.00

Fairy Ware Teapot £9.50

Gemma Puzzle Teapot
£16.50

Grafton Mustard Pot
& Lid No. 502 £6.50

Gemma Kettle £12.00

Swan Puzzle Teapot £13.50

Gemma Diamond
Shaped Teapot £14.00

Gemma Hot Water
Jug £10.00

Gemma Miniature Cup
and Saucer £6.50

Clifton Bagware Cup
and Saucer £6.50

Shelley Persian
Cafeterre £16.50

Arcadian Bird Series
Sugar Bowl £8.50

Tuscan Lemon with
Open Top £12.50

Arcadian Shaving Mug £9.50

Shelley Shaving Mug
£12.50

Gemma Shaving Mug
(Green) £12.50

Gemma Shaving
Mug £9.50

Arcadian 'Hair Pins' Oval Box £8.50

Florentine Hair Brush (Moulded Bristles) £14.00

Carlton Circular Pot with Curved Lid £6.50

Robinson and Leadbeater Oval Box and Lid £12.50

Florentine 'Trowel' Box and Lid £14.00

Carlton Rectangular Pin Box and Lid £7.50

Arcadian Heart Shaped Pin Box and Lid £6.50

Rectangular Box and Lid £6.50

Carlton Swedish Kettle £5.50

Carlton Bottle £7.00

Gemma Square Teapot £10.00

Arcadian Oval Trinket Box and Lid £6.50

Oval Box and Lid £6.50

German Teapot £8.50

Gemma Moustache Cup £8.50

Gemma Cup and Saucer £6.50

Pearl Arms Coffee Pot £9.50

Ornate Butterfly Vase £10.00

Grafton Comic Cruet Happy & Sad £30.00 Pair

Wilton Ashtray £17.50

Gemma Cheese Dish £8.50

Arcadian Cheese Dish £10.50

Gemma Shaving Mug £9.50

Carlton Coffee Pot £9.50

Carlton Kettle 'Polly Put....'£12.50

Grafton Hereford Kettle 11.50£

Gemma Teapot £8.50

Florentine Teapot £9.50

Carlton Pepper & Salt Pair £12.00

Cyclone Coffee Pot £9.50

Arcadian Turquoise Kettle £12.50

Silver Rimmed Tankard £16.50

Arcadian Comical Teapot £65.00

Shelley Teapot £20.00

Gemma Cheese Dish & Lid £8.00

Crown Devon Gravy Boat & Saucer£20.00

Gemma Shaving Mug £7.50

Fenton Cheese Dish and Cover £9.50

Arcadian Flower Vase £8.00

Carlton Cheese Dish and Cover £10.50

Foreign Cheese Dish and Cover, One-Piece £7.50

Carlton Cup & Saucer £6.50

Arcadian Match-Holder & Striker £7.50

Foreign Ashtray £8.50

Arcadian Ring Stand £12.00

Carlton 'Hair Tidy' & Lid £7.50

Grafton Cup & Saucer £9.50

Willow Horseshoe Match-holder & ashtray £15.00

Arcadian Fluted Beaker £9.00

Foreign Souvenir Ware Egg Cups Each £10.00

Victoria Lucky White Heather Mustard Pot & Lid £9.50

Carlton Lustre Vase £12.50

Willow Horseshoe Tray £6.50

Willow Club-shaped Dish £7.50

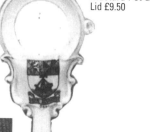

Foreign Butterfly Vase £10.00

Arcadian Heart-shaped Dish £4.00

Willow 'Cards' Box & Lid £12.00

Willow Mirror £25.00

Arcadian 'Hair Pins' Box & Lid £6.50

The Concise Encyclopaedia and Price Guide to Goss China
2000 Edition
Nicholas Pine

Now in its seventh edition, this latest guide has much fresh information including numerous new pieces, many announced for the first time. It has been completely re-typeset and each of the 1400 photographs has been digitally reproduced for maximum clarity and sharpness.

The dimensions and inscription for every piece are given and the Historic Models and Special Shapes section contains the correct matching arms for each model - all separately priced. The very latest revised prices are given right through the book which is also a complete descriptive listing of every piece of Goss ever produced.

The guide is the standard work on Goss china and is used by collectors, dealers and auctioneers worldwide.

The prices given form the base prices of pieces to which the values for particular arms or decorations should be added.

The work is well illustrated and is superbly bound in hardcover with colour jacket. It is a pair with **The Price Guide to Crested China** and the sequel to **The Price Guide to Arms and Decorations on Goss China** by the same author.

THE CONCISE ENCYCLOPAEDIA AND PRICE GUIDE TO GOSS CHINA

Nicholas Pine

The major features of the Concise Encyclopaedia and Price Guide to Goss China include:

- Every chapter revised and updated, incorporating over two thousand detailed amendments to the previous edition.
- Over 1400 illustrations - including both common and rare items.
- An illustration of every model and most other items.
- All pieces designated into First, Second and Third periods.
- The original inscription on every piece given, over 1000 in total.
- Every correct matching arms recorded and priced.
- Dimensions given for each piece and variations.
- Over 2500 pieces listed and separately priced.

- A complete chapter on factory marks with 40 illustrations encompassing every known mark - with dates.
- American Wares chapter re-written and clarified.
- An informative history of Goss China and many notes for collectors.
- Additional chapters on Goss Postcards, Goss Cabinets, The Goss Records and The League of Goss Collectors.
- Every photograph has been digitally reproduced for maximum clarity and sharpness.
- Numbered Models listed and identified.
- Glossary of terms - all technical terms explained.

215mm x 155mm 1400 Illustrations 464 pages. Casebound. £40.00

The Price Guide to Arms and Decorations on Goss China

Nicholas Pine

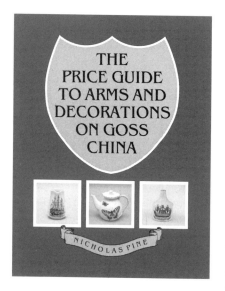

After ten years of research, Nicholas Pine and his late editor Norman Pratten have produced a complete listing of all known Goss arms and decorations in a magnificent 320 page, large format Hardback book with full colour jacket.

The book provides a unique and comprehensive listing, with values, of the 10,000 plus coats of arms and decorations which adorned Goss China during its period of production spanning 80 years.

Also included are chapters on the manufacture and decoration of Goss china and a history of W H Goss and his factory.

The largest section, geographical place names, contains 2,200 entries, including those introduced by Arkinstall & Son (Arcadian) when they took-over the works in 1929. All these Arcadian place names, 4,400 in all, are listed in a special section of the book so that collectors for the first time can ascertain the arms used only by the Goss factory.

The book encompasses the complete range used by the factory including: Chapters on all Civic arms in the British Isles and overseas; Royal, Nobility and Personal; Educational, Medical and Ecclesiastical, Commemoratives and Exhibitions; Transfer Printed Pictorial Views and Enamelled Illustrations; Regimental Badges and Naval Crests; Flora and Fauna; Armour, Flags and Masonic, and late decorations known as Third Period.

The Guide contains over 2,000 illustrations, and every piece listed is priced or valued, sub-divided into over 100 easy-to-use sections.

The book has been designed for use in conjunction with *The Concise Encyclopaedia and Price Guide to Goss China* by the same author. Collectors and dealers who possess a copy of the Encyclopaedia are strongly advised to acquire this book so that accurate up-to-date values may be obtained for each piece, for, as often as not, the decoration on a particular piece is worth much more than the piece itself.

Published 1992 260mm x 215mm. 320pages. 2000 illustrations. £19.95

William Henry Goss

*The story of the Staffordshire family of Potters
who invented Heraldic Porcelain.*
Lynda & Nicholas Pine

In this first ever biography of the man who is credited with inventing heraldic porcelain and his family who worked with him and at times against him, the authors tell the story of Goss china in fascinating detail.

From a promising start as a literary student, William Henry Goss used the important contacts he made in London to carve himself a career in the pottery industry in Stoke-on-Trent. At first he produced a limited, expensive range of Parian busts and figurines, but with the entry of his sons, Adolphus and later Victor and Huntley into the business, production switched to the small white models bearing colourful coats of arms for which the firm became famous.

The authors recount the stories of Godfrey, who ran away to New Jersey with a factory paintress, began a pottery there and founded the American branch of the family; the surprising Falkland Islands connection, still continuing today; why William refused to speak to his wife for the last twenty years of his life and how he came to have four homes all at the same time. The history of the three periods of production is complemented by fascinating chapters on how the porcelain was both manufactured and sold through virtually every town in the country.

The book is illustrated with over 350 photographs and maps, includes much material not previously published and comprehensive family trees.

As the story unfolds you can discover:

- About the three periods of Goss manufacture and how the trade developed leading eventually to mass popularity nationwide.
- The amazing Falkland Islands connection, how Port Stanley and the Upland Goose Hotel came to be so-named and the exciting story of how the Goss family came to emigrate to those barren islands - and the dreadful fate that befell them.
- Why youngest daughter Florence married a bewiskered Bostonian millionaire older than her father.
- The truth about the rumour that second son Godfrey got a factory girl 'into trouble' and was banished to America. Why did Godfrey emigrate to America? and did he start a US Goss factory?

- The beginnings of William's potting career. Why did he decide to become a potter?
- How the romantic young William became an obstinate and pedantic father and eventually a near recluse.
- Why William did not speak to his wife for the last 20 years of his life - and how he came to have four homes all at the same time.
- His amazing generosity towards his friends and workforce and his unbelievable meanness and cruelty towards his wife and children.
- How William viewed his two sons Adolphus and Victor as rivals.
- Who really invented heraldic porcelain and how it was manufactured and marketed.

260mm x 217mm 350 Illustrations 5 Family Trees 256 pages. Bibliography and Glossary. Casebound. £19.95

The Goss & Crested China Museum

For some 30 years, Nicholas and Lynda Pine have been collecting Goss family memorabilia and this is now on display at the Goss & Crested China Centre and Museum at Horndean, Hampshire.

In the museum, the story of heraldic porcelain is told on a series of illustrated wallboards around the rooms.

William Henry's personal photograph album is on display. Contained within its pages are the photographs of Royalty, the Nobility, poets and writers which Goss used to model his range of portrait busts.

Elsewhere can be found much ephemera of the Goss factory and family including many of William Henry's original recipe books and dozens of his eldest son Adolphus' original transfer printed views used to pictorially decorate the wares.

The museum also boasts family paintings, William's original seal, Adolphus' chair from Alsager District Council where he was chairman and a magnificent turquoise jewelled plaque made by William for his daughter Georgiana.

All books written by William Henry are on view - his own copies - and a number of important related books from Goss' own library as well as many letters from William and from Adolphus, the firm's commercial traveller writing back to the factory with orders.

Also on permanent show are displays of Goss China and ever changing temporary displays of particular collections or themes.

Entry to the museum is free of charge between 9.00am - 5.00pm six days a week. Why not visit The Goss & Crested China Centre to see both the showroom containing over 5000 pieces for sale and the museum?

The Goss & Crested China Museum
62 Murray Road, Horndean, Waterlooville, Hampshire, PO8 9JL

Would you like to join

The Goss & Crested China Club?

Exclusively for collectors and customers of Goss & Crested China Ltd. Membership will provide answers to question such as:

How do I find the pieces I am looking for?
What is a fair price?
Where can I obtain information on Goss China and Goss collecting?
Where can I exchange or sell pieces I no longer require?

Join the Goss & Crested China Club without delay and receive the following benefits:

FREE Specially designed enamel membership badge.

FREE Membership card and number.

FREE Telephone and postal advice service.

FREE Information on books about heraldic china collecting.

FREE Especially favourable Club members part-exchange rates for pieces surplus to requirements.

FREE Without obligation search-and-offer service for any items and decorations that you seek.

FREE Invitations to Club open days.

EXCLUSIVE Valuation service for your collection

EXCLUSIVE Club Members only special offers announced regularly in Club members monthly catalogue *Goss & Crested China.*

Membership is free and is available to subscribers to Goss & Crested China the club's monthly catalogue of pieces for sale.

To join, just send £24.00 or £40.00 (US$60) overseas airmail annual subscription* to The Goss & Crested China Club, 62 Murray Road, Horndean, Waterlooville, Hampshire PO8 9JL, and you will receive a membership application form with your first copy of the catalogue. Upon receipt of the completed form, you will be sent your enamel badge, membership card and full details of the club's special offers and services.

*For Airmail outside Europe add £16.00 or US$24

Goss & Crested China Ltd. are the leading dealers in Heraldic China.

We have been buying and selling for over 25 years and our experienced staff led by Lynda and Nicholas Pine will be able to answer your questions and assist you whether you are a novice or an experienced collector.

A constantly changing attractively priced stock of some 5,000 pieces may be viewed at the Goss & Crested China Centre and Museum in Horndean, including Goss cottages, fonts, crosses, shoes, lighthouses, models etc. and the full range of crested ware including military, animals, buildings etc. covering all the other manufacturers.

Visitors are welcome to call during business hours of 9.00 - 5.00 any day except Sundays and Bank Holidays. Those travelling long distances are advised to telephone in advance so that they may be sure of receiving personal attention upon arrival, but this is not essential.

Most of our business is by mail order and we publish *Goss & Crested China*, a monthly 32 page illustrated catalogue containing hundreds of pieces for sale from every theme and in every price range. The catalogue is available by annual subscription; please refer to the following page for details of this and the Goss and Crested China Club.

In addition, if you specialise, we will be pleased to offer you particular pieces or crests from time to time as suitable items become available. Please let us know your wants as with our ever-changing stock we will probably have something to suit.

Our service is personal and friendly and all orders and correspondence are dealt with by return. You will find us fair and straightforward to deal with, as we really care about crested china and this is reflected in our service.

Finally, we are just as keen to buy as to sell and offers of individual items or whole collections are always welcome. These will be dealt with by return and the very highest offers will be made.

Goss & Crested China Ltd,
62 Murray Road,
Horndean,
Waterlooville
Hampshire
PO8 9JL
Telephone: Horndean 023 9259 7440
Facsimile: 023 9259 1975
e-mail: info@gosschinaclub.demon.co.uk

Visit our website on:
www.gosscrestedchina.co.uk

ARKINSTALL & SON,
ARCADIAN WORKS,
STOKE-ON TRENT.

Arcadian Arms China

Over 500 Shapes. Comprising Latest Military Novelties.

SPECIAL FEATURE COAT OF ARMS TEA WARE.

PROMPT DELIVERY NOW GUARANTEED.

"PRATT" WARE Reproductions of Famous Old Blue Prints.
SPECIALITY 1919—BLUE CHARIOTS.

FLOWER POTS, VASES, CANDLESTICKS, SALAD BOWLS, TEAPOTS, HOT WATER JUGS,
AND A COMPLETE RANGE OF USEFUL AND FANCY ARTICLES.

The same assortment is also made and shown in PRATTS BLACK
"KAN-SU," and "CHERUBS" which have proved an immense success.

Advertisement by Arkinstall & Son for the 1919 British Industries Fair depicting their newly introduced range of War models which became popular after World War 1.